of eclipsing binaries developed by H. N. Russell and [illegible]. Period-luminosity relation of variable stars in Small Magel[illegible] noticed by Miss H. S. Leavitt.   **1913** Reflection spectr[illegible] nebulosity in Pleiades discovered by V. M. Slipher. N. Bohr proposes his theory of atomic structure. Photoelectric photometry developed, particularly by Stebbins. Reversal of polarity of magnetic field in sunspots noticed at the beginning of a new cycle. Russell presents the spectral class-luminosity diagram (H-R diagram) and proposes a theory of stellar [illegible]   **1914** Shapley proposes the pulsation the[illegible] criteria developed by W. [illegible]ic parallax method. Sha[illegible] [illegible] of cepheids.   **1915** Shapley first notices different stellar population in globular clusters. Adams determines spectral type of Sirius B. Einstein's General Theory of Relativity.   **1916** A. S. Eddington begins investigation of stellar structure. A. van Maanen measures proper motions in spirals, implying short periods of rotation.   **1917** G. W. Ritchey discovers nova in NGC 6946; this leads to a search for novae in galaxies and a method estimating the distances of galaxies.   **1918** Shapley proposes new model of galaxy. 100-in. Hooker telescope completed at Mount Wilson Observatory. Nova Aquilae: the brightest nova of modern times.   **1919** International Astronomical Union established.

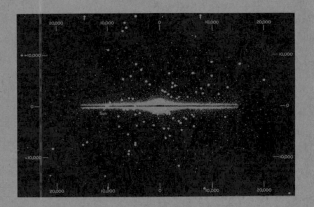

1920 "Great Debate" regarding the size of the Milky Way galaxy and the status of spiral nebulae between H. Shapley and H. D. Curtis. M. N. Saha develops the theory of excitation and ionization in stellar atmospheres.   **1922** E. P. Hubble investigates bright nebulae, and the theory of nebular emission lines is soon developed by H. Zanstra.   **1923** A cepheid variable definitely identified by Hubble in Andromeda galaxy.   **1924** Mass-

(Continued on rear endpapers)

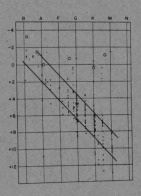

Astronomy of the 20th Century

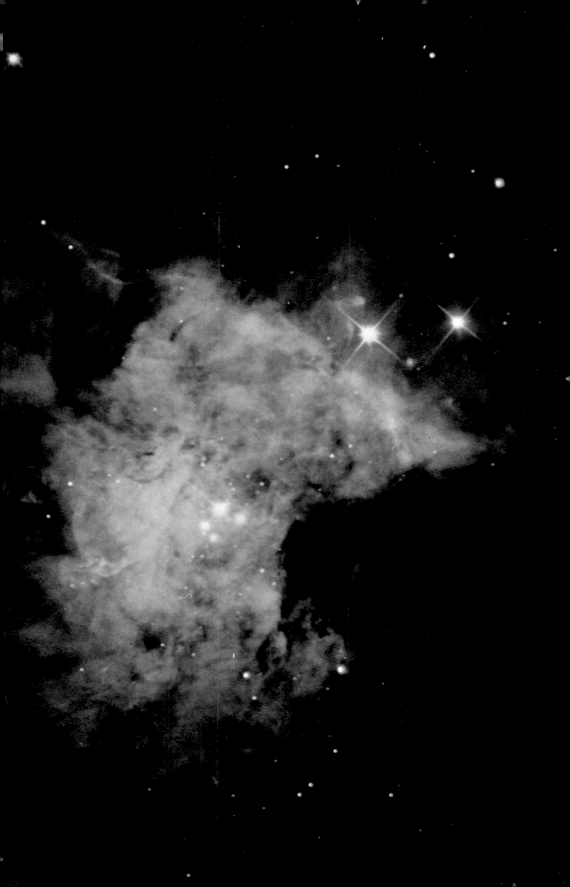

ASTRONOMY
OF THE *20*TH
CENTURY

Otto Struve *and* Velta Zebergs

Illustrated with photographs and diagrams

THE MACMILLAN COMPANY, NEW YORK

MACMILLAN NEW YORK, LONDON

Fig. 1.   The inner part of the Orion Nebula, photographed with
the Lick Observatory's 120-in. telescope. (*Lick Observatory*)

Library of Congress catalog card number: 62-21206

First Printing

Printed in the United States of America

The Macmillan Company, New York
Collier-Macmillan Canada, Ltd., Galt, Ontario
Divisions of the Crowell-Collier Publishing Company

PREFACE

ASTRONOMY IS usually spoken of as the oldest of the sciences. It started under the guise of astrology when man believed that he could predict his own future from the planets and the stars. About the seventeenth century, astronomy was recognized as a truly useful science. The location of the stars and planets enabled navigators to determine their position at sea, and for several centuries astronomers were predominantly occupied with the problems of navigation. During the past 5 years, astronomy has again become "useful"—presumably because man now hopes that his increasing knowledge of the universe will bring him material benefits. However, between the era of navigation by the stars and the present era of space exploration, there was what might be called "the Golden Age" of astronomy. During this time, astronomers were detached from a search for any practical applications and only sought truth for its own sake. It is with this Golden Age of astronomy, particularly the last half-century of it, that the present book is primarily concerned.

The purpose of this book, however, is not to present a detailed and comprehensive listing of all astronomical research during this century. Rather, the authors wish to describe, by means of specific examples chosen from different branches of astronomy, some of the great advances that have been made by astronomers and to indicate their working techniques. This has necessitated a somewhat uneven coverage of the different branches of astronomy. For example, there is no separate discussion of positional astronomy, even though many of the investigations discussed would not have been possible without the increased amount of data and greater accuracy achieved in the determination of star positions and proper motions during this century.

An attempt has been made to divide the material into topics that follow one another logically, but since most of the chapters cover the entire span of 60 years, it occasionally has been necessary to run ahead of the story. Footnotes and numerous cross references have been supplied to overcome any difficulties that may arise due to this organization.

The many illustrations throughout the book will serve to acquaint the reader with the astronomers of the Golden Age, their instruments, and the celestial objects studied by them. Whenever appropriate, quotations have been used for either of two reasons: to present the original ideas of an investigator, or to give a summary or an evaluation of a problem by a person particularly qualified to do so.

The two authors have both been the victims of East European terrorism, though their experiences were separated by about a quarter of a century. However, they have made a sincere effort to present the results of astronomy since 1900 in an unbiased manner. Undoubtedly, there is in the book a strong preference for sources that were originally written in the English language. This is only natural, and it does not represent an attempt to exaggerate the contributions of English-speaking scientists. In a few cases, the pronoun "I" is used in connection with events that are personally known to the elder of the two authors, O. Struve.

The authors are indebted to many individuals and observatories for illustrative material and to many scientific journals and publishers for granting permission to use material originally published by them. Special thanks are due to Columbia University and the American Museum–Hayden Planetarium for permission to use their libraries, and to C. A. Federer, Jr., Editor of *Sky and Telescope* for the use of many illustrations and paragraphs previously printed in that periodical. Nearly all of the work connected with the preparation of the manuscript was carried out while Mr. Struve served as the director of the National Radio Astronomy Observatory at Green Bank, West Virginia, and Mrs. Zebergs was a member of the Observatory's scientific staff, with headquarters at the New York offices of the Associated Universities, Inc.

O. Struve

V. Zebergs

CONTENTS

ILLUSTRATIONS

I

THE FORTUNE
OF ASTRONOMERS

SCIENTISTS, AND particularly astronomers, often are imagined as leading "ivory-tower," or cloistered lives, pursuing their scientific interests independent of outside pressures and influences. However appealing this romantic notion, it is far from true. Economic, political, and ideological factors have always shaped the lives of astronomers and influenced their productivity.

As recently as 1940, astronomy was the purest of sciences, almost devoid of practical application. This purity perhaps lent a certain charm to the subject, but it also resulted in meager financial support from governments, universities, and private foundations. There were few openings, even in so rich a country as the United States, for young astronomers, and many of the most talented students turned to other professions. Only those who were inspired by their teachers or who had developed an exceptional desire to carry on research in astronomy persisted in the often hopeless task of supporting themselves as astronomers.

After World War II, however, astronomy emerged as a science of national importance; vast sums have become available for new instruments and research centers. Thousands of people who 25 years ago would have studied physics, mathematics, chemistry, or geology now turn to astronomy, but they are not enough to fill the many positions which have come into being. Perhaps the most important problem confronting astronomers today is training sufficient numbers in astronomy and the related basic sciences to meet the new demand.

GROWTH IN ASTRONOMICAL FACILITIES

University Observatories

At the beginning of this century the lot of the professional astronomer was uncertain. The more advanced countries usually had one large government observatory, staffed with 10 to 20 scientists and assistants, often even fewer. Principal universities in Germany, France, Russia, England, and the United States usually provided one chair of astronomy (which meant, of course, only one regular professorship). Many universities employed one or two additional astronomers as assistant professors or instructors; they were expected to teach some of the required courses but rarely were given time to conduct research. Unless the professor could secure money from private sources, he had few if any assistants and computers. Budgets in university observatories, always small, were usually insufficient for proper maintenance of the instruments. Observatory libraries existed mainly through the world-wide exchange of publications among observatories, and funds for the publication of research rarely were provided on a continuing basis. Until around 1925, the library budget of a typical university observatory was about $50 per year, not even enough for subscriptions to the few available periodicals, such as the *Astrophysical Journal,* started by G. E. Hale at the Yerkes Observatory, Williams Bay, Wisconsin, or the *Astronomische Nachrichten* ("Astronomical Bulletin") published by Akademie-Verlag, Berlin. Libraries grew, but only because the observatory directors usually donated publications acquired for their personal use.

Since most astronomers were trained in observational work, upon their appointment as professors they usually attempted to secure university funds for one modern instrument, which almost invariably remained in use for 50 years or more. They could not get appropriations for additional

Fig. 2   Pulkovo Observatory around 1900.

Fig. 3. The main building of the Paris Observatory, with a statue of
U. J. J. Leverrier in front. (*Courtesy Paris Observatory*)

modern equipment, other than small auxiliary attachments. Students,
therefore, were compelled to develop interests related to the instrumentation available at their universities. Thus an observatory with a precise
meridian circle° as its principal instrument was not prepared to train
students in *stellar spectroscopy*.† These special interests could only be
pursued by obtaining a fellowship or other form of grant that enabled
the young astronomer to go to a national observatory—perhaps Pulkovo
in Russia, Paris in France, or Greenwich in England, observatories established to investigate navigational and geodetic problems but that were,
around 1900, expanding into other fields.

Privately Endowed Observatories

In addition to the many small university astronomy departments, a few
relatively large observatories were built around the turn of the century.
These larger facilities can be attributed to the mid-19th-century rise of
capitalism in the Western world. Wealthy persons, honoring institutions in
the cities where they lived or had been born, created such outstanding facilities as the Lick and Yerkes Observatories in the United States. J. Lick, a
Pennsylvania-born piano and organ maker, who amassed his fortune
through real-estate speculation during the Gold Rush, gave the funds for

° An instrument used to determine accurate stellar positions.
† The analysis of light coming from the stars by means of an instrument called a
spectroscope, which separates the light from a particular source into its component
wavelengths.

the construction of the Lick Observatory to the University of California about 1875. Similarly, the name of C. T. Yerkes, a Chicago streetcar magnate, will be remembered for the considerable sums he donated to the University of Chicago for a large telescope and subsidiary buildings and instruments. The large dome of the Yerkes Observatory in the foreground of the photograph contains the 40-inch (40-in.) refractor, largest instrument of its type in the world. Mount Wilson Observatory, started by the Carnegie Institution of Washington, acquired its 100-in. telescope through funds that were a gift from J. D. Hooker, a Los Angeles businessman. The widespread interest created in New England by the appearance of a bright comet was partly responsible for the founding of the Harvard Observatory in 1839, but its instruments too were paid for by a few wealthy individuals.

The last observatories built with private or foundation funds are the McDonald Observatory of the University of Texas, whose 82-in. reflector was completed in 1939, and Palomar Observatory in California, in 1947, financed by the Rockefeller Foundation.

In Europe, neither capitalism nor the consequent philanthropy achieved the peaks they did in the United States. Still, a private foundation created the observatory at Nice in France, and the Simeis Observatory in the Crimea, Russia, opened about 1909 as a private observatory, later was given by N. S. Maltzef, to the Pulkovo Observatory, and it functioned thereafter as a southern observing station for Pulkovo. The Engelhardt Observatory was V. P. Engelhardt's gift to the University of Kazan. In Great Bri-

Fig. 4.   Yerkes Observatory.

Fig. 5. The 40-in. refractor of the Yerkes Observatory. (*Yerkes Observatory*)

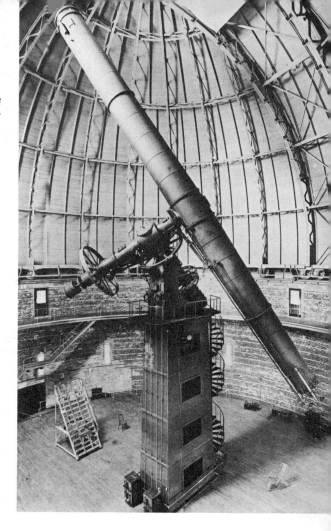

Fig. 6. G. Van Biesbroeck at the objective of the Yerkes 40-in. refractor.

Fig. 7   The 200-in. Hale telescope dome, with shutter open in moonlight. (*Mount Wilson and Palomar Observatories*)

Fig. 8   The 200-in. Hale telescope. (*Mount Wilson and Palomar Observatories*)

tain a number of small observatories were created as private institutions; some are still in operation. One of the most important of these was the Norman Lockyer Observatory in southern England; Sir Norman Lockyer, one of the first astrophysicists, obtained funds from wealthy friends after he had decided to leave the Solar Physics Observatory in London.

As a rule, the large, privately endowed observatories were equipped by the donors with one or more powerful instruments that could be expected to provide useful results for several decades. In most cases, the institutions accepting the gifts undertook to maintain the observatories, but there rarely was enough money to provide even modest auxiliary instruments and never enough to replace the principal refractors or reflectors* with more modern telescopes. Thus the Lick Observatory depended for about 70 years upon the 36-in. refractor built from money willed by Mr. Lick and the 36-in. Crossley reflector, a gift of a wealthy English amateur astronomer, E. Crossley. Similarly, Yerkes has had to rely completely on its 40-in. refractor completed in 1897, until a 24-in. reflector was constructed by G. W. Ritchey a few years later.

Government Observatories

Completely new types of observatories began to be built after World War II. The flood of funds from the wealthy had diminished to a trickle, and further progress could be achieved only by governments' assuming responsibility for the development of new facilities. In the United States, the first new type of observatory, the Kitt Peak National Observatory near Tucson, Arizona, was "born" in 1953 at a small conference of astronomers interested in *photoelectric photometry*, the determination of stellar brightnesses (see Chapt. V). The astronomers, who had been accustomed only to very meager resources, recommended to the National Science Foundation (NSF) of the United States† that a small optical telescope be financed by the government and made available to photoelectric experts from eastern universities. The typical facilities at these institutions are inadequate and atmospheric conditions invariably unfavorable for determining stellar brightnesses. The NSF convened a small committee and upon its recommendation decided to create a large national optical observatory wholly financed by the NSF and operated by a board of trustees known

---

* Refractors are telescopes employing lenses as light-gathering elements, while reflectors are telescopes with parabolic or spherical mirrors.

† The National Science Foundation is an organization established by the federal government and supported by federal funds for the purpose of encouraging and financing research in the basic sciences.

by the designation AURA (Association of Universities for Research in Astronomy, Inc.).

Under its original charter the NSF is not permitted to operate scientific institutions directly, but the foundation is permitted, and even encouraged, by the government to provide funds for appropriate governing bodies such as AURA, which consists of eighteen members from nine institutions (the Universities of California, Chicago, Harvard, Indiana, Michigan, Ohio State, Princeton, Wisconsin, and Yale). A. B. Meinel was named the first director of the Kitt Peak Observatory with headquarters in Tucson, Arizona. The choice of the Kitt Peak site and the observatory's early organization were mainly Meinel's work. Observations, started with two 16-in. reflecting telescopes mounted on trucks that could be moved rapidly from one site to another, indicated that the atmospheric conditions on Kitt Peak are at least as good as any that can be found in the United States at altitudes below 7,000 feet. The observatory recently has constructed a 36-in. general-purpose reflector for photoelectric work, and is now engaged in building an 80-in. reflector for stellar observations and a very large tower telescope for solar work. It is expected that in the future a huge optical telescope of a diameter not less than 200 in. will be built for Kitt Peak. Since its exact aperture has not been determined, it is usually referred to as the "X-in." telescope. At one time Meinel thought that X could be as large as 600 in., but it is improbable that so large a telescope will be constructed in the foreseeable future.

About 1956, the NSF decided to create a National Radio Astronomy Observatory in Green Bank, West Virginia, resembling in character the Kitt Peak National Observatory. A steering committee under chairmanship of the Dutch-born astronomer B. J. Bok, then of Harvard, recommended to the Foundation that the governing body of the observatory should be the board of trustees of the Associated Universities, Inc., which consists of representatives from nine northeastern universities (Columbia, Cornell, Harvard, Johns Hopkins, Massachusetts Institute of Technology, Princeton, Pennsylvania, Rochester, and Yale).* The National Radio Astronomy Observatory in Green Bank, West Virginia started active astronomical observations upon the completion of the 85-ft. paraboloid antenna (the Tatel radio telescope) early in 1959. A 140-ft. *equatorial telescope*† is now

---

* Associated Universities, Inc., had undertaken already the operation of the Brookhaven National Laboratory, which grew out of the government's Manhattan Project for development of the uranium fission bomb. The laboratory, however, is devoted to basic and applied research without any direct military application.

† An equatorial telescope is mounted so that there are two axes at right angles, one parallel to the earth's axis of rotation.

Fig. 9. A drawing of the 300-ft. transit-type radio telescope nearing completion at the National Radio Astronomy Observatory. (*Courtesy Associated Universities, Inc.*)

under construction and a 300-ft. *transit-type dish** is nearing completion.

Both of these national observatories are financed wholly by the government; the NSF realizes that it is no longer justifiable to build one large telescope and then provide only minimal additional funds for relatively inexpensive auxiliary equipment. Hence, both observatories are expected to take advantage of new inventions and build new and improved instruments more or less continuously. Both were instructed to acquire relatively small permanent scientific staffs who would carry on their own research and also would be of assistance to visiting scientists from all parts of the United States and possibly even from other countries.

Similar observatories are being developed in the Soviet Union, France, Germany, and other countries. Institutional observatories, such as those connected with a university, probably will have to commit themselves to continuous development in telescope construction—this is being done by the University of California at Lick, where a 120-in. reflector was completed recently—or they gradually will cease to function as observatories and be converted into purely instructional departments. Although other

* A radio antenna shaped like a dish that can move only in one coordinate.

national observatories have come into being, they are still few in number, and scientists from other institutions must be allowed time to visit them in order to acquire the necessary observational material for research.

ASTRONOMERS, WORLD EVENTS, AND IDEOLOGIES

The development of astronomy during this century is traced in Fig. 10, which gives the number of active astronomers based upon the *Astronomischer Jahresbericht* ("Yearly Astronomical Report"), originally published by the Deutsche Astronomische Gesellschaft (the German Astronomical Society, founded in Heidelberg in 1863), a bibliography of all astronomical publications from 1900 to 1959. There was little change during the period 1900–1910, years that probably represent a relatively stagnant stage in astronomy. Although a few very distinguished astronomers were making important discoveries and developing theories, the majority of young astronomers were involved in determining *stellar coordinates* on the *celestial sphere*° and compiling some of the most important astronomical catalogues. However, many astronomers regarded this identification and compilation as unrewarding, and that attitude undoubtedly induced some of them to turn to such fields as physics and chemistry. Major projects such as the *Astrographic Chart* and *Catalogue,* a photographic chart and catalogue of star positions covering the entire sky, initiated in 1887 at an international conference in Paris and only now nearing completion, were headed by elderly men who could not devote themselves unstintingly to observational work. This responsibility was shifted to assistants who carried out observations, reduced them, and prepared them for publication.

The decline in astronomical work that began about 1910 probably reflects the uncertain peace in the years just before 1914 and no doubt was accelerated by World War I. Also, early volumes of the *Jahresbericht* in-

° Any one of a set of values that is used to specify the position of a point on the celestial sphere is known as a coordinate; the celestial sphere is imaginary and assumed to be of infinite radius, and the celestial objects appear to be placed upon it.

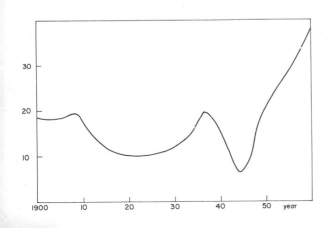

Fig. 10.   The number of active astronomers, by hundreds, during the 20th century.

cluded not only authors but also institutions and organizations and, additionally, many unimportant brief notes not in the later volumes. The marked acceleration between about 1929 and 1936 may have resulted from the emergence of astrophysics, which, of course, had started much earlier, as the dominant field in astronomy. The second decline in the years after 1936 probably resulted from international tensions preceding World War II. On the other hand, the almost linear and very rapid increase that began in 1947 and still continues suggests that the number of authors increases at the rate of about 150 per year. Of these only about a third have been trained in astronomy. The rest were educated in such fields as physics, electronics, engineering, and chemistry.

World events have had a decisive influence upon the volume of astronomical research in all countries. Astronomy almost ceased to exist in Russia during the civil war of 1917–1920, and the increase of astronomical research in the Soviet Union after the recovery from the revolution and the years of famine was even more rapid than indicated by the curve. Similarly, there was a drastic reduction in astronomical research in Germany during World War II and in the first few years after it.

The history of 20th-century astronomy differs radically from that of the 19th century, which was relatively unaffected by wars and revolutions. One must go back to the late 16th and 17th centuries to find similar turbulence affecting the lives of the few great astronomers of that time— for example, the German Johannes Kepler, the Italians Galileo Galilei and Giordano Bruno, and a handful of others.

Astronomical research recovered very quickly after World War II, partly as a result of the dramatic rise of *radio astronomy*, the offspring of developments in radar techniques during the war (see Chapt. VI), but very slowly after World War I. It is perhaps surprising that the linearity of the curve between 1948 and 1959 apparently does not reflect the emergence of research by means of rockets and satellites. It is to be expected that this new area may cause an even more rapid increase during the next few years.

Individuals and World Events

The tragic figure of Kepler was molded by the 16th- and 17th-century German religious wars. Twentieth-century upheavals, beyond the impact made on the field of astronomy as a whole, had an enormous effect on the lives of individual astronomers. No one can estimate the numbers of young astronomers and astronomers-to-be who were sacrificed to two world wars, or whose lives and interests were affected adversely by the economic disruptions that followed these holocausts. Since Russian astronomers probably were affected more than those of any other country, a few examples, taken mostly from Russian sources, may illustrate this point.

P. K. Sternberg was a member of the Moscow Observatory before World War I. He had been born in 1865, the son of a small-town merchant and contractor for a Russian railroad. His student years were spent in Moscow during one of the most reactionary periods of the czarist regime, and this undoubtedly had a decisive effect upon Sternberg's entire outlook. A quiet person, he constantly was observing star positions for the determination of the variation of latitude in Moscow, and taking gravity measurements in and around Moscow for determination of the region's gravitational anomaly. No one knew, however, that since the early days of this century, and especially since the unsuccessful revolution of 1905, he had been interested in politics and had become an active member of the underground Bolshevik party. Sternberg is reported to have hidden in the observatory a large quantity of bombs and explosives intended for a future revolution. Upon the former director V. K. Cerasky's retirement in 1916—still under the czarist regime—Sternberg, then a full professor at the university, became the new observatory director. A year later, he took an active part in the bloody struggle between the Bolsheviks and their adversaries that led to the conquest by the former of the entire city. In 1919–1920 he served as political and military commissar of the Red Army that defeated the White Army forces of Admiral A. V. Kolchak, the famous anti-Bolshevik leader.

Unfortunately, during the fighting in Siberia, Sternberg contracted a serious lung ailment that caused his death on February 1, 1920. His name has been attached to the Astronomical Institute of Moscow University, where many of his students and their present pupils are carrying out astronomical research that he himself was unable to engage in, due to his involvement in the revolution and relatively early death. Sternberg was an "old Bolshevik" and, though I did not know him intimately, the reports of others leave no doubt of his sincerity. One wonders what would have happened to him had he lived until the time of the great Stalinist "purges" of 1937.

No such curiosity need be attached to the fate of another Russian astronomer, B. P. Gerasimovich, who was younger than Sternberg, but whose socialistic position was so strong that the czarist police refused to issue him the certificate of political loyalty required before application could be made for a passport to travel in other countries. His rise in the astronomical world was rapid and spectacular. From a rather obscure professorship at the University of Kharkov, he was appointed about 1930 by the Soviet Government as director of the Pulkovo Observatory. But in 1937, for reasons still obscure, Gerasimovich was accused of treason and sentenced to 10 years of imprisonment. He and several other well-known Russian astronomers—B. V. Numerov and N. I. Komendantov among them —disappeared completely. Their names were blocked out in articles already in press and did not reappear in any Soviet publication until the government cast off the Stalin "cult of personality."

There is no information concerning those Russian astronomers who lost their lives during World War I and the Russian civil war, but there is at least some indirect information concerning the effects of the following years of famine.

About 1922, after the end of the Russian Revolution, the food situation in the Soviet Union had become so serious that substantial aid from more prosperous countries was required. Pitiful letters from Russian astronomers reached the United States, and Edwin B. Frost, Director of the Yerkes Observatory, communicated about the problem with Frank Schlesinger of Yale University, who was at that time the president of the American Astronomical Society (AAS). At a meeting of the Society a small gift of food was sent to the eminent Russian astronomer A. A. Belopolsky to help his fellow astronomers; but this token would not keep alive even those who resided at Belopolsky's own observatory at Pulkovo.

In order to save as many Russian scientists as possible from starvation, Frost organized a small, informal committee at Yerkes Observatory. He undertook to serve as its chairman, and the Belgian-born astronomer G. Van Biesbroeck at Yerkes and I served as its members. I also acted as the secretary of the committee, and carried on the correspondence necessary in ordering food packages. Several hundred American astronomers made small monthly contributions out of their relatively meager salaries, and at the end of the project many dozen food packages had been mailed to all the principal observatories in the Soviet Union.

The naming by the Simeis Observatory of the minor planet Ara* (the initials of the "American Relief Administration," organized by former President Herbert Hoover to furnish food to starving Russians) was one of many indications of gratitude that came to the committee during its existence. Among those who felt that their lives had been saved through the generosity of their American colleagues were Professor and Mrs. Cerasky of Moscow, and Professor N. P. Belyayev of the Crimea. Most of

* The minor planets, or asteroids, are small bodies orbiting between Mars and Jupiter.

these men and women are no longer living, but the few who are undoubtedly remember the feeling of friendship that bound them to the astronomers of the United States. No such altruistic undertaking by individuals, and directed at a scientific group, occurred before or after the great Russian famine.

During World War II many of the established Russian observatories and their senior staff members were evacuated before the advance of the German armies. But one of the better-known scientists, K. F. Ogorodnikov, a professor of astronomy at the University of Leningrad, found himself among the defenders of that great city during the long siege. His family had been evacuated to an eastern province, but he himself remained at his post and witnessed the indescribable horrors of starvation and repeated bombings of the city. Ogorodnikov's own life probably was saved because, due to a small injury, he was flown out of Leningrad toward the end of the siege.

Loss of life among the younger Russian astronomers during World War II was not recorded systematically, but an indication of what happened may be gathered from occasional comments in various publications. Thus one learns from a "History of the University of Kharkov during 150 years of its Existence," by A. I. Slastenov,[1] that the young astronomer G. L. Strashny, whose work had just become familiar to Western scientists, was shot by German occupation authorities, as was M. S. Savron. U. N. Fadeiev and A. I. Rasdolsky of the same observatory died of starvation. The astrophysicists I. Timoshenko and V. Perzov were killed in action. The woman astronomer Lialia Oubijvovk became the leader of a band of guerrillas in the Poltava region; she was arrested and tortured to death by the German S.S. As far as can be judged from subsequent events, all of these severe losses in personnel at a single, relatively small provincial university were overcome by the rise of younger generations of able, highly trained, and presumably ambitious and nationalistically inclined persons.

These are but a few examples of the effects of wars, revolutions, and famine upon astronomers. Since their ranks were decimated in other countries as well, the increase in astronomical research since 1948 is all the more astonishing. It probably can be concluded that the almost miraculous rejuvenation of astronomy in the 20th century was an indirect result of these catastrophes and the enormous upheaval they evoked.

The Quest for Prestige

But what has made an astronomer "tick" during the past 60 years? In an article in *Science*[2] F. Reif of the University of California vividly described the tremendous pressures that have evolved in the quest of prestige and success in the field of physics during the past 10 or 20 years. A highly competitive atmosphere has been created in a pure science, encouraging work of the most spectacular kind and discouraging advances in the older and therefore less appealing fields. This atmosphere encourages, as well, rapid and often premature publication of preliminary results, as contrasted to prolonged and careful routine studies.

Astronomers are exposed to the same pressures. Their number is not so great as to cause a "Letter to the Editor" signed by 24 co-authors such as described by Reif. But the motto "publish or perish" drives many young astronomers to choose the "most fashionable areas of scientific activity" for their research, and to establish claims to priority rather than to concentrate upon those areas most important from a long-range point of view.

The American astronomer J. L. Greenstein recently wrote in a personal communication: "I am appalled at the absolute ignorance of so many of our graduate students [whom he described as "extremely bright"] about the major problems of contemporary astronomy and of historical accomplishments, defining by history anything more than ten years old."[3] And in a similar vein A. Sandage of Mount Wilson and Palomar Observatories wrote: "A modern history of astronomy will be one of the great stimuli for students, who of late just do not read the literature, either current or ten years old."[4] This is a far cry indeed from what an astronomer was supposed to do, and often did do, in the years before the outbreak of World War II.

An astronomer whose active scientific life goes back to the early years of this century must feel as though he were one of the few surviving dinosaurs of a rapidly disappearing species. At his antediluvian universities he learned: that the "royal road to success" in science first required the accumulation and slow digestion of a broad basis of observational and theoretical facts discovered by his elders; that only after this would a new idea, more or less suddenly, occur to him; that he would then test this idea by all possible means and certainly not announce it publicly until he had done so; and that if observational data were lacking or were insufficient to supply the test, he would forget the idea or postpone it until some later time. This dinosaur now finds to his amazement that the new species replacing him, while still utilizing a wide range of knowledge acquired in a limited field, often finds it expedient to substitute a "good guess" when test material is unavailable. The guess may or may not be good, and consequently the idea may or may not be sound. The new method does bring faster results and often stimulates the imagination, but it is certainly quite different from the old slow and tortuous road to scientific success.

Ideological Pressures

A great deal has been written, especially in the Soviet Union, about the effect of ideological differences upon astronomical research. Nearly every prominent 20th-century Western astronomer has at one time or another been described as being naive, a religious mystic, a tool of the bourgeoisie, or an agent of counter-revolution. The earlier writings on this topic, between about 1935 and 1955, usually were boastful in tone, claiming that only the followers of the Lenin-Stalin line of dialectic materialism were able to draw correct conclusions from observations. Western scientists were insultingly described as idealists who spread confusion in astronomy and distorted and falsified facts in order to find support for their bourgeois or capitalistic world picture. I refer to such addresses as that by the Russian V. E. Lvov, presented in 1953, at a Soviet conference on cosmogony. Russian-born G. Gamow, G. E. Lemaître, F. Hoyle, H. Bondi, and T. Gold, together with several "more serious scientists, such as O. Struve, C. F. von Weizsäcker, and Bart Bok," as well as Pope Pius XII, were all summarily accused of having attached some religious or pseudo-scientific significance to what was thought to be a coincidence in the age determination of stars and galaxies—from the redshift, the lines in the spectra of the latter, and from the physical and kinematic properties of the stars. This boastful attitude never seemed to be consistent with statements by Soviet astronomers at international scientific meetings, which were usually friendly and complimentary.

For example, at the 1952 meeting of the International Astronomical Union in Rome, the Soviet astronomer V. A. Ambarzumian, then a vice president of the Union, and since 1961 its president, made the following declaration:

... We, the Soviet astronomers, depend for our studies upon the enormous amount of factual data collected at observatories throughout the world, and upon theoretical investigations of scholars of different nationalities. It is for this reason that we attach the greatest importance to the peaceful collaboration of astronomers of the entire world. Because we experience a feeling of deep respect with regard to the research by these scientists ... we believe that the joint study of such large problems as that of the evolution of celestial bodies will contribute to the cultural rapprochement of different nations, and to a better understanding among them. This is our modest contribution to the noble efforts toward maintaining peace throughout the world.[5]

Fig. 11. A group of U.S.S.R. astronomers at the Rome meeting of the International Astronomical Union in 1952. (Left to right: U. A. Rjabov, P. G. Kulikovsky, D. J. Martinov, E. K. Kharadse, O. Melnikov, A. B. Severny, M. S. Nemiro, V. A. Ambarzumian, A. G. Massevich, B. V. Kukarkin, M. Zverev.)

However, the ideological differences—Leninist-Marxist materialism on one side, and capitalistic idealism on the other—are still very much on the minds of many distinguished Russian astronomers. The most sophisticated discussion of this problem was by the Russian B. V. Kukarkin, formerly vice president of the International Astronomical Union. He maintained that at the present time the Western idealists are trying to "reconcile" the requirements of science with their religious or idealistic views. In doing so they, in effect, are trying to revive the philosophy of the 18th-century German philosopher Immanuel Kant and, perhaps unconsciously, are "hiding" these efforts within the axiomatic postulates of their theories. Further, Kukarkin states that some of the "most remarkable contemporary scientists" are doing this, and that they themselves are often unaware of their erroneous initial concepts.[6]

The following chapters of this book give no indication of the idealistic dichotomy described by Kukarkin. They do suggest that Western astronomy is the same as Soviet astronomy, and that it makes no real difference whether we use the word "empiricism," as was done by the distinguished Italian astronomer G. Abetti in the preface to his history of astronomy,[7] or the words "dialectic materialism," as is done by the Soviet writers. It is true that one can find in the publications of Western astronomers occasional statements that must sound strange to young Soviet ears. The late English astronomer J. H. Jeans' remark about the "finger of God" that set the planets spinning around their axes can be twisted to mean something different from what was intended, and so also can the American physicist A. H. Compton's remark at the dedication of the McDonald Observatory in 1939: "... when rightly interpreted we have in religion our greatest hope of reaching a stable and satisfying life."[8] Neither can one find much scientific value in the philosophical sections of E. B. Frost's autobiography, published in 1933,[9] with his ideas of the orderliness of a "purposeful creation" of the universe. Are these personal views any more misleading than, for instance, the final sentence of the Russian astronomer P. P. Parenago's book *The World of the Stars*, which hails the "greatest genius of all mankind, comrade Stalin"?[10]

All of astronomy is materialistic or based upon empiricism. This book shows that while there are no perceptible differences in method or execution of scientific research based upon varying ideologies, there are large and significant differences in the ways in which individual astronomers have reached their goals. There were those such as G. E. Hale, the famous American solar physicist, former director of Yerkes and Mount Wilson Observatories, and the initiator of Palomar Observatory, who invented new instruments or built more powerful telescopes to answer questions that could not be approached with existing facilities. Many others who lacked skill in instrumentation made notable advances through what one may call successful hunches, while still others exploited their knowledge of mathematics and theoretical physics.

II

ASTRONOMY
IN 1900

A BRIEF SURVEY of the main astronomical events, the activities of astronomers, and some of the ideas they expressed in 1900 will provide a useful introduction to this discussion of the development of astronomy during the 20th century.

PRINCIPAL EVENTS

... Astronomers believed the closeness to the earth in 1900 of the minor planet Eros would permit determination of the value of the *astronomical unit** with much greater precision than was formerly possible. They intended to apply Kepler's third law: The squares of the orbital *periods*† of the planets are proportional to the cubes of their orbital *semimajor*

---

* The mean distance between the earth and the sun (abbreviated a.u.). The most recent value of the astronomical unit is 92.96 million miles.

† The periods of revolution around the sun.

Fig. 12. Trail of the minor planet Eros, on January 26, 1931. (*Courtesy Sky and Telescope*)

Fig. 13. Photograph of the solar corona, taken by E. E. Barnard and G. W. Ritchey, during the eclipse of May 28, 1900. (*Yerkes Observatory*)

axes.* Since the periods of the major and minor planets were accurately known, exact measurement of *one* distance between two bodies revolving around the sun would enable astronomers to determine the scale factor of the solar system. Realizing that the direct measurements of the distance between the sun and the earth are subject to many very serious errors, the astronomers recognized that better results would be obtained by measuring the distance, by *geocentric parallax*† of a starlike object, such as Eros, which happens to come close to the earth at certain times in its orbit.

. . . A total solar eclipse occurred on May 28, 1900, observable in the United States, Portugal, Spain, and Africa.

Both events attracted the attention of astronomers throughout the world, and the year's astronomical publications provided numerous accounts of successful observations of the eclipse and of detailed plans for the observations of Eros' celestial coordinates.

The famous American mathematician and astronomer, Simon Newcomb, discussed the importance of the Eros observations in his introductory remarks to the 1900 meeting of the American Astronomical Society:

Some one has divided astronomers into two classes, those who talk about things to be done, and those who go to work and do them. In the present case I am afraid we shall have to enroll ourselves in the first class, because it is not easy to do anything in this matter, the situation in this

* The mean distance of the planet from the sun.

† The apparent change of position of a heavenly body due to a shift of the observer by the rotation of the earth; hence only observed in bodies sufficiently close for the earth's radius to subtend a measurable angle.

country not being favorable to the determination which we have in view. You are doubtless all aware of the great interest attaching to this remarkable asteroid. It may be said to supply us with what we have long been wanting, an object admitting of exact observation, which at proper intervals will come so near the earth that the solar parallax can be determined with greater precision than by any other method. It would hardly be possible to get one more exactly to fill the bill. The minimum distance of Eros from the earth is 0.15 of the distance of the earth from the sun. It follows, therefore, that at certain times it will be about as near to us as observations can advantageously be made. Were it to come very much nearer the additional advantage would be slight, for the reason that the elements of its orbit could hardly be known with sufficient accuracy to give us greater advantage: 0.15 is all that we can ask for, since that distance will diminish the effect of errors of observation by six or seven times. We have made very little progress in this direction for fifty years, and may now hope for something more. Yet in Eros, the Fates or whoever rules our destiny, have supplied us with something very tantalizing. It turns out that the nearest approach of Eros to the earth occurs only on rare occasions. A nearest approach occurred in 1894, and another approach as near as that will not occur until after the middle of the coming century. But an approach as near as can occur in the next twenty years will take place in the coming autumn, when its minimum distance from the earth will be about 0.3 or twice its absolutely shortest distance. It is very desirable that astronomers who devote their attention to the determination of the solar parallax, should take advantage of this opportunity for we shall have a parallactic displacement of Eros exceeding three times and possibly five times the solar parallax. But there are many drawbacks, the planet is faint; it will probably be, when nearest to us, but little above the ninth magnitude, and it will therefore be scarcely possible from its rapid motion to photograph it, or to ascertain its true position upon the plate at any given time. It is difficult to ascertain just how the observations upon it should be made.[1]

An International Astrographic Conference was held in Paris in July, 1900, and "in conformity with the expressed objects of the conference, a special committee was appointed to prepare a general plan for systematic observations of Eros at the coming opposition, by which the widest cooperation of the observatories of the world would be secured."[2] This committee prepared a set of resolutions and recommendations to guide the astronomers in the most effective planning of their work.

Determining the astronomical unit from the parallax of Eros involved an enormous amount of work. The coordinates of Eros with respect to certain comparison stars had to be measured with the utmost accuracy; but first the positions of the comparison stars had to be determined with respect to brighter stars whose coordinates and *proper motions**

* The rate of change of the star's apparent place on the celestial sphere.

already were adequately known. The results of this investigation were published in 1910 by the Cambridge astronomer A. R. Hinks, who found 8″.806 (″ is seconds of arc) for the solar parallax, or 92.83 million miles (mi) for the astronomical unit. A similar campaign was conducted at the next close approach of Eros in 1930–1931, under Harold Spencer Jones, then Astronomer Royal of Great Britain. Eros probably will not be used again for measurement of the solar parallax, because several new methods employing recent advances in radar and electronic techniques and artificial satellites are capable of giving much higher accuracy. These are, for example, measurements of the *Doppler displacement** of transmitters located in space vehicles, and radar contact with other planets. The most recent determination of the astronomical unit, 92.96 million miles, was made at the Jet Propulsion Laboratory of the California Institute of Technology from radar contact with Venus in early 1961.

ASTRONOMICAL SOCIETIES

By 1900, the principal national astronomical societies were already active. The Royal Astronomical Society (RAS), for example, held regular meetings in London under the chairmanship of George Darwin and E. B. Knobel. At the turn of the century, the RAS had 635 fellows and an additional 48 foreign associates, who had been elected by the Society from countries outside the British Empire.

A special issue of the *Monthly Notices of the Royal Astronomical Society*[3] was devoted to accounts of the eclipse expeditions from Great Britain, led by Sir Norman Lockyer, H. H. Turner, and H. F. Newall, J. Evershed, R. Copeland, and W. H. M. Christie (Astronomer Royal) and F. W. Dyson (secretary of the RAS). The observations included direct photographs of the *corona*† and photographs of the coronal spectrum as well.

An important event in 1900 for the RAS was the award of the Society's Gold Medal to the famous French theoretical astronomer H. Poincaré. In his presidential address, George Darwin described three aspects of Poincaré's theoretical work: his mathematical study of the tides of the oceans, his memoir on the figures of equilibrium of rotating liquids, and his monumental work in celestial mechanics.[4] Darwin's concluding paragraph was:

The leading characteristic of M. Poincaré's work appears to me to be

---

* The shift in wavelength of sound or light waves due to relative motion of the source and the receiver, named for the formulator of the theory, the 19th-century Austrian physicist Christian Doppler.

† The outermost tenuous envelope of the sun.

Fig. 14.   H. Poincaré.

the immense wideness of the generalisations, so that the abundance of possible illustrations is sometimes almost bewildering. This power of grasping abstract principles is the mark of the intellect of the true mathematician; but to one accustomed rather to deal with the concrete the difficulty of completely mastering the argument is sometimes great. To the latter class of mind the easier process is the consideration of some simple concrete case, and the subsequent ascent to the more general aspect of the problem. I fancy that M. Poincaré's mind must work in another groove than this, and that he finds it easier to consider first the wider issues, from whence to descend to the more special instances. It is rare to possess this faculty in any high degree, and we cannot wonder that the possessor of it should have compiled a noble heritage for the men of science of future generations. In handing this medal to you, M. Poincaré, I desire to say on behalf of the Society that in seeking to pay honour to you we feel ourselves honoured.[5]

Many astronomers agree that with Poincaré and his contemporaries, especially F. Tisserand, the French school of mathematical astronomers founded by P. S. de Laplace, J. B. T. Delambre, and others almost 100 years earlier, reached the apex of its development and only one other group, H. Gyldén's in Sweden, could compete with it.

Poincaré's posthumous book *Leçons sur les hypothèses cosmogoniques (Lectures on Cosmogonical Hypotheses)*[6] is based, as are his other writings, entirely upon the study of Newtonian gravitation. With consummate skill he discussed—often much more lucidly than the original authors—the hypotheses advanced to explain the origin of the solar system. The *Leçons* inspired many of the astronomers who received their training in the first quarter of this century. Even now, 50 years later, Poincaré's results are quoted (for example, in some of the papers by D. Layser of Harvard University). Surely the *Leçons* is one of the most significant astronomical books ever written.

The Deutsche Astronomische Gesellschaft was the only astronomical society that attempted to maintain an international character. Meetings usually were held alternately one year inside and the next year outside of Germany. The Council, its governing body, always consisted of approximately equal numbers of German and non-German astronomers.

The 18th meeting of the Gesellschaft was held in Heidelberg, August, 1900. Hugo von Seeliger of Munich was the president, and the members of the Council were E. Weiss of Vienna, N. Dunér of Upsala, Sweden, M.Nyrén of Pulkovo, G. A. C. Oudemans of Utrecht, the Netherlands, R. Lehmann-Filhés of Berlin, G. Müller of Potsdam, and E. H. Bruns of Leipzig.

In the early years of the century von Seeliger, president of the Gesellschaft for many terms, was Germany's most influential astronomer. He still held this post at the time of the 1913 meeting at Hamburg in connection with the completion of the Bergedorf Observatory. I, then a high-school student, attended with my father, and vividly remember the famous astronomer. Some of the younger astronomers felt von Seeliger had been in power too long and should be replaced by someone from their ranks. But the "revolution" failed, and von Seeliger was re-elected by a large majority.

One of the most interesting papers presented at the 1900 Gesellschaft meeting was K. Schwarzschild's "Concerning the Possible Measure of Curvature of Space." Although the theory of relativity was still unknown in 1900, Schwarzschild apprehended the importance of non-Euclidian geometry. Referring to an article by H. Helmholtz, the German physicist, he comments:

We find ourselves— if we want to—in a geometrical fairyland, but it is the beauty of this fairyland that we do not know whether it may not in the end be real after all. The question should now be considered how far have we pushed the borders of this fairyland, how minute the curvature of space is, and how large a radius of curvature should be assumed.[7]

Schwarzschild's final conclusion is:

... it is possible, without contradicting the evidence, to think of the universe as contained within a hyperbolic (pseudospherical) space with a radius of curvature larger than 4,000,000 radii of the earth's orbit, or within a finite, elliptical space with a radius of curvature larger than 100,000,000 radii of the earth's orbit, while assuming in the latter case an absorption of light equal to 40 magnitudes in one journey around this space.[8]

Although it is now known that the possible radius of curvature of the universe must be much larger than the minimum values quoted by Schwarzschild, his paper represents a challenging effort to solve what is now referred to as the "cosmological problem."

An important service rendered by the Gesellschaft in the course of approximately a half-century was the publication (in its *Vierteljahrsschrift*, "Quarterly Journal") of a catalogue of variable stars. In 1900 E. Hartwig of Bamberg, Germany, listed 360 variable stars. The latest catalogue, published by the Russian astronomers B. V. Kukarkin, P. P. Parenago, U. I. Efremov, and P. N. Kholopov, lists 14,708 variables.

Fig. 15. (Left) H. von Seeliger.
Fig. 16. (Right) K. Schwarzschild.

Another 1900 publication was the German astronomer A. Auwers' report on the catalogue (the AGK1 catalogue) of star positions determined by many observatories cooperating under Gesellschaft auspices. The star positions contained in the AGK1 were redetermined about 30 years ago, under the same sponsorship, and reported in the AGK2 catalogue. At present, the positions are being determined for the AGK3 catalogue under the auspices of the International Astronomical Union (IAU); this will result in accurate calculations of the proper motions of stars.

The Gesellschaft maintained its international character until World War I and attempted to renew it in the years of peace following the Versailles treaty. A more representative international society of astronomers, the International Union for Cooperation in Solar Research, had been created through the initiative of G. E. Hale in 1904. In 1919, this group and several others conducting cooperative research merged to become the International Astronomical Union, which still is the only truly international association of astronomers. By 1959 the IAU had 1,120 members.

The organization of an American Astronomical Society was proposed in 1897 during the dedication of the Yerkes Observatory. The organizing conferences held at Yerkes in 1897 and at Harvard in 1898 were followed in 1899 by the Society's first regular meeting at Yerkes. The 1900 meeting at Columbia was held in connection with the 49th annual meeting of the American Association for the Advancement of Science. By that year the AAS membership had grown from 113 to about 150; present membership is close to 1000.

Fig. 17. Group picture taken at the meeting of the American Astronomical Society at the Yerkes Observatory in 1941. (*Courtesy* Sky and Telescope)

ASTRONOMICAL PUBLICATIONS

A glance at articles that appeared in 1900 in the *Astrophysical Journal* gives a good idea of the problems in astrophysics considered by astronomers at the turn of the century. C. Easton of the Netherlands published his famous hypothesis that the Milky Way is, in effect, a spiral galaxy whose center is at a considerable distance from the sun.

The name "Milky Way" originally was used to describe the conspicuous band of dense star clouds that forms almost a complete circle around the sky. However, it is now used also (as is done here) to denote the large, strongly flattened aggregate of stars, nebulae, and dust—the Milky Way galaxy—outlined by these star clouds. The Milky Way band results from the greater concentration of stars and the extent of the system in this plane, near which the sun is located. The Milky Way, also often referred to simply as "the galaxy" or "our galaxy" is similar to the spirals, such as the Andromeda galaxy (see Fig. 214) or M 81 (see Fig. 195). The latter are often referred to as *extragalactic nebulae* as distinguished from *galactic nebulae*, the nebulous gas clouds within the Milky Way. Since that time, Easton's hypothesis has been revised drastically. According to Easton, for example, the center of the Milky Way is located approximately in the direction of the constellation Cygnus; actually the center is located almost 75° farther south in Sagittarius. Nevertheless, as will be seen in Chap. XIX, P. 428, Easton's article profoundly affected study of the structure of the Milky Way.

Still another outstanding contribution to astronomy in 1900 was an article by J. E. Keeler, director of the Lick Observatory, on the observatory's Crossley reflector, an instrument that has rendered great services to photographic astronomy during this century. Keeler says in the first sentence of his paper: "The Crossley reflector, at present the largest instrument in its class in America, was made in 1879 by Dr. A. A. Common, of London, in order to carry out a test by practical observations, of certain ideas of his respecting the design of large reflecting telescopes."[9] The reflector was later presented to the Lick Observatory where it still is used for the direct photography of nebulae, for spectroscopic studies of various types of stars and emission nebulosities, and for the measurement of the *radial velocities** of exceedingly faint objects. Keeler's article contains reproduction of a photograph of the Trifid Nebula in Sagittarius. When this early photograph is compared with a recent photograph made with

* Motions along the line of sight toward or away from the observer.

Fig. 18. (Top) The Lick Observatory around 1900: (left) large dome containing the 36-in. refractor; (right) smaller dome containing the 12-in. refractor. (*Lick Observatory*)

Fig. 19. (Below left) The 36-in. Crossley reflector as it appeared in 1900. (Lick Observatory Publications, *VIII, 1908, p. 16*)

Fig. 20. (Below right) The Crossley reflector with its modern mounting. (*Lick Observatory*)

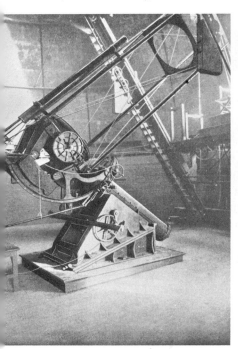

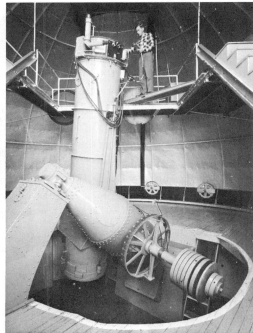

Fig. 21. Keeler's photograph of the Trifid Nebula. (*Lick Observatory Publications, VIII, 1908, plate 55*)

the 200-in. telescope, it is seen that the latter, taken in the red region of the spectrum, does not show the companion nebulosity, which is very strongly blue.

Unfortunately, Keeler died later in 1900, after only two years' work at the Lick Observatory. His biography by W. W. Campbell, the next director of the observatory was printed in the *Astrophysical Journal*.[10]

H. C. Vogel of the Potsdam Observatory, whose main contribution was the discovery of spectroscopic binary stars, published a long article on "Progress Made in the Last Decade in Determination of Stellar Motions in the Line of Sight."[11] Most of Vogel's work was done prior to 1900, but his article contains a useful summary of the earlier measurements by Sir William Huggins, the English astronomer of the 19th century, in London, as well as his own and those of other astronomers in the latter part of the 1800's. The precision of Vogel's measurements, made with a small prism spectrograph, is comparable to the precision obtained now with much better instruments (see Chap. IV).

The American theoretical astronomer F. R. Moulton published the im-

Fig. 22. The Trifid Nebula, photographed in red light with the 200-in. Hale telescope. (*Mount Wilson and Palomar Observatories*)

portant article, "An Attempt to Test the Nebular Hypothesis by an Appeal to the Laws of Dynamics." In this article he criticized the then accepted theory of the origins of the solar system as proposed by Laplace (see P. 169). His principal conclusion that " . . . certain phenomena . . . contradict the hypothesis so flatly that candid minds must admit that its validity in the form considered is open to serious question . . . "[12] was not accepted for many years, mainly because of the appeal Laplace's work held for those who were mainly interested in the simpler aspects of the nebular hypothesis. However, Moulton's conclusions have been confirmed so many times during the past 60 years that their validity is unchallengeable.

In the *Astronomical Journal* of 1900 Moulton published his meteoric theory of the *Gegenschein* or counterglow. During a visit by Moulton to the Yerkes Observatory, the American astronomer E. E. Barnard, who was an extremely keen observer, had pointed out to him the faint glow that can be seen in the night sky in a direction opposite the sun's. While the *Gegenschein* is always faint, it can be distinguished fairly easily at those times of the year when it does not merge with the Milky Way. Moulton's theory is based upon the properties of particles of very small mass traveling in the gravitational field produced by the sun and the earth.

These particles, which tend to linger near the Lagrangian point that lies about 70,000 mi. beyond the apex of the earth's shadow, are illuminated by the sun. Because of their relatively greater concentration in the vicinity of the Lagrangian point, they produce an additional illumination, except at the very center of the glow. At the center, according to Moulton, there should be a minimum of intensity that may be described as an annular eclipse of the sun as seen from each individual particle. The sun's disk is not completely covered by the disk of the earth during such an eclipse, as would be the case if the particles were inside the earth's shadow, and a luminous outer ring of the sun remains visible.

The accumulation of the observational data required to test the theories formulated by 1900 and to develop new ones during the 20th century has been greatly facilitated through the introduction of new observational techniques and the improvement of those already in use around 1900. One such important method of accumulating observational information is by photography.

III

PHOTOGRAPHY OF
THE MILKY WAY

OF THE SIGNIFICANT contributions to the application of photography in astronomy, the work of E. E. Barnard was particularly important. During the first two decades of this century, he was not only the most notable member of the Yerkes Observatory staff, but was recognized universally as the most capable and productive observer throughout the world. I still vividly remember my first impression of him. When I arrived at the Yerkes Observatory in 1921 as a refugee from war-torn Russia, one of the first persons I met was an elderly gentleman—Barnard—who was looking at the barograph in the library of the observatory, quietly complaining to himself that the barometric pressure was going down and the sky would presumably be cloudy. This concern was typical of Barnard and according to another of his associates, the American astronomer Philip Fox:

One could always tell what the night had been by his reaction from it. If clouds or bad seeing had marred the observing, his unconscious sighs were clearly audible. If the sky had been kind, his spirit was gay with song.[1]

Although Barnard's bibliography (which he maintained as a card index in his office) includes the titles of some 900 papers, his name is now seldom mentioned in astronomical literature. Yet all active astronomers are in one way or another building upon the foundation of accurate measurements of celestial bodies and utilizing the thousands of photographs of the Milky Way he obtained, first at the Lick Observatory and later at

Yerkes. It is astonishing that Barnard's contributions are not often mentioned by those who are so indebted to him. His name and work have become a part of the history of astronomy sooner, perhaps, than is normal. Astronomers have found Barnard's contributions to be sound and have long associated his with the great names of earlier decades.

EARLY YEARS OF E. E. BARNARD

Edward Emerson Barnard was born in Nashville, Tennessee, on December 16, 1857. Because his family was poor he had to leave public school after attending only 2 months. When he was only 9 years old, he started to work as a photographer's assistant in Nashville. At this time sunlight was used as the source of illumination, and Barnard's principal duty was to point a heavy enlarging camera at the sun. In order to make the work easier and use the time for reading and study, he built a simple equatorial mounting operated by a driving mechanism, so that the camera automatically followed the diurnal motion of the sun. One of the books he read during these years was Thomas Dick's *Practical Astronomer*,[2] from which he gained his early knowledge of astronomy.

By 1877 Barnard had saved enough money to buy a 5-in. equatorial telescope, and he was soon well known as an active amateur astronomer. Barnard joined the American Association for the Advancement of Science, and at a meeting of the association in Nashville he met Simon Newcomb of the United States Naval Observatory. Newcomb advised Barnard that in order to accomplish something important in astronomical research, he must first be well grounded in mathematics, but Barnard could not afford formal study. True, by reading at home he became proficient in elementary mathematics, but he was never thoroughly acquainted with the more advanced developments, and his fame rests upon his achievements as an observer, not as a theoretician.

BARNARD'S VISUAL OBSERVATIONS

The Search for Comets

On May 12, 1881, the 23-year-old Barnard discovered his first comet in the morning sky near α Pegasi. Formal announcement of his discovery was not made, however, and the comet went unobserved by other astronomers. The first comet officially discovered by him was observed on the night of September 17, 1881, in the constellation Virgo. Searching the sky over a period of years, he discovered many more comets,

Fig. 23.   E. E. Barnard.

and five times received the $200 prize established by Mr. H. H. Warner of Rochester, New York, for each unexpected comet discovered by an American observer. With this money Barnard bought the modest home known in Nashville as "Comet House."

The Fifth Satellite of Jupiter

A small fellowship offered Barnard in 1883 at Nashville's Vanderbilt University enabled him to attend courses while taking care of the observatory, and he received his B.S. degree in 1887. In the same year, E. S. Holden, the Lick Observatory's first director, offered Barnard a position. He remained at Lick until 1895 making some of his greatest discoveries with the observatory's 36-in. visual refractor.

On September 9, 1892, Barnard discovered Jupiter's fifth satellite. This represents perhaps the most remarkable visual observation ever made. A most difficult object to discern with any telescope, it can be seen only during elongations, when the satellite is at its greatest angular distance from Jupiter, and then only under conditions of excellent seeing. In recognition of his achievement, in 1897 Barnard was awarded the RAS Gold Medal. Commenting on the award, Simon Newcomb recalled their first meeting in Nashville:

... I did not for a moment suppose that there was a reasonable probability of the young man's doing anything better than amusing himself. At the same time feeling it a duty to encourage him, I suggested that there was only one thing open to an astronomical observer situated as he was, and that was the discovery of comets.

I had never even looked for a comet myself and knew little about the methods of exploring the heavens for one, except what had been told me by H. P. Tuttle. But I gave him the best directions I could and we parted. It is now rather humiliating that I did not inquire more thoroughly into the case. It would have taken more prescience than I was gifted with to expect that I should live to see the bashful youth awarded the gold medal of the Royal Astronomical Society for his work. . . .[3]

ADVANCES IN PHOTOGRAPHY

Experiments in the application of photography to astronomy had begun even before Barnard was born. His major contribution, however, is the refinement of astronomical photography through the use of different types of instruments, especially in the case of photographic objectives of large angular field.

Both the daguerreotype process, invented in 1839, and the colloidal process, introduced around 1850, were extremely slow, and early experiments were necessarily devoted to photography of the sun, moon, planets, and some of the brightest stars. By 1900, many photographs of the planets, comets, and asteroids had been obtained. To the surprise of many astronomers, however, the greatest advances had been made in photography of the stars and nebulae, a field of observations that seemed at first to hold little promise.

In the fall of 1882, a few years after the relatively fast dry plates had become available, the English astronomer D. Gill photographed a bright comet in the southern sky over the Cape of Good Hope. He used a camera borrowed from a local photographer. Gill's pictures showed the comet well, but the large number of stars recorded was even more impressive. At this time the brothers Paul and Prosper Henry of Paris were busy charting the stars along the *ecliptic.*° They were discouraged by the immense numbers encountered in the region of the Milky Way until Gill's photographs indicated the possible value of photography in making charts. It may be assumed that the active application of stellar photography dates from this incident.

Nebular photography started in 1880 when the American astronomer Henry Draper obtained the first photograph of the Orion nebula. In the 1880's the best photographs of nebulae were obtained by A. A. Common in England with the 3-ft. reflector that later was to become the Lick Observatory's Crossley reflector. Astronomers on the whole were rather skeptical about the advantages of nebular photography. A controversy had raged for some time over the existence of a nebula connected with the star Merope, of the Pleiades cluster, and when the Henry brothers constructed their photographic telescope one of the photographs

. . . showed the Merope nebula just as the best observers had drawn it and at the same time filled the entire group of stars with an entangling

---

° The apparent path of the sun on the celestial sphere due to the orbital motion of the earth.

system of nebulous matter which seemed to bind together the different stars of the group with misty wreaths and streams of filmy light clearly all of which is entirely beyond the keenest vision and the most powerful telescope. This was a revelation. . . . It began to dawn upon astronomers what great possibilities lay in the photographic plate for the detection and study of nebulae. . . .[4]

One of Common's photographs of a nebula, and another taken by the Henry brothers of a densely crowded region of a part of the constellation Cygnus, indicated to Barnard the astronomical value of photographs. Thus he conceived the idea of photographing the Milky Way.

During the wet-plate period of photography, the Willard photographic lens (named after a photographic stock dealer) had been used for making portraits. The lens was valuable because its great relative aperture shortened the time of the sitting. The Lick Observatory purchased the lens after it had been used by an amateur astronomer to obtain excellent photographs of the solar eclipse of January 1, 1889. The necessary funds were donated by C. F. Crocker, a Regent of the University of California, also noted for his support of several expeditions from the Lick Observatory to observe solar eclipses. After arriving at Yerkes in 1895, Barnard tried for several years to interest someone in purchasing a portrait lens similar to the Willard lens. Miss Catherine W. Bruce, who had already given money for the construction of several photographic telescopes and other astronomical equipment at various institutions, donated the sum needed for a photographic telescope consisting of a 5-in. guiding telescope and two photographic doublets of 10 and 6¼ in. in aperture, rigidly bound together on the same mounting.

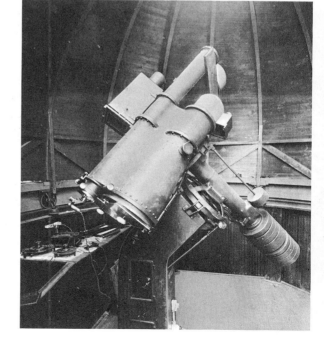

Fig. 24. The Bruce photographic telescope of the Yerkes Observatory. (*Yerkes Observatory*)

Fig. 25. Comet Morehouse photographed by E. E. Barnard with the Bruce photographic telescope.

Barnard's photographic observations of the Milky Way were published in many issues of the *Astrophysical Journal* and collected in two important volumes. The earlier volume[5] contains 129 photographs, mainly of the Milky Way and comets, made with the 6-in. Willard lens. His last series of photographs, an *Atlas* published in 1927,[6] includes 50 obtained with the Bruce telescope at the Yerkes and Mount Wilson observatories (Barnard had spent part of 1905 as guest investigator at Mount Wilson, taking with him the Bruce telescope).

An amusing incident occurred during the preparation of prints for the *Atlas*. All prints were made in Chicago and shipped to Yerkes by truck. During one of the "mob wars" in Chicago a gangster's bullet pierced a shipment of photographs. The photographs had to be remade, but for years the damaged prints remained objects of curiosity to visitors at Yerkes.

"HOLES" IN THE HEAVENS

An important feature of the *Atlas* are the charts identifying the brightest stars and the dark and luminous nebulae. Barnard also included a catalogue of dark nebulae in his Introduction to the *Atlas*.

The existence of dark regions in the Milky Way had been known to astronomers since the English astronomer W. Herschel announced their existence in the late 18th century with the famous words: "Surely, this is a hole in the heavens!" It took some time, however, before these "holes"

Fig. 26. Star cloud in the region of Sagittarius, photographed in red light w$\cdot$ the Palomar 48-in. Schmidt telescope. (*Mount Wilson and Palomar Observatorie*

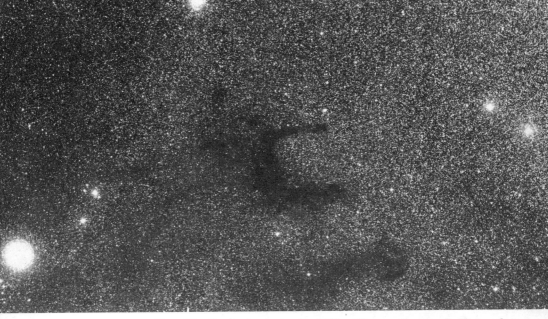

Fig. 27. Dark clouds in the Milky Way northwest of Altair, photographed with the Palomar 48-in. Schmidt telescope. © *1955 National Geographic Society – Palomar Observatories*)

were correctly interpreted. In 1903 Miss Clerke* wrote:

> ... That dark stars exist, singly and in systems, and dark nebulae no less, we have been almost inevitably led to conclude; but the galactic clefts cannot be reckoned among their manifestations. They are, on the contrary, what they appear to be, intervals of starless space between neighboring star clouds, and suggest processes of disintegration advancing with inconceivable slowness towards unimagined issues.[8]

And in 1919 Barnard noted:

> I did not at first believe in these dark obscuring masses. The proof was not conclusive. The increase of evidence, however, from my own photographs convinced me later, especially after investigating some of them visually, that many of these markings were not simply due to an actual want of stars, but were really obscuring bodies nearer to us than the distant stars. In this way it has fallen to my lot to prove this fact. I think that there is sufficient proof now to make this certain.[9]

Barnard's was the only catalogue of dark clouds until 1960, when D. Sh. Khavtasi's six-chart atlas of galactic dark nebulosities was published in the Soviet Union.[10] This new atlas confirms earlier findings that dark nebulae have a strong tendency to be distributed along the *galactic equa-*

*tor** and that the widest distribution in *galactic latitude*† occurs in the vicinity of the galactic center, where it is approximately uniform between galactic latitudes −10 and +15°. In the region of Cygnus and Vulpecula the range is from about −7 to +5° in latitude.

The Russian astronomers G. A. Shajn and W. F. Hase reported in 1952 that the dark clouds of the Milky Way usually are elongated in directions parallel to the galactic plane. Their finding suggests the existence of an interstellar magnetic field whose lines of force lie predominantly in the galactic plane. A trend toward such orientation also is suggested by Khavtasi's atlas, but individual clouds often depart strikingly from this general rule.

Another catalogue has just been completed at the National Radio Astronomy Observatory by Mrs. B. T. Lynds, who has made use of the National Geographic–Palomar Observatory *Sky Atlas* photographs discussed below, and has recorded and mapped the various objects.

WIDE-ANGLE PHOTOGRAPHIC TELESCOPES

Barnard worked exclusively with photographic lenses, never with reflectors. The Estonian-born optician B. Schmidt invented the wide-angle reflecting telescope in Germany in 1932, after Barnard's death. The best photographs of large regions of the Milky Way are obtained with either Schmidt reflectors or Maksutov-type reflectors (similar instruments developed in the Soviet Union) in which the *spherical aberration*‡ is corrected by means of a suitably figured, thin correcting lens before the rays reach the spherical surface of the reflector. The *coma*§ is eliminated by making the aperture, or diameter, of the correcting lens smaller than the aperture of the spherical mirror. For example, the 48-in. Schmidt telescope on Mount Palomar has a spherical mirror with a 72-in. aperture.

A similar but slightly smaller Schmidt telescope is used at the Bergedorf Observatory near Hamburg, Germany. Several Maksutov telescopes are used in the Soviet Union, and excellent photographs have been obtained, for instance, by astronomers at the Crimean Astrophysical Observatory and the Burakhan Observatory in Armenia. Recent experiments indicate that the Schmidt reflector's optical performance is somewhat better

---

* The intersection of the plane of the Milky Way and the celestial sphere.

† The angular distance north or south of the galactic equator.

‡ The failure of light rays from the outer and inner parts of a lens or mirror to converge at the same focal point.

§ A distortion present only in reflecting telescopes, producing elongated, comet-like images at the outer edge of the field (see Fig. 188).

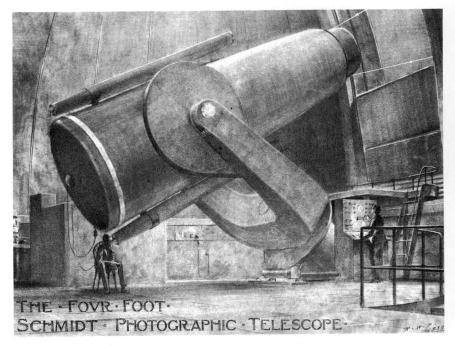

Fig. 28. Drawing by Russell Porter of the 48-in. Schmidt telescope. (*Mount Wilson and Palomar Observatories*)

than that of the Maksutov telescope, but both have been used to cover regions of the sky of the order of 6½° on the side. The National Geographic-Palomar Observatory *Sky Atlas* photographs have been obtained with this instrument. The *Atlas* consists of photographic reproductions of red- and blue-sensitive photographs of 879 fields, 6.6° square (sq), and covers the entire sky north of −27° declination. This *Atlas*, published in 1954, has the most complete coverage and the best quality of any in existence and contains an enormous wealth of information that is just beginning to be explored. The more recent development of wide-angle optical systems occurred in the 1940's at Yerkes Observatory and is largely the result of the work of L. G. Henyey and J. L. Greenstein. A representative photograph of the Milky Way obtained with a camera of this kind covers a region of the sky of 140° (see Fig. 29).

"WOLF CURVES"

While Barnard was interested primarily in the peculiar shapes of cosmic clouds, Max Wolf of Heidelberg, Germany, another significant contributor to the application of photography in astronomy, was con-

Fig. 29. The Milky Way from Sagittarius to Crux, photographed by A. D. Code with a wide-angle Henyey–Greenstein camera.

cerned with a different aspect of the problem. He invented a method for estimating the distance of a dark cloud from the apparent magnitudes of the foreground stars. When the nebula is not completely opaque, the stars showing through make it possible to derive an approximate value of the absorption of the cloud. Wolf's method was a simple one: He plotted the numbers of stars per unit area of sky against their mean apparent magnitudes (brightnesses) and compared plots made in transparent regions with plots made in the regions of dark nebulosities. In the graph of the ob-

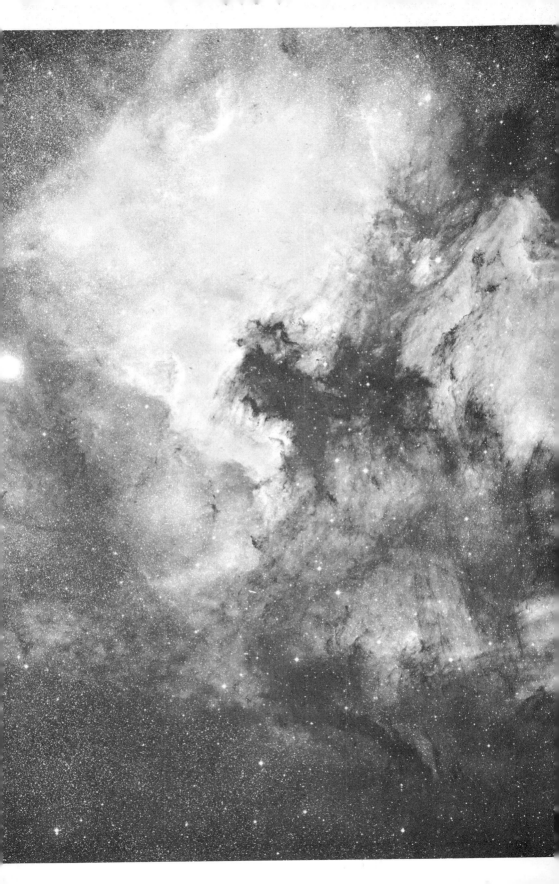

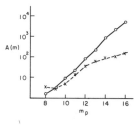

Fig. 31. Observed "Wolf curves" for the region of the North America Nebula. (*From O. Struve, B. Lynds, and H. Pillans, Elementary Astronomy, New York, Oxford University Press, 1959, Fig. 27.6*)

served "Wolf Curves" for the region of the North America Nebula, the solid curve represents the unobscured region, the dashed curve the region of the dark cloud. This method never was intended to produce more than a very crude estimate of the distance of a cloud and its absorption of optical light. Other astronomers often have used the same method, sometimes exaggerating its importance and attempting to derive more accurate values than Wolf himself anticipated. In 1937, B. J. Bok critically examined the use of Wolf curves, pointing out that the large differences that exist in stellar intrinsic brightnesses often obscure and complicate the real effects of the dark nebulae to such an extent that the distance, total absorption, and even the number of nebulae in line of sight can be greatly misjudged from an inspection of these curves. In his review of a book by the German astronomer W. Becker,[11] O. Struve also pointed out that it is unrealistic to apply the Wolf curves to dark nebulae, the fringes of which are nearly transparent, while the central regions are almost completely opaque. Exaggerated applications of Wolf's method have produced very questionable results.

Although photographs of dark cosmic clouds have been accumulating for 70 years, as yet there is no reliable information about their motions. But there is every reason to believe that soon it will be possible to find displacements of the edges of certain dark nebulae and probably also to observe the gradual obscuration of stars by the clouds, as well as the emergence of hitherto invisible stars. Earlier investigators attempted to attribute certain types of stellar variability to the obscuration-emergence process, but as yet no case has been proved in which the variation in brightness is attributable to changes in the opacity of the interstellar material in the line of sight.

IV

RADIAL
VELOCITIES

PHOTOGRAPHY GIVES A record of the position and appearance of celestial objects and, in special cases, the angular displacement on the celestial sphere. On the other hand, the analysis of their spectra enables the determination of their radial velocities.

In 1842, Christian Doppler, then at the University of Prague, announced the effect of the approach or recession of a light source upon its *spectrum.*[*]

Doppler was familiar with the analogous effect of motion upon the pitch of a sound wave: The whistle of an approaching locomotive appears to be higher in pitch than that of the same locomotive when it is receding. He concluded that in a similar way the spectrum of an approaching light-source should be displaced toward the violet (or shorter wavelength) while the spectrum of a receding light-source, should be displaced toward the red (or longer wavelength). Hence he believed that light would redden if the distance between the earth and a star were increasing and become more violet if the distance were decreasing. However, no such effect occurs with relative motions of tens or even hundreds of kilometers per second. For a receding light-source the invisible near ultraviolet

---

[*] The spectrum of a star, as formed by a conventional *spectrograph* (described on P. 65), consists of a continuous bright background, the continuous spectrum, ranging from red for the longest visible wavelengths to violet for the shortest. The continuous spectrum is crossed by narrow dark or bright lines, the *absorption* or *emission* lines, respectively, the origin of which will be discussed in more detail in Chap. XI. The wavelength of light is usually measured in *Angstrom units* (abbreviated A): $1A = 10^{-8}$ cm. The common abbreviation for wavelength is λ.

radiations may become visible, while the visible red radiations are shifted into the infrared region that cannot be detected by the human eye, but the photographic plate, properly sensitized, can record the infrared radiations.

In 1913, W. W. Campbell, in his famous volume on *Stellar Motions*,[1] stated that Doppler had erred and that in 1848 the French physicist and astronomer H. Fizeau had correctly pointed out that the continuous spectrum would not change as a consequence of radial motion. Campbell maintained that the Doppler shift can be seen only in the displacements of the absorption and emission lines of a stellar spectrum.

The contention that Doppler had erred is no longer acceptable. When the relative motion of the earth and the light source is very large, roughly in the range of 0.2 to 0.5 times the velocity of light (186,000 mi/sec), there is a detectable change in the continuous spectrum of the source. The American W. A. Baum at Mount Wilson Observatory has made extensive use of his measurements of the energy distributions of very distant and rapidly receding galaxies with normal spectra. These spectra would resemble that of the sun if the galaxies were stationary, but observed spectra show a striking shift of the entire *energy curve*,* especially of the maximum of the energy spectrum toward the red. In the drawing of spectral intensity curves on P. 62, the solid line applies if the galaxy is at rest relative to the earth, the dashed line if it is receding from us at half the velocity of light. Such a rapidly moving object would appear markedly reddened. The dotted ordinate is the wavelength of maximum sensitivity of ordinary photographic plates (see also Fig. 238). However, in the case of stars belonging to the Milky Way, relative motions with respect to the earth are never larger than a few hundred kilometers per second (km/sec), and the shift of the energy curve of the continuous spectrum, therefore, cannot be detected.

PIONEERS IN RADIAL-VELOCITY DETERMINATION

The first practical application of the Doppler principle was achieved in the second half of the 19th century by Sir William Huggins at his private observatory with a visual spectroscope attached to a small refractor. Such observations, however, were affected by serious systematic errors. For example, one observer reported 73 km/sec, but another found 89 km/sec as the velocity of recession of the bright star Arcturus. The first reliable visually determined radial velocities were obtained at Lick Ob-

* A plot of the intensity of the continuous spectrum as a function of wavelength.

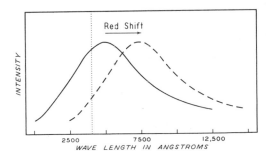

Fig. 32. Spectral intensity curves for a typical galaxy. (*Courtesy* Sky and Telescope)

servatory around 1890 by J. E. Keeler, who not only was a skilled observer but also had the powerful 36-in. telescope, a good spectroscope, and ideal atmospheric conditions. Keeler obtained a velocity of approach of 6 km/sec for Arcturus. The currently accepted radial velocity of approach is 5.2 km/sec, obtained from the measurement of 628 spectrograms from 16 observatories. In the photograph of two spectra of the star Arcturus, the two light bands represent the continuous spectrum of the star and the black vertical lines are the absorption bands produced by various atoms in the stellar atmosphere. The white vertical lines at the top and bottom were produced by an iron arc comparison source. The shift of the stellar absorption lines toward the right (red) in *a* and toward the left (violet) in *b* are well shown by the iron absorption lines which match the emission lines of the comparison source.

Fig. 33. Two spectra of the star Arcturus taken about six months apart: (a) July 1, 1939, measured velocity +18 km/sec; (b) January 19, 1940, measured velocity −32 km/sec. The velocity difference of 50 km/sec is entirely due to the velocity of the earth. (*Mount Wilson and Palomar Observatories*)

42⁵

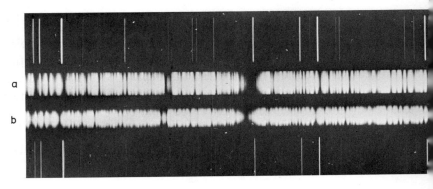

Fig. 34. W. W. Campbell.

Anyone who has attempted to observe a stellar spectrum with a visual spectroscope attached to a refractor or reflector realizes how difficult it is to see any absorption lines on the relatively weak continuous background. It is surprising that, considering this difficulty and that of producing a comparison spectrum of a terrestrial source in a visual spectroscope, Keeler and others determined the radial velocities of even a few stars with any degree of precision.

One of the first attempts to photograph stellar spectra on wet plates was made by Huggins in 1863. Draper in the United States obtained stellar spectrograms in 1872, still using the wet-plate method. Both men welcomed the development of dry plates, but their results with these also reflected serious errors. Hence, the era of accurate radial velocity measurements began with the work of the German astronomers H. C. Vogel and J. Scheiner at the Potsdam Observatory from 1888 to 1891. Their average probable error was only 2.6 km/sec, an improvement by a factor of almost 10 over earlier results. Many a non-German astronomer went to Potsdam to learn radial-velocity measurement techniques from Vogel and

4271.8

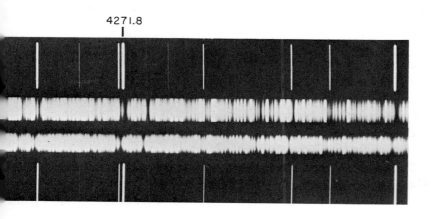

Fig. 35. E. B. Frost (left), A. A. Belopolsky (seated), and F. Ellerman in 1899 at the entrance of the Yerkes Observatory.

his associates. Among these students were E. B. Frost, who applied these techniques at Yerkes, and A. A. Belopolsky, who remained active in this field for about 25 years at Pulkovo. At the Lick Observatory, highly accurate measurements were initiated by Campbell, who constructed the famous 3-prism Mills spectrograph that is, with minor improvements, still used.

At the end of the 19th century, Huggins, commenting on the future of radial-velocity determinations, concluded: "This method of work will doubtless be very prominent in the astronomy of the near future, and to it probably we shall have to look for the more important discoveries in side-real astronomy which will be made during the coming century."[2] In the early years of this century, the possibility of measuring a star's radial velocity by means of the Doppler effect was so promising and rewarding that those who had access to large telescopes were highly enthusiastic about their work. I recall that E. B. Frost often said he would rather measure stellar radial velocities than engage in any other type of scientific activity.

Now, much of the glamour of such work has faded; indeed, many astronomers now consider it a necessary but tiresome occupation.

PROS AND CONS OF RADIAL-VELOCITY MEASUREMENT

An enormous amount of valuable information can be derived from radial velocities. For example, the study of several types of stars—such as spectroscopic binaries and pulsating variables, of the expansion of gaseous shells, of motions within gaseous nebulae, and statistical studies of stellar motions—come largely from radial-velocity investigations.

The work may become tedious because of the extensive labor involved both in the measurement of the displacement of the spectral lines and in the reduction of measurements. Many observations often are required to obtain a significant result. This brings up an important aspect of astronomy in general. Perhaps the most outstanding differences between astronomy and its related sciences are the time required to discover new facets in the universe and the enormous accuracy of measurement that is required to produce valuable astronomical information. Ordinarily, an astronomer is not able to experiment. Natural phenomena are usually complicated superpositions of many different processes. Thus even a very simple problem, such as the determination of the mass of a binary star using Kepler's third law (see P. 294), may require hundreds of years of observations before an accurate determination of the binary orbit can be made. Similarly, in the study of pulsating variable stars, astronomers often find superpositions of several distinct periods. It may take many years to disentangle these periods and determine from them and from the radial velocities the corresponding changes in the diameters of radially expanding and contracting variables.

In order to achieve the required accuracy, it is necessary to beware of many possible sources of error and, to illustrate this point, several sources of instrumental error in the determination of radial velocities will be discussed in some detail.

DESIGNING SPECTROGRAPHS AND SOURCES OF ERROR

Illumination of the Slit

In the photographic method, the image of a star usually is trailed along a part of the slit of the spectrograph, in the focal plane of the image-forming telescope. The comparison spectrum typically is an iron arc or a titanium spark, and its light is projected in a direction that coincides with the plane of the slit.

All the early spectrographs (beginning with Vogel's and continuing with those of Campbell at Lick, Frost at Yerkes, Belopolsky at Pulkovo, F. Küstner at Bonn, and, somewhat later, J. S. Plaskett at Ottawa and Victoria) employed glass prisms for the dispersing units and doublet lenses for the *collimators* and *cameras*.* Astronomers soon recognized

---

* The collimator renders the light that has passed through the slit parallel before it reaches the prism (or prisms); the camera focuses the dispersed light. Instead of glass prisms, most modern spectrographs have dispersion gratings, usually made by ruling a series of fine parallel lines on an aluminized plane glass plate.

that to conserve light the collimator should be made as long as possible, the spectrograph aperture as large as possible, and the cameras of shorter focal length. In the photograph of the Bruce spectrograph, equipped with 3 prisms, the collimator is at the bottom and the camera, which is parallel to the collimator, is at the top. Typical ratios of collimator to camera lengths were 2 (or 3):1. In recent years, several spectrographs have been constructed with a ratio of 10 (or more):1. This refinement enables the observer to open the slit wider than with a 1:1 ratio, where the camera lens, in combination with the collimator and the *prism* (or grating), produces a monochromatic image of the slit whose width is equal to that of the slit. Hence the earlier spectrographs employed slit widths of 0.01 to 0.03 millimeter (mm). Even in very good seeing, the star image in a large telescope's focal plane may be 1″ in diameter, which for the Yerkes 40-in. refractor would correspond to 0.1 mm. By opening the slit to a width of several tenths of a millimeter, a large fraction of the starlight is utilized in forming the spectrum, and the exposure times are correspondingly reduced.

All stellar spectroscopists no doubt wish to utilize the starlight ordinarily intercepted by the jaws of the slit. The only constructive idea for accomplishing this was published by I. S. Bowen, the present director of the Mount Wilson and Palomar Observatories, in 1938. His *image slicer* consists of a series of thin glass plates or mirrors, which displace slices of the original star image, lining them up on both sides of the principal image. No method exists—and Bowen says that none can be invented—that would enable the observer to superpose the slices of the image on top of the narrow spectrum produced by the central strip. Hence Bowen's procedure produces a series of narrow spectra and makes it possible to decrease the exposure time normally required to widen the spectrum by trailing the star image along the slit.

Opening the slit introduces a possible source of error carefully investigated about a quarter of a century ago by Plaskett. If the star image is not held accurately in the middle of the slit, between the jaws, but illuminates one edge more than the other, a spurious shift of the spectral lines is found. The diffuse light of the comparison source, on the other hand, illuminates the slit uniformly and gives the correct wavelength. Ordinarily, an observer holds the star image accurately between the two edges of the slit, but in most parts of the sky, atmospheric dispersion causes the image to be slightly unsymmetrical—blue on one side and red on the other. Hence if the yellow light of the image is used for guiding the telescope visually, but the blue light is dispersed and photographed,

Fig. 36. The Bruce spectrograph of the Yerkes Observatory.

Fig. 37. Diagram of the 80-in. telescope of the Kitt Peak National Observatory showing the mirror system and the light path for different focal arrangements. (*Courtesy* Sky and Telescope)

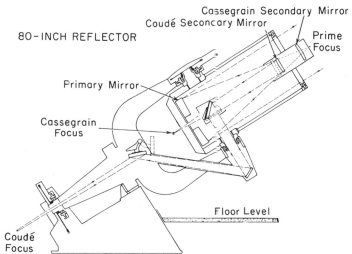

80-INCH REFLECTOR

Cassegrain Secondary Mirror

Coudé Secondary Mirror

Prime Focus

Primary Mirror

Cassegrain Focus

Floor Level

Coudé Focus

an error of several kilometers per second easily can occur. This problem becomes especially serious when the dispersing unit is a quartz prism or a diffraction grating and the resulting spectrum is in the invisible ultraviolet domain.

The American astronomer D. M. Popper has shown that, with the McDonald Observatory's Cassegrain spectrograph (a type of spectrograph named after the Frenchman who invented an improved reflecting telescope in 1672), atmospheric dispersion at zenith distances of 50° or more may cause the ultraviolet star image to be completely off the slit. The result is an underexposed spectrogram produced by occasional errors in guiding that may from time to time allow the ultraviolet light to pass through the slit. This effect is less serious in poor seeing than in good seeing. On the other hand, it is difficult for the observer to focus the star image accurately when seeing is poor and the image several seconds of arc in diameter. In exceptionally poor seeing, the image at the Cassegrain focus of the McDonald telescope may have a diameter of nearly 1 centimeter (cm).

Incorrect focusing on the slit causes nonuniform illumination of the collimator and the dispersing unit, leading to yet another possible error, because no such nonuniformity exists in the comparison spectrum.

Flexure

A major source of error recognized and avoided if possible by all early spectroscopists is the instrument's flexure when attached to the telescope's moving tube. The only satisfactory precaution against flexure is a stationary spectrograph, which can be placed at the telescope's Coudé focus, in which the image is brought completely outside the telescope; this procedure is adopted in most modern instruments.

The field of the Coudé-type spectrograph rotates, while the slit remains in a fixed position — usually horizontal. Because of this, guiding along the slit must be done in two coordinates, except when the star is in the *meridian**. At the McDonald Observatory, a slow drive in *declination*† was built into the telescope; thus the observer can automatically correct for changes in declination while he guides in right ascension. At Mount Wilson and Palomar an auxiliary *image rotator* that makes one revolution in 48 hours is placed in front of the slit (because of the reflection of starlight in the rotator, the angle is twice as large per unit of time as the angle of rotation of the field).

Slippage

There are many practical advantages to a Cassegrain-type spectrograph, because the observer is on the observing floor and can see both the spectrograph and the telescope. However, the slippage of optical parts as the angle between the optical axis and the horizon changes during the exposure has not been investigated adequately as a source of possible error. The lenses or mirrors of the collimator and camera and the dispersing unit must be mounted in such a way as to inhibit movement within their cells. However, because pressure causes deformation of optical parts, in practice each part may move within the cell by as much as 0.1 mm. If this slippage occurs uniformly the spectrum lines appear

* The meridian is the great circle passing through the observer's zenith and the north and south *celestial poles* (the two points where the earth's axis of rotation, extended indefinitely, would pierce the celestial sphere). The *celestial equator* is the great circle in which the plane of the earth's equator cuts the celestial sphere, and its intersection with the ecliptic (see P. 50) is known as the *vernal equinox*.

† *Right ascension* (α) and *declination* (δ) are the equatorial coordinates and are defined as follows: α is the arc of the celestial equator, measured eastward from the vernal equinox to the intersection of the equator and the object's hour-circle; δ is the angular distance north (+) or south (−) of the celestial equator.

broadened, but if it takes place at irregular intervals the lines may be double or multiple.

All such difficulties are avoided in the stationary Coudé spectrographs, always used for *high-dispersion* studies*. Yet even now, work with small- and medium-dispersion spectrographs often is carried out at the prime or Cassegrain foci.

Temperature Control

During the early 1900's Campbell, among others, recognized that the dispersion of a prism changes with temperature, and that if the temperature of mechanical parts varies during an exposure additional displacements result. Hence they sought suitable thermostatic devices. Attempts to achieve 0.01°C (centigrade) temperature control were illusionary, because as a rule the thermostat was actuated only one-half hour before the astronomer started his work. In observatory domes the temperature tends to rise above the seasonal environmental average during the day and then drop rapidly immediately after sunset, becoming almost constant during the night. Campbell reported that at Lick the temperature remains almost constant (to within about 3°C) on an average night after the rapid cooling at sunset. Nevertheless, even small Cassegrain spectrographs require several hours for adjustment to a preset, constant temperature. Hence it usually is possible to achieve only 0.1°C temperature control.

Unfortunately, this degree of control persuades many observers that they are "safe" when they should be aware of possible difficulties. I vividly remember a program of spectrographic observations of the binary π Scorpii† carried out simultaneously by my colleague C. T. Elvey (using a newly constructed spectrograph at Northwestern University's Dearborn Observatory) and me (using the Bruce spectrograph at Yerkes). We obtained some spectrograms during the same nights at the same hours. But many of Elvey's results differed from mine — some by as much as 100 km/sec. Elvey then discovered that close agreement had resulted when he had turned off his thermostat and later learned that the thermo-

---

* The dispersion refers to the amount of separation of light of different colors by the spectrograph. Thus a dispersion of 3 A/mm means that two absorption lines whose wavelengths differ by 3 A are recorded on the photographic plate with a separation of 1 mm. This is referred to as *high dispersion*, achieved only with some of the largest telescopes and for relatively bright stars whose light can be greatly spread out while a sufficient intensity still can be recorded. A *low-dispersion* spectrogram may have, for example, 250 A/mm—that is, two lines differing in wavelength by 250 A separated by 1 mm.

† Stars in constellations are assigned Greek letters in descending order to signify their brightness; thus α Canis Majoris is the brightest star in the constellation, β, the second brightest and so on.

stat controlled a stream of warm air directed against one of the principal structural members of the spectrograph frame. When hot air was blown against this member the entire spectrograph was bent; hence an erroneous value for radial velocity was obtained if the thermostat was on while the stellar spectrum was photographed but off when the comparison source was exposed (Elvey was in no way responsible for the design of the Dearborn spectrograph).

In the 1920's and 1930's, W. S. Adams and his associates at Mount Wilson attempted to control the Coudé spectrograph to better than 0.1°C. Heating units were placed outside the main spectrograph box, and fans were used to blow the warm air into the spectrograph. The stratification of air inside the spectrograph proved difficult to control, but could be handled by occasionally readjusting the fans and placing baffles inside the box, thus producing the maximum possible mixing of air within. Recent experience indicates that on the average night, when the temperature inside the spectrograph drops less than 1° in 12 hours, better results may be secured without any thermostatic control, because the enormous mass of iron and cement that constitutes a large Coudé spectrograph varies its temperature only slightly as a function of the outside temperature.

A few astronomers have attempted thermostatic control of a spectrograph at the usual maximum temperature where the spectrograph is located, hoping thus to avoid the long interval required for adjustment of the spectrograph after sunset to the temperature chosen by the observer. Results have not been encouraging. When spectrograph temperature differs greatly from outside air temperature, problems of stratification become very serious. When plateholders are removed and inserted, temporary temperature change causes unpredictable variations.

Using a modern Coudé spectrograph with a dispersion of 3 A/mm, Adams has derived radial velocities of Arcturus with a precision of 0.01 km/sec. This level could be exceeded if a stellar spectrograph were built and maintained with as many precautions against instrumental error as modern meridian circles. Instead, spectrograph cameras and dispersing units are changed at frequent intervals, and hence collimation and other adjustments cannot be maintained close enough to theoretically attainable precision.

Changes in the Mirror System

With large reflectors, such as the 100-in. instrument at Mount Wilson shown in the drawing, additional sources of error arise from changes in the telescope's mirror system. In the illustration, (1) is the slit, (2) the

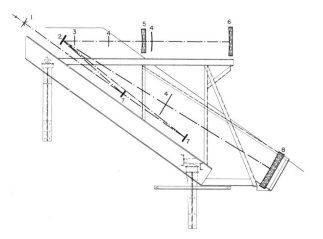

Fig. 38. Path of light in the Coudé spectrograph of the 100-in. telescope of the Mount Wilson Observatory.

grating, (3) the correcting plate, (4) plateholder, (5) camera mirror of shortest focus, (6) intermediate camera mirror, (7) two collimating mirrors one of which is chosen by the observer for use, and (8) long-focus camera mirror. For example, to achieve the highest possible accuracy, illumination of the collimator (at Mount Wilson a parabolic mirror) must be kept constant. This cannot always be attained. The beam of star light reflected from the large principal mirror first falls upon a hyperbolic mirror near the principal focus and then is returned with a greater effective focal length along the telescope's optical axis. At the intersection of this axis and the polar axis, an elliptical plane mirror reflects the beam through an opening into the polar axis and is focused on the spectrograph slit. Declinations greater than +30° give a projected image of the elliptical mirror that no longer is circular, but rather smaller in declination than in right ascension. When approximately +51° declination is reached, the projected width of the plane mirror is about zero, and no light is reflected into the spectrograph. This effect causes differences in collimator illumination between stars of different declinations and also, of course, between star light and comparison source. Since no optical instrument is absolutely perfect, only a part of the collimator, diffraction grating, and camera mirror is illuminated by the star, while the full aperture is utilized for the comparison source. Perhaps this difficulty could be avoided by observing only one star, as Adams did in the case of Arcturus. Unfortunately, the rotation of Mount Wilson's plane Coudé mirror is irregular and subject to occasional jumps that usually cannot be corrected by resetting and are detected by the observer only if they are very large. Hence, if the plane mirror makes a series of small changes in angle during a single exposure, the observer tends to correct them by the slow-motion control in declination. The result is that illumination of optical parts by star light undergoes a change during exposure not matched by a corresponding change in illumination by the comparison source.

THE ACCURACY OF DIFFERENT METHODS

The Doppler formula shows that the displacement of a spectral line in wavelength ($\Delta \lambda$) is proportional to the wavelength. The dispersion of a grating is constant, and hence if the spectrum is produced by a grating, spectral line displacement measured in fractions of a millimeter also is proportional to the wavelength and is twice as large at wavelength 7,500 A (red) as at wavelength 3,750 A (violet). Thus, it would seem advantageous to measure radial velocities in the red, rather than the violet, region of the spectrum. However, most photographic plates have more contrast and are more sensitive in violet than in red light. In practice, therefore, most radial velocities have been determined from photographs of the violet and blue regions of stellar spectra.

Because modern radio receivers are so sensitive, remarkably precise radial-velocity measurements can be obtained from the hydrogen emission or absorption line at 21-cm wavelength (see Chap. VI). Radial velocities of neutral interstellar hydrogen gas obtained at the Netherlands Foundation for Radio Astronomy, Dwingeloo, Holland, and at other radio observatories, with only one discrete line known in the centimeter and meter wavelength ranges, are at least 10 times more precise than measurements from the optical spectrum.

Application of a Fabry-Perot interferometer provides another very accurate method of determining radial velocities of emission nebulae, such as the Orion Nebula (see Frontispiece). The Fabry-Perot instrument is one of a group that utilizes the phenomenon of *interference**. Depending on the type of interferometer used, alternating dark and light lines or rings are observed. The spacing of the *maxima* (or fringes) depends on the angle of incidence, the separation of the beams, and the wavelength. In the case of two sources with small angular separation, or an extended source with nonuniform intensity, the modification of the fringe patterns depends on the separation of the sources or the intensity distribution of a single extended source. In recent years, G. Courtès, the French astronomer, and his associates have used the Fabry-Perot instrument successfully.

Attainable precision (0.1 km/sec in the French work) depends upon the properties of the interferometer. The advantage of this instrument

* The modification of intensity obtained by the superposition of two or more beams of light derived from the same source.

over slit spectrographs is that it enables the observer to detect small irregularities in the interference rings when they cross large nebulous structures.

Finally, a word should be said about determining radial velocities by means of *objective prisms*. One of the prisms is placed in front of a telescope's objective; this produces low-dispersion spectra, rather than point images of all stars in the field of view (see P. 190 and Fig. 93). The principal problem in using this method of radial-velocity determination is the difficulty of providing a comparison spectrum. The most successful method has been that employed by C. Fehrenbach and his associates at the Haute Provence Observatory in France. It depends upon the measurements of relative displacements of lines when photographed with two different orientations of the objective prism Fehrenbach's precision compares favorably with the best obtained with slit spectrographs of smaller dispersion. This method makes it possible to measure radial velocities of many stars on a single photograph.

SUMMARY OF RESULTS

Radial-velocity measurements of single stars and spectroscopic binaries are listed in a catalogue containing 15,107 stars compiled by the American R. E. Wilson, an astronomer at the Mount Wilson and Palomar observatories.[3] Wilson investigated the systematic differences among the principal observatories and adopted the Lick Observatory system as the standard. These differences depend to some extent upon the spectral class of the star, because they are caused in part by differences in the adopted wavelengths of the absorption lines. The various spectral classes or types, designated by the letters, O, B, A, F, G, K, M, in order of decreasing temperature, are distinguished by the prominence of different characteristic absorption lines and will be discussed in detail in Chaps. X and XI. For example, the systematic corrections for the results of Mount Wilson Observatory, which furnished almost one-half the data, are 0.0 for spectral type A, $+0.5$ km/sec for classes F and G, and -0.5 for classes K and M. The largest systematic corrections applied by Wilson are those for the velocities (-9.8 km/sec), obtained mostly by Belgian-born F. Henroteau in 1920–1922 at the Dominion Observatory in Ottawa, Canada.

Since Henroteau died some years ago in Liège, Belgium, astronomers have not been able to ascertain definitely the source of this large systematic difference. Some astronomers believe that he used a narrow slit for the comparison spectrum, widening the slit by changing the position of one slit jaw during the stellar exposure. It is inconceivable that Henroteau would not realize that to do so would introduce a serious displacement of the stellar absorption lines. Whatever the merits of criticism of Henroteau's work, the importance of his establishing the periodicities of a number of β Canis Majoris pulsating variables is incontestable. He is also responsible for other valuable contributions to stellar spectroscopy.

It is difficult to ascertain the total number of spectrograms that have been obtained and used for radial-velocity measurement since 1900. Wilson's results for single stars represent the mean of four or five spectrograms; for spectroscopic binaries, however, several hundred spectrograms have been needed to establish the line-of-sight velocity of the center of gravity of the system. The number has probably been about 200,000.

Radial-velocity measurements are scientifically valuable, principally because of their statistical significance. Long ago, spectroscopists detected a correlation of the mean radial velocity and the spectral type: The hot B-type stars have slower motions than the cooler main-sequence K and M stars of relatively low luminosity, also referred to as dwarfs, in contrast to luminous K and M giants (see Chap. X, P. 202). However, the very hot O-type stars occasionally have large radial velocities. This phenomenon, though originally attributed to equipartition of energy among stars of different masses (the B stars are known to have larger masses than K or M stars), has more recently been interpreted as representing motions in different galactic orbits (see Chap. XIX, P. 421).

Of special interest are the motions of stars belonging to clusters and *associations* (loose clusters covering a large area of the sky). The moving cluster of the Hyades has been known for many years and the radial velocities of its members have been very precisely determined by the Canadian astronomer J. A. Pearce of the Dominion Astrophysical Observatory in Victoria, B.C. Measurements of radial velocities and proper motions of stars in associations have led some spectroscopists to believe that the associations are expanding with velocities of the order of 10 km/sec. However, this result has not been completely accepted and there is need for additional accurate measurements.

A star's true space motion can be determined only if, in addition to radial velocity, its proper motion in angle and its distance are known. Still, many interesting conclusions are based solely on radial velocities. Since a star's space motion is always greater than its radial velocity, a very large value for the latter, say 100 to 500 km/sec, implies a space motion greater than that of the velocity of escape from the Milky Way. A star with this great motion would become extragalactic.

V

PHOTOMETRY

THE DETERMINATION OF stellar *magnitudes* is one of the oldest fields of astronomy, dating from the Greek astronomers Hipparchus (c. 130 B.C.) and Ptolemy (2nd century A.D.), who first divided stars visible to the naked eye into six magnitudes, the sixth being the faintest and the first the brightest stars. Their crude scale, used and extended to fainter magnitudes after telescopes were introduced, was, in fact, roughly logarithmic; that is, equal ratios in light intensity corresponded to equal steps in magnitude. For northern observers, the North Star, Polaris, was assigned a magnitude (mag) of 2, and other magnitudes were determined with respect to Polaris. However, the European astronomer, E. Hertzsprung, discovered in 1911 that Polaris is a peculiar, pulsating variable star, whose brightness fluctuates by several tenths of magnitude, and hence is an unreliable standard.

In a sense, all stellar magnitudes have been determined in terms of the brightness of the sun; an intermediate sequence of stellar magnitudes, proposed by the American astronomer E. C. Pickering, the North Polar Sequence, was adopted at the beginning of this century to provide both a smaller range and a source of known brightnesses that could be used at night. Aside from the sun, the brightest star ʼ(Sirius, −1.5 mag) and the faintest stars that can be recorded now represent a range of about 20 mag. This range corresponds to a ratio of 1:100 million in the intensity of light.

Many observations using different instrumentation have been made on purely arbitrary scales, connected with neither the North Polar Sequence nor the sun. Because of variation in atmospheric absorption, the best results are obtained by measuring a star's brightness with respect to comparison sources in the immediate vicinity. Recently, accurate magnitudes have been determined for standard stars in all parts of the sky and the North Polar Sequence is seldom used directly, even though all standards are to a certain extent based upon it. As a result of these difficulties, all early scales of stellar magnitudes are grossly in error, and astronomers have been compelled only recently to revise drastically the *apparent magnitudes** of stars located in distant galaxies without introducing errors due to unreliability of scale.

VISUAL PHOTOMETRY

Argelander's Method

Prior to 1900 the methods developed by the German astronomer F. W. A. Argelander in the early part of the 19th century were used widely to determine stellar brightnesses. Stars were compared visually and brightness estimates made in arbitrary steps, one step indicating the smallest detectable difference. On the average, the steps equalled 0.1 mag, but observers differed considerably in the magnitudes they reported. This method of visual photometry was used particularly in the study of variable stars. Comparison stars, chosen to resemble the variable star to within two or three steps at most, were regarded as of constant brightness. However, brightness of a variable star often changed considerably, forcing the observer to use a series of comparison sources.

Argelander's very simple method is still used by many professional astronomers as well as by amateurs, with whom it is particularly popular. Among the several organizations of amateur astronomers throughout the world, the American Association of Variable Star Observers (AAVSO), with several hundred members, including many from other countries, has produced the most significant results. The AAVSO has prepared suitable charts of several hundred variable stars, and it accumulates roughly 50,000

---

* It is customary to use the term *apparent magnitude* in referring to the measured brightness of a celestial object. In order to compare intrinsic brightnesses, the *absolute magnitudes* are employed, defined as the apparent magnitude the object would have if it were located at a distance of 10 parsecs (32.6 light-years or 2×10^6 A.U.) from the solar system. The *parsec* is defined as the distance at which the radius of the earth's orbit would subtend an angle of $1''$ (that is, the star would have a parallax of $1''$. This is actually the *heliocentric* parallax, in contrast to the geocentric parallax for which the radius of the earth is used as a base line, as defined on P. 36).

observations per year from its members. Because the Argelander method is not highly accurate, amateurs are limited for the most part to stars showing large changes in brightness, such as *long-period variables, Cepheid variables* (named after δ Cephei, the first of this type to be observed; see Chap. XV, P. 313) and some *eclipsing variables* (see Chap. XIV, P. 313).

The AAVSO was founded 50 years ago by E. C. Pickering at the Harvard Observatory in Cambridge. The man most responsible for its success, however, is the elder Leon Campbell, a Harvard Observatory staff member who collected individual members' observations and plotted many very useful *light curves** (see, for example, Figure 288). Some have proved particularly valuable to P. W. Merrill in his spectroscopic studies at Mount Wilson and to a few other professional astronomers. The AAVSO now is independent of the Harvard Observatory and is headed by Mrs. Margaret Mayall.

Visual Photometers

During the last quarter of the 19th century, several types of visual photometers were developed. Among them was the *polarizing photometer,* invented by the German astronomer F. Zöllner, in which two *Nicol prisms* were rotated so that when parallel they transmitted almost all light passed through the device. When one prism was at an orientation of 90° to the other, however, the light was completely extinguished.† An artificial star whose brightness could be regarded as constant was reflected into the telescope's eyepiece, and the brightness of the variable star was made to resemble that of the artificial one by rotating one of the prisms. The reading was expressed as the angle between the prisms. The artificial star usually was produced by using a light-source in the observatory dome and a pinhole.

All observers who used the Zöllner photometer discovered they could not make the artificial image resemble a real star in appearance; hence the observer always was aware that the two sources appeared slightly

---

* Graphs of stellar magnitude plotted against time.

† Light may be considered as consisting of transverse waves vibrating at right angles to the direction of propagation. Star light is made up of vast numbers of electromagnetic waves, each having its own plane of vibration. When all planes of vibration are present, the light is said to be *unpolarized* if only one plane is present, the light is *plane-polarized*. Polarized light can be detected with a Nicol prism, an optical device made from a calcite crystal, which transmits only one plane of vibration. The prism is named after the 19th-century Scottish astronomer William Nichol, who first proposed it. If unpolarized light is passed through a Nicol prism, the transmitted beam will be polarized. If this polarized light is passed through another Nicol prism oriented at 90° to the first, the second prism will transmit only the vibrations in a plane at right angles to those transmitted by the first, and hence no light will emerge.

different when seen in the eyepiece. An accurate comparison was difficult to achieve.

At the end of the 19th and the beginning of the 20th centuries, the greatest progress in visual photometry was made at the Harvard Observatory under E. C. Pickering's directorship. He and others realized that the magnitude scales devised by 18th- and 19th-century observers, such as William Herschel and the Russian astronomer F. G. W. Struve, differed greatly. A star one observer might describe as of 20 mag would be listed by another as of 15 mag. Pickering adopted the definition of *magnitude scale*, proposed by the English amateur astronomer N. Pogson around 1850 and still accepted: The ratio of light intensity of successive magnitudes equals the 5th root of 100 (approximately 2.512).

Pickering also devoted much effort to establishing a zero point of the sequence. Thus, according to S. I. Bailey's history of the Harvard Observatory, "The Harvard observations were undertaken not only to extend the knowledge of the relative brightnesses of faint stars, but especially to determine the relations of the scales of magnitudes used by different observers."[1] For this purpose, Pickering developed the Harvard *meridian photometer*. This instrument is fixed in an east-west direction and employs two objectives of equal aperture and focal length. By means of a mirror or prism, Polaris is kept in the field of view of one objective while another mirror can be tilted to bring the beam of light from any star, at the time it crosses the meridian, through the other objective close to that of the pole star. The two beams of light are analyzed by means of a Nicol prism. This method avoids using an artificial star, but complications are introduced by Polaris' variability (see P. 75).

The Harvard work (later extended to the southern hemisphere) re-

Fig. 39.   Harvard Observatory around 1900. (*Courtesy* Sky and Telescope)

Fig. 40. E. C. Pickering.

sulted in the *Harvard Photometry*,[2] a catalogue of 4,260 stars north of declination −30°, published in 1884. At about the same time another extensive catalogue was published by the English astronomer C. Pritchard at the Oxford University Observatory from observations with a *wedge photometer*, in which a plate or wedge of gradually increasing opacity is used to decrease the brightness of one of the light sources. A more precise investigation undertaken at Potsdam by G. Müller and P. Kempf resulted in the *Potsdamer Photometrische Durchmusterung* ("Potsdam Photometric Catalogue").[3]

According to Bailey, by 1906 Harvard observers had made more than a million comparisons of nearly 50,000 stars; some, particularly the brighter stars, had been measured a number of times. Pickering revised the magnitudes of stars of 6.5 mag or brighter for the *Revised Harvard Photometry*,[4] published in 1908, which became the standard reference work for the magnitudes of the brighter stars.

PHOTOGRAPHIC PHOTOMETRY

Around 1900, photographic methods were introduced into photometry. In many respects, photographic procedure was far superior to that of even the best visual photometers. Early workers incorrectly assumed, however, that the photographic emulsion produced identical images of stars whose apparent brightnesses differed by a factor of 2 when the exposure time was made twice as long for the fainter star as for the brighter star. They found that by prolonging the time of a photographic exposure corresponding to the ratio of 5 mag, they obtained a photographic gain of only 4 mag. Thus if the intensity ratio of two light-sources is 100, the ratio of the exposure time on a blue-sensitive emulsion required to obtain identical stellar images is, on the average, about 150, not 100. This effect was particularly investigated by J. A. Parkhurst at Yerkes and F. E. Ross, who was at that time connected with the Eastman Kodak Company. They and others discovered what is known as the *reciprocity failure of the photographic emulsion*. This effect usually is described by the *K. Schwarzchild exponent* (p): The photographic density of a stellar image is not solely a product of the intensity of the source and the duration of the exposure, but is a function $I \times t^p$, where I is the intensity of the source, and t is the length of the exposure; p is constant for a given photographic emulsion with an average value of about 0.8, but may be close to 1.0 for certain yellow- and red-sensitive emulsions (in which case there is no appreciable reciprocity failure), while for others it may be somewhat less than 0.8.

Of the many different kinds of emulsions tested throughout the past half-century, those produced by the Eastman Kodak Company are among the best. Even they, although fairly well standardized, still vary in over-all sensitivity and the characteristic value of p. Obviously, the accuracy of a photographic determination of brightness depends on a detailed study of the emulsions to be used. Two emulsions, for example, labeled with the same numbers and letters, may have been produced at separate times and may contain slightly different quantities of the same ingredient.

Because the ordinary photographic plate is most sensitive to blue light, while the eye is most sensitive in the yellow region, visual and photographic magnitude scales differ somewhat; the type of magnitude used always must be specified. The difference between visual and photographic magnitudes for any star, $mag_{phot}-mag_{visual}$, is called the *color index*, and often is used as an equivalent for spectral type. The scales are so adjusted that the color index is zero for A-type stars of surface temperature of about 10,000°. For hotter, blue stars, the color index is negative, for cool, red stars it is positive. (See, in particular, Chap. XIII, P. 261). A more recent development is the photographic plate with a sensitivity very similar to that of the eye; it produces *photovisual* magnitudes.

PHOTOELECTRIC PHOTOMETRY

The history of *photoelectric photometry*, the breakthrough in astronomical photometry that began around 1910, is for the most part the "story" of J. Stebbins, director of the University of Illinois Observatory from 1903 to 1922, and of the Washburn Observatory of the University of Wisconsin from 1922 until his retirement in 1948.

When he arrived at Urbana, Illinois, Stebbins found a Pickering visual polarizing photometer attached to a 12-in. refractor. With this instrument he started a program of measuring the relative magnitudes of double stars. At an American Astronomical Society dinner in Urbana on August 20, 1957, Stebbins described the conditions under which he had been expected to conduct research:

Fig. 41. The present director of the University of Illinois Observatory, G. C. McVittie (left), with two of his predecessors: J. Stebbins (center), and R. H. Baker. (*Photograph by Walter J. Miller, S.J., courtesy* Sky and Telescope)

One significant item of the situation was that the observatory had no operating budget, not a dollar. Of course you can run a mathematics department with a library and a few boxes of chalk, but not an observatory. I paid for minor items out of my own pocket, and at the end of the year I presented and collected the accumulated bill for eight dollars; e-i-g-h-t, eight. As I look back now, I should have been fired for being so cheap. Later, both the University and I learned better how to spend money. This early experience has made me a poor member of any committee or panel with the responsibility of distributing funds for research. When it costs thousands of dollars even to start a project, I find myself living in a different world.[5]

For a few years observations were made visually, and Mrs. Stebbins often acted as a recorder while her husband dictated hundreds of readings to determine the brightness of only one star. In order to increase the efficiency of his work, Stebbins decided to develop an electrical method. At a physics department open house, he met a young instructor, F. C. Brown, who demonstrated a *selenium cell* that rang a bell when a lamp was used to illuminate it. Stebbins notes:

Let me explain here that the so-called selenium cell is actually a bridge. Two wires are wound in parallel in double spiral around a flat insulator, and the area between them on one side is smeared with amorphous selenium, which, when heated and properly treated, takes the crystalline form that changes its electrical resistance when exposed to light. The dimensions can be, say, from two inches by one inch down to a square centimeter. The best commercial cells at that time were by J. W. Giltay of Delft, Holland, the same firm that now makes the Moll microphotometer.

I soon made friends with Brown, and in due time we had a selenium cell on the 12-inch refractor; I operated the telescope and a shutter while Brown looked after the battery, galvanometer, and scale. The first trial was on Jupiter—no response; several more trials, still no response. I said to myself, "I'll fix him." The moon was shining through a window; I took the cell with attached wires off the telescope and exposed it to the moon. The galvanometer deflection was measurable with plenty to spare. Result: we spent a couple of months measuring the variation of the moon's light with phase. The cell was mounted in a wooden or cardboard box which, when held by hand on a window sill, could be sighted at the moon. After exposure to the moon the cell was moved to a crude optical bench and exposed at different distances to a standard amyl-acetate lamp. At full moon the match was obtained at slightly more than 2 meters. Our resulting light curve turned out to be the first since the time of Zöllner in the 1860's.[6]

With some improvements and a new selenium cell, Stebbins finally detected a barely measurable response from the light of the mag 1 star α Tauri. Then one clear, cold night he noticed that the cell's sensitivity had increased by a factor of about 2 (from room temperature to 0°F), while the irregularities in the electrical circuit had decreased by a factor of 10.

The next refinement came quite accidentally:

After an exhibit at a meeting I wrapped a cell in a handkerchief for safety and put it in my pocket. Later I forgot about the cell, pulled out the handkerchief, and dropped the cell on a hard floor. It had been a good cell, but now I had two cells each twice as good as the original. Since the extra area of two square inches had only produced irregularities, a smaller cell was all to the good. With this much to go on, I got up my nerve, placed our best cell in a vise, and with a hammer and a chisel gave it a whack to break off about a quarter of it to make a really good cell.[7]

With this broken fragment, placed in an icepack, mag 2 stars could be measured with some accuracy and Stebbins was able to obtain a light curve of Algol that showed a slight decrease of the double star's brightness when the fainter component of the pair was obscured partially from view by the brighter one—a secondary eclipse (see Fig. 149, and P. 288).

At about the same time H. Rosenberg and P. Guthnick in Germany had begun experimenting with *photoelectric cells*, in which an electric current was generated by the ejection of electrons from a metal surface exposed to light. Rosenberg was a wealthy man, who before World War I had built a private observatory near Tübingen, Germany, that was destroyed during the war. Afterward, he was named director of the university observatory in Kiel, Germany. Although Rosenberg was familiar with the properties of photoelectric cells, he never applied them directly to the stars at the focus of a telescope; his photoelectric measurements were made on photographs. At the 1913 Astronomische Gesellschaft meeting there was a lively discussion of the advantages of photoelectric cells over the selenium cells used by Stebbins. Those in favor of the photoelectric cell emphasized its somewhat greater sensitivity and faster operation. After 1913 Stebbins began using photoelectric cells made by his University of Illinois colleague Jacob Kunz.

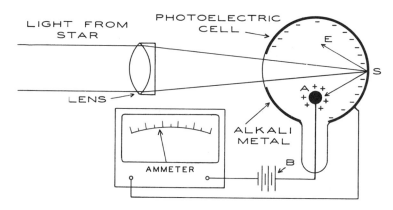

Fig. 42. The simplest form of photoelectric photometer. (*Courtesy* Sky and Telescope)

The simplest form of photoelectric photometer is shown in the diagram. As light falls on the cell, the ammeter readings are accurately proportional to brightness. The battery B applies a positive potential to the anode A so that it collects the photoelectrons E released from the cathode at S.

Stebbins' years at Washburn were productive. He described some of his experiences there at the dedication of the observatory's Pine Bluff station on June 30, 1958:

When the observatory was founded [around 1880] the methods of observational astronomy were practically all visual; astronomers actually looked through their telescopes. I do not need to remind the present audience how photography has supplanted visual observations. At the Washburn Observatory, however, the whole field of photographic research was skipped, and we jumped directly from visual to photoelectric methods. For the past thirty-five years the energies of the staff have been confined to the application of the photoelectric cell to astronomical observations. Among the fields of investigation have been the detection of small variations in the light of stars, studies of eclipsing and pulsating stars, measurements of magnitudes and colors of stars, and studies of interstellar material from the effects of selective absorption in space. My colleague Morse Huffer has been associated in all this work from the beginning, and Albert Whitford for about twenty-five years.

An epoch-making event took place here when Whitford devised the combination of a photocell and an amplifier[*] in a vacuum tank, mounted it on a board, and pointed it through a tube out of a basement window at the Pole Star. After successful measures of Polaris, the device was transferred to the 15-in. refractor where it worked without difficulty. We

[* The so-called *photomultiplier tubes* take advantage of the fact that the electrons released by light rays will release additional electrons when they strike another suitable metal surface. For example, a typical modern photomultiplier tube may have nine successive stages of amplification, and as many as a million electrons may be released from the ninth surface in the chain reaction started by one electron released from the first surface. This enormous multiplication of the photoelectric effect accounts for the sensitivity of modern photomultiplier tubes.]

used to say that his photometer, even without a telescope, would detect a candle a mile away. We said this so often that we felt constrained to try it at least once with a real candle at a real mile. When we did so by setting up a standard candle on Picnic Point, a mile across the lake from the observatory, we found that with no optical aid, except a blank tube to eliminate stray light, the photocell would not only give a conspicuous response in galvanometer current when exposed to the candle, but would show a detectable effect when the light was cut down to about one-fiftieth of a candle at the mile, or, say, a candle at seven miles. Since the effective aperture of the cell was about one inch, it followed that on the 15-in. refractor the limit of detection would be a candle at about one hundred miles. Now with the installation of the new 36-in. reflector we should be able to detect a candle at 1000 miles. Here we allow a factor of 5 for the larger telescope and of about 20 for the improved light receivers and techniques. If we extrapolate into the future, improvements by a factor of 100 every 25 years should be satisfactory all around.[8]

Early experiments with photoelectric cells were not always reassuring. A well-known observer once got no response from his cell when he pointed it to the sun. Later he improved the performance of his equipment and was able to measure the brightnesses of the stars to about mag 5 or 6. In the early days of photoelectric photometry, cells varied greatly in sensitivity. (Stebbins usually managed to get the best cells, leaving those of second-best quality to other observatories.)

Since voltage was required to make the cell respond to faint radiation from stars and nebulae, it always was necessary to disconnect the electrical circuit when the cell was not in use and might be exposed to the strong radiation of daylight. One of the best photoelectric cells at Yerkes was damaged seriously because the observer failed to follow this procedure. Even relatively short exposure to fairly bright light could result in drastic changes in a photoelectric cell's properties; therefore, cell performance had to be tested at frequent intervals.

Most of these difficulties have been overcome, but even now photomultiplier tubes made by the same manufacturer often differ in sensitivity, as well as in other characteristics. It has become standard practice for a manufacturer to issue different price lists, one for the astronomer willing to take a chance on the possibility of getting a good cell, another for him who insists on a guarantee that the cell has been fully tested in the laboratory and be performing according to his specifications before it is received by the observatory.

Incidentally, photoelectric cells are more sensitive than selenium cells in another respect. According to Stebbins: ". . . once I dropped a selenium cell, and then there were two; once and only once in forty years have I managed to drop a photoelectric cell, and then there was none."[9]

Because Yerkes is fairly near Washburn there was a lively exchange of ideas and information between the personnel of the two institutions. Stebbins' students all became competent in photoelectric studies, and several Yerkes astronomers, among them C. T. Elvey, introduced photoelectric photometry to Yerkes.

Photoelectric measurement of star brightnesses is precise to about 0.01 mag, a limit set not by the photoelectric cell or the telescope, but by the length of time it takes to move the telescope from one star to another. In order to increase the accuracy still further, G. Kron and others have developed a reflecting device placed in a telescope's focal plane. With it, a nearby comparison star can be recorded photoelectrically a few seconds after the star being investigated has been measured. In cases where it is necessary only to observe changes in a single star or to observe the transmitted starlight's amount of polarization, precision to 0.001 mag can be attained.

Photoelectric photometry has not replaced photographic methods completely. It is an accurate but relatively slow process, since only one star at a time can be observed, while many star images can be recorded on a photographic plate. Thus, to find the magnitudes of several hundred stars in a cluster, a number of them may be chosen as reference standards and their magnitudes determined photoelectrically with great precision. The magnitudes of the rest are then found photographically by referring to the standard stars. This situation probably will change with the development of *image converters*, discussed on Pp. 87-89, able to record an extended image of a starfield, for instance, not just a single point source.

PHOTOMETRY OF FAINT STARS AND NEBULAE

In their efforts to measure the apparent brightnesses of stars and nebulae, astronomers have encountered many practical difficulties in establishing an accurate photometric sequence for the brighter stars, even though in principle this problem is relatively simple. However, two fundamental problems are encountered in the photometry of faint stars and nebulae:

1. Reducing the time required to make a measurement. Using photography, the time can be reduced with telescopes of larger aperture or with faster emulsions. With photoelectric devices, it is hoped that a reliable value of the electron count will be obtained in as short an interval

as possible. The importance of this consideration is indicated by W. A. Baum's estimate that to attain an accuracy of 0.05 mag (in only one color) for a star of mag 23, one full night of good seeing with the 200-in. Hale telescope would be required.

2. Enhancing the contrast between the diffuse background luminosity of the night sky and the light of faint stars and nebulae. This is especially important in reaching the faintest objects. The light of the night sky always is present; it results from air glow, the diffuse scattering of starlight by cosmic dust clouds, and unresolved stars and galaxies. *Air glow* is variable and depends in part upon the manner in which air molecules are excited during the day by solar radiation. *Diffuse light,* coming from cosmic dust clouds, varies from one part of the sky to another; the same is true of the light from unresolved stars and galaxies. On the average, the brightness of the night sky is 300 stars of mag 10 per square degree. The night sky's light sets a limit that cannot be overcome by building larger telescopes or by inventing more sensitive emulsions or photoelectric receivers. As a matter of fact, there now are photomultiplier tubes that can record brightnesses of all stars that can be photographed with the largest existing telescopes.

There have been marked advances during the past few years in attempts to solve these problems. The second, in some respects the more fundamental, has been discussed by Baum, who started his investigation by considering photographic methods. He has, for example, made a 12-times enlargement of a relatively short exposure of a field of stars and galaxies obtained on a night of good seeing with the 200-in. Hale telescope. The background sky appears as a light-gray surface upon which the star images are superposed. Baum learned that doubling the exposure brings out more stars but also increases the photographic density of the background sky. His experience with the 200-in. telescope indicates that after about 30 minutes (min) on a fast, blue-sensitive emulsion, this background becomes so dark that no additional images of faint stars are brought out, even if exposure time is increased to 1 hour (hr). A better contrast could be attained and fainter stars recorded with even more fine-grained emulsions. Up to a certain point, this procedure is sound, but in practice it is limited by the prohibitive slowness of all fine-grained emulsions.

Baum also concludes that no photographic procedure now being developed can reduce this background. Photography used by itself seems limited to the blue magnitude of 24 attainable with the 200-in. telescope.

However, some novel electronic techniques may speed solution of both fundamental problems.

Baum has considered two objectives to be achieved by electronic techniques: (a) intensification of the image so that very fine-grained emulsions too slow for direct photography may be used, and (b) elimination of most of the brightness of the night sky by means of electronic methods before the intensified image is photographed.

Several procedures have been proposed for the accomplishment of the second objective. For example, there are: a conventional television system, television designed for image storage over long intervals of time (as developed in RCA's Vidico), and the image-storage systems having a *photoemissive cathode* suggested by J. D. McGee in England. McGee's design particularly appears quite promising, but, according to Baum, good definition and high yield have not been achieved yet.

Regarding the first problem, the greatest progress has been made by A. Lallemand of the Paris Observatory with image converters containing a magazine of photographic plates. A design perfected by Lallemand and M. Duchesne is shown schematically in Fig. 43. First the photocathode R is prepared in a small evacuated tube Q, which is sealed in a larger pyrex glass tube A. Light enters through the window G. The chamber N contains a number of Kodak-type NT2a photographic plates used for nuclear research.

After the larger tube A has been evacuated and the plates sufficiently outgassed, a magnetically operated hammer M breaks and destroys the small tube Q. The photocathode then is pulled magnetically by means of the coil S into the operating position at O. The electrons are focused and

Fig. 43.   Diagram of the Lallemand image tube. (*Courtesy* Sky and Telescope)

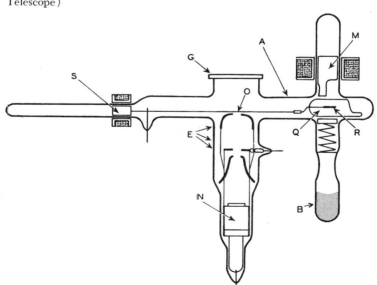

accelerated by means of the three electrodes indicated by E, and they pass from the photocathode at O to the topmost of the plates at N. During this process, the vacuum is preserved by activated charcoal at B, which absorbs residual gases.

The photographic emulsion is highly sensitive to fast electrons having energy of about 40,000 electron volts. Hence Lallemand's method achieves an important reduction in exposure time. The response of the emulsion is almost linear, and trouble caused by reciprocity failure in direct photography is avoided. The whole apparatus has been designed so it can be attached to the eye end of a movable telescope; there is also less general fogging than in direct photography.

Lallemand's procedure may be affected by several serious technical difficulties. The antimony-cesium photocathode can be ruined by various gases occluded in the photographic emulsion and gradually escaping after the space around them is evacuated. Therefore, the plates must be outgassed before actual observing can begin. This procedure takes time and requires refrigeration, which disintegrates the emulsion's gelatin. Although during outgassing, the photocathode is safe from contamination in its small tube Q, it loses some sensitivity during the exposure because all gases cannot be eliminated. It is completely spoiled when the device is opened to extract the plates for developing, and a new, sealed photocathode is required for the next series of exposures.

The French astronomers have coped successfully with some of these problems. They have tried more resistant antimony-cesium photocathodes containing an excess of cesium and have introduced various devices for improving the vacuum without spoiling the emulsion.

By 1951, Lallemand had succeeded in photographing a laboratory source completely invisible to the eye. An early test photograph of the Trapezium in Orion is shown at the left in Fig. 44. The exposure was for 5 seconds. The picture on the right is an ordinary photograph, exposure time 3 minutes, taken with the same telescope the same night. The second picture does not show the fourth star in the Trapezium. True, his method, which has achieved an average saving in exposure time of at least a factor

Fig. 44.   The multiple star θ Orionis.
(*Courtesy* Sky and Telescope)

of 50, cannot accomplish the discovery of stars and galaxies beyond the present limit of mag 24. However, it permits the use of slower, fine-grained emulsions possessing higher contrast, and it also can be used to observe high-dispersion spectra of faint stars now beyond the reach of conventional spectrographs on even the largest telescopes.

In 1959, Lallemand and Duchesne brought their electronic camera to the Lick Observatory, where it has been used successfully with the 120-in. telescope. M. F. Walker of the observatory has been able to obtain the spectra of faint variables in several young clusters, down to apparent mag 14 to 16, with a dispersion of 65 A/mm. G. Kron has developed a modified form of the image tube (a valve is added between the cathode and plate sections) that preserves the cathode through a number of exposures.

I. S. Bowen summarized the present status of observational techniques at the December, 1960, meeting of the American Association for the Advancement of Science:

> The fifteen years since the war have seen drastic changes in astronomical equipment and observing techniques. Photomultiplier receivers have replaced the photographic plate for perhaps one-fourth to one-third of the observing time of most large telescopes, and this use is still increasing. Image-intensifier tubes are just beginning to become available. When these are perfected they will almost certainly replace the direct recording of starlight on a photographic plate for much of the remaining observing time.[10]

In accordance with this prediction, it is likely that the design of future optical telescopes will be influenced strongly by efforts to take full advantage of photoelectric photometers and photoelectric image intensifiers. Optical ground-based telescopes would be capable of recording the brightnesses of the most luminous galaxies, whose absolute visual magnitudes are −20, at distances of 10 billion light-years. Although optical images of more distant galaxies cannot be detected with the available instruments, radio telescopes can record the radio emission of peculiar galaxies (discussed in Chap. VI, P. 107) beyond the reach of optical instruments. It is possible that both optical and radio techniques will extend the radius of the observable part of the universe beyond the range now thought attainable.

Some astronomers are less optimistic. They agree with A. C. B. Lovell, the director of the Nuffield Radio Astronomy Laboratory at Jodrell Bank, England:

> Today our telescopes are so powerful that they probably penetrate to the limits of the observable universe. We may therefore be near the limit of our scientific knowledge of the universe as regards its extent in time

and space and the cosmological implications of the observations now in progress have assumed an unparalleled significance.[11]

Still, although all stars except the sun are, in fact, point sources, their images as produced by a telescope are small spots of measurable size. If these were of uniform brightness, there would be no advantage in constructing telescopes with apertures larger than those now in use. But the star images in the focal plane have peaks of intensity at the spot centers, and this feature encourages the belief that a telescope larger than the 200-in. reflector at Palomar might bring out stars even fainter than can be recorded now. Thus, many astronomers advocate the construction of a telescope with a 400- or 500-in. mirror, a project that is by no means impossible.

VI

RADIO
ASTRONOMY

ALTHOUGH THE NEW techniques discussed in the preceding chapters greatly facilitate the recording and analysis of
radiation collected by ordinary telescopes, observations are based essentially upon the same range of wavelengths that has been employed for
centuries. True, this has been extended somewhat—the ordinary photographic plate is sensitive to shorter wavelengths than the eye, while red-
and infrared-sensitive emulsions extend to slightly longer wavelengths.
The span of observation is still limited to the *optical window*, from about
3,000 to about 10,000 A. Radiation beyond these limits is cut off by the
opacity of air. At the short wavelength, this occurs principally because of
the presence of ozone, and at the long end because of water vapor.

A completely new window has been opened recently. The earth's
upper atmosphere is transparent to electromagnetic waves in the radio
wavelength range, from about 1 cm to almost 15 m. At the turn of the
century, the English physicist Sir Oliver Lodge and others failed in their
attempts to detect radio waves from the sun. No efforts were made to explore the "radio window" in the first decades of this century, and the first
extraterrestrial radio waves were discovered accidentally in the 1930's.
However, not until 15 years after this first observation did the science of
radio astronomy begin to make noticeable progress.

THE DISCOVERY OF EXTRATERRESTRIAL
RADIO WAVES

The science of radio astronomy had its beginning in 1931–1932, when in the course of experiments designed to investigate high-frequency radio disturbances in the atmosphere (that is, high frequency in conventional radio broadcasting, but low frequency in terms of radio astronomy), K. G. Jansky of the Bell Telephone Laboratory found that:

Data obtained . . . show the presence of three separate groups of static: group 1, static from local thunderstorms; group 2, static from distant thunderstorms, and group 3, a steady hiss type static of unknown origin.

The direction [of the third type of static] varies gradually throughout the day, going almost completely around the compass in 24 hours. The evidence indicates that the source of this static is somehow associated with the sun.[1]

This conclusion was based on occasional observations, extending over a relatively short interval of time, but Jansky soon started more regular investigation of the third type of static. His apparatus consisted of a sensitive shortwave radio receiving system, to which he had connected an automatic signal intensity recorder. The antenna system was highly directive in the horizontal plane and was rotated continuously about a vertical axis once every 20 min, so that the *azimuth** of the direction of arrival of the radio noise could be established with a reasonable degree of accuracy, while the altitude of the signal could not be measured with precision. The wavelength used was 14.6 m, but a few additional runs were obtained at 15 and 13 m without any appreciable difference in the resulting tracings.

A year later Jansky stated that "Records of these waves have now been taken at frequent intervals for a period of more than a year. The data obtained from these records, contrary to the first indications . . . indicate that the direction remains fixed in space. . . ."[2]

Since the position of the sun among the stars shifts gradually eastward due to the orbital motion of the earth, it was ruled out as a source of the radio waves.

The position of maximum intensity of the waves obtained at this time was $\alpha = 18$ hrs, $\delta = -10°$, the latter having a large uncertainty. Jansky further speculated on the origin of the waves. "The apparent direction of

---

* Azimuth is analogous to *bearing* in surveying; it can be defined as the arc of the horizon measured westward from the south point to the intersection of the horizon and a vertical circle passing through the celestial object.

Fig. 45. K. G. Jansky and his rotatable directional antenna.

arrival of the waves has not yet been definitely associated with any region fixed in space; however, there are two such regions that should be seriously considered."[3]

The two suggested regions were:

1. the center of the Milky Way system, at approximately $\alpha = 17$ hrs 30 min, and $\delta = -30°$; and

2. the direction in space, in the constellation Hercules, toward which the sun is moving with respect to the stars in its neighborhood. The coordinates of this direction are about $\alpha = 18$ hrs, $\delta = +30°$.

It is now known that the first alternative is correct, and the radio waves Jansky detected come from the direction of the center of the Milky Way, relatively more conspicuous in the radio frequencies than in optical light. This is due to the fact that radio waves from the central regions of the galaxy can penetrate through the extensive dust clouds absorbing the light of optical frequencies.

These first two papers by Jansky were published in the *Proceedings of the Institute of Radio Engineers,*[4] but did not receive much notice. Even his next paper in *Popular Astronomy,* in 1933,[5] did not attract much attention among astronomers. It seemed that the only astronomers actively interested in Jansky's results were F. L. Whipple and J. L. Greenstein, both of the Harvard Observatory, who presented a theoretical discussion of Jansky's results and established that the radio noise he observed could not be explained in terms of secondary solar radiation produced in the earth's atmosphere.

Most astronomers, however, took little interest in Jansky's work; some were not acquainted with the technical aspects of radio engineering and others were not sufficiently receptive to the new discovery's revolutionary aspects.

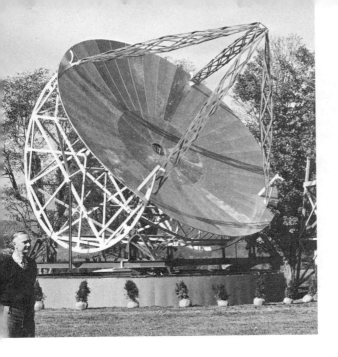

Fig. 46. G. Reber and his 31-ft. reflector, erected on a turntable at the National Radio Astronomy Observatory. (*National Radio Astronomy Observatory*)

THE LONE INVESTIGATOR

The next great step in radio astronomy was made by the American radio engineer, Grote Reber, who had read Jansky's papers and was able to appreciate their importance. During the middle 1930's he built the first parabolic radio antenna, which was fixed in azimuth to coincide with the meridian of his home in Wheaton, Illinois, but could be rotated around a horizontal axis to point toward different altitudes. He obtained a long series of measurements that he published, some in the *Proceedings of the Institute of Radio Engineers*[6] and some in the *Astrophysical Journal*.

Reber was completely unknown to astronomers. I remember his first visit to the Yerkes Observatory, after he had taken a course in astrophysics under B. Strömgren at the University of Chicago to learn the astronomical data he required to explain his observations. Reber was convinced that he, by using a shorter wavelength of 1 or 2 m, had obtained a remarkable confirmation of Jansky's early work.

He brought to Yerkes a large stack of tracings, on which his instrument had recorded the intensity of radiation from the sky at a wavelength of slightly less than 2 m. A definite increase of intensity was shown by a general bulge of the red line, drawn by the recording instrument at the exact time the Milky Way passed over his antenna. The presence of numerous violent and sharp disturbances was an annoying factor, which Reber explained as the result of various electrical appliances, such as a dentist's drill a block or two away, a trolley line on a street in his vicinity, or a passing car's faulty ignition.

We at the observatory continued our discussions with him, and Dutch-born G. P. Kuiper of the staff visited his home to inspect the remarkable radio telescope he had built at his own expense and according to his own designs. We were beginning to realize that a completely new branch of astronomy was emerging.

The publication of Reber's first results in the 1940 *Astrophysical Journal*[7] was the beginning of a concerted effort on the part of astronomers and radio engineers to explain the source of the radio radiation. In this paper, he announced the occurrence of a maximum of intensity coinciding with the transit of the Milky Way. Astronomers were surprised to learn that radio radiation intensity was greatest from the Milky Way. This area of intensity closely followed the optical *isophotes*, lines of equal intensity, that had been drawn by the Dutch astronomer A. Pannekoek and others. Reber also reported that a few bright stars, such as Vega, Sirius, Antares, Deneb, and the sun, gave negative results. His next paper announced the discovery of a relatively faint radio emission from the sun.[8] But Reber apparently was not the first to detect the solar radiation, even though his results were published first. According to G. C. Southworth, a research engineer at the Bell Telephone Laboratories who knew Jansky and was acquainted with his early work, experiments had been designed for the detection of *thermal* radiation° at radio wavelengths emitted by the sun. Southworth noted that: "During the summer months of both 1942 and 1943, the writer and certain of his associates observed a small but measurable amount of microwave radiation coming from the sun."[9]

That the sun is a relatively faint source at radio frequencies in comparison with the Milky Way was a startling discovery, and one of the reasons why astronomers at first were suspicious of the work done by Jansky, Reber, and other pioneers. It is now well known that most of the observed radiation from the sky comes from diffuse spots of different kinds located in the Milky Way or other galaxies. No real star, other than the sun, has been found to possess a measurable amount of radio radiation. Nevertheless, because the sun is a radio source whose intensity is

---

° *Thermal* or *black body* radiation refers to a particular type of intensity distribution in the spectrum, characteristic of the *perfect radiator*, that is, one that radiates the maximum amount of energy at any given temperature, and is perfectly black when cold. This intensity distribution can be calculated theoretically (from a formula developed by the German physicist Max Planck) for any given temperature. Decrease in temperature affects the energy curve (*Planck curve*) in two ways: The total amount of energy radiated per square centimeter of surface decreases and the maximum of the energy curve shifts to longer wavelengths. For all stars, the maximum occurs within or close to the visible region and the curve drops first rapidly, then more gradually, toward longer wavelengths.

enormously enhanced during the outburst of a *solar flare,** it is likely that many stars that resemble the sun in other physical characteristics also emit measurable amounts of radio radiation during their flare activities.

Reber's radio-frequency isophotes of the Milky Way indicated not only a strong source toward the center of the galaxy in Sagittarius but also several other regions of increased intensity (see Fig. 47); three discrete radio sources are recognizable: Cassiopeia A is at the upper left, Sagittarius A at lower right, with Cygnus A between them, all superposed on the general radio emission from the Milky Way. Reber commented upon these results as follows:

> Too little is known about the cause of this phenomenon to read a great deal from Figure [47]. However, it is suggested that the disturbance is in some way connected with the amount of material in space ... various maxima point to the direction of projections from the Milky Way. These projections may be similar to the arms often photographed in other spiral nebulae. In the case of the Milky Way this general picture would call for the center toward Sagittarius, and arms in the direction of Cygnus, Cassiopeia, and Canis Major.[10]

His work, more than Jansky's, made a strong impression upon astronomers. It was frequently discussed in meetings, and led to efforts by Walter

* A sudden increase of brightness of certain areas of the sun.

Fig. 47.   Radio map of the sky by G. Reber. (*Courtesy* Sky and Telescope, *as adapted from the* Astrophysical Journal)

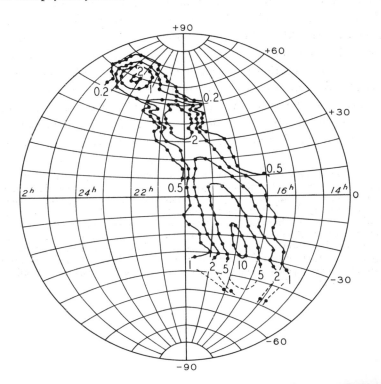

Baade and German-born Rudolph Minkowski of the Mount Wilson Observatory to start some radio-astronomical observations in California. These were temporarily halted because of the outbreak of World War II.

WAR EFFORTS AND RADIO ASTRONOMY

An important discovery was made accidentally when the British early-warning radar system was jammed severely during February 26–28, 1942. The jamming, first attributed to the enemy, was investigated by the English radio astronomer J. S. Hey, who concluded that it originated from the sun and that "this unusual intensity, of the order of 10^5 times that corresponding to the calculated black-body radiation, appears to have been associated with the occurrence of a big solar flare reported to be in a central position on February 28, 1942."[11]

Increases in radio noise before and after radio fadeouts had been noticed earlier; however, according to the American radio astronomer, F. T. Haddock, in most investigations concerned with shortwave radio fadeouts "it appears that the question of the origin of this enhanced noise attracted the least attention."[12] Thus Hey was the first to suggest that radio radiation originates from the sun and is related to solar activity.

Hey, together with his English colleagues S. J. Parsons and J. W. Phillips, made another discovery that also resulted from studies of radar. When some new equipment did not perform as expected, J. M. C. Scott, a theoretical physicist, suggested to Hey ". . . that the limitation in effective noise factor might be attributable to cosmic noise, about which something was already known from the work of Jansky and Reber."[13]

Hey, Parsons, and Phillips were soon able to verify that much of the noise came from the galaxy. In a more detailed survey, they found that radio noise received from the direction of Cygnus was not constant, often fluctuating rapidly by as much as 15 per cent of the mean power received. They described the implications of this observation as follows:

> We were able to rule out the possibility of terrestrial or solar causes, and the interpretation of the results was consistent only with origin in the direction of Cygnus. . . . It appears that such marked variations could only originate from a small number of discrete sources.[14]

Although the fluctuations were attributed later to disturbances in the earth's ionosphere (the upper atmosphere), this was the first reference to "*discrete sources*," the Cygnus A source* discussed on P. 107. The an-

* The capital letters following the names of constellations refer to the radio sources of the constellation, "A" being the strongest source.

nouncement of Hey, Parsons, and Phillips stimulated great interest in the search for other discrete sources and in the determination of more accurate positions of radio sources in order to identify them with optically observed objects.

The most important theoretical investigation of this period also can be indirectly attributed to the war. During the German occupation, astronomers in the Netherlands were deprived of most of their facilities, and several among them, including the young astronomer H. C. van de Hulst, devoted themselves to theoretical work. According to van de Hulst:

In the spring of 1944 Oort° said to me: "We should have a colloquium on the paper by Reber; would you like to study it? And, by the way, radio astronomy can really become very important if there were at least one line in the radio spectrum. Then we can use the method of differential galactic rotation as we do in optical astronomy."[15]

Van de Hulst prepared the colloquium, held at Leiden Observatory and in doing so took up Oort's suggestion about spectral lines, investigating in particular the structure of the hydrogen atom (see Chap. XI, P. 214 for a discussion of atomic structure) which is the most abundant element in space. He found that:

The ground level of hydrogen is split by hyperfine structure into two states of distance 0.047 cm^{-1}. In the one state the spins of the electron and the proton are parallel, in the other antiparallel. At the spontaneous reversal of the spin a quantum of 21.2 cm would be emitted.[16]

Even though in any individual atom such spontaneous reversal occurs, on the average, once in 11 million years, the cumulative effect of the large number of hydrogen atoms in interstellar space might be observable. Confirmation of van de Hulst's prediction was provided in 1951 by the American physicists H. I. Ewen and E. M. Purcell at Harvard and shortly afterward by Dutch and Australian astronomers as well. An extremely important line of investigation has resulted from this discovery, enabling us for the first time to map with some success the structure of the Milky Way (discussed in Chap. XIX). Attempts have been made to discover the 21-cm absorption line in distant galaxies so that the interpretation of the redshift of galaxies could be tested (see P. 471).

The following comment was made by Ewen shortly after the discovery of the 21-cm line, which has a frequency of 1420 megacycles (mc):

° J. H. Oort, the director of the Leiden Observatory, is famous for his studies of the structure of the Milky Way. He developed the method of differential galactic rotation (discussed in Chap. XIX, P. 422).

Fig. 48. H. C. van de Hulst at a colloquium at Leiden Observatory. In front of van de Hulst, in the first row, is J. H. Oort.

The radio broadcasts coming to us from outer space can be compared to sounds from a boiler factory: they are a jumble of vibrations, covering a broad band of frequencies. It has not been easy to figure out what these messages mean. But about a year and a half ago a single significant note was discerned through the din. Today listening posts all over the world are tuning in on this high-pitched monotone at 1420 megacycles, and from it they are obtaining a new picture of the universe.[17]

RADIO TELESCOPES

The advances in electronic devices made during the war, especially radar, resulted in receivers for radio observations much more refined than the relatively simple devices of Jansky and Reber. Thus the stage was set for the development of radio-astronomical instruments and the rapid progress of radio astronomy. These developments were exploited first in England and Australia, and somewhat later in the Netherlands, France, Canada, the Soviet Union, and the United States. English and Dutch astronomers eagerly turned to radio astronomy. Optical observations in their countries are greatly hampered by unfavorable weather conditions of clouds and fog, which, however, are penetrated by radio waves. In the United States most large optical observatories are in the southwest, and radio astronomy first made noticeable progress in the less favorable climate of the eastern states.

Optical telescopes look very much alike, but there is enormous diversity among radio telescopes, and it is impossible to describe here all the varieties designed. Such diversity exists because wavelengths in the radio range differ by a factor of 1,500 between the shortest, about 1 cm, and the longest radio waves of about 15 m. Thus, different structures serve best for the wavelength at which observations are to be made. Since *telescopic resolving power** is inversely proportional to the wavelength and proportional to the aperture, radio telescopes have a much lower resolving power than optical telescopes of similar aperture; however, various structural arrangements are designed in order to increase the effective aperture

* A telescope's ability to separate close stars or points of light.

and thus obtain a higher resolving power. In this respect, radio-telescope design is fundamentally different from optical-telescope design. The Australian J. G. Bolton explains:

In building large optical telescopes, the main aim is to achieve a large collecting surface. Little gain results from the high resolving power because of atmospheric scintillation. In the cm and dm wavelength region of the radio spectrum, advantage can be taken of both the resolving power and the collecting area of large antennae. . . . However, in the meter wavelength region, receiver sensitivities and radio star [now called "discrete radio source"] luminosities are such that, with quite small antennae, more objects can be detected than can be resolved by the instrument. Both the sensitivity of the whole receiving system and the resolving power of the antenna vary directly as the area of the antenna, in the antenna of the conventional type. . . . As the area of the antenna is increased, the number of stars detectable increases faster than the number discernible. Thus great advantage can be taken of antennae so designed that a higher resolving power is obtained than the physical area would suggest.[18]

To equal the resolving power of the 200-in. telescope (of 0″.03 achieved in optical light) at a wavelength of 1 m, an aperture of 2.5 x 10^7 ft, approximately the earth's radius) would be required. Obviously, this resolving power cannot be achieved; but very large apertures are required even for resolving power of only a few minutes of arc. Most radio sources, however, are more intense in the meter than in the centimeter range, and instruments had to be planned for these wavelengths. Because with the conventional telescope it is difficult to achieve the required apertures, interferometers were used. In 1947, L. L. McCready, J. L. Pawsey, and R. Payne-Scott in Australia designed an ingenious *"cliff"* interferometer that employed an antenna array on a high cliff and was used for observing the interference pattern between the direct beam and the beam reflected from the surface of the sea. M. Ryle and F. G. Smith at Cambridge, England, started experimenting with two separate arrays. The first observations, which provided accurate location and hence led to the identification of the intense radio sources, were made with an interferometer consisting of two 27-ft paraboloids separated by about 1,000 ft. The two 90-ft paraboloids recently built at the California Institute of Technology radio field station in Owens Valley will play an important role in determining radio-source positions and extended source brightness distributions.

Another type of interferometer was designed at the *CSIRO* (Commonwealth Scientific and Industrial Research Organization) Radio Physics Laboratory near Sydney, Australia, by B. Y. Mills and A. G. Little. The collecting area of the Mills Cross (Fig. 50) is equal to the physical area of

Fig. 49. The twin 90-ft. radio telescopes at the Owens Valley radio observatory of the California Institute of Technology. (*Courtesy California Institute of Technology*)

the arms. Resolving power is determined by the length of the arms; thus it achieves a high resolving power at a relatively low cost. The arms of the aerial are 1,500 ft long; only one is shown at its full length in the photograph. Later modifications of the same principle have been incorporated into the Christiansen Cross, also near Sydney.

During the early years of radio astronomy, *arrays,* consisting of a large number of individual elements, were most popular, particularly in interferometer arrangements, because of their lower cost and easier construction. Development of arrays was dictated also because most sources are fainter in short wavelengths and hence work had to be carried out at longer wavelengths, where the required resolution could not be achieved in a paraboloid reflector of the type used by Reber. However, a steerable reflector is preferred in many types of observations, and the trend has recently changed. According to Bolton:

Such a telescope has none of the restrictions of an array, such as limited frequency, band width, or difficulty in position changing. For wavelengths below 50 cm it is almost a necessity, for stellar and galactic investigations

Fig. 50. The Mills Cross at the CSIRO Radiophysics Division, Sydney, Australia. (*CSIRO photograph; courtesy* Sky and Telescope)

require collecting area, as well as resolving power, and in many cases tracking of an object or region is desirable. With the ever-increasing sensitivity of receivers in the microwave range due to improvements in conventional receivers and new advances, such as the traveling wave tube and the maser, it is likely that much routine work such as the determination of position or brightness distribution of radio sources, will in the future be carried on with large reflectors working in the microwave range rather than arrays and interferometers in the meter wavelength range. . . . There is no doubt that a large reflector for the cm wavelength range is more expensive than a large array for the meter wavelength range; however, the higher initial cost is probably offset by a longer working life and greater versatility.[19]

In the United States there are a number of paraboloid reflectors up to 90 ft in diameter, and a 300-ft transit-type dish has been constructed at the National Radio Astronomy Observatory. Several other antennae are in the design and construction state: for example, a 140-ft equatorial telescope for the National Radio Astronomy Observatory. The first large-size, and still the biggest steerable paraboloid (250-ft aperture) is at the Nuffield Radio Astronomy Laboratory at Jodrell Bank, England, and the second largest (210-ft aperture) was recently completed in Australia. The 250-ft telescope, a tremendous step forward in radio telescopes, was proposed in 1949 by A. C. B. Lovell, the director of Jodrell Bank.

Sir Ben Lockspeiser, Britain's Secretary of the Department of Science and Industrial Research, said in an address introducing Lovell:

Shortly after the war I was sitting in my office, when a young man came and asked me to let him have £1,000 in order that he might build a radio telescope. After he had explained about his idea, I realized that he was proposing a very promising and new line of enquiry, and he got his £1,000.

Two years afterwards, the same young man walked into my office and said he wanted £100,000 to build a new radio telescope. He pointed out that this would provide a new method for investigating the universe, and because it was independent of cloud and other climatic conditions which

Fig. 51.   An aerial view of the 250-ft. radio telescope nearing completion at Jodrell Bank. (*British Information Services; courtesy* Sky and Telescope)

make observational astronomy in this country so difficult, he felt sure that here was an opportunity for this country to regain its leadership in this field.[20]

After a more thorough investigation, the cost was estimated at £500,000 (approximately $1,410,000) and was shared by the Trustees of the Nuffield Foundation. The telescope was to have a diameter of 250 ft, an *altazimuth* mounting, and a surface of coarse open wire mesh (like the mesh of the California Institute of Technology telescopes); it was designed for investigations in the meter wavelengths. During construction, the 21-cm emission line of hydrogen was discovered, and because of this line's great importance the design had to be changed to permit observations at 21 cm. Because of the shorter wavelengths, solid surface had to be substituted for the wire mesh. Completed in 1957, the telescope has been used successfully in a large number of investigations.

A radically different radio telescope has just been completed at Ohio State and Ohio Wesleyan Universities Radio Observatory. The reasoning leading to its design is described by J. D. Kraus, who has been heading the project:

With the introduction of radio telescopes a new window has been opened on the universe. However, at present only one hundred or so radio sources are reliably known. This is hardly a statistically significant sample of the radio universe. Although the largest telescopes now or soon to be in operation may raise the number into the thousands, it is doubtful if the number will approach that of the stars that can be observed with the unaided eye (about 5,000). Hence, until much larger radio telescopes are built radio astronomy will remain in the primitive status of even smaller numbers than the pre-Galilean era of optical astronomy.

The only way out is with telescopes of larger apertures. But it is not sufficient merely to plan bigger completely steerable parabolic dish telescopes. These cost millions of dollars for diameters of only 100 to 200 feet and the cost mounts exponentially as the size is increased. What is needed in order to break through the "aperture barrier" is an approach or design which can achieve apertures of several acres for thousands instead of millions of dollars, since then apertures of dozens of acres for a few millions of dollars become feasible.[21]

The telescope (see Fig. 52) consists of a 360-ft, tiltable flat reflector at the right to be extended to 720 ft and a fixed paraboloid reflector (at the left). A horn containing receiving equipment is located a short distance in front of the flat reflector. This design was chosen, according to Kraus, because:

Since a flat surface can be very easily checked for any unevenness, it is not necessary that the tiltable reflector be a rigid structure. This results

Fig. 52. Radio telescope at the Ohio State – Ohio Wesleyan Radio Observatory. (*Tom Root Air Photo, Plymouth, Ohio; courtesy* J. D. Kraus, Ohio State University)

in a larger saving in cost. . . . It is much more difficult to maintain tolerances on a curved surface such as a paraboloid, especially if it is movable. This problem is avoided and the cost correspondingly reduced by making the paraboloid fixed. . . . By making the length of the reflectors considerably greater than the height there is an additional saving in cost since the expense of a structure is approximately proportional to the cube of its height . . . the number of sources which an antenna can resolve or detect is a function of the size of the aperture area and not its shape. For example, an antenna with an aperture 100 feet long by 25 feet wide (2,500-square foot aperture area) can resolve the same number of sources as an antenna of the same aperture but 50 feet square.[22]

On the other hand, although the sensitivity of radio-emission receivers has been increased greatly since World War II, and ingenious new types have been designed, progress still depends mostly upon the ability to build larger and larger antennae. Technological and financial limitations prevent the construction of radio telescopes markedly superior to those now available. The interval in wavelength between about 1 micron (μ) and 1 cm probably will be bridged by a new type of instrument that conceivably could be placed in a satellite in order to avoid absorption in our atmosphere. At the long end of the radio-frequency window, the resolving power of any instrument now under construction is so low that its usefulness is severely limited. Space scientists have suggested that two satellites revolving in circular orbits around the earth could be used as an interferometer, but no serious attempt has been made to exploit this idea.

THE RADIO UNIVERSE

Progress in radio astronomy has been rapid, and an enormous amount of observational and theoretical material has accumulated since the end of World War II. Radio astronomy, which has provided some of the most exciting postwar discoveries and has greatly increased our understanding of the universe, at the same time has presented many new problems that still await solution.

Cosmic Background Noise

It is useful to distinguish between the general cosmic background noise, discovered by Jansky and Reber, and discrete radio sources. The exact distribution of background noise depends upon the frequencies at which observations are made, and much has been learned from these differences about the various contributing factors. One component has been attributed to emission nebulae, associated with hot O and B stars and concentrated in a thin disk in the galactic plane. A second component, whose width corresponds roughly to the stellar distribution in the Milky Way band, appears to be associated with later-type stars. The German astrophysicist A. Unsöld suggested that this component might originate in flare stars; but it may also result from a superposition of large numbers of faint, discrete, radio sources not associated with optically observable objects and of unknown nature. The third component is distributed uniformly over the sky and sometimes has been attributed to unresolved, faint, extragalactic sources. A more probable identification, first suggested by J. E. Baldwin, is the galactic "halo" similar to that surrounding the Andromeda nebula—a region from which radio waves can be detected that is 10 times larger than the optically visible galaxy.

Discrete Radio Sources

The discrete sources fall into three groups: sources associated with the solar system, galactic sources, and extragalactic sources. In the solar system, the strongest emission originates in the sun, and both the "quiet" sun and the solar radio bursts have been investigated extensively. Jupiter was found to be a radio source in 1955 (see P. 159), and since then radio emission has been detected from Venus, Mars, and Saturn. Attempts to detect radio emission from comets have failed.

The first discrete radio source identified outside the solar system was Taurus A, third brightest radio source in the sky. In 1949, J. G. Bolton and G. J. Stanley of the Radiophysics Laboratory at Sydney, Australia, obtained an accurate position and found it to coincide with the Crab nebula —the remnant of a Type I supernova that exploded in 1054. By 1959 the remnants of the 16th-century Danish astronomer Tycho Brahe's nova of 1572 and Kepler's nova of 1604, both of Type I, had been found as weak radio sources. In 1951, Minkowski and Baade at Palomar Observatory identified the strong source Cassiopeia A as the remnants of a supernova of Type II. (Both the Crab nebula and the Cassiopeia A source will be discussed in Chap. XVI.)

Some of the strongest galactic emission nebulosities (see Chap. XVIII) such as the Orion, the Rosette, and η Carinae nebulae, also exceed the background noise sufficiently to be considered discrete sources.

Extragalactic Radio Sources

Identified extragalactic sources fall into two broad groups—normal, relatively nearby galaxies, such as the Andromeda galaxy (M 31), the Magellanic Clouds, M 81, M 51, and so forth,* and a large variety of what may be called *peculiar* galaxies.

R. Hanbury Brown and C. Hazard in England first detected weak emission from the Andromeda galaxy in 1950. Since then, they and B. Y. Mills have investigated several other normal galaxies. The radio emission of these galaxies usually can be observed over the galactic *halo*, or *corona* (see P. 407n). The normal galaxies are relatively faint at radio frequencies, and the total amount of energy emitted in this range is only about a millionth of that emitted at optical wavelengths.

The *peculiar* galaxies are much stronger radio sources, and some of them are radiating as much, and even more, energy at radio frequencies than in the optical range.

The strongest of peculiar galaxies, the Cygnus A source, discovered by Hey, Parsons, and Phillips, was identified by Baade and Minkowski with an object first interpreted as two galaxies in collision 700 million light-years away. (A light-year is the distance traversed by light in one year and equals 9.5×10^{17} cm, or 6.3×10^4 a.u.) Using radio telescopes with greater resolving power, astronomers have learned that radio emission originates in two separate regions, placed symmetrically on both sides of the optical object, at distances of about 100,000 light-years from it. Similar highly displaced radio sources have been discovered recently in several

---

* The brighter galaxies and nebulae are usually referred to by the numbers assigned to them in either of three catalogues: Messier's catalogue, published in 1781 (in which case the number is preceded by M), the New General Catalogue (NGC) published in 1888, or the Index Catalogue (IC), extension of the NGC and published in 1895 and 1908.

Fig. 53. (Top) Cygnus A radio source, photographed with the 200-in. Hale telescope. (*Mount Wilson and Palomar Observatories*)

Fig. 54. (Lower left) Globular galaxy M 87 in Virgo, photographed with the 200-in. Hale telescope. (*Mount Wilson and Palomar Observatories*)

Fig. 55. (Lower right) Short-exposure photograph of M 87, in blue light, with the 120-in. telescope. (*Lick Observatory*)

peculiar galaxies. Other examples of peculiar galaxies are the Centaurus A source identified with NGC 5128, and Virgo A, identified with M 87. NGC 5128 appears as an elliptical galaxy crossed by a wide band of dust; M 87 appears on long-exposure photographs to be a normal globular galaxy. On short exposures made in blue light, a luminous "jet" is seen to project about 300 parsecs (see Fig. 55) from the nucleus.

Many attempts have been made to explain the great intensity of radio emissions from peculiar galaxies, and a recent suggestion by the English astronomer G. R. Burbidge, now at the University of California, will be discussed in Chap. XVI, P. 342. Interpreting Cygnus A in terms of colliding galaxies has been questioned occasionally, and efforts are being made to account for it with a more comprehensive theory, including peculiar galaxies of different kinds.

All discrete sources discussed here have a continuous spectrum, and the changes in intensity are gradual. Energy distribution is not thermal, except in a few cases, such as the galactic emission nebulae. It cannot be attributed to the radiation from a hot body, since thermal radiation decreases toward longer wavelengths, while most radio sources exhibit the opposite effect (radiating more strongly at meter wavelengths than in the centimeter range). This effect has been attributed to the *synchrotron mechanism,* the spiraling of high-energy electrons along magnetic lines of force (this will be discussed in more detail in connection with the Crab Nebula).

In a recent article, I. S. Shklovsky has described the discovery of "radio-galaxies" and their interpretation in terms of nonthermal, synchrotron radiation as the greatest achievement of astronomy in the 20th century. The discovery of many very intense radio galaxies required skill and knowledge, but given large radio-telescopes and sensitive receivers any qualified person could have found such objects as Cygnus A. But the synchrotron mechanism (for the discovery of which Shklovsky was himself mainly responsible) was entirely new in astronomy. Its use required not only extensive knowledge of theoretical physics, but a brilliant new idea was needed, which resulted in the discovery of vast clouds of "relativistic electrons," associated with the galaxies, with electron velocities close to the velocity of light; these electrons emit radiation when they are placed in a magnetic field. Contrary to what is observed in thermal sources (free-free electrons), the synchrotron radiation increases in intensity with the wavelength, in the centimeter and decimeter range. There must be a cut-off at still longer wavelengths, but it has not yet been definitely observed.

To date, only a very small percentage of the detected radio sources have been identified with optical objects. Of the several thousand sources contained in surveys made at Sydney and Cambridge, only a little over a hundred have been identified. The difficulty is attributable to a lack of accurate positions for fainter sources and possibly to sources (some of the peculiar galaxies, for instance) that are more intense in the radio than in the optical region.

THE SEARCH FOR ARTIFICIAL SIGNALS

In recent years, considerable theorizing and some observing have been devoted to the possibility of detecting radio signals from intelligent beings elsewhere in the universe. The problem of intelligent life or of other forms of life on planetlike bodies is not new. A book published in the 18th century by the Frenchman B. le B. de Fontenelle, dealt with this problem at great length; it was translated into many foreign languages and stimulated a great deal of interest. At the beginning of this century, the topic was debated vigorously in connection with the Martian canals (see Chap. VIII).

This renewal of interest, which resulted from the invention of radio telescopes, was greeted suspiciously at first by most scientists, who made it the butt of jokes and an object of scathing criticism. But the possibility of intelligent life in space cannot be brushed aside. The number of solar-type stars in the Milky Way and other galaxies is very large, and life appears to be an intrinsic property of certain types of complicated molecules.

The American astrophysicist, Chinese-born S. S. Huang, has discussed the physical conditions that would be required for life to exist on a planet outside the solar system. He concludes that a very massive star's lifespan probably is much too short to allow the formation of complicated living organisms on planets that may travel in approximately circular orbits around such stars. For example, the total lifespan of a star having a mass 50 times that of the sun is only a few million years. On the other hand, the evolution of a star of very small mass proceeds very slowly, while stars with masses smaller than that of the sun are much cooler so that the space in which planetary temperatures would be approximately similar to the earth's is quite restricted.

The possibility of life may be seriously considered only on planets of solar-type stars with masses and lifespans (about 10^{10} years) similar to the sun's. Among the billions of such stars in the Milky Way and other billions of similar stars in distant galaxies, planets that support some form of life may very well exist. There is, however, less justification for concluding that such forms of life have developed the kind of intelligence required for transmitting understandable signals into space.

Several distinguished physicists and astronomers have discussed this problem. In 1959, P. Morrison and G. Cocconi, physicists at Cornell, were among the first to suggest that the Jodrell Bank 250-ft radio telescope should be used to probe for artificial signals. Lovell has recently published an article in *The New York Times* that describes his own reactions to this proposal. At first, apparently, he dismissed the suggestion as preposterous and its authors as a pair of cranks (Lovell did not know then that Morrison and Cocconi are eminent physicists).

F. Drake of the National Radio Astronomy Observatory calculated that with the 85-ft radio telescope, artificially produced radio signals could be detected with sufficient intensity if the distances were not greater than about 10 light-years. However, only two solar-type stars at distances of approximately 10 light-years, τ Ceti and ν Eridani, are single (because binary motion probably destroys the longevity of a planetary orbit). No signals could be detected from them by Drake, and it would be an extraordinary coincidence indeed if there were intelligent beings on planets associated with these particular stars. A more thorough discussion of the entire problem was published by S. von Hoerner.[23] Since most of the factors determining the existence of intelligent life on other planets are unknown, von Hoerner assumed average values for those properties not now observable.

Von Hoerner concluded that, to achieve a reasonable probability of detecting another civilization, the search should be extended to a distance of about 1,000 light-years. If the number of suitable stars in Drake's survey is typical for this larger volume, the radio emission of approximately 2 million stars, rather than two stars, would have to be examined. At present this is impossible, not only because of the tremendous amount of work required, but also because at a distance of 1,000 light-years the signals would have to be very much more intense than any signals that man can transmit into space in the centimeter wavelengths.

Although many distinguished scientists are actively interested in this problem, those responsible for spending government money on scientific research are necessarily skeptical about financing so expensive a project that does not promise quick results. Thus Lovell, though he apparently no longer considers the ideas of Morrison and Cocconi as mad, is undoubtedly right when he says that the time has not yet come to divert the observing time at the 250-ft radio telescope from other pressing needs. It is unlikely, therefore, that in the near future anyone will be able to embark on a full-scale program of searching for artificial radio signals from other worlds.

In their excitement about the probability of artificial radio signals, a crucial point seems to have been overlooked by many astronomers. Before any such full-scale program is initiated, there should be a systematic search for planetary bodies accompanying solar-type stars and perhaps also relating to stars having other physical properties that may yet be amenable to life. This now can be done in several ways.

Assuming, as is reasonable, that the orbital inclinations of such companions are distributed at random, a fairly large percentage of solar-type stars should show periodic occultations by the planetary body. In the case of the sun and Jupiter, diminution in brightness would be about 1 per cent, which would be easily detectable but would require many years of continuous search coupled with an effort to distinguish the occultation's geometrical effects and the irregular fluctuations in the parent star's brightness that are caused by spots. Another way to discover bodies of small mass is to measure changes in the parent star's radial velocity; such changes would be about 0.01 km/sec, which is within the range of existing spectrographs. In this case also, continuous observations would be needed to study one or more orbital cycles. The third method, measuring the proper motions of parent stars, is essentially the same used for the last 25 years in the United States by Dutch-born P. van de Kamp and his associates at the Sproul Observatory in Swarthmore, Pennsylvania. They have found several stars whose motions through space are not rectilinear or, in the case of binaries, are not strictly elliptical and have inferred the masses of the companion stars (as will be discussed in more detail in Chap. XIV, P. 297). In a few cases, masses of about 0.01 solar mass have been inferred, but since the low-mass companions are invisible, it cannot now be decided whether to regard them as dark planets or as stars of very low intrinsic brightness. However, at the present time this method is applied only in the case of bright stars that have attracted the attention of astronomers interested in determining stellar parallaxes, and in a few binary stars that have been accurately observed by means of visual micrometers over intervals of many decades.

VII

THE SUN

THE RELATIONSHIP between improved observing methods and facilities, discussed in the preceding chapters, and theoretical developments is well illustrated by the progress of solar research during this century.

In 1904 H. H. Turner presented the Royal Astronomical Society's Gold Medal to George Ellery Hale, who was honored for his method of photographing the solar surface and for other astronomical work. Turner's presentation speech began with:

"It cannot be too often repeated," remarks Prof. Hale himself in a recent memoir, "that the sun is the only star whose phenomena can be studied in detail." We also assent at once not only to the proposition itself, but to the obvious corollary that particular attention should be paid to solar phenomena; and yet it would appear from the history of astronomy that the statement, however often repeated, has fallen on deaf ears.[1]

THE "NEW ERA" IN SOLAR RESEARCH

With few exceptions ears were deaf until almost the end of the 19th century. Around 1890, however, a period of intensive and detailed study of solar phenomena commenced, in large part because of the efforts of Hale in the United States and H. Deslandres in France. Both men used new methods and invented new instruments: notably the *spectroheliograph* (Hale) and the *spectral velocity recorder* (Deslandres).

The *spectroheliograph* is a slit spectrograph that employs a second slit immediately in front of the photographic plate to isolate the light of a single line in the solar spectrum. With synchronized motion of the two slits, one across the solar image, the other across the photographic plate, a complete image of the sun in the light of the chosen line can be obtained. The double-slit method had been discussed in the 19th century by J. Janssen at the Meudon Observatory in France and others, who, however, never tried to apply it. C. A. Young at Princeton University and O. Lohse at Potsdam, Germany, had tried the procedure but failed in its application. Hale, apparently, was not familiar with these earlier speculations or experiments.

The *spectral velocity recorder* employs a widened slit moved a short distance between exposures and gives the spectral displacements of the complete calcium (Ca) line. These displacements are interpreted as movement of the calcium clouds.

Hale and Deslandres made several important discoveries almost simultaneously, and considerable controversy about priority resulted, particularly in regard to the invention of the spectroheliograph. Most recent texts state that in 1891 Hale and Deslandres independently invented the spectroheliograph. The inventors, it seems, felt quite strongly about each other's claims. In 1905 Deslandres in a pointed discussion of the question of priority stated that:

> I have not been ignorant ... of the advantages of the spectroheliograph, which I have continuously used for the recording of vapors in my first notes of August 1891 and February 1892, which Hale always fails to mention. Not only have I used the spectroheliograph ... but even the spectral velocity recorder. I have considered the instrument ... [spectroheliograph] neither as very new or as very difficult to construct. ... In addition, the spectroheliograph ... obeys certain simple optical rules which I have been the first to propound in 1893 ... and which alone assure me of a clear and complete image. These rules have been followed subsequently by all, and in particular by Hale in his last researches of 1903.[2]

In Hale's riposte:

> Before 1893 when he also obtained a spectroheliograph ... Deslandres devoted special attention to a study of the K-line in successive sections of the sun's disk. The spectrograph employed for this purpose was moved a short distance between each exposure, but the exposures were made when the instrument was at rest, and the resulting photographs are photographs of spectra ... the principle of continuous relative motion of solar image and slit, essential in a spectroheliograph, is lacking. ...[3]

A just appraisal of the situation was made by F. W. Dyson, when he presented the Royal Astronomical Society Gold Medal, also for research on solar phenomena, to Deslandres in 1913:

... the spectroheliograph was realized in actual practice first by Hale, but Deslandres has not only contributed greatly to its development, but he has also constructed another instrument, the "Spectroenregistreur des vitesses," or velocity recorder, which is of equal and may prove of even greater importance. Thanks to this discovery, we can follow and study the varying movements of the solar atmosphere, as well as the forms of the different layers.[4]

Although the atmospheres of the sun and the stars and their spectra will be discussed in more detail in Chap. XI, a short description and definition of some terms is essential at this point. The *photosphere* is the lowest layer of atmosphere, forming the apparent surface of the sun (Fig. 56). It displays a finely grained appearance and at times other more conspic-

Fig. 56.   Photograph of the sun, taken on July 31, 1949, under excellent conditions, showing large sunspots and fine structure of the sun's surface. (*Mount Wilson and Palomar Observatories*)

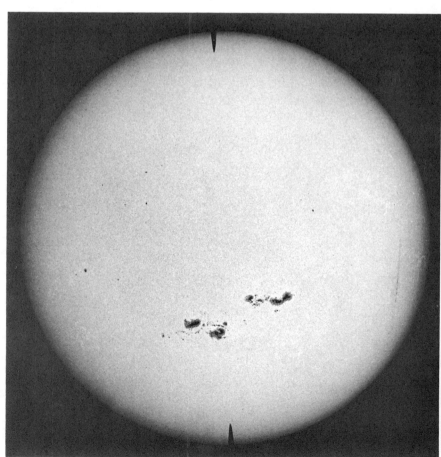

uous features, such as darker, roughly circular regions, called *sunspots*. (The central dark part of a sunspot is called the *umbra*, the surrounding lighter region the *penumbra*.) In calcium spectroheliograms, sunspots are surrounded by regions of high luminosity called *flocculi*. Near the edge of the sun, flocculi are visible in white light as well and are then called *faculae*. *Prominences* are masses of luminous gas rising above the solar photosphere and best seen at the edge of the solar disk, where they are projected against the sky. Above the photosphere are the more tenuous layers, the *chromosphere* and the *corona*.

The *solar absorption lines* (Fig. 57) originate in different layers of the photosphere but principally in the upper one, usually referred to as the *reversing layer*. The Bavarian optician and physicist J. von Fraunhofer first detected dark lines in the solar spectrum at the beginning of the 19th century and assigned letters to the most conspicuous ones. He began with the red and called the first conspicuous line A; C is the hydrogen-alpha

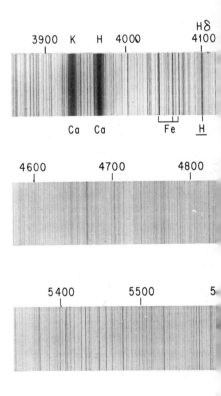

Fig. 57. The spectrum of the sun between 3,900 and 6,900 A. (*Mount Wilson and Palomar Observatories*)

(H α) line; D are the two famous close sodium lines in the yellow; and the H and K lines are of ionized calcium, at 3968 and 3933 A, respectively. The absorption lines in the solar spectrum (or in the spectra of stars similar to the sun) are often referred to as the Fraunhofer lines. In the figure the wavelength scale and Fraunhofer's original designations are marked at the top of each strip. A few of the modern identifications are indicated at the bottom. The black vertical lines are the absorption lines of the solar atmosphere.

Early photographic plates were insensitive to red light, and the H α line, the most conspicuous in visual observations, could not be used to obtain spectroheliograms. Hale, however, found the calcium H and K lines strong not only in the chromosphere and prominences but also near sunspots and in other areas across the solar disk. Since the Fraunhofer lines are produced in the upper photosphere and thus give a picture of the solar atmosphere at relatively high levels, the spectroheliogram of the

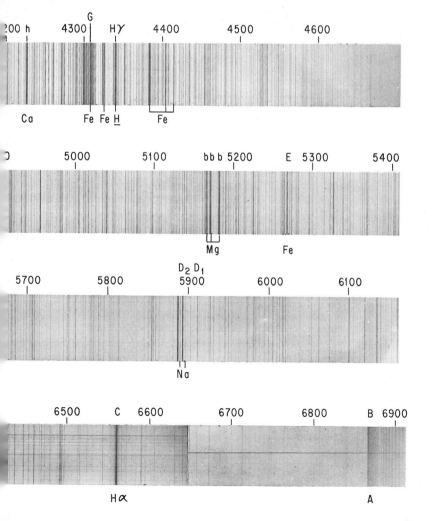

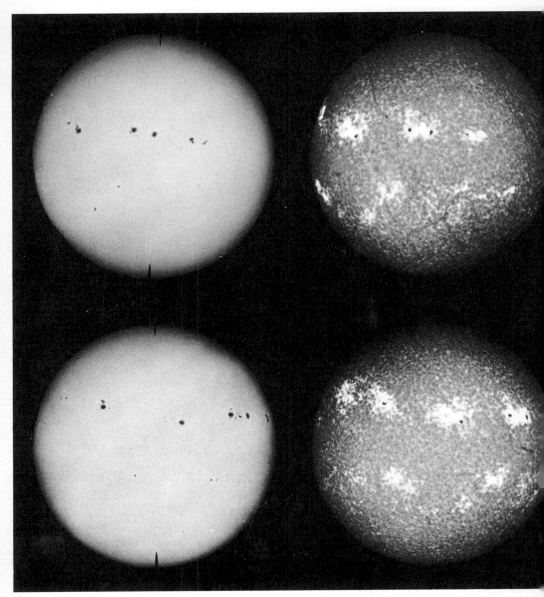

solar disk is quite different from a photograph made in integrated white light, and it varies from line to line. At the left of each series of photographs in Fig. 58 is a direct photograph of the sun in white light, in the center a simultaneous photograph in the light of ionized calcium, and on the right a photograph in the light of the Balmer-alpha line of hydrogen. The top series was taken on October 10, 1926, the bottom, on October 14, 1926. In calcium light the entire disk shows a mottled appearance in addition to the bright flocculi occurring around sunspots and in other disturbed areas across the solar disk.

The absorption lines in a spectrum are not infinitely narrow but

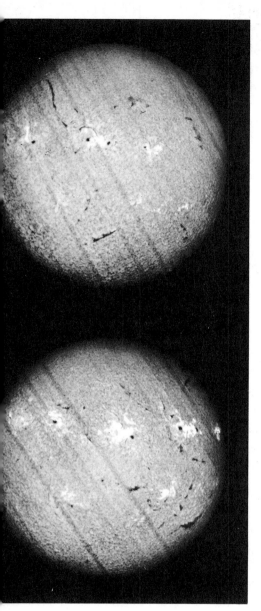

Fig. 58. The sun. (*Mount Wilson and Palomar Observatories*)

possess a certain width, with the maximum absorption in the center (core) of the line, decreasing smoothly toward the edges (wings). A plot of the amount of absorption against wavelength is referred to as the profile of the line (see Fig. 113). The broadening of the lines is due to many factors, which will be discussed in Chap. XI and in the Appendix, and differs from star to star as well as for different lines in the same spectrum. Thus the H and K lines of calcium are conspicuously broadened in the solar spectrum. Since the atoms most effective in producing absorption in the core and the wings of a line do not occur in the same layer of the solar atmosphere, Deslandres first suggested that different levels of the atmos-

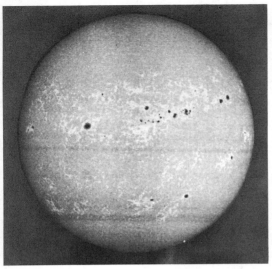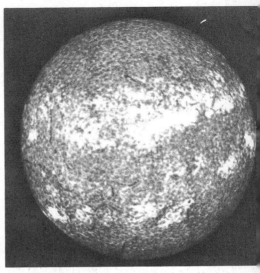

Fig. 59. Left: solar image in the wing of the K line; right: in the center of the K line. (*Meudon Observatory*)

phere can be photographed by centering the slit of the spectroheliograph on different parts of the H and K line—the center of the line produces a picture of high-level clouds, the wings produce one of the lower levels.

Low-level calcium spectroheliograms more closely resemble direct photographs: The sunspots appear dark and the faculae seen near the edge of the sun in ordinary photographs are shown. Faculae were known to be often associated with sunspots and in a sense to be more fundamental than the spots themselves. Faculae usually precede the development of sunspots and linger on after their disappearance. Moreover, prominences seem to be directly associated with them. In white light, however, faculae are visible only near the edge of the sun; elsewhere the lack of contrast with the surrounding photosphere does not allow them to be seen. The spectroheliograph permitted the study of flocculi across the entire solar disk.

High-level calcium spectroheliograms, on the other hand, do not resemble direct photographs: The calcium clouds are much more extensive, often completely covering the sunspots.

THE LIFE AND WORK OF GEORGE ELLERY HALE

While many astronomers made important contributions to solar research, Hale is the "New Era's" preeminent figure. Any discussion of his work must emphasize his role in the development of the Yerkes, Mount Wilson, and Palomar observatories. His research progressed along with his improvement of solar telescopes and auxiliary equipment, and Hale's most valuable contribution to astronomy may well be his unceasing effort to provide the best equipment—including the world's largest refracting and reflecting telescopes—for solar and stellar studies.

Hale combined good training in physics and mathematics with extraordinary inventiveness in developing new instrumentation. The naming of the 200-in. telescope of the Palomar Observatory "the Hale telescope" is a tribute to these unusual qualifications. Few astronomers of any generation have been equally competent as instrumentalists and as observers and theoreticians.

Early Years

George Ellery Hale was born in Chicago, Illinois, on June 29, 1868. As a young boy, with the help and encouragement of his family, he built a workshop equipped with various physical and chemical apparatuses, and delighted in examining microorganisms with his microscope. After becoming interested in astronomy at the age of 13 or 14 he met two famous double-star observers, S. W. Burnham and G. W. Hough of Chicago, but soon found that

... I could not have devoted my life to such work as they were doing, valuable as it was to science. The reason lay in the fact that I was born an experimentalist, and I was bound to find the way for combining physics and chemistry with astronomy.[5]

This emphasis on the interrelatedness of astronomy, physics, and chemistry was later reflected in his own research and also in his attitude toward astronomical research facilities.

Hale became fascinated with the solar spectrum after acquiring a spectrometer and grating:

... Nothing could exceed my enthusiasm in observing the solar spectrum and in measuring the principal lines. I bought Lockyer's "Studies in Spectrum Analysis" and began the observations of flame and spark spectra and their comparison with the sun. At last I had found my true course and I have held to it ever since.[6]

However, Hale did not devote his energies exclusively to solar research, which he saw in a broader framework:

I must emphasize the advantages I gained from my earlier work in other fields. It gave me a broad interest in many branches of science and taught me something of their mutual dependence. It led me to read *The Origin of Species*, and initiated a lasting desire to study evolution. It taught me to regard the sun as a typical star, a link in the long evolutional chain, and thus helped me to avoid becoming exclusively a specialist in solar research.[7]

Fig. 60.   G. E. Hale.

In his *The Study of Stellar Evolution* (1908) Hale explained his attitude toward the study of the subject:

We are now in a position to regard the study of evolution as that of a single great problem, beginning with the origin of the stars in the nebulae and culminating in those difficult and complex sciences that endeavor to account, not merely for the phenomena of life, but for the laws which control a society composed of human beings. Any such consideration of all natural phenomena as elements of a single problem must begin with a study of the Sun, the only star lying near enough the Earth to permit of detailed investigation. . . .

It will be the object of this book to show how the student of astrophysics attacks this problem of stellar evolution, through the development of special instruments and methods of research, and the accumulation and discussion of observations. . . .

It must not be forgotten that such a study comprises only the earliest and simplest elements in the general problem of evolution. The province of the student of astrophysics may be said to end with an understanding of the production of a planet like the Earth.[8]

Hale obtained a thorough background in mathematics, physics, and chemistry during his studies at the Massachusetts Institute of Technology (1886–1890). He also served at this time as a volunteer assistant at the Harvard College Observatory, where he experimented unsuccessfully with the first form of a spectroheliograph. In 1891, he developed a working instrument at his private observatory in Kenwood, a suburb of Chicago, where he made spectroscopic observations of sunspots, obtained the first photographs of the ultraviolet spectrum of prominences (this was achieved very shortly thereafter also by Deslandres and C. A. Young of Princeton), and identified some of the higher members of the Balmer series of hydrogen (see P. 215). Hale was interested particularly in sunspots, because when he started his work,

. . . the widest differences of opinion prevailed among astronomers concerning the nature and origin of sunspots. Some regarded them as cooler regions in the solar atmosphere resembling terrestrial clouds, while others insisted upon their very high temperature. Faye and Reye, in harmony with an early suggestion of Sir John Herschel considered them to resemble cyclones or tornadoes, but Faye's theory involved a downrush of the surface vapors while Reye, agreeing with the views of other meteorologists, was equally emphatic in favor of an uprush.[9]

He soon realized that he needed larger instruments to make further progress.

Yerkes Observatory

In 1897, Hale was appointed associate professor of astrophysics at the University of Chicago and learned by chance that glass disks for a 40-in. refracting telescope ordered by the University of Southern California were for sale. He began the first of his many struggles to obtain money for large instruments. This time funds were donated by Chicago's streetcar magnate C. T. Yerkes, mentioned in Chap. I—who first gave money "only" for the lenses, then "only" for the mounting, and, finally, for the building.

In 1897 the Yerkes Observatory, boasting what is still the largest refractor in the world, was dedicated, with Hale serving as its director. Hale moved his Kenwood equipment, including the laboratory, to Yerkes, and had an instrument shop built at the observatory. He insisted that laboratories and instrument shops were an integral part of an observatory, arguing that observational data must be supplemented with laboratory tests and that astronomers must be provided with the instruments required by specific problems. Hale's then novel approach, time and again has been proved essential for efficient planning of observations and evaluation of observational data, and it now is adopted by all large observatories.

With the Rumford spectroheliograph attached to the 40-in. telescope, Hale discovered in 1903 the dark calcium and hydrogen flocculi, elongated, dark patches, which turned out to be prominences seen in projection on the solar disk. Thus prominences could be studied not only at the edge, but also across the entire disk of the sun.

The Development of the Mount Wilson Solar Observatory

The size of auxiliary instruments for solar observations was limited by the weight a moving telescope could carry. Even at Kenwood, Hale had planned to build a fixed solar telescope in which, by a system of moving mirrors, sunlight would be reflected in a fixed direction. Because of poor atmospheric conditions, the fixed horizontal Snow telescope built at Yerkes did not give the desired results, and it became clear that only in a better location would a solar observatory be effective.

Fig. 61. The Rumford spectrohelio-graph, attached to the Yerkes 40-in. refractor. (*From G. E. Hale. The Study of Stellar Evolution, Chicago, University of Chicago Press, 1908, Plate 37*)

Fig. 62. (Opposite) spectrum of a sunspot. (*From* Astrophysical Journal, *LXXV, 1932, Plate 15; courtesy Mrs. C. Moore-Sitterly*)

Prospects were quite dim until the Carnegie Institution of Washington was founded in 1902, and Hale became secretary of a committee studying the feasibility of supporting extensive astronomical research. The committee recommended the establishment of a large solar observatory, and soon a grant was obtained to study possible sites. Mount Wilson in southern California was judged the most favorable. However, money for the solar observatory was not obtained until after 1904, when Hale, on his own, made observations on Mount Wilson to persuade the foundation's trustees of the site's advantages. Hale was then appointed director of the new observatory. The Snow telescope, moved from Yerkes, gave better results, but air stratification in the long horizontal path of the light rays often caused image distortion. Realizing that these difficulties could be avoided in a vertical telescope, Hale devised a 60-ft tower telescope with a 30-ft spectrograph in a vertical, underground tunnel. High-dispersion, good-quality spectrograms and spectroheliograms obtained with it led to further progress in the study of sunspot phenomena.

Analysis of Sunspot Spectra

There are conspicuous differences in relative intensities of lines in sunspots and the solar disk, as shown in Fig. 62. The slit of the spectrograph was placed across the spot so that the spectrum of the photosphere was recorded above and below the sunspot spectrum. The changes in

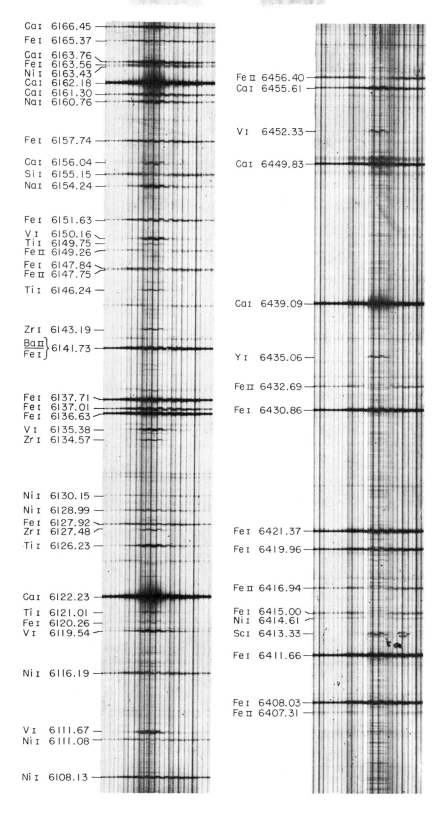

Ca I 6166.45
Fe I 6165.37
Ca I 6163.76
Fe I 6163.56
Ni I 6163.43
Ca I 6162.18
Ca I 6161.30
Na I 6160.76

Fe I 6157.74

Ca I 6156.04
Si I 6155.15
Na I 6154.24

Fe I 6151.63
V I   6150.16
Ti I 6149.75
Fe II 6149.26
Fe I 6147.84
Fe II 6147.75

Ti I 6146.24

Zr I 6143.19

Ba II
Fe I } 6141.73

Fe I 6137.71
Fe I 6137.01
Fe I 6136.63
V I   6135.38
Zr I 6134.57

Ni I 6130.15
Ni I 6128.99
Fe I 6127.92
Zr I 6127.48
Ti I 6126.23

Ca I 6122.23
Ti I 6121.01
Fe I 6120.26
V I   6119.54

Ni I 6116.19

V I   6111.67
Ni I 6111.08

Ni I 6108.13

Fe II 6456.40
Ca I 6455.61

V I   6452.33

Ca I 6449.83

Ca I 6439.09

Y I   6435.06

Fe II 6432.69

Fe I 6430.86

Fe I 6421.37

Fe I 6419.96

Fe II 6416.94

Fe I 6415.00
Ni I 6414.61
Sc I 6413.33

Fe I 6411.66

Fe I 6408.03
Fe II 6407.31

intensity toward the center of the spot are well shown. The zig-zag appearance is due to the Zeeman effect discussed below. At the beginning of this century, the intensity differences were suspected to result from differences in temperature between the photosphere and the sunspots. Lockyer already had noticed that, in passing from the solar disk to the spots, the spectrum is modified in a manner similar to that observed when passing from spark to arc spectra in the laboratory. It was known, too, that vapors in the spark attain a higher temperature than in the arc. Comparison of spot spectra with extensive laboratory observations (particularly those of A. S. King, W. S. Adams, and H. G. Gale at Mount Wilson) of the effects of temperature and density on spectral-line behavior established the lower temperature and higher density in spot regions. This work also provided a basis for the Indian astronomer M. N. Saha's ionization and excitation theories (discussed in Chapter XI) and contributed to Adams' and A. Kohlschütter's establishment, also at Mount Wilson, of luminosity criteria, and hence contributed to the spectroscopic parallax method (discussed in Chap. X, P. 201). Additional evidence of a lower temperature in sunspots was provided in 1906 by the identification of titanium oxide (TiO) and other molecular bands in sunspot spectra by Hale and his collaborators and by A. Fowler of London University in England.

Another puzzling aspect of the sunspot spectrum was the doubling of certain lines, attributed for a long time to an emission line—resulting from an overlying, hotter layer of vapors—superposed on the absorption line. While this explanation accounted for the calcium H and K lines and the Hα line, it did not account adequately for the behavior of many fainter lines observed with the 60-ft tower telescope. The H-α spectroheliograms obtained in 1908, when photographic plates sensitive to red light became available, represented an even higher level in the solar atmosphere than the calcium spectroheliograms and showed striking vortex patterns around sunspots, which suggested to Hale a new line of investigation:

We know from the investigations of Rowland that the rapid revolution of electrically charged bodies will produce a magnetic field, in which the lines of force are at right angles to the plane of revolution. Corpuscles emitted by the photosphere may perhaps be drawn into the vortices, or a preponderance of positive or negative ions may result from some other cause. When observed along the lines of force, many of the lines in the spot spectrum should be double, if they are produced in a strong magnetic field. Double lines, which look like reversals, have recently been photographed in spot spectra with the 30-ft spectrograph of the tower telescope, confirming the visual observations of Young and Mitchell. It should be determined whether the components of these double lines are circularly polarized in opposite directions, or, if not, whether other less obvious indications of a magnetic field are present.[10]

When a source of light is between the poles of an electromagnet, each spectral line is split into components, which are polarized. The unique combination of splitting and polarization effects was discovered by the Dutch physicist P. Zeeman in 1896. Hale detected the features of the Zeeman effect and derived an estimated field strength of several thousand gauss. Recent observations have established that a spot's field strength depends on its maximum area—100 gauss in the smallest measurable spots, up to 4,000 gauss in large spots. The field decreases from the center to the edge.

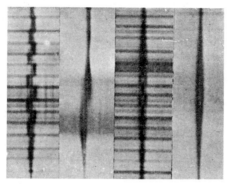

Fig. 63.   Zeeman effect in sunspot spectra. The second strip shows reversal of polarity in two adjacent spots. (*From G. E. Hale and S. B. Nicholson,* Magnetic Observations of Sunspots, *Part I. Washington, D. C., Carnegie Institution, 1938, Plate 6*)

If the magnetic field were produced by the whirling of charged particles, then (analogous with reversal of current in an electromagnet) a reversal in the direction of the revolution should produce opposite polarities in sunspots. This relationship seemed to be confirmed when late in 1908 two spots on opposite sides of the solar equator with hydrogen vortices indicating revolution in opposite directions were found to have opposite polarities. In Fig. 64, (a) is a bipolar group of sunspots, (b) unipolar groups on opposite sides of the equator (represented by the black line). Subsequently, the relationship was found not to hold true for all spots: The direction of the whirl in the hydrogen vortices does not necessarily correspond to that in the underlying spot vortices. Rather, the vortex structure observed on spectroheliograms is not caused by the magnetic field at all, but is similar to a cyclone, and thus is a purely hydrodynamic phenomenon.

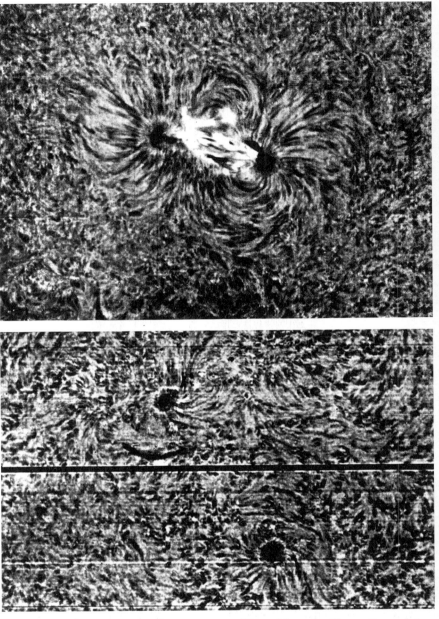

Fig. 64. Hydrogen vortices above sunspots. (*From* Magnetic Observations of Sunspots, *Part I. Washington, D.C., Plate 3*)

The most recent evidence indicates that sunspots actually are exceptionally calm areas on the solar surface; the strong magnetic fields impart so much rigidity to the hot gases that little heat transport by convection can occur. The surrounding areas thus show a higher-than-average convection and consequent turbulence. In this connection, it is interesting to note that in *Our Sun,*[11] published in 1949, the American astronomer D.

H. Menzel devoted a chapter to "Sunspots—Solar Cyclones." In the revised 1959 edition this chapter is called "Sunspots—Magnetic Islands."

Only fairly large sunspots could be observed with Mount Wilson's 60-ft telescope, and to extend observations to smaller spots with weaker fields a 150-ft tower telescope with a 75-ft spectrograph was built in 1910. From studies of smaller sunspots with the new telescope it was learned that most groups have a bipolar character, the leading and following spots having opposite polarization. The order of polarity is reversed in the two hemispheres of the sun; that is, the leading (in the sense of the sun's axial rotation) spots in the southern hemisphere have opposite polarities from the leading spots in the northern hemisphere. Discovery of the common dipolar characteristics led to a search for "hidden" companions of single spots in extended regions of calcium flocculi; weak magnetic fields often were detected.

A completely unexpected phenomenon occurred at the beginning of the new sunspot cycle in 1913, when the polarities within the groups were found to be arranged in opposition to those observed during the sunspot cycle just ending. The frequency of sunspots and their location on the solar surface were known to show a periodicity of 11 years. At first, systematic errors were feared, but none was found; a similar reversal of polarities at the beginning of the next cycle in 1923 confirmed the phenomenon. Thus 22 years may be considered a complete sunspot cycle. An adequate explanation of changes in polarities in successive 11-year cycles has been the principal stumbling block in all sunspot theories.

None of the hypotheses to explain sunspots is completely satisfactory. Hale suggested that the bipolar spots were ends of a U-shaped vortex, formed in the outer layers of the sun, within which gases are spiraling upward and outward. The Norwegian physicist Bjerknes in the 1920's posited a doughnut-shaped vortex below the surface encircling the sun and occasionally breaking through the surface layers. The theories of Swedish physicists H. L. Alfvén and C. Walén assume that a strong field exists in the sun's core and that a sudden disturbance in the core may cause a wave to travel outward, carrying with it some of the magnetic field and proceeding as a small, doughnut-shaped vortex.

General Magnetic Field of the Sun

The existence of a general magnetic field in the sun has been suspected at least since the eclipse of 1878, when the resemblance of the coronal streamers to magnetic lines of force was noted. The earth's magnetism was well established, and the English astronomer A. Schuster had asked whether other great rotating bodies such as the sun also might not be magnets. In 1912 Deslandres suggested that the forms and motions of prominences appeared to be influenced by a general magnetic field. Attempts in 1908 and 1911 to detect it with Mount Wilson's 60-ft tower telescope were inconclusive, but the observations were renewed with the 150-ft telescope during the sunspot minimum of 1913. Even though the general field was not expected to be strong enough to produce splitting of spectral lines it would produce a shift in widened lines with different orientations of polarizing apparatus. Hale and his collaborators at first estimated a field strength of 50 gauss at the poles, later revised it to 25 gauss, then found negative values, and finally returned to 50 gauss.

The most extensive measurements of the broadening of the lines attributable to a Zeeman effect in a general magnetic field were made by Hale's associate at Mount Wilson, Dutch-born A. van Maanen, who has made many important contributions to the study of stellar motions—a famous white dwarf is known as "van Maanen's star." It is believed now that van Maanen's measurements of the solar spectrum were erroneous, perhaps because of the method and the measuring instrument employed. This is not surprising, since the observed displacements are extremely small. When J. Evershed re-examined Hale's plates in 1938, he concluded that the observed displacements could also be caused by small-scale, irregular currents in the solar atmosphere.

According to recent measurements using improved techniques the astronomers at Mount Wilson have found that a general field of about 1 gauss exists in high solar latitudes. A magnetogram by the American astronomers H. D. and H. W. Babcock is reproduced in Fig. 65 and shows the location, polarity, and intensity of weak magnetic fields. Each

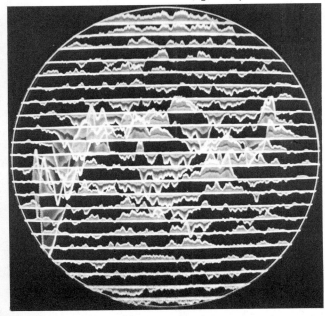

Fig. 65.   Magnetogram of the sun. (*Mount Wilson and Palomar Observatories*)

Fig. 66. Air view of the Mount Wilson Observatory: (top right) dome of the 100-in. Hooker telescope; (lower right) 60-in. reflector; (left) the two solar towers and behind them the horizontal Snow telescope building. (*Mount Wilson and Palomar Observatories*)

trace interval is equivalent to about 1 gauss. A deflection upward from a fiducial line indicates that the field vector is toward the observer, and vice versa. North is at the top, east at the right. Evidence for the field is found in the deflections near the poles, positive in the north, negative in the south. The large deflections near the equator are produced by several extended bipolar magnetic regions. As shown in the magnetogram, the general field is of opposite polarity in the two hemispheres and it also undergoes reversals that, however, do not coincide with reversals of sunspot polarity. Thus, any adequate theory of solar magnetism has to account for the behavior of the general magnetic field, as well as for the magnetic phenomena of sunspots.

Growth of Mount Wilson Observatory and Birth of Palomar Observatory

After 1910, because of ill health, Hale gradually decreased the time devoted to research and concentrated on planning better research facilities and on scientific organization. The original plans for Mount Wilson included a 60-in. telescope for the study of stellar evolution; a 60-in. glass disk given him by his father was soon shipped to Pasadena, figured

Fig. 67. The 100-in. Hooker telescope. (*Mount Wilson and Palomar Observatories*)

in the Mount Wilson shops, and was erected in 1908. Hale knew that the 60-in. telescope would not be powerful enough to solve the many astrophysical problems requiring great light-gathering power, and he tried to obtain funds for an even larger telescope. In 1906, J. D. Hooker promised enough money for an 84-in. mirror, but later increased it for a 100 in. mirror. Hale's announcement of the gift noted:

> ... no provision has yet been made for the mounting and the dome. It is not known from what source funds for this purpose will come, but I believe a donor will be found by the time they are needed.[12]

Happily, even though much effort and patient waiting were required, Hale always found a donor for his projects. The great American industrialist and philanthropist Andrew Carnegie greatly increased the Carnegie Institution's endowment and, thus, money became available for the mounting. It has been said that Hale already had learned as a boy, when asking money from his father for his scientific projects, to present his case well and to prove convincingly that the outlay would be worthwhile; certainly he had the conviction and patience required for persuasion. His attitude toward larger instruments is seen in his comment on the 100-in. Hooker telescope:

The huge dimensions of such a powerful engine of research as the Hooker telescope are not in themselves a source of satisfaction to the astronomer, for they involve very heavy expense, justifiable only in case important results, beyond the reach of other instruments, can be secured.[13]

In 1923, deteriorating health forced Hale to resign the directorship, but he remained honorary director until the end of his life. He was replaced as director by W. S. Adams, one of Yerkes' first staff members, who had joined the Mount Wilson group when Hale moved to Pasadena. During Hale's lifetime, Adams always conferred with him about all important problems. In order to continue whatever research his health would permit, Hale built a private solar observatory in Pasadena where he invented the *spectrohelioscope*. Similar in principle to the spectroheliograph, it had oscillating slits (later rotating prisms), which enabled visual observation of prominences to be made. While only a static picture is registered on spectroheliograms, with the spectrohelioscope "...objects familiar for years on hydrogen spectroheliograms suddenly seem to come to life, while difficulties in the interpretation of their complex structure are greatly reduced by its aid."[14]

By the late 1920's, the 100-in. telescope had solved many problems, but still more were unresolved, and the possibilities of even larger instruments were considered. Thus in 1928 Hale wrote:

... The 100-inch Hooker telescope of the Mount Wilson Observatory has solved many fundamental astronomical and physical problems beyond the reach of our 60-inch reflector, and prepared the way for an attack on still more important problems that demand greater light-gathering power for their solution. ... A larger telescope would not only furnish the necessary gain in light, space-penetration, and photographic resolving power, but permit the application of ideas and devices derived chiefly from the recent fundamental advances in physics and chemistry. These advances which have suddenly transformed spectroscopy from an empirical into an exact and rational science, would undoubtedly render possible many new discoveries with such an instrument.[15]

After prolonged negotiations, the International Education Board of the Rockefeller Foundation provided money for a 200-in. telescope to be erected on Mount Palomar and to be operated by the California Institute of Technology in close cooperation with the Mount Wilson Observatory. Delays in construction of the 200-in. Hale telescope were long and frustrating (it was not finished until 1948), but by the time of Hale's death in

1938 work had progressed far enough to assure him of its successful completion.

RECENT IMPROVEMENTS IN OBSERVATIONAL TECHNIQUES

As discussed above, Hale's contributions in the field of solar physics started with the construction of the small spectroheliograph at Kenwood and the larger *Rumford spectroheliograph* at Yerkes, for which he used relatively cheap, commercially available lenses as collimator and camera. In the 1930's the American astronomer G. W. Moffitt discovered that internal reflections of sunlight by the many glass surfaces in the Rumford spectroheliograph cannot be eliminated completely by means of appropriately placed baffles and diaphragms. Hence the quality of the spectroheliograms obtained at Yerkes was never quite adequate because of the effects of out-of-focus sunlight. Hale's next great step was the construction of a *horizontal-type stationary spectroheliograph* (the Snow telescope). He realized that the difficulties he encountered—caused by thermal heating of the air in the instrument—would be eliminated for the most part in vertically mounted solar towers, two of which have been mentioned. Even these instruments are beset by difficulties that arise because the sun's image is projected vertically downward by means of plane mirrors. An ordinary glass mirror, such as that used by Hale on Mount Wilson, is rapidly distorted by the sun's heat when the small dome is opened in the morning. Much better results have been obtained at Mount Wilson with plane quartz mirrors, which are almost impervious to thermal deformations.

Still other difficulties are caused by the heating of the vertical shaft during the day. R. B. Leighton recently has improved the performance of the Mount Wilson tower telescopes, by using paint that reflects most of the sun's damaging heat. Some of Leighton's photographs of the fine-structure granulation of the solar surface approach the results obtained with a balloon-supported solar telescope by German-born M. Schwarzschild of the Princeton University Observatory (see Fig. 68, picture taken August 17, 1959, at an altitude of 80,000 ft). The best observations of the solar granules during the latter part of the 19th century were made by J. Janssen in France and A. P. Gansky at the Simeis Observatory in the Crimea and these were actually better than any but the most recent photographs of Leighton and Schwarzschild.

Even now, the best photographs of the sun, either in direct light or

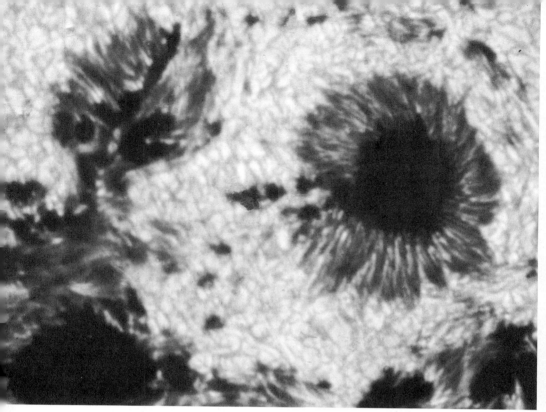

Fig. 68. Structural details in the sun's surface and sunspot penumbrae. (*Project Stratoscope; courtesy* Sky and Telescope)

by means of a spectroheliograph, are obtained at Mount Wilson and other ground-based observatories during the early morning. Solar observers at Mount Wilson start their work immediately after sunrise, when the earth's atmosphere is relatively quiescent and the seeing is often very good.

Although the average size of granules (about 1″ in diameter) was established by Janssen's and Gansky's work, for many years some astronomers were either unaware of these earlier results or thought them incorrect. Direct photographs of the sun, especially those made in England, suggested to H. H. Plaskett of Oxford University Observatory, among others, that granules are never smaller than about 5″ in diameter. The original results were confirmed at Yerkes by P. C. Keenan in the 1940's and, of course, later by Schwarzschild. Some asked whether there may not be even smaller solar granules. Schwarzschild's balloon-supported telescopes have ascertained definitely that the average size of granules is about 1″ and that their lifespans are a few minutes. Leighton, among others, has pointed out that at longer intervals the pattern of the granulation is approximately reproduced. These data bear upon the theory of convection with which Indian-born S. Chandrasekhar of the University of Chicago has been concerned during the past 10 years.

A spectacular advance in the construction of solar observatories resulted from R. R. McMath's work at the McMath-Hulbert Observatory, now a part of the University of Michigan. McMath studied engineering at the University of Michigan and was a successful businessman before he became interested in astronomy. When still an amateur, he secured the best photographs of the moon to have been shown on movie films. After the observatory was established, he built a powerful tower telescope with a vacuum spectrograph in a horizontal chamber. Because of the vacuum, stratification of air below the slit was eliminated. Photographs of the sun were obtained with a spectroheliograph and certain spectral lines were photographed with very high-dispersion spectrographs. The spectrograms revealed that the solar granules often described as *rice-grains* represent updrafts of gas in the sun's atmosphere with violet shifts of absorption lines; the interspaces between the granules indicate velocities of recession and therefore downdrafts.

McMath, in collaboration with L. Goldberg, O. Mohler, and Miss H. W. Dodson, at the McMath-Hulbert Observatory, produced some of the most spectacular films of the sun's changing features. Equally good instrumentation has been developed at the high-altitude observatory on Sacramento Peak by J. W. Evans and D. H. Menzel and by W. O. Roberts at the High Altitude Observatory at Climax, Colorado.

The invention of image intensifiers has been responsible in large part for the improved techniques developed since the end of World War II. The Lallemand tube was discussed on P. 88. The Orthicon television-type instrument produces on a screen an image of a solar spectral line that shows the features first photographed at the McMath Observatory. The Orthicon screen also registers easily recognizable changes resulting from the changes in the sun's granulation, and these in turn can be recorded by photographing the screen. An instrument of this type has been installed at the Sacramento Peak Observatory by E. W. Dennison.

Until the 1930's, coronal pictures could be obtained only during total eclipses, when the sun's entire disk is hidden by the moon's disk. Hale made several attempts to photograph the sun's corona in full daylight. However, scattered light prevented his obtaining satisfactory results. The first successful construction of a coronograph was made in 1931 by the French astronomer B. Lyot, who used essentially the same technique as Hale. Lyot painstakingly eliminated all scattered light in the instrument; even small bubbles in the glass of the various optical parts and scratches on the surfaces had to be avoided. An artificial screen was used to block out the brilliant image of the sun's disk. At the present time, photographs of the inner corona are obtained on every clear day at several mountain observatories where atmospheric scattering presents no great problem.

Solar-eclipse photographs established that the corona changes from year to year, approximately in accordance with the solar-activity cycle. At times of minimum solar activity, the corona shows a striking series of bright filaments emerging from the sun's polar regions and strongly resembling effects of magnetic fields. At these same times, the corona's equatorial regions are usually long and extended, producing a very unsymmetrical picture of the corona. At maximum solar activity, the corona is more uniform and has approximate, but not exact, circular symmetry.

One of the problems that has intrigued astronomers through the present century is that of the corona's temperature. It must be very high, probably a million degrees, a fact indicated by the presence in the coronal spectrum of atomic lines that correspond to very high stages of ionization. True, degree of ionization depends on both the temperature and density of the gases (see P. 217), and high ionization thus may result from low density rather than from high temperature. However, this cannot explain the presence of the solar corona. The density required to produce the state of ionization at a temperature of a few thousand degrees would be so low that its features would be unobservable. Different methods applied by astronomers for determining the corona's temperature give results that vary between 750,000° and 1,500,000°. The best-informed theoretical solar physicist of the present generation, A. Unsöld, believes that it is not yet possible to give preference to either of these values.

The sun's continuous spectrum is produced by the photosphere. Between it and the corona is the layer of gas, several thousand kilometers in height, that is designated the *solar chromosphere* and produces mostly emission lines. Until recently, observations of the solar chromosphere could be made only during solar eclipses, when the sun's bright disk and the thin (100 km or less) reversing layer are covered by the moon's disk. (see Fig. 69, taken at the total solar eclipse of 1952). During these very

Fig. 69.   High-dispersion flash spectrum of the sun, made by the High Altitude Observatory's expedition to Khartoum during the total solar eclipse in 1952. (*High Altitude Observatory; courtesy* Sky and Telescope)

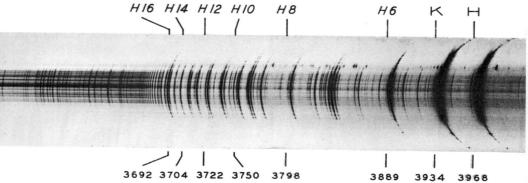

brief intervals, the spectrum of the remaining crescent of sunlight consists mostly of emission lines; some are the same as absorption lines originating in the reversing layer, while others, such as those of neutral helium, require a higher temperature and a lower density than those of the reversing layer. Numerous studies have been made at solar eclipses of the sun's "flash spectrum."

Sensitivity of the human eye differs from person to person and reaches into the violet part of the spectrum to about 3,900 A. Ordinary photographic emulsions are sensitive to shorter wavelengths, and special emulsions developed for X-ray studies are used in all hospitals. However, the earth's atmosphere is opaque to all wavelengths shorter than about 3,000 A, the ultraviolet limit to which the solar spectrum could be photographed, until a tremendous advance came after World War II through the application of high-flying rockets, for example, see Fig. 70. In the United States, R. Tousey at the Naval Research Laboratory has obtained photographs of the solar spectrum to wavelengths shorter than 1,000 A whose quality matches that of the best spectrograms obtained in the ordinary region of the spectrum.

At first, the appearance of the solar spectrum in the extreme ultraviolet was a surprise to astronomers. In passing toward the ultraviolet, the intensity of the continuous spectrum decreases, at first gradually and then quite abruptly, while the ordinary Fraunhofer lines appear as emission features on top of the weak background of the continuous spectrum. In retrospect it is easy to see that this should have been expected. Solar gases contain atoms and molecules of different kinds and produce emission lines when the background continuous spectrum is weak. Currently, several astronomers are studying the strong solar emission line of hydrogen at 1,216 A (Lyman-α). This is the most important line in the hydrogen spectrum, and its intensity and profile are expected to yield significant information regarding the sun's physical properties.

As yet, no spectra of the sun have been obtained in the even shorter wavelengths of the X-ray spectrum. However, direct X-ray pictures of the sun have been obtained and analyzed by H. Friedman and his associates of the Naval Research Laboratory. In the photograph, sufficient resolution was achieved to reveal the radiation's source distribution. The images of discrete X-ray sources were, however, smeared through about 170° due to motion of the rocket. Comparison with calcium K line photographs

Fig. 70.   The extreme ultraviolet spectrum of the sun, photographed from a Aerobee-Hi rocket on April 19, 1960. (*Official U.S. Navy photograph; courtesy R. Tousey, U.S. Naval Research Laboratory*)

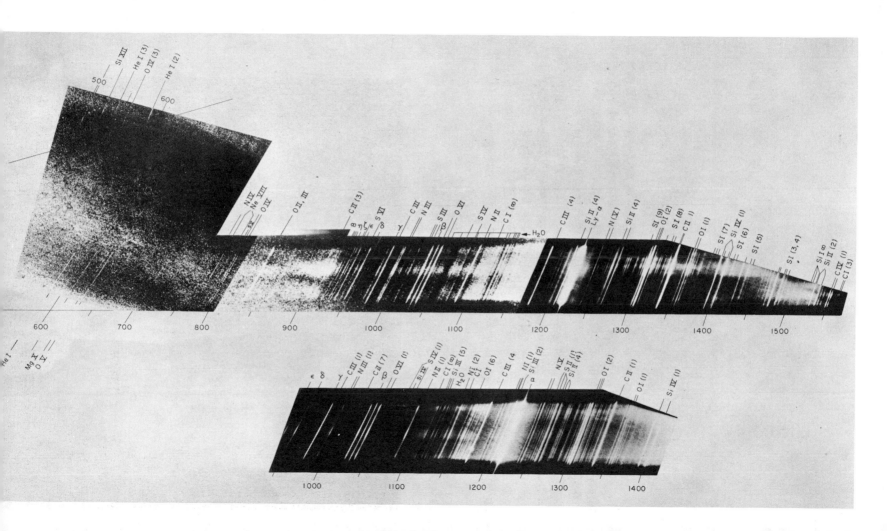

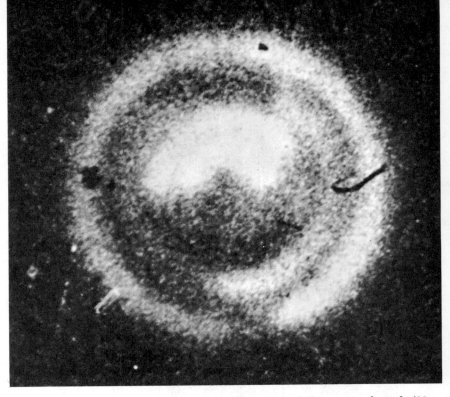

Fig. 71. The first successful photograph of the sun in the soft (20 to 60 A) X-ray region, photographed from an Aerobee-Hi rocket on April 19, 1960. (*Official U.S. Navy photograph; courtesy H. Friedman, U.S. Naval Research Laboratory*)

shows a correlation between X-ray emission and bright plage areas on the sun.

As mentioned in Chap. VI, Pp. 95, 97, the sun has been observed as a radio source, and important investigations of solar longwave radiation are now in progress at many radio observatories. Even though it is not possible at centimeter and meter wavelengths to obtain direct solar images containing the same amount of detail shown on optical photographs, it is now possible to observe, even in radio wavelengths, the principal structural features of the solar surface, such as flares and sunspots.

VIII

PHYSICS OF THE
SOLAR SYSTEM

AS POINTED OUT in the preceding chapter, the study of
the sun is only the first step in the larger endeavor—the study
of stellar evolution—that was stressed repeatedly by Hale and is the major
concern of present-day astrophysicists. Before passing on to the studies
concerned with this question, problems of a slightly different nature will
be considered. Many areas of study have been found in the investigation
of all those nonluminous bodies (the planets with their satellites, the
minor planets, or asteroids, the comets, meteors, dust and gas) that are
gravitationally controlled by the sun and comprise the solar system. The
discussion will be divided into two main topics: the physics and the
origin of the solar system.

THE LIFE AND WORK OF PERCIVAL LOWELL

Up to the end of the 1900's, planets were visually observed
mainly by amateurs using relatively small instruments. At the present
time, most large observatories devote a considerable proportion of their
observing time to planetary studies, and some of the best-known astrophysicists are attempting to interpret these observations. This change in
attitude can to a large degree be attributed to the efforts of one man,
Percival Lowell, and to his part in one of the greatest astronomical con-
troversies of this century: the existence of life on Mars.

Lowell was born into a prominent Boston family in 1855; his brother

Fig. 72.   P. Lowell.

A. L. Lowell became President of Harvard University. In his boyhood he read books on astronomy and observed through a small telescope set up on the flat roof of the family house. While at Harvard he studied mathematics, physics, classics, and history, excelling particularly in mathematics. Upon graduating in 1876, Lowell entered the family enterprises, and after acquiring sufficient wealth from shrewd investments, he went to Japan and Korea to study Oriental languages and customs. He expressed his fascination and enthusiasm for the Orient in several books. During this period, he did not pursue astronomy actively, but according to his brother: "This interest he never lost, and after lying half dormant for many years, it blazed forth again as the dominant one in his life...."[1]

Lowell was intrigued by the reports of the Italian astronomer G. Schiaparelli's observations of Mars' surface features, particularly the fine linear markings discovered in 1877 and named the *"canali"* ("channels"), somewhat misleadingly translated in English as "canals." Schiaparelli's work apparently had a decisive effect on Lowell's plans:

> Talking later to George Agassiz, Percival attributed the change to the fact that Schiaparelli, who had first observed the fine lines on the planet Mars . . . found that his failing eyesight prevented his pursuing his observations further, and that he [Lowell] had determined to carry them on.[2]

Thus, in 1894, at the time of the *close opposition of Mars,*＊ Lowell established an observatory devoted to planetary studies, particularly of Mars, ". . . put up for the purpose of getting as good air as practicable, at Flagstaff, Arizona."[3] Lowell explained and predicted that

> A steady atmosphere is essential to the study of planetary detail: size of instrument being a very secondary matter. A large instrument in poor

＊ At opposition, Mars (or any other planet beyond the orbit of the earth) is in a direction opposite to that of the sun and at its closest distance to us. Due to differences in the shapes of their orbits, the distance between Mars and the earth is not always the same at opposition. It differs by a factor of almost 2 between close, or favorable, oppositions occurring at intervals of about 15 years, and the most unfavorable oppositions. In the former case, the disk of the planet subtends an angle of about 25″, in the latter about 14″.

air will not begin to show what a smaller one in good air will. When this is recognized, as it eventually will be, it will become the fashion to put up observatories where they may see rather than be seen.[4]

This prediction has certainly come true.

Life on Mars

The 1894 observations and the conclusions drawn from them were described by Lowell in the first volume of the Annals of the Lowell Observatory[5] and in his popular book Mars,[6] upon which the following discussion mainly will be based. These observations were confirmed during the 1905 opposition, and essentially the same ideas were expressed in his later books Mars and Its Canals[7] and Mars As the Abode of Life.[8] It is impossible to describe adequately the wealth of observations included in these books, and only points pertinent to his argument will be reviewed, as much as possible in Lowell's own words.

He reported first that, "... we have proof positive that Mars has an atmosphere; we have reason to believe this atmosphere to be very thin —thinner at least by half than the air upon the summit of the Himalayas— and in constitution not to differ greatly from our own."[9] He also thought that the mean temperature of Mars is about 48°F. and that the polar caps of Mars (white areas at the poles, varying in their extent with Martian seasons) consist of frozen water. During the Martian summer, the polar caps melt and water is released. Lowell agreed with an earlier suggestion by W. H. Pickering of Harvard, who had observed Mars extensively at the South American station of the observatory at Arequipa, Peru. Both believed that the so-called Martian seas (dark areas, retaining their positions, but undergoing seasonal changes in color and changes in shape and distribution from one Martian year to the next) may have been true seas in the distant past but that at the present time, "... the blue-green regions of Mars are not water, but generally at least, areas of vegetation; from which is follows that Mars is very badly off for water, and that the planet is dependent on the melting of its polar snows for practically its whole supply."[10]

The most important part of Lowell's argument rested on the observations of the "canals" and "oases." The former were described as

... a network of fine, straight, dark lines. The lines start from points on the coast of the blue-green regions, commonly well-marked bays, and proceed directly to what seem centres in the middle of the continent, since most surprisingly they meet there other lines that have come to the same spot with apparently a like determinate intent. ... The lines appear

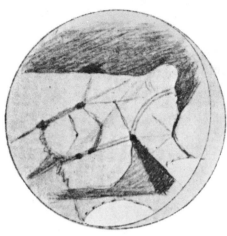

Fig. 73. Surface features of Mars, drawn by P. Lowell. (*From P. Lowell*, Mars and its Canals, *New York, The Macmillan Company, 1907, P. 254; courtesy* Sky and Telescope)

either absolutely straight from one end to the other, or curved in an equally uniform manner. There is nothing haphazard in the look of any of them . . . each line maintains its individual width, from one end of its course to the other . . . their length is usually great, and in cases enormous.[11]

Schiaparelli had only seen the canals in the disk's reddish-ochre portions. These areas cover most of the surface, do not exhibit seasonal changes, and are often referred to as Martian deserts. Pickering in Arequipa, and later A. E. Douglass at Flagstaff, found that the dark areas are also traversed by canals and that the ". . . canals in the dark regions end at the very points at which the others begin, and they do this invariably. There is no canal in the dark areas which does not so connect with one in the bright regions."[12] Lowell also agreed with Pickering's suggestion that: ". . . what we see is not the canal proper but the line of land it irrigates."[13]

The "oases"—small dark areas observed at the meeting points of canals—"constitute so many hubs to which the canals make spokes."[14]

The final line of reasoning and conclusions were as follows:

We find, in the first place, that the broad physical conditions of the planet are not antagonistic to some form of life; secondly, that there is an apparent dearth of water upon the planet's surface, and, therefore, if beings of sufficient intelligence inhabited it, they would have to resort to irrigation to support life; thirdly, that there turns out to be a network of markings covering the disk precisely counterparting what a system of irrigation would look like; and, lastly, that there is a set of spots placed where we should expect to find the lands thus artificially fertilized, and behaving as such constructed oases should. All this, of course, may be a set of coincidences, signifying nothing; but the probability points the other way. As to details of explanation, any we may adopt will undoubtedly be found, on closer acquaintance, to vary from the actual Martian state of things; for any Martian life must differ markedly from our own.[15]

Irrigation, unscientifically conducted, would not give us such truly wonderful mathematical fitness in the several parts of the whole as we there behold. A mind of no mean order would seem to have presided over the system we see—a mind certainly of considerably more comprehensiveness than that which presides over the various departments of our own public works. Party politics, at all events, have had no part in them; for the system is planet-wide ... Certainly what we see hints at the existence of beings who are in advance of, not behind us, in the journey of life.[16]

Lowell's estimates of physical conditions, such as atmosphere and temperature, were not quite correct. Several other parts of his argument—particularly the efficiency of conducting an extremely scant amount of water over such vast distances—were questioned. However, the greatest arguments raged over his description of the "canals." Several observers confirmed the detail seen by Lowell, while other experienced observers, with similar or even better equipment and observing conditions, such as E. M. Antoniadi in France and E. E. Barnard in the United States, were unable to see them. To Barnard, Mars gave

... the impression of a globe whose entire surface had been tinted a slightly pink color, on which the dark details had been painted with a grayish colored paint, supplied with a very poor brush, producing a shredded or streaky and crispy effect in the darker regions.... No one could accurately delineate the remarkable complexity of detail of the features which were visible in moments of greatest steadiness.[17]

Among the supporters of Lowell's views was Swiss-born R. J. Trumpler of the Lick Observatory. Indeed the dispute between those who could and could not see the Martian canals seems to occasionally have been an inter-institutional controversy.

Unfortunately, these observations cannot be checked objectively by photography. The exposure time required to bring out any detail is longer than the moments of exceptionally good seeing, and photography cannot reproduce the detail the eye may glimpse during an instant. Photographs do, however, show some of the more distinctive linear markings. The general concensus now is that, while there are certain linear markings, they are neither as numerous nor as regular as seen by Lowell, who sincerely believed he had reported his observations accurately. The main difficulty may have resulted from individual differences among observers. The Astronomer Royal of Great Britain, H. Spencer Jones, noted:

The eye of one may tend to bridge the gap between faint details and to draw a marking as uniform, straight, continuous line unless he could clearly see that there are irregularities, bends and discontinuities in it. Another may only draw it this way when he can see beyond the possibility of doubt that it is uniform, straight, and continuous.[18]

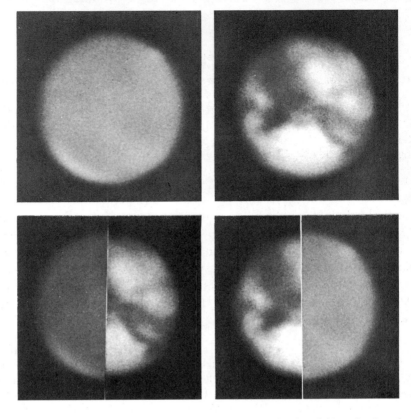

Fig. 74. (Above) Mars, photographed in ultraviolet (top left) and infrared (top right) light with the Crossley reflector on Nov. 2, 1926. Halved images for comparison of apparent size of the planet. (*Lick Observatory*)

Fig. 75. (Below) Mars, photographed by B. Lyot at the Pic du Midi Observatory on September 23, 1941. (*Courtesy A. Dollfus, Meudon Observatory*)

An excellent final comment on the Mars controversy is given by the English astronomer R. L. Waterfield in his historical *A Hundred Years of Astronomy:*

Now the story of the "canals" is a long and sad one, fraught with back-bitings and slanders; and many would have preferred that the whole theory of them had never been invented. Yet whatever harm was done was more than outweighed by the tremendous stimulus the theory gave to the study of Mars, and indirectly of the planets in general. Whether in a positive way to champion it, or in a negative way to oppose it, it attracted many able observers who otherwise might never have taken an interest in the planets. . . . So the pistol which Schiaparelli had so unwittingly let off, though it shocked the finer feelings of many, had undoubtedly been the starting signal of that race for discovery which the planetary astrono-mers are still successfully pursuing.[19]

The Lowell Observatory was devoted during these years, as it still is, to many different aspects of planetary study. Among the most noteworthy are: (1) the first attempts to measure planetary temperatures. These were made in 1921–1922 by the American scientists W. W. Coblentz and C. O. Lampland; (2) Lowell and the American astronomer V. M. Slipher's spectroscopic determination in 1912 of the rotation period of Uranus; and (3) photographs of planetary spectra and direct photographs of the planets, particularly those of E. C. Slipher. Aside from the Mars contro-versy, however, Percival Lowell is best remembered for his association with the discovery of Pluto, the ninth planet of the solar system.

The Discovery of Pluto

As early as 1905, Lowell had predicted the position of a trans-Neptunian planet, referred to as "planet X," from perturbations in the motion of Uranus; that is, the motion of Uranus could not be represented completely by taking into account the gravitational attraction of the sun and of the known planets, and the differences (residuals) between the observed and calculated motion were attributed to a planet beyond Nep-tune. The mass and orbit of the unknown, disturbing planet were pre-dicted from these residuals, but the early search yielded no results. With better values of the residuals and improved and more extensive methods of calculation, Lowell repeatedly revised the predicted position, and his final "Memoir on a Trans-Neptunian Planet" was read to the American Academy of Arts and Sciences on January 13, 1915. A certain sense of humor is evident in Lowell's letter of December 14, 1914, to Lampland, who was mainly responsible for the search conducted at the Lowell Observatory: "I am giving my work before the Academy on January 13. It would be thoughtful of you to announce the actual discovery at the same time."[20] However, according to his brother, A. L. Lowell, "That X was not found was the sharpest disappointment of his life."[21]

Lowell died on November 12, 1916. After an extensive search, the discovery of a planet close to the predicted position was announced on March 13, 1930. The planet was found by an assistant at the Lowell Observatory, C. Tombaugh, using a blink microscope on plates taken on January 23 and 29, 1930.

According to Tombaugh:

> ... when one-fourth of the way through this pair of plates (centered on delta Geminorum), on the afternoon of February 18, 1930, I suddenly came upon the images of Pluto! The experience was an intense thrill, because the nature of the object was apparent at first sight. ... In all of the two million stars examined thus far, nothing had been found that was as promising as this object. ... The images were quickly found on both plates on January 21, the position conforming with the motion indicated by the plates of January 23 and 29. Thereupon, I informed the Director and other members of the staff, who came to take a look.[22]

Announcement of the discovery was withheld until it was checked on later photographs. A statement was released on the anniversary of Lowell's birth, giving due credit to his role in the discovery. It is interesting to note that a certain amount of controversy ensued regarding the prediction and discovery. In December 1930, H. N. Russell, the most famous and revered American astronomer at the time, commented:

> The orbit, now that we know it, is found to be so similar to that which Lowell predicted from his calculations 15 years ago that it is quite incredible that the agreement can be due to accident.[23]

A few years later, however, the mass of Pluto was estimated to be considerably less than Lowell had predicted, and E. W. Brown, a well-known mathematical astronomer, after extensive calculations and review of the data used by Lowell, concluded that the available data had been insufficient to determine the correct elements. Russell wrote to A. L. Lowell:

> The question arises ... why is there an actual planet moving in an orbit which is so uncannily like the one he predicted? ...
> There seems no escape from the conclusion that this is a matter of chance. That so close a set of chance coincidences should occur is almost incredible, but the evidence employed by Brown permits of no other conclusion. ...

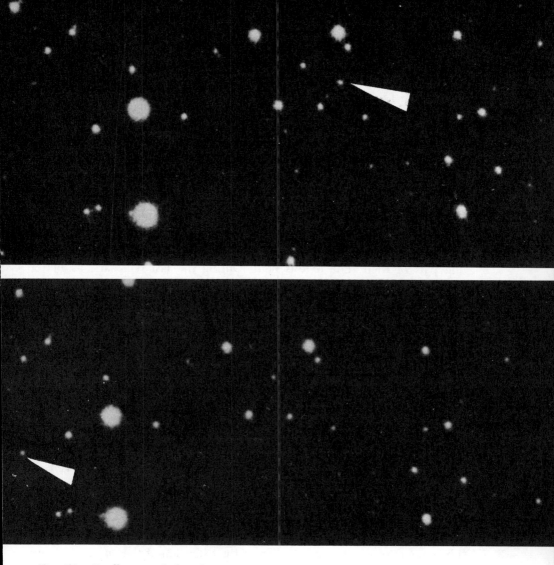

Fig. 76. Small parts of the plates blinked by C. Tombaugh on February 18, 1930, showing the discovery positions of Pluto, marked by the arrows: (top) January 23 and January 29 (bottom). (*Lowell Observatory*)

Fig. 77. Percival Lowell's predicted orbit of Planet X compared with the observed orbit of Pluto. (*Courtesy Sky and Telescope*)

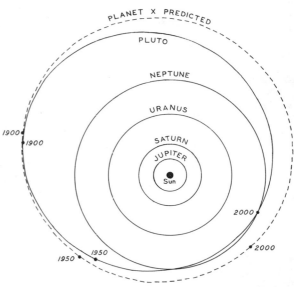

In any event, the initial credit for the discovery of Pluto justly belongs to Percival Lowell. His analytical methods were sound, his profound enthusiasm stimulated the search, and, even after his death, was the inspiration of the campaign which resulted in its discovery in the observatory which he had founded.[24]

ATMOSPHERES AND SURFACE FEATURES OF PLANETS

The Lowell Observatory was the first well-equipped institution devoted to planetary research, and soon other observatories began devoting part of their time to this field. During the last 60 years, as better instruments and new methods have been introduced, a considerable amount of information about the physical conditions of the planets has been gathered. The present status of our knowledge is summarized in Tables 1 and 2.

To avoid fragmenting the discussion by focusing on details about each planet, planetary observations will be approached from the point of view of observational techniques introduced in this century.

Photography

Direct photography first was applied successfully by Lampland at the Lowell Observatory. Photography is still inferior to visual observations in glimpsing minor details erased by atmospheric turbulence. However, photography gives a more objective and permanent record of the major features and their changes, both intrinsic and caused by the planet's rotation. While photography "washes out" sharp details, it can "bring out" other phenomena of small contrast, such as the extension of the cusps of Venus (indicating an extensive atmosphere and, occasionally, high-level clouds).

Many interesting results have been obtained by using color filters. W. H. Wright's photographs of Mars in the 1920's at Lick Observatory showed that the planet's disk appears considerably larger in ultraviolet than in infrared light. This difference, attributed to the scattering of ultraviolet light by the atmosphere, indicates an atmospheric thickness of about 100 km. However, while observing Mars visually through filters in 1952, Kuiper was unable to detect any difference in the diameter.

Much information about the types of atmospheric formations present in planetary atmospheres has been provided by photography using filters. For example, several types of clouds have been identified on Mars: yellow clouds, visible to the eye but not recorded on blue-sensitive plate; blue

Table 1.

PLANETARY ELEMENTS[25]

	Semi-major Axis of Orbit (a.u.)	Equato-rial Radius* + = 1	Mass ⊕ = 1	Density (gm/cm³)	Sidereal Rotational Period‡	Oblate-ness§	T″ °K#	Velocity of Escape** (km/sec)	Albedo††	g‡‡ (cm/sec²)	No. of Satellites Known: 1900	No. of Satellites Known: 1960
MERCURY	0.39	0.38	0.053	5.3	(88 days)	0.0	48°	4.2	0.060	360	—	—
VENUS	0.72	0.97	0.815	4.95	(224.7 days)	0.0	35	10.3	0.61	850	—	—
EARTH	1.00	1.00	1.000	5.52	23ʰ 56ᵐ	0.0034	30	11.2	0.34	982	1	1
MARS	1.52	0.53	0.107	3.95	24ʰ 37ᵐ	0.0052	24	5	0.15	376	2	2
JUPITER	5.20	11.20	318.00	1.330	9ʰ 50ᵐ	0.062	13	61	0.41	2,600	5	12
SATURN	9.55	9.47	95.22	0.687	10ʰ 14ᵐ	0.096	10	37	0.42	1,120	9	9
URANUS	19.2	3.75	14.55	1.56	10ʰ 49ᵐ	0.06	7	22	0.45	940	4	5
NEPTUNE	30.1	3.50	17.23	2.27	15ʰ 40ᵐ	0.02	5	25	0.54	1,500	1	2
PLUTO	39.5	(1.1)†	(0.9)	(4.0)				10	0.16	800	—	—

* The equatorial radius of the earth, used here as the unit, is 6,400 km or 6.4×10^8 cm, and the mass of the earth equals 6×10^{27} gm. ⊕ is the symbol for the earth.

† Quantities marked in parentheses are uncertain.

‡ The sidereal rotation period is the time required for a complete rotation of the planet with respect to the stars.

§ Oblateness is the ratio of the difference between the equatorial and polar radius of a planet to the equatorial radius.

″ Average temperature (T) calculated for a black body.

K refers to the Kelvin (or absolute) scale of temperatures, which has the same divisions as those of the centigrade scale, but has its zero point at −273°C. 0° K is the so-called absolute zero, the lowest temperature that can exist according to theoretical considerations.

** Velocity of escape is the velocity required to overcome the force of gravity and escape into space.

†† Albedo is the ratio of the total light reflected from a sphere to the total light incident on it.

‡‡ The acceleration of gravity, that is the velocity acquired by a freely falling body, started from rest, at the end of the first second.

Table 2.

CONSTITUENTS OF PLANETARY ATMOSPHERES[*]

Planet	Substance	Detected	Amount cm atm (NTP)	Basis of Estimate	Remarks
MERCURY					Probably fluorescing free radicals and ions produce haze
VENUS	CO_2	yes	10^5	Spectroscopic	Much below the cloud layer
	H_2O	yes	oceans	Polarization of clouds	
MARS	CO_2	yes	3,600	Spectroscopic	
	H_2O	yes	?	Polarization of clouds	Polar caps consist of ice. Some clouds have the polarization of ice crystals
	N_2	no	1.8×10^5	Total pressure measurement	N_2 is accepted as the most likely non-condensable element
JUPITER	CH_4	yes	1.5×10^4	Spectroscopic	
	NH_3	yes	700	Spectroscopic	
	H_2	yes	10^6		
	He	no	5.6×10^6	} Density of the planet	} Assumed to be present in solar proportions relative to methane
	N_2	no	4×10^3		
	Ne	no	1.7×10^4		

Planet	Substance	Detected	Amount cm atm (NTP)	Basis of Estimate	Remarks
SATURN	CH_4	yes	35,000	Spectroscopic	
	NH_3	yes	200	Spectroscopic	
	H_2	no	6.3×10^7	Density of the planet	Assumed to be present in solar proportions relative to methane
	He	no	1.3×10^7		
	N_2	no	9.5×10^3		
	Ne	no	2.7×10^4		
URANUS	CH_4	yes	2.2×10^5	Spectroscopic	1. He and H_2 are assumed to be effective molecules in producing transitions of H_2
	H_2	yes	9×10^6	Calculated on assumption 1	
	He	no	2.7×10^7		
	H_2	yes	4.2×10^6	Calculated on assumption 2	2. N_2 and H_2 are assumed to be effective molecules in producing transitions of H_2. Solar proportions of He and H_2 are assumed.
	He	no	8.6×10^5		
	N_2	no	4.2×10^6		
NEPTUNE	CH_4	yes	3.7×10^5	Spectroscopic	
	H_2	yes	Larger than in Uranus	Spectroscopic	Assumed to be effective molecules in producing transitions of H_2. Solar proportions of H_2 and He assumed
	N_2	no			
	He	no			

Kuiper (1952) has been unable to detect N_2O, CH_4, C_2H_4, C_2H_6, and NH_3 on Venus; SO_2, O_3, N_2O, CH_4, C_2H_4, C_2H_6, and NH_3 on Mars; O_3 and SO_2 on Saturn and Uranus. In most cases, the substances could not be expected to be present because of thermodynamic instability under the known conditions of the planet involved.

* Adapted from H. C. Urey, with corrections suggested by him.[26]

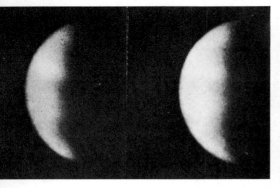
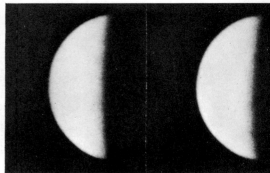

Fig. 78. Venus, in violet light (first two) and red light (latter two), photographed by G. P. Kuiper with the 72-in. reflector of the McDonald Observatory. (*Courtesy Yerkes Observatory Photographic Service*)

clouds, photographed in blue and violet light but invisible in yellow and red light; and white clouds, equally visible in all colors. In blue and violet light, Mars often is enveloped in a dense haze or fog, which, however, is transparent to red and yellow light. Hence, Martian surface features are visible in red and yellow light, except when obscured by the yellow clouds. These observations, while providing descriptive information of the features, do not reveal their physical nature.

Spectroscopy

The constituents of the atmospheres, and of the planetary surfaces have been identified primarily by spectroscopy and *polarimetry.*[*] The light we receive from the planets basically is reflected sunlight, altered somewhat by its passage through the planet's atmosphere and/or reflection from the surface. In addition, the light passes through the earth's atmosphere, and hence any constituents also present in our atmosphere —for example, water vapor, nitrogen, and oxygen—are extremely difficult to identify. Either the absorption lines have to be very intense or the spectra must be photographed at the times of greatest relative approach and recession between the planet and the earth when a shift or asymmetry of the spectral lines can be observed. Thus, in 1932, while looking for

[*] A method of analyzing light by means of a polarimeter in order to determine the way in which light is affected upon reflection.

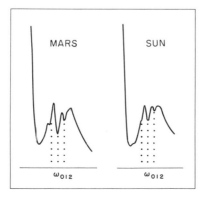

Fig. 79. Tracings by G. P. Kuiper of CO_2 bands in the infrared region of the spectrum of Mars. (*Yerkes– McDonald Observatories chart; courtesy* Sky and Telescope)

evidence of water vapor in the infrared spectrum of Venus, W. S. Adams and T. Dunham, Jr., at Mount Wilson Observatory found certain bands greatly strengthened and identified these with carbon dioxide (CO_2). CO_2 is present in Venus' atmosphere in considerable amounts, compared to its presence in the earth's atmosphere. In 1952, Kuiper found the same molecule in the Martian atmosphere, the detection being more difficult due to smaller concentrations of CO_2 in the case of Mars. The most extensive attempts to detect the presence of oxygen and water vapor in Martian atmosphere were those conducted by Adams and Dunham in 1934. From observations at the time of greatest relative velocity of approach and recession, they hoped to detect asymmetries in the spectral lines. They were able to set an upper limit of only 0.0015 for the ratio of the amounts of oxygen and water vapor present on Mars to those in our atmosphere.

Conspicuous bands not resembling any observed in the solar spectrum were detected in the spectra of Jupiter and Saturn by V. M. Slipher as early as 1905. These bands were not identified until 1931 when R. Wildt, a German astronomer now at Yale University Observatory, attributed them to ammonia and methane. Exact comparisons with laboratory spectra were carried out by Dunham in 1933. It appeared that all earlier attempts at identification had failed because the laboratory spectra of ammonia and methane had been observed at much lower concentrations than those necessary to reproduce the observed bands. Dunham found that the best match of the intensity of the bands in the spectrum of Jupiter and in the laboratory can be obtained by using a 40-m tube filled with ammonia at a pressure of 1 atmosphere (14.7 lb/in.² at sea level). In the photograph of spectra of Saturn and Jupiter between 7,700 and 8,100 A, (a) is the sun, (b) Saturn, (c) Jupiter, (d) 40-m tube.

Spectrograms of the light reflected from the different areas of the surface of Mars have also been studied extensively. In 1924, V. M. Slipher showed that the reflection spectrum of the dark areas did not resemble that of chlorophyll, the substance that produces the green color of terrestrial plants and hence such plant life probably does not exist on Mars. These results were confirmed by Kuiper's more extensive observations of 1956, from which he found, instead, a resemblance to the reflection spectrum of lichens, which probably could thrive in the Martian climate. Kuiper also identified the yellow, "desert" regions of Mars with a brownish igneous rock, felsitic rhyolite (aluminum and potassium silicate with quartz grains in occlusion).

From a comparison of the reflection from the Martian polar caps with hoarfrost, Kuiper has concluded that the caps must consist of water in the form of a thick layer of hoarfrost rather than CO_2, since both ice and the polar caps appear nearly black in infrared light, while frozen CO_2 remains white. However, to the authors' knowledge, Kuiper has not published any tracings, a fact commented upon also by H. C. Urey.

Polarimetry

Polarimetry has provided much observational information on atmospheric and surface features, because, as described by the French astronomer A. Dollfus:

> Light reflected by illuminated substances shows polarization whose properties depend on the nature of the surface and on the angles of incidence and observation. This is caused by reflection, scattering, diffraction, single and double refraction, and absorption. All these processes are taking place simultaneously in the surface layers to which the light penetrates.[27]

The pioneer in this field was B. Lyot, who started polarization measurements at the Meudon Observatory in 1922; only since 1948 have his observations been extended by Dollfus and his collaborators using improved equipment and techniques. Observations are made at different times; changes in polarization characteristics with changes in *phase angle**
are compared with similar observations of terrestrial substances.

The polarization curve for Venus found by Lyot in 1929 differs completely from those of solid materials. It is analogous to the curves found for clouds and droplets. Therefore, Venus must be covered by a layer of opaque clouds whose upper part consists of fine droplets (a little over 2μ in diameter) with the *reflective index†* of water. Very small transparent crystals could give similar polarization.

Mars' desert regions were first investigated by Lyot in 1922, and their polarization is especially well reproduced by limonite (a hydrated iron oxide) in a finely pulverized condition. This finding, however, has been challenged recently by Kuiper, as mentioned on P. 155. The polarization of the dark areas varies with the Martian seasons and with latitude. Seasonal variations in polarization appear related to the changes in contrast

---

* The angle, at the planet, between the direction to the sun and to the earth.

† The ratio of reflected to incident light.

Fig. 80. Spectra of Saturn and Jupiter. (*T. Dunham, Jr., Mount Wilson Observatory*)

and color of these regions; the growth and decay of some microorganisms could account for this. The polar caps show polarization similar to that of hoarfrost under low pressure (as also noted from their spectra), while in some small areas different polarization characteristics, similar to those of ice crystals, are found. Dollfus suggests that there may be ice deposits in several areas of higher elevation. The white clouds must consist of veils of crystals, as do our cirrus clouds, and it is interesting to note that polarization studies occasionally detect white clouds too faint to be observed visually. The blue clouds, or fog, consist of droplets about 3μ in diameter. During December, 1924, when a large part of the Martian surface remained covered for weeks by a yellow veil of exceptional density, Lyot discovered a considerable reduction in polarization. This does not invalidate the hypothesis that the yellow clouds are dust storms, even though the constituents of these clouds have not been identified.

Polarization measurements do contradict the assumption that Jupiter's atmosphere consists of an optically opaque cloud layer overlaid by transparent gases. The atmosphere must be contaminated by thin fog containing particles about 1μ in diameter.

Since Saturn's phase angle attains much smaller values, the variation of polarization is more difficult to observe. It appears that Saturn's atmosphere contains particles somewhat different in nature from Jupiter's, but it has been impossible to draw definite conclusions.

As seen from Table 2, some constituents of planetary atmospheres have been inferred from theoretical considerations reviewed in detail in Urey's paper[26] but are too involved to be discussed here.

Use of Thermocouples

Extensive measurements of planetary temperatures with thermocouples* were begun in the 1920's by Coblentz and Lampland at Lowell

* A thermocouple consists of wires or strips of two dissimilar metals, soldered at their junction and connected to an *ammeter*, an instrument that measures electric current. When exposed to radiation, the temperature increases at the junction and causes a weak electric current to flow through the ammeter. Temperature differences of $1/1,000,000°$ between the heated junction and the rest of the electrical circuit can be measured.

Fig. 81. Jupiter, photographed in blue light with the 200-in. Hale telescope, showing the large Red Spot, the satellite Ganymede, and its shadow. (*Mount Wilson and Palomar Observatories*)

Observatory, and by E. Pettit and S. B. Nicholson at Mount Wilson. Coblentz and Lampland found that the temperature of both hemispheres of Venus is 241°K while the temperature of Mercury, which does not have any atmosphere and is much closer to the sun, is about 610°K on the sunward side. Pettit was especially successful in making his own thermocouples by sputtering small fragments of metal upon a glass plate.

Radio Astronomy

Most recently radio-astronomical investigations of the planets have yielded new and puzzling data. Thermal radio radiation is of particular interest for planets possessing extensive atmospheres, since it would be expected to originate in a deeper layer than optical light. However, according to a review by C. H. Mayer, the American radio astronomer:

Radio observations of Venus and Jupiter have already supplied unexpected experimental data on the physical conditions of these planets.
The observed intensity of the radio emission of Venus is much higher than
the expected thermal intensity, although the spectrum indicated by
measurements at wavelengths near 3 and 10 cm is like that of a black body
at about 600°K. This result suggests a very high temperature at the solid
surface of the planet, although there is a possibility that the observed
radiation may be a combination of both thermal and nonthermal components and that the observed spectrum is that of a black body merely
by coincidence. In the case of Jupiter, the radio emission spectrum is
definitely not like the spectrum of a black body radiator, and it seems
likely that the radiation reaching the earth is a combination of thermal
radiation from the atmosphere and nonthermal components.[28]

Even more puzzling was the discovery in 1955 of strong, long-wave-
length radio bursts from Jupiter by B. F. Burke and K. L. Franklin at the
Department of Terrestrial Magnetism of the Carnegie Institution. Modern
astronomers rarely look at the sky while they are engaged in astronomical
observations. First, Burke and Franklin noticed an unidentified discrete
radio source where no such source had been known to exist. A few days
later they found no radio emission in or near the spot at which they had
found a signal, but later observations again indicated a discrete source a
short distance away from the original location. Only accidentally did they
examine the night sky and discover that the intermittent radio radiation
came from Jupiter, which moves across the sky in accordance with its
orbital motion around the sun. The radio bursts from Jupiter are observed
only at wavelengths of 10 to 15 m. After this discovery, similar bursts,
previously assumed to result from terrestrial interference, were found by
the Australian radio astronomer C. A. Shain on some records taken in
1950 and 1951. Shain discovered that the principal region of activity is
associated with one of the white spots in the South Temperate Belt.
Franklin and Burke subsequently established a correlation between the
large Red Spot and radio bursts. From his work at the Ohio State University, J. D. Kraus has suggested the possibility that the mechanism producing the radio bursts may be triggered by particles emitted from the sun.

INTERIOR STRUCTURE OF PLANETS

Knowledge of planetary interiors is derived by complex theoretical reasoning. Paradoxically, it is much easier to analyze stellar interiors because the properties of gases are much better known and easier
to predict than are those of liquids and solids, particularly at high pres-

sures. The conspicuous differences in size, shape, mass, and density of
the terrestrial planets (Mercury, Venus, Earth, and Mars) and the Jovian
(or giant) planets (Jupiter, Saturn, Uranus, and Neptune) indicate a
drastically different constitution. The terrestrial planets are believed to
resemble the earth in structure and probably also in chemical constitution; that is, these planets are believed to have a surface layer of clays
and limestone, a lower layer of silicates (the mantle) and an inner core.
According to the American physicist W. C. de Marcus:

> Opinion as to the material forming the earth's core is divided. The
> opposing views are basically that the core is a high-pressure silicate phase
> of high density and that the earth's core is iron, or nickel and iron. Gener-
> ally, the silicate camp favors the view that all the terrestrial planets save
> Mercury are, for practical purposes, chemically identical, while the iron
> camp considers that the terrestrial planets are similar in constitution but
> definitely differ quantitatively.[29]

Because of the low density of the Jovian planets, arguments were presented in favor of a gaseous constitution as late as 1933, mainly by the
Russian astronomer N. Lvov. The present model of the giant planets is
mainly Wildt's work, although suggestions of models similar to those he
developed had been presented earlier. His model has been extended and
refined since 1947, when the principal ideas were crystallized in his "Report on the Progress of Astronomy" to the Royal Astronomical Society.

Wildt considered spectroscopic results as well as the dimensions and
masses of the planets, since

> ... the principal chemical differences between the atmospheres of the
> terrestrial and the giant planets, namely, the prevalence of hydrogen com-
> pounds in the latter, can qualitatively be understood as a consequence of
> an enormous surplus of hydrogen which was prevented from escaping
> into space by the great surface gravity of the giant planets. Moreover,
> this view of the atmospheric constituents of the giant planets is in good
> accord with their low mean densities, as was first pointed out by F. R.
> Moulton [in 1905].[30]

While hydrogen thus should be the main constituent of these planets,
from more detailed considerations "... on plausible assumptions concerning the interior composition and the compressibility of planetary matter,"[31]
it appeared that the planet could not be of uniform composition throughout. Wildt concluded that the planets must have a relatively small core,
with a density (ρ) equal to or greater than that of terrestrial rocks, surrounded by a deep shell of very small density, $\rho \le 0.78$ gm/cm^3 for Jupiter
and $\rho \le 0.425$ gm/cm^3 for Saturn. "The only substances known to give

Fig. 82.   Saturn, photographed with the 100-in. Hooker telescope. (*Mount Wilson and Palomar Observatories*)

such low densities are the so-called permanent gases in the state of high compression, which may lead even to solidification."[32] Wildt also pointed out that the gaseous atmosphere above the shell would be extremely thin; that its depth would be less than 1 per cent of the planet's radius, because the gases would solidify under their own weight as a result of the great force of gravity exerted by the planet's large bulk. Similar conclusions were reached by V. G. Fessenkov in the Soviet Union.

COMETS

Concerning smaller bodies in the solar system, the opinion expressed 10 years ago by the Russian-born astronomer N. T. Bobrovnikov of Ohio State and Ohio Wesleyan Universities, one of the scientists most active in cometary research, is still true to a great extent:

In general, in the rapid development of astrophysics in the last 50 years, the smaller members of the solar system have been largely neglected. The difficulty of maintaining continuous and systematic observation, as well as lack of observers, accounts for this situation. The lure of the great universe, with its stars and nebulae, where a striking development of theory goes hand in hand with an equally striking development of observational technique, has been too strong to resist. The attention of the majority of observers and theoreticians has been directed to these larger problems. Yet the presence of the diffuse matter in the solar system is undoubtedly connected with similar diffuse matter elsewhere in the universe, and the progress of our study of the universe in general may be facilitated by our thorough understanding of the behavior of the lesser members of our solar system.[33]

Investigations of comets during this century have been hampered also by the lack of great comets, such as were observed during the 19th century. Despite these handicaps, some of their mysteries have been cleared up. For centuries, comets were believed to represent evil spirits. Even after such superstitions had disappeared, for the most part, near-panic was caused by the predicted passage on May 18, 1910 of the earth through the *tail*[*] of Halley's comet. Similar fears of contamination and destruction were created by the close approach of the small periodic comet Pons-Winnecke in 1927.[†] The appearance of comet Delevan of 1914 was believed to prophesy the disasters of war. However, the earth's passage through a comet's tail remains completely unobservable. The passage of the earth through the outer layers of a comet nucleus (the main body of the comet) results in a meteor shower, such as that observed in 1833 and 1866 and referred to as the "Leonid shower," because its apparent origin was in the constellation Leo. A collision of the earth with the central nucleus of a comet has been estimated to occur at intervals of about once in about 100 million years. Although there is no direct observational evidence that such collision has occurred during recorded history, the event would not necessarily be harmless.

There is now a fair understanding of the nature of cometary nuclei and of the processes occurring in comet tails. The exact mechanism causing the ejection of material from the nucleus and the formation of the tail is less well understood. Formation of cometary tails has been attributed mainly to the pressure of solar radiation, which drives the molecules and atoms in a direction radially away from the sun. Many peculiarities about the forms of and changes in cometary tails still require satisfactory explanation. The German astronomer L. Biermann recently suggested that solar corpuscular radiation, or the ejection of high-velocity particles from

[*] A luminous extension from the main body of the comet, directed roughly away from the sun and consisting of extremely rarefied gases, that was believed to contain poisonous substances capable of contaminating the earth's atmosphere.

[†] Comets are designated by the year of discovery and then the order of discovery in that year. A relatively bright comet is usually known also by the name of its discoverer (or discoverers).

the sun, also may play an important role; he found confirmation for his theory in the study of the influence of solar magnetic storms in Comet Whipple-Fedtke (1942g).

The size and mass of cometary nuclei have been inferred indirectly. The Great Comet of 1882 passed at a distance of 500,000 km from the sun and must have been subject to temperatures of at least $4,500°K$, sufficient to vaporize a body 1 m or more in diameter. The comet's brightness did not change noticeably, and hence it must have been fairly large. However, it could not be seen when in front of the sun, so that the diameter could have been no more than 70 km. The average diameters of cometary nuclei are estimated to be about 1 km.

An upper limit to cometary masses is set by the fact that while their paths are perturbed greatly by planets, the comets do not exert any observable gravitational influence on even the minor planets. The lower limit of mass is estimated mainly from the rate of loss of mass at perihelion, particularly for periodic comets. The masses are believed to be between 10^{15} and 10^{17} grams (gm); between 60 billion and 6,000 billion comets would be equal to the mass of the earth.

The constitution of the cometary nucleus is inferred from spectrographic observations of the *coma*, a mass of gas surrounding the nucleus and consisting of atoms and molecules liberated by the nucleus. The commonest substances are simple groups of atoms (radicals) that are fundamental parts of compounds consisting of two light atoms, such as oxygen and hydrogen (OH), nitrogen and hydrogen (NH), carbon and hydrogen (CH), carbon and nitrogen (CN), or the carbon molecule, C_2. Since most of these molecules are not very stable, they are readily decomposed by the action of the sunlight and are driven into the comet's tail.

The unstable radicals could not have existed very long in the nucleus and must be the decomposition products of other, more stable molecules. It has been shown, particularly by K. Wurm in Germany, P. Swings in Belgium, and N. T. Bobrovnikov, that the cometary nucleus contains water (H_2O), ammonia (NH_3), methane (CH_4), and other molecules. The comets spend most of their lifetimes at great distances from the sun where these parent molecules form solids: ordinary ice and ices of ammonia, methane, and so forth. Probably the best description of a comet has been given by F. L. Whipple, who pictures it as a mixture of these ices, with grains of meteoric material—mostly iron (Fe), calcium (Ca), magnesium (Mg), manganese (Mn), silicon (Si), nickel (Ni), aluminum (Al), and sodium (Na)—embedded in them. These grains probably range all the way from free atoms, which produce metallic emission lines in cometary spectra, to large blocks some centimeters or even meters in size. Thus the comet is thought of as a solid body, a "dirty iceberg." As it approaches the sun, some of the lighter molecules evaporate and create both the coma and the tail.

The spectra of these tails show that they consist of two substances: ionized molecules emitting radiation by the process of fluorescence (by the absorption of sunlight and re-emission of the absorbed energy in the characteristic wavelengths of the molecules); and small, solid particles reflecting sunlight without absorption (this same process provides the light of the moon and the planets).

From the brightness distribution observed in the tail of Halley's comet, K. Schwarzschild and E. Kron concluded in 1911 that "... [the observed distribution] is immediately explained if we assume that in the tail of comets we are concerned with fluorescent or resonance radiation excited by the solar radiation."[34] The theory of fluorescence was developed by the Dutch astronomer H. Zanstra and the German K. Wurm, who showed that the predicted luminosity agreed with that observed for comets showing strong emission spectra. Another and most important application of the fluorescence hypothesis was developed by Swings in 1941, while he was at the Lick Observatory.

It was known that the intensity distribution within cometary bands differs from that found in laboratory sources even at low temperatures; moreover, the intensity distribution varies from comet to comet and for any comet at different heliocentric distances. Many unsuccessful attempts had been made to explain these phenomena. According to the Canadian astronomer A. McKellar, of the Dominion Astrophysical Observatory at Victoria, B.C., who soon quantitatively confirmed Swings' work:

This problem was solved in a most satisfactory manner by Swings. He pointed out that if it be assumed that the bands are produced by pure resonance, the exciting radiation being sunlight, consideration must be given to the fact that the wavelength distribution of this exciting radiation would be far from smooth because of the irregular contour of the solar spectrum, resulting from the presence of many strong absorption lines.[35]

Swings had also pointed out that:

... certain relative intensities may be very sensitive to change in the radial velocity which could bring the cometary absorption line inside or outside a strong Frauhofer line.... It does seem likely that the differences between the CN structure of comets of similar heliocentric distances is mainly due to the difference in radial velocity.... This may, of course, also be applied to one comet at different heliocentric distances.[36]

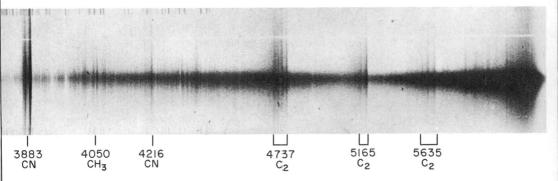

| 3883 | 4050 | 4216 | 4737 | 5165 | 5635 |
| CN | CH₃ | CN | C₂ | C₂ | C₂ |

$$\begin{array}{cccccc} 3883 & 4050 & 4216 & 4737 & 5165 & 5635 \\ \text{CN} & \text{CH}_3 & \text{CN} & \text{C}_2 & \text{C}_2 & \text{C}_2 \end{array}$$

Fig. 83. The spectrum of Comet 1948 I, photographed by P. D. Jose and P. Swings with the 82-in. reflector of the McDonald Observatory.

Fig. 84. P. Swings at a Yerkes Observatory measuring machine.

Even though the effect was best observed in CN bands, similar considerations would apply to the bands of OH, NH, and CH.

THE MOON

Although advances made in lunar studies will not be discussed in detail, attention is called to G. P. Kuiper's lunar observations based on photographs made at several observatories and to a similar study by the Czechoslovak-born astronomer Z. Kopal of Manchester University at the observatory on the Pic du Midi, in the Pyrenees. The moon has no atmosphere, and its thousands of craters are probably the result of meteoric impacts. There has been some controversy about lunar volcanic action occurring at the present time, and plans are under way to place upon the moon an instrument for the detection of possible tremors resembling earthquakes. There also has been some controversy about the existence of lunar gases escaping from craters, such as Alphonsus. About 10 years ago, D. Alter, the former director of the Griffith

Planetarium in Los Angeles, felt certain that his photographs of Alphonsus showed at times that the bottom of the crater appeared washed out by a gaseous medium. Independently, the Russian astronomer N. A. Kozyrev announced that he had observed an emission spectrum in the central peak of the crater Alphonsus, which resembled the emission spectrum of C_2. His results have not been accepted by many astronomers, and there is at present no confirmation of the single observation he published. Kuiper, who has become one of the leading authorities on the moon, has reversed his originally critical opinion of Kozyrev's work and accepts the results of the observations without attempting to identify the emission features with known terrestrial molecules.

An amusing incident occurred in the mid-1920's, when a Russian pseudoscientist wrote to me claiming he had been able to observe the side of the moon hidden from direct view because of the coincidence of the periods of lunar rotation and revolution around the earth. He complained that he could not receive the credit due to him from the leading Russian astronomers, because (he felt) all of them were counter-revolutionaries, and hence the only hope for recognition rested with Western astronomers. Thirty years later a Soviet satellite circled the moon and produced a crude, but nevertheless spectacular, picture of the major formations of its invisible part.

Other important results have already been obtained with instruments located in interplanetary space vehicles, such as the discovery of the Van Allen belts of particles surrounding the earth. Even more spectacular discoveries in the solar system may be expected in the next few years—information that may make all of our present knowledge of the planets and their satellites appear insignificant by comparison.

IX

ORIGIN OF THE
SOLAR SYSTEM

AT THE TURN of the century, astronomers recognized the
universal force of attraction as the only force that could produce stars and planets. In the laboratory this is usually a small force, and
in physics it plays a subordinate role. Thus, two 1-gm particles, separated
by 1 cm, attract each other with a force of 6.7 x 10^{-8} dyne. However, all
stars and many other bodies in the universe have such large masses (2 x
10^{33} gm for the sun) that gravitation provides an important, perhaps even
the overwhelming, force operating in the universe. In the meantime, other
forces, such as those of magnetism and gas pressure, have played an increasingly important role in all theories of the origin of the solar system.

Another development in cosmogonic thinking during the present century is the recognition of the existence of many solar-type stars whose
origin presumably is the same as that of the solar system. It is, therefore,
not sufficient for a theory to explain only those properties of the solar
system that cannot be due to chance—for example, the fact that the orbital
planes of the planets and the directions of planetary motion nearly coincide with the sun's equatorial plane and its direction of rotation. Because
these theories also must account for the existence of billions of other stars
in the Milky Way, astronomers were forced to break with the old tradition
and depart entirely from the conventional form of cosmogonic research.
The transition has not been an easy one, and it has taken at least half a
century to adopt a new approach. Among the astronomers primarily responsible for this transition was C. F. von Weizsäcker in Germany, who

adapted the physical theory of turbulence to the stars. He also attempted to explain why many hot stars have large rotational velocities, while all single, main-sequence stars of low surface temperature have slow equatorial rotational velocities resembling the sun's 2 km/sec equatorial rotation. In the Soviet Union, V. A. Ambarzumian has stressed the departures from the old-type cosmogony, which reached its highest development in H. Poincaré's *Leçons sur les Hypothèses Cosmogoniques* (see p. 39). The Russian astronomer V. G. Fessenkov, partly in collaboration with A. G. Massevich, has discussed the possible effects upon a star's evolution of a loss of mass occurring in the form of *corpuscular radiation*. In America, the most significant contributions to modern cosmogony have been made by G. P. Kuiper; in Great Britain, F. Hoyle and more recently the theoretician W. H. McCrea have led in this field.

THE SOLAR SYSTEM AS A UNIQUE PHENOMENON

Tidal and Collision Hypotheses

All theories of the origin of the solar system date from 1755, the year Immanuel Kant suggested that the sun and the planets had originated from the condensation of a diffuse mass of tenuous material, the clots of gas and dust growing by accretion to form planets and satellites; the remainder of the nebula contracts to form the sun. This is called the *nebular hypothesis* and was independently developed by Laplace in 1796.

Fig. 85.   Diagram of Kant's theory of the origin of the solar system. (*From T. L. Page*, Physics Today, *I, 1948, 6, P. 14; courtesy* Sky and Telescope)

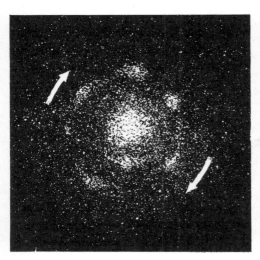
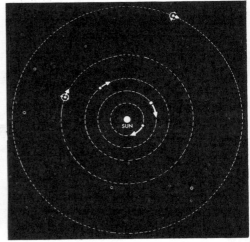

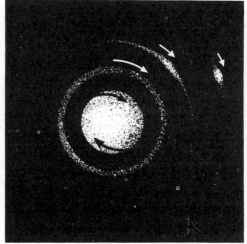

Fig. 86. The origin of the solar system as envisaged by Laplace. (*From* Physics Today, *1, 1948, 6, P. 14; courtesy* Sky and Telescope)

It was accepted generally until about 1900. Its first serious challenge was on the grounds that the sun could not have rotated fast enough to shed rings that condensed into planets as proposed by Laplace. "Tidal" theories were developed by J. H. Jeans in England and T. C. Chamberlin and F. R. Moulton at the University of Chicago, among others. These theories suggested that a close encounter (even a grazing collision) between the sun and another star caused the ejection of solar material that ultimately condensed, forming the planets and their satellites. According to Chamberlin and Moulton, violent tidal eruptions would be produced on the near and far side of the sun as follows:

Fig. 87. Diagrams depicting the Chamberlin-Moulton "planetesimal" hypothesis. (*From* Physics Today, *1, 1948, 6, P. 15; courtesy* Sky and Telescope)

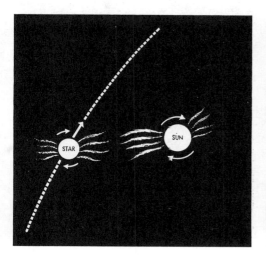

It is supposed that our system has developed from a spiral nebula, perhaps something like those spiral nebulae which Keeler showed are many times more numerous than all other kinds together. The spiral nebula is supposed to have originated when another sun passed very near our sun. The dimensions of the nebula were maintained almost entirely by the orbital motions of the great number of small masses of which it was composed and only very little by gaseous expansion. . . . The planets have been formed around primitive nuclei of considerable dimension by the accretion of the vast amount of scattered material which was spread throughout the system.[1]

While all other theories assumed gradual condensations in a gaseous nebula leading to the formation of planets, Chamberlin and Moulton proposed that the nebula quickly cooled and solidified, creating small chunks of matter, the *planetesimals*. Hence their theory is often referred to as the *planetesimal hypothesis*.

Jeans and H. Jeffreys, the English astronomer, hypothesized that a large, cigar-shaped filament had been pulled out of the sun by a star passing within two or three solar radii from it. According to this conception, the amount of matter attracted by the passing star would have increased until its closest approach and thereafter would have decreased again, creating a filament thicker in the middle than at the ends, thus accounting for the large size of Jupiter and Saturn (formed in the middle) and the smaller planets (formed at the ends).

These theories, as well as others developed during the first decades of

Fig. 88.   Schematic diagram of the Jeans-Jeffreys hypothesis of the solar system's origin. (*From* Physics Today, *I, 1948, 6, P. 19; courtesy* Sky and Telescope)

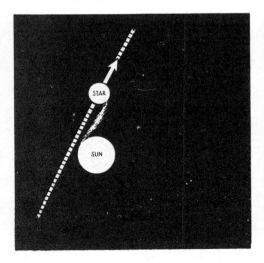
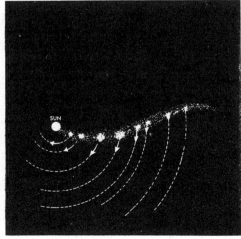

this century, were concerned mainly with those properties of the solar system about which a great deal was known. All the theories were intended to explain these properties in terms of classical mechanics. While advances gradually were made in theories of stellar evolution, including the origin of binary stars, the general feeling was expressed by Jeans that, "... the great disparity of weight between the sun and planets distinguishes a sun and planet formation from that of the normal binary star, and so suggests entirely different origins for the two formations."[2]

Difficulties Encountered

Several difficulties, however, were encountered by the tidal theorists. Thus L. Spitzer, Jr., of Princeton University, showed in 1939 that matter pulled out of the sun could not condense, but rather would expand and form a gaseous nebula surrounding the sun. About the same time W. J. Luyten of the University of Minnesota published a severe criticism of the near-approach theories on dynamic grounds.

The distribution of *angular momentum** in the solar system was recognized gradually as the greatest stumbling block for all theories. This difficulty, which has been stressed frequently, was ingeniously described by H. N. Russell in his *The Solar System and Its Origin:*

The major planets, which have less than 1/700 of the whole mass, carry 98 per cent of the angular momentum; the Sun, with practically all the mass, only 2 per cent. The puzzle is why the Sun has so little, not why the planets have so much—for any bodies revolving in orbits of the same cross-diameter must necessarily have as much angular momentum per ton as the planets do, so long as the central mass is as great as the Sun's. Whether this mass is expanded into a nebula extending almost to the planet's orbit, or concentrated into a star, makes no difference at all.

But if all the mass and angular momentum of our system could be collected in the Sun, it would then rotate in about twelve hours, and be less flattened at the poles than Jupiter. The centrifugal force at its equator would be about 5 per cent of gravity, and and it would be far from any danger of breaking up. . . .

No one has ever suggested a way in which almost the whole of the angular momentum could have got into so insignificant a fraction of the mass of an isolated system. . . .[3]

* Angular momentum may be defined as the product of the mass of a moving particle and the area swept out in unit time by the line joining it to a given point. For a planet moving in a circular orbit, the angular momentum is the product of its mass, its distance from the sun, and its orbital velocity, the latter quantity depending on the mass of the sun. For a rotating body, it is the sum of the products of the mass of each particle, its distance from the axis of rotation, and its rotational velocity. The total angular momentum of a system can be changed only by an outside force; it cannot be altered by internal forces.

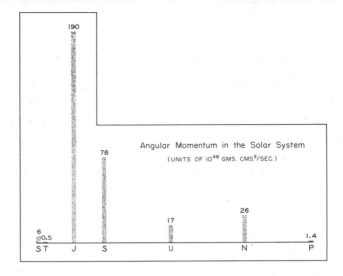

Fig. 89. Distribution of angular momentum in the solar system. The sum of the contributions of the four terrestrial planets is labeled "T". Left of it is the sun's value. (*Courtesy* Sky and Telescope)

While early versions of the tidal theories attempted to attribute the large angular momentum carried by the planets to the action of the passing star, closer calculation, particularly attempts to account also for the angular rotation of the planets and the orbital revolution of their satellites, showed they had not succeeded. Jeffreys, in a revision of his earlier ideas, proposed a grazing collision rather than a close passage, and thus accounted for more features of the solar system. The English astronomer R. A. Lyttleton meanwhile suggested that the sun originally had been a member of a binary system and that a close approach of a third star had separated its companion.

Attempts also were made to consider the nebular hypothesis by exploring additional assumptions regarding magnetic and electrical fields. Thus the Norwegian physicist K. Birkeland speculated in 1914 about the possibility of electrically charged particles leaking out from the sun and forming rings, the radii of which depend on the ratio of the electrical charge to the mass of the particles. In 1942 H. Alfvén considered the effect that would have been produced by the sun's motion through a dense nebula containing charged particles. While the above theories account for the distribution of angular momentum, they do not account for the process of condensation into planets, which appears highly doubtful under the assumed conditions. And as H. Spencer Jones noted in 1940: ". . . each new objection raised against any theory of the origin of the solar system has to be overcome by the introduction of some new additional assumption, making the theory in itself less probable."[4] Appearing to be near total despair, Spencer Jones concluded:

The solar system must have had an origin; if we cannot account for it except by the introduction of many special and somewhat artificial hypotheses, we shall have to conclude that the probability of other stars having systems of planets is very small.[5]

THE NEW COSMOGONY

Frequency of Planetary Systems

By this time, however, many astronomers realized that the formation of the solar system must be connected closely with the processes that create stars. One reason for this reversal of opinion was the fatal defect of all collision theories: These stellar encounters are much too rare. The sun, for example, is more than 4 light-years from its nearest stellar neighbor, and with a relative velocity of 20 km/sec it would take roughly 10^5 years to travel that distance.

But the sun, as seen from a distance of 4 light-years, occupies only about 10^{-16} of the entire sky; the other star, as viewed from the sun, may be regarded as covering an equal solid angle. Thus the probability of the two objects striking one another after 100,000 years is only 2×10^{-16}. If this value is increased to allow for near misses, the probability of a particular star colliding with another during the galaxy's entire past life (say 5 billion years) is only about 5×10^{-11}. Even if allowance is made, as by Jeans, for the fact that the planets might have been formed before the sun had contracted to its present size, the probability of collision is not increased sufficiently.

Since our galaxy contains roughly 2×10^{11} stars, perhaps only one or two collisions have occurred during the past 5 billion years (collisions may occur more often in the dense, but relatively small central condensation of the Milky Way). If the sun had been one of the partners in such an encounter, our solar system would be practically unique. However, evidence from other solar-type stars indicates that planetary systems are common in space. Collision theories, therefore, should be discarded.

The evidence for this conclusion comes from comparing the rotational velocities (see Chap. XI, p. 228) of stars of different spectral types. Table 4 shows that most main-sequence stars hotter than F5 (surface temperature 6,500°) are rotating rapidly, while cooler stars, such as the sun (as well as giants, long-period variables, and others), have slow rotations. Since other stellar characteristics, such as color and mass, fail to show any similarly abrupt change at F5, it must be inferred that some unobservable property accounts for this discontinuity.

The property's significance becomes clear if the change in solar rotational velocity is considered that would result if all the angular momentum of the planets, from their orbital motion and rotation, were added to the sun's. If all the present planets were combined with the sun, its rotational velocity would be increased by a factor of 50. It would then be spinning fairly rapidly at 100 km/sec, as the hotter stars do.

These considerations indicate that all, or most, solar-type stars have low rotations because they possess planetary systems but do not give any clue to the process by which the planets were formed, nor how any star, single or with planets, could have acquired as small an angular momentum as the sun's.

Most astronomers now believe (see Chap. XIII, P. 273) that stars originate in the gravitational contraction of large "cells" of interstellar gas and dust. Such a cell may be visualized as a cloud, perhaps 4 light-years in radius, with a mass roughly that of the sun. It is assumed that gravitationally stable condensations of gas form and grow more massive, at length becoming visible as black globules when seen in front of a bright nebula. How will this process lead to the formation of a solar system?

Von Weizsäcker's Theory: Turbulence

Nebulae that are typical birthplaces of stars have turbulent internal motions with velocities from 5 to 10 km/sec. These are chaotic movements, though sometimes occurring in well-defined stream patterns. If a cell of such nebulosity, containing as much material as the sun, were to contract from an original density of 10^{-22} gm/cm^3 to that of the sun, 1.4 gm/cm^3,

Fig. 90. Diagram of von Weizsäcker's theory of the origin of the solar system (*From* Physics Today, *I, 1948, 6, P. 21; courtesy* Sky and Telescope)

the chaotic motions would never completely cease; some angular momentum, more than the solar system now has, would remain.

The first application of the physical theory of turbulence to the problem of the origin of the solar system was provided by von Weizsäcker in 1943. In the introduction to his paper proposing the new theory, von Weizsäcker explained:

It is assumed that the planets originated from a strongly flattened nebula which rotated around the sun and contained, as does the sun, only about 1 per cent of its weight in the form of heavy elements from which the earth was formed. Such a nebula must have been formed at the time of creation of the sun and will be destroyed within 10^7 to 10^8 years due to turbulent motions within it. Systems of convection currents must originate in it. . . . The planets grow from the combination of smaller chunks of condensed heavy elements. The satellites originated likewise in smaller nebulae formed around the planets; the convection currents explain the direction of revolution of satellites and of rotation of planets.[6]

Von Weizsäcker assumed the original nebula to have a density of about 10^{-9} gm/cm^3, containing about $\frac{1}{10}$ of the mass of the sun. He postulated that the greater part of the nebula was dissipated into space, carrying with it some of the angular momentum. According to a review of von Weizsäcker's paper by G. Gamow and J. A. Hynek in 1945, in the *Astrophysical Journal* (which brought von Weizsäcker's theory to the attention of English-speaking astronomers), these whirlpools can be thought of as the balls in a ball bearing. If the outer bearing (vortex) moves clockwise and the inner bearing counterclockwise, the balls will rotate in the "direct" sense, as the planets do.

Gamow and Hynek doubted that the growth of planets can occur in the manner suggested by von Weizsäcker, and other objections to the theory have been raised since. For example, Kuiper showed that the vortices and, in particular, the small whirlpools could not have persisted long enough for growth to proceed as von Weizsäcker suggested. However, it is certain that ". . . Weizsäcker has directed a fresh stream of thought into the long-stagnant pool of theories of planetary origin."[7]

McCrea's Theory: Random Flights

An idea proposed by McCrea, first applied to a system of planets extending to about 40 a.u., can be applied to a much larger volume of nebulous gas, perhaps of the order of 2 light-years, or 2×10^{18} cm. If the condensing nebulosity is considered to consist of N separate blobs, each having a velocity of the order of 5 km/sec, or 5×10^5 cm/sec, and a mass of $2 \times 10^{33}/N$ gm, the statistical theory of random flights can be applied to the problem. If the original cloud were composed of very few blobs, all having the same velocity, but randomly distributed directions of motions, the rotational momentum of the blobs with respect to their center of gravity would almost never be close to zero. As McCrea has shown, the most probable rotational momentum of the entire mass would be the product of the total mass (2×10^{33} grams) times the velocity (5×10^5 cm/sec) times the radius of the cloud (2×10^{18} cm) divided by $\sqrt{N}$. The result is $2 \times 10^{57}/\sqrt{N}$. If the solar system's rotational momentum is the same now as it was before the cloud condensed (3×10^{50} gm cm^2/sec), there would be approximately 10^{14} blobs.

It is necessary to emphasize that the statistical theory gives only the most probable rotational momentum of the N blobs, and does not indicate directly how this value may differ from one interstellar cloud to another. However, it can be shown that rotational momenta differing by a factor of, say, 10 from the most probable value may be regarded as exceedingly rare. The number $N = 10^{14}$ is unexpectedly large. It is not consistent with the known dimensions of the turbulent eddies in the Orion nebula and in other similar gas clouds. In the course of the condensation of the gas cloud, almost certainly a much smaller number of blobs resulted in the observed rotational momentum of 3×10^{50} gm cm^2/sec. Moreover, in the original nebula, clouds of the size contemplated here would collide with other clouds, and therefore would exchange energy and angular momentum.

McCrea at another time discussed this same problem of turbulence in connection with the formation of the solar system. He disregarded the early stages of condensation and started with a fairly dense cloud possessing a radius of some 40 a.u., ultimately leading to a distribution of rotational momentum in the ratio of 50:1 between the planets and the sun itself. The known turbulent motions in gaseous nebulae indicate that a star could not have been formed through the process of *Kelvin contraction** unless a large part of the rotational momentum of the initial cloud were lost during the early stages of contraction, or the number of turbulent eddies is vastly greater than are now observed. Incidentally, McCrea's expression for the expected rotational momentum of an aggregate of N blobs could only approach zero if N were very large. It would be al-

---

* Kelvin or Helmholtz contraction refers to the hypothesis proposed in the 19th century to account for the radiation of the sun. According to this theory, stars tend to cool down and contract during their lifetimes and in doing so are converting gravitational potential energy into heat (see Chap. X, P. 200). This process is now believed to occur in the early stages of stellar evolution (see Chap. XIII, P. 271).

most exactly zero if the cloud consisted of single atoms whose individual motions were distributed at random and whose velocities were approximately those that correspond to the temperatures of the nebulae.

All cosmogonical theories based upon Kelvin's contraction hypothesis must overcome two other difficulties:

1. The condensing cloud must retain its identity, despite the action of tidal forces exerted upon it by the bulk of the Milky Way and by nearby stars. This, in effect, means that the cloud must possess an initial density greater than about 3×10^{-22} gm/cm^3, or roughly 100 H atoms/cm^3. Observations indicate that very dense gaseous nebulae may have as many as 10,000 H atoms/cm^3.

2. The condensation also must overcome the so-called Jeans' criterion of instability, which implies that only very cold clouds whose individual particles have velocities of about 0.2 km/sec can produce stars.

Kuiper's Theory: Tidal Stability

The importance of the tidal-stability criterion in cosmogony was first demonstrated by Kuiper, long before McCrea's theory became known. No attempt has been made as yet to integrate the two theories, but they seem to be entirely compatible.

Kuiper assumes that the sun was formed in a fairly dense interstellar cloud, and that a disk-shaped nebula several tens of astronomical units in radius was left behind and revolved around the sun. The inclinations of the planetary orbits indicate that Kuiper's solar nebula would have had an appreciable thickness at right angles to its plane of original rotational symmetry. The latter may be identified with what is called the "invariable plane" of the solar system. It represents the average for the system, and its orientation in space can be altered only by external forces. If the inclination of the orbit of any one planet changes as a result of perturbations, the inclinations of one or more of the other orbits must change in the opposite direction.

With the exclusion of Pluto, which probably was a satellite of Neptune, the innermost planet, Mercury, has the largest orbital inclination to the invariable plane (which remains unchanged by any of the mutual actions of planets within the solar system), amounting to about 6°.5 at a distaance from the sun of 0.4 a.u. A protoplanet, moving in such an orbit, indicates a thickness of about 0.1 a.u. for the solar nebula. Farther out, at about Jupiter's distance of 5 a.u. from the sun, the orbital inclination of 1° again roughly suggests a thickness of 0.1 a.u.

If the nebula is assumed to have had a cylindrical shape, its volume up to a distance of 30 a.u. from the sun would have been 10^{42} cm^3. If it is assumed that the original solar nebula contained as much mass as that of all the planets at the present time, 2×10^{30} gm, the mean density of the solar nebula would have been 2×10^{-12} gm/cm^3. Even allowing for possible departures in the assumed values of the nebula's thickness and radius, it is difficult to see how the density could have been more than about 10^{-11} gm/cm^3. However, according to the tidal criterion, the density must have been greater than 4×10^{-9} gm/cm^3.

The discrepancy Kuiper found between the two values is a factor of at least 100, and therefore he concluded that the presently observed planetary masses account for only 1 per cent, or less, of the mass of the original solar nebula. At least 99 per cent of the nebula must have been driven out of the solar system. This conclusion is consistent with the fact that the terrestrial planets are strikingly deficient in hydrogen. Even Jupiter and Saturn, which consist mostly of hydrogen, must have accumulated within their bodies only a fraction of the material that was located inside their rings of "dominance." The nebula's original mass must have been about 0.1 times the mass of the sun, or 2×10^{32} gm. Had all of it been collected into one companion star, the solar system would now be a normal double star of mass ratio $\frac{1}{10}$. Such ratios occur frequently—in about 20 per cent of all double stars, the smaller component has $\frac{1}{10}$ (or less) the mass of the primary star. In Kuiper's own words:

> Since roughly half the stars are binaries, one may say that about 10 per cent of the stars are attended by companions not over 0.1 times as massive. Several astrometric binaries with secondaries having masses between 0.1 and 0.01 sun strengthen the belief that binaries with large mass ratios are no exception.[8]

Kuiper also found support for his hypothesis from an investigation of the frequencies of semimajor axes of binary stars. He found that they range between 0.01 and 100,000 a.u.; the average is 20 a.u., which is about the average distance of the major planets from the sun.

The theories of von Weizsäcker, McCrea, and Kuiper are based upon purely gravitational considerations. Although progress has been made lately by many astronomers, including Alfvén and Spitzer, in studies of

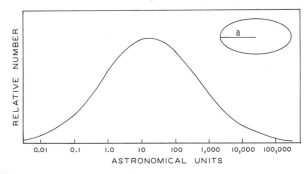

Fig. 91.   Distribution of the major axes of binary stars after G. P. Kuiper. (*Courtesy* Sky and Telescope)

the effect of magnetic forces in the Milky Way, these ideas are still in the process of development.

ADDITIONAL THEORIES REGARDING THE LESSER BODIES OF THE SOLAR SYSTEM

The theories thus far discussed are concerned principally with the solar system's larger bodies: the planets and their satellites. However, the origin of asteroids, meteors, comets, and cosmic dust in the solar system also must be accounted for by some additional hypotheses.

The formation of asteroids and meteors often has been attributed to the break-up of a planet between the orbits of Mars and Jupiter, or to the failure of the matter occupying this region to condense into a single body. Kuiper has suggested that, while more than one condensation formed in the "asteroid belt," further fragmentation was created by subsequent collisions between these parent masses. The smaller fragments produced in such collisions are observed now as meteors, the larger ones as asteroids.

A number of theories about the origin of comets have been proposed. More than a century ago, Laplace suggested that comets come from interstellar space. This theory was developed in detail by Schiaparelli, the French astronomer C. Fabry in the 19th century, and more recently by N. D. Moisseiev in the Soviet Union. However, Laplace's theory attributes to interstellar comets velocities with respect to the sun that are characteristic of objects moving in hyperbolic orbits.*

E. Strömgren, the Danish astronomer, and the father of B. Strömgren, emphasized in 1914 that there were no records of comets whose orbits definitely were hyperbolic in character before they came into the region of the planets. It is true that some observations have given values of eccentricity greater than 1. According to the concepts of celestial mechanics, this means that they were moving in hyperbolic orbits while the observations were being made. However, Strömgren's computations give convincing evidence that long before the comets approached the sun their orbits had eccentricities smaller than 1. Only because of perturbations by the major planets did the orbits become hyperbolic. They often remained so after they had left the solar neighborhood; such a comet would be lost

---

* Hyperbola is one possible path of an object traveling under the gravitational influence of the sun. It is an open curve; the object approaches the sun from infinity and recedes to infinity. In a circular or elliptical orbit, the path is closed and the object traverses it periodically. These curves are usually described in terms of a quantity called *eccentricity*, which is greater than 1 for a hyperbola and less than 1 for an ellipse. The same definitions apply to orbits of binary stars, to stellar orbits due to rotation around the galactic nucleus, and other orbits.

permanently and would become a true interstellar object, whose probability of returning to our vicinity is excessively small. Strömgren's work has been extended by several investigators who have reached the same conclusion: Those comets that appear to move with hyperbolic velocities when they are close enough to be observed originally had greatly elongated, elliptical orbits.

Because of the weakness of Laplace's model, there was a revival some years ago of another hypothesis originally proposed by the French mathematician J. L. Lagrange in the 18th century. This theory attributes the origin of comets to violent explosions on the larger planets, a process believed to be going on even at the present time. It has been revived principally by S. K. Vsekhsviatsky and several other Russian astronomers, who argue that some of the comets have orbits approaching Jupiter to such an extent that it is possible they once occupied the same point of space. For example, according to A. D. Dubiago and M. Kamiensky, the orbit of comet Brooks II in 1886 approached the orbit of Jupiter to about 0.01 a.u., or less than 1 million miles. Vsekhsviatsky thinks that small changes could have resulted in the actual crossing of the orbits at an earlier approach. There is, however, one great difficulty in connection with this theory: The short-period comets that can be explained readily in this manner are only a small fraction of the thousand or more recorded.

There are approximately 42 comets in Jupiter's "family" that would be explainable by this theory. Their motions are usually in the same direction, as are the motions of the planets. The planes of their orbits do not differ greatly from the plane of the ecliptic. Their aphelia, or greatest distances from the sun, approach quite closely to Jupiter's orbit. There can be no doubt that these comets are related to Jupiter in some way. If they did result from an explosion on the surface of the planet, it would be difficult to explain why the rest of the comets show no preference for the plane of the ecliptic, being distributed more or less at random in inclination and in perihelion distance.

Oort's Theory

In order to explain the striking difference between the long- and short-period comets, J. H. Oort in 1950 made use of Strömgren's work and that of other investigators, notably G. Van Biesbroeck who in 1927 computed the definitive orbit of Comet Delavan. Van Biesbroeck found a hyperbolic orbit when the object was near the sun. By computing backward and allowing for planetary perturbations, he found that Comet Delavan originally moved in an ellipse with a semimajor axis of 170,000 a.u. and a period of 24 million years. For Comet Morehouse (1908 c), Van Biesbroeck found that the original orbit was a greatly elongated ellipse with a period of about 500,000 years.

Collecting all available information, Oort found that there is a decided maximum of frequency among cometary orbits having major axes of about 150,000 a.u., which is not very different from the distance to the nearest star. This does not mean that these comets are interstellar. On the contrary, Oort believes that they must be members of the solar system, because they share the motion of the sun through interstellar space. Oort next attempted to explain the remarkable tendency of the comets to move in orbits that reach out beyond the confines of the domain of the planets to distances that are truly interstellar.

A few years earlier, one of Oort's associates at the Leiden Observatory, A. van Wörkom, investigated in detail the effect of planetary perturbations upon the different types of cometary orbits. His conclusions are highly technical in nature, but he established that, on the average, a long-period comet like Delavan's, once it had reached the relatively small volume of space in which the planets revolve around the sun, will be thrown out of its original elliptical path and will be found to pursue a new orbit, which may be one of short period (in which case the comet may become temporarily a member of Jupiter's family of comets), or it may become hyperbolic (in which case the comet is ejected from the solar system for all time).

Suppose, then, that a cloud of comets is revolving in different kinds of orbits, with aphelia of about 150,000 a.u. What are the conditions under which some of them may have perihelion distances of about 1 or 2 a.u.; that is, come close enough to be detectable? If it is assumed first that the cloud of distant comets has a random distribution of directions with respect to the sun, then the overwhelming majority never will cross the small sphere (with the sun at its center) whose radius is 2 a.u. and never will be bright enough to be seen from the earth. But a small number of comets similar to Delevan's and Morehouse's will have velocities so directed that they cross this sphere. However, by applying van Wörkom's computations, it appears that planetary perturbations are so large that nearly every comet that comes within 2 a.u. is "diffused" out of its original orbit, and either is converted into a short-period comet or is removed altogether from the solar system. How then is it possible that there are any comets within the outer cloud having the required velocities and directions to bring them into the observable region? Since the distant comets have orbital periods of a few million years, it is certain that all those that could have come to within 2 a.u. must have done so long before the present era.

One might ask whether the supply is replenished constantly by comets whose original distances were greater than 150,000 a.u. It is at this point that Oort made one of his intuitive deductions: The cloud cannot extend greatly beyond 150,000 a.u., because at very great distances the perturbations produced by the stars are large enough to disturb their orbits and remove them permanently from the solar system. It is this idea—the effect upon comets of perturbations produced by the stars—that is essentially new in Oort's hypothesis. Not only do these perturbations set an upper limit to the size of the comet cloud, but they also produce appreciable changes in the motions, even within the cloud itself. At the critical distance of 150,000 a.u., where a comet spends most of its multimillion-year period, the stellar perturbations, though not sufficient on the average to remove the comets from the solar system, are strong enough, nevertheless, to alter their velocities gradually. This immediately provides an explanation for the continuous supply of comets that can reach the critical sphere of 2 a.u. It is only necessary to suppose that within the outer cloud the number of comets is very great, perhaps 100 billion. In that case, there always will be new comets perturbed by stellar attractions in such a way that they may reach the small inner sphere and become visible from the earth. This process will stop only after a considerable fraction of the 10^{11} comets have been thrown into the domain of the planets and perturbed by them in such a way that they leave the solar system in hyperbolic orbits. It can be shown that during the solar system's lifetime no great progress has occurred in this slow diffusion of comets from the outer cloud. Oort's theory also shows why the inclinations of the orbits of the long-period comets have no relation to the plane of the ecliptic. On the other hand, he was able to show that comets captured by Jupiter, either through a single, large perturbation or through the cumulative action of many small perturbations, will have substantially the observed distribution of major axes and will favor direct rather than retrograde motion.

Probably the greatest significance of Oort's distant comet cloud is that it drastically altered our estimates of the size of the solar system. At the beginning of this century, the distance of Neptune, 30 a.u., was believed to be the extent of the solar system. The discovery of Pluto increased the radius to 40 a.u. (and conceivably there could be even more distant planets yet to be discovered at distances of tens, and possibly hundreds, of a.u.). Now it must be concluded that the solar system extends to at least 150,000 a.u. or somewhat farther—that is, to about one-third the distance to our nearest stellar neighbor, α Centauri—and the volume assigned to the sun touches the volume assigned to its neighboring stars. Thus Oort's conclusions have led to the concept of the Milky Way divided into adjoining cells of dominance whose radii are roughly equal to one-half the average distance between neighboring stars.

Although Oort was not concerned primarily with the origin of comets, in his discussion he suggested that the comets may have originated, together with the minor planets and the meteors, from the explosion of a planetlike body between the orbits of Mars and Jupiter. Those fragments that from the beginning had approximately circular orbits and those that were rapidly thrown into circular orbits remained stable members of the solar system's interior group. Being constantly exposed to radiation from the sun, these objects lost their gaseous constituents and became minor planets and ordinary meteors. But some fragments had elliptical orbits and, therefore, were subjected immediately to large perturbations by Jupiter and other planets. Van Wörkom's theory suggests that the perturbations, in general, increased the major axes of the orbits of these fragments, but the exact amount and the direction of the perturbing forces depended upon the circumstances of each approach. It can be shown that the diffusing action of the planets is such that all but about $\frac{1}{30}$ of the orbits were converted into hyperbolas, and consequently 97 per cent of the exploded material was lost quickly to interstellar space. But since the perturbations cover a continuous range of values, an appreciable fraction, about 3 per cent of the total, was thrown into orbits with major axes between 25,000 and 200,000 a.u. These fragments formed the outer cloud of comets. Many of them would have been thrown into the cloud within a few years after the explosion. Hence these fragments may have retained many of their icy constituents, and it is possible that the solid stones or pieces of iron were embedded in a solid magma of ice, ammonia, methane, and the like, in the manner suggested by Whipple. At a distance of 100,000 a.u., the brightness of the sun would be 10 billion times less than that observed from the earth, and throughout almost the entire lifetime of such a distant comet, the sun never would appear brighter to it than Arcturus. It is not surprising, therefore, that within the cloud the original constitution of the exploded planet may have been preserved over several billion years. Once the comet finds itself in the outer regions, it does not return to the point in space where the explosion took place—perturbations by the stars will see to that.

It is probable that at the present time the number of minor planets and of other small fragments being thrown into long-period cometary orbits is very small. It is impossible to estimate the length of time required to sift out the three groups of fragments effectively: the 97 per cent of the material that was quickly eliminated from the solar system; 10 billion comets thrown into the outer comet cloud; and the small remaining masses that, in the form of minor planets and meteors, revolve around the sun in stable orbits.

Kuiper's Theory

An alternative theory of cometary origin was presented in 1951 by Kuiper. He observed that, if comets have the same composition as asteroids, it is difficult to explain the great intensity of cometary emissions, as well as the occasional disintegration of comets. Recent evidence suggesting that meteors originate solely from disruption of comets and that the crystal structure of the less frequent large meteorites is similar to the probable structure of asteroids, combined with the knowledge that the rate of meteorite fall is not increased during meteor showers, led Kuiper to conclude that

> . . . it is probable that the two phenomena are not connected. The very finely divided disintegration products of comets (probably including the dust that gives rise to the zodiacal light) point to a structure very different from meteorites or asteroids and are consistent with such a composition as would follow from condensation outside the orbit of Neptune and subsequent evaporation of 99 per cent of the material.[9]

Kuiper also noted:

> In summary, it is assumed that the comets are the condensation products of the outer parts of the solar nebula which formed the planets. Planetary perturbations lifted many of them to great distances from the sun, where stellar perturbations altered their orbits once more, making them rounder and of random inclination. This will preserve the comets for 10^{10} years, on the average. But stellar perturbations occasionally send comets back to the planetary system; some of them are captured by Jupiter and become periodic comets. Periodic comets will either slowly evaporate or break up by tidal action, or both, and the fragments will form shower meteors, and the zodiacal light; a few comets will sustain such perturbations (mostly by Jupiter) as to be thrown out of the solar system in hyperbolic orbits.[10]

Thus it appears that a large number of comets have escaped from the solar system and become interstellar objects. The question arises whether other stars also may not have many freely moving comets that, from time to time, may enter the inner regions of our planetary system and then give rise to a truly hyperbolic comet. The fact that we have not observed such phenomena does not mean that they do not exist. The number of comets for which computations in the manner of E. Strömgren have been made is quite small. Most other comets have been observed insufficiently to permit the computers to determine the form of their orbits before they came into the domain of the planets.

If it is assumed that all stars produce interstellar comets at the same rate as the sun, then it can be estimated that there are about 10^{12} interstellar comets per cubic parsec of space. Each comet will be perturbed in its motion by the neighboring stars, but from the time of its birth it will carry with it the velocity of its star of origin. Unless the cometary velocities are redistributed very greatly during the age of the galaxy, they will retain, on the average, a distribution of motions similar to that of the stars. By using a formula derived by Jeans, one can compute the interval of time between two successive "encounters" of the planetary domain of the solar system and an interstellar comet on the above assumptions. The result is about 100 years; thus an interstellar comet is by no means impossible. F. L. Whipple has pointed out that some of the ideas discussed in this chapter were first advanced by E. Öpik, then of Tartu Observatory, Estonia. Whipple's own work at the Smithsonian Astrophysical Observatory is providing new and exciting results on meteors and meteoric particles of cometary nuclei.

X

SPECTRAL
CLASSIFICATION

IN PASSING on to the study of the stars and their evolution,
it is well to realize that, as pointed out by A. Wolf, one-time
professor of logic and scientific method at the University of London:

Classification is one method, probably the simplest method, òf discovering order in the world. By noting similarities between numerous distinct individuals as forming one class or kind, the many are in a sense
reduced to one, and to that extent simplicity and order are introduced
into the bewildering multiplicity of nature.[1]

In astronomy the method of classification finds many uses, but ordinarily it is thought of as referring to the study of stellar spectra.

BEGINNINGS OF SPECTRAL CLASSIFICATION

Pioneers in Classification

At the beginning of the 19th century, the German Joseph von
Fraunhofer compared the spectra of the sun and the stars, but the first
fairly comprehensive attempt at classification was undertaken by the
Italian astronomer Father A. Secchi in the 1860's "to see if the composition
of the stars is as varied as the stars are innumerable."[2] He noticed that
while the stars are exceedingly numerous, their spectra can be grouped in
certain distinct types. Secchi classified about 4,000 stars into four main
types. In 1902, Miss A. Clerke noted in *Problems in Astrophysics* that,

... Father Secchi's four "types" continue fundamental. It is well, then, to keep their characteristics steadily in mind. The first is marked by strong hydrogen absorption. It consists of radiantly white stars. The second by innumerable fine metallic rulings; the sun is an example. The third type includes red stars with banded spectra like Antares, the bands being sharply terminated towards the violet, diffuse towards the red. The fourth is composed of deeply tinted, mostly faint objects, showing wide bands facing redward, due to carbon absorption. These four groups form irremovable landmarks; but beside and between them many subordinate divisions have been set up.[3]

A similar scheme had been arrived at by H. C. Vogel while he was developing a classification representing what he believed to be successive stages in stellar evolution—from the young white stars to the old red ones.

First Attempts to Interpret the Spectral Sequence

Although some turn-of-the-century astronomers still argued, as the English astronomer E. W. Maunder did, that ".... spectrum type does not primarily or usually denote epoch of stellar life, but rather a fundamental difference of chemical constitution,"[4] Miss Clerke concluded that: "Modes of classifying the stars have come to be equivalent to theories of their evolution."[5]

Two questions were involved in the attempts to connect spectral classifications and stellar evolution:

1. What are the factors causing the observed differences in stellar spectra?

2. Does every star, at different stages in its development, pass through all the types of the spectral sequence?

Before the atomic theory and the theory of radiation had been developed, astronomers were able to suggest a number of possible causes of spectral differences, but could offer no conclusive proof of the merits of their theories. As W. S. Adams aptly commented: "We could hardly hope to understand the behavior of matter in the distant stars when the mechanism of the light given out by a candle flame was still quite unknown to us."[6] Thus differences in spectra conceivably could be produced either by real differences in the chemical composition of stellar atmospheres, or by varying atmospheric conditions.

According to the theories developed mainly by Helmholtz and Lord Kelvin in the second half of the 19th century, a star derived its energy of radiation from the gravitational energy of contraction. As long as the star remained gaseous, the temperature of the inner layers increased, but once it reached a liquid state (because of compression) it no longer was compressible; nor would it generate energy. Hence the star would cool quickly.

Both of the best-known theories at the turn of the century were based on the Helmholtz-Kelvin assumptions, according to which a star would exhibit successive spectral types in the process of its development.

The theories of Schuster and Huggins about how real differences in the composition of the atmosphere are produced were described by G. E. Hale:

In describing the process of condensation, Schuster points out that the expansion caused by the rising temperature of the gaseous bodies must at first result in the rejection of helium, hydrogen, and other light gases, on the supposition that the gravitation is not sufficient to retain them. These light gases will thus be left to constitute diffuse nebulous masses. . . . In the process of time, however, the star will have condensed sufficiently to retain hydrogen and helium, and these gases will then begin to diffuse into the interior, where they will be absorbed at a rate which depends upon the star's mass. Helium, which is denser than hydrogen, will be retained first, thus giving rise to the helium, or Orion, stars. As this gas diffuses inward, its place will be taken by hydrogen, which will thus become predominant in the spectrum. In its turn, the hydrogen will diffuse into the star, and the increasing convection currents will cause a more and more complete stirring-up of the low-lying metallic vapors, which will therefore play an increasingly prominent part in the spectrum. Thus the solar stage will ultimately be reached.[7]

Sir Norman Lockyer, on the other hand, stressed the importance of the effect of atmospheric temperature on the appearance of the spectrum. His conclusions were based in part on laboratory experiments, during which he had observed differences between arc and spark spectra of the same element (higher temperature is associated with the latter). Lockyer visualized the transition from spark to arc spectrum as a dissociation of the known elements into protoelements. Thus, while the arc spectrum of iron is produced by ordinary metallic iron vapors, in the spark the particles are split up into more elementary building blocks. This, in a way, hints at the ionization theory developed about 30 years later, but too little was known of atomic structure for him to develop any solid theoretical basis for these ideas. At the same time Lockyer formulated his *meteoritic hypothesis*. The matter from which stars are formed is provided by swarms of meteors, with random motions analogous to wandering molecules, rather than matter in the gaseous state. Even though the meteoritic hypothesis has been discredited, Lockyer's ideas of stellar evolution and his

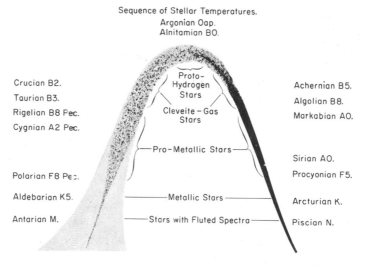

Sequence of Stellar Temperatures.
Argonian Oap.
Alnitamian BO.

Crucian B2.
Taurian B3.
Rigelian B8 Pec.
Cygnian A2 Pec.

Proto-Hydrogen Stars
Cleveite – Gas Stars
Pro–Metallic Stars

Achernian B5.
Algolian B8.
Markabian AO.

Polarian F8 Pec.
Aldebarian K5.
Antarian M.

Metallic Stars
Stars with Fluted Spectra

Sirian AO.
Procyonian F5.
Arcturian K.
Piscian N.

Fig. 92. Lockyer's temperature-condensation curve. (*From* Hill Observatory Bulletin, *II, 1915, P. 1*)

system of classification stressing the influence of temperature deserve consideration. Again, Hale provides a good description:

Starting from the meteoritic hypothesis, and assuming that the chemical elements, at the temperature of the hottest stars, are dissociated into simpler substances, Lockyer has developed a plan of stellar evolution which comprises a classification of stellar spectra on a temperature basis. He supposes that the meteoritic swarms represented by the nebulae gradually condense into stars, by processes whose details are still uncertain. According to his classification, the gaseous and bright-line stars, in which the temperature is supposed to be higher than that of the less condensed nebulae, lie just above the latter in point of development. Then come the red stars of Secchi's third type: .... Further condensation, still involving a rise of temperature, would produce stars analogous to the Sun, but differing in the important particular that, while their temperature is increasing, that of the Sun is supposed to be decreasing. Finally, at the point of maximum temperature, Lockyer places stars of Secchi's first type. Here the meteorites, long since completely transformed into the gaseous state, have reached the condition ... at which the rise in superficial temperature, due to continued condensation, is just balanced by the loss resulting from radiation. The declining period, then setting in, results in the development of stars like the Sun, which can be only arbitrarily distinguished from stars of equal, but rising, temperature, lying on the opposite branch of the temperature curve. After the solar stars come the red stars of Secchi's fourth type, and after these, final extinction of light.

This system of classification, considered apart from the hypotheses with which it is connected, has the advantage of providing for both the ascending and descending branches of the temperature curve. Unfortunately, we are perhaps not yet in a position to distinguish clearly between stars of the same surface temperature, in one of which the gain of heat is more rapid than the loss, while in the other the reverse is true.[8]

Although progress in the interpretation of spectral differences was not possible without new developments in atomic theory, extensive spectral classifications were undertaken, particularly at the Harvard Observatory.

THE HENRY DRAPER CATALOGUE AND
THE HARVARD SYSTEM

As a memorial to Henry Draper, a survey of the spectra of bright northern stars was started in 1886 at Harvard under E. C. Pickering's direction. Draper was one of the outstanding pioneer American spectroscopists of the 19th century. Objective prisms, rather than slit spectrographs, were used at Harvard in order to photograph spectra of all the brighter stars in the field of the telescope. In his *One Hundred Years of Astronomy,* the English astronomer R. L. Waterfield commented upon the introduction of this method: "It was at this juncture that America, always appreciative of mass-production, stepped in with a method for photographing stellar spectra wholesale."[9]

The Draper Catalogue of Stellar Spectra,[10] containing 10,351 stars north of −25° declination and down to about 8 mag, was published in 1890; an additional volume published in 1897 included southern stars. The classification in the original volume generally followed Secchi's, but his types were subdivided into 16 classes denoted by the letters A through Q (except J). The notation was changed in Part I of the next volume; but at the beginning of this century, when a repetition and extension of the catalogue was undertaken, the original system was retained in a somewhat modified form. Some groups were omitted or combined, and the order of several classes was changed so that a smoothly changing sequence would be achieved. Thus the well-known spectral sequence of O, B, A, F, G, K, and M types (with the relatively rare types N, S, R as a branch at the red end) was established. *The Henry Draper Catalogue,*[11] published between 1918 and 1924 (with two extensions up to 1949), contains 359,082 stars. Subdivisions now are indicated by a number after the letter, from 0 to 9. The sun, for example, is classified as G2. The spectral types at the beginning of the sequence (O,B) are sometimes referred to as "early," those at the end as "late" spectral types. In Fig. 94 of some representative stellar spectra, (a) is λ Cephei, spectral type O6; (b) γ Scorpii, BO; (c) α Coronae Borealis, AO; (d) δ Aquilae, FO; (e) Sun, G 2; (f) ε Cygni, KO; (g) α Herculis A, M5.) The sharp absorption line of ionized calcium (CaII) in λ Cephi is of interstellar origin.

The Harvard classification is the greatest single work in the field of

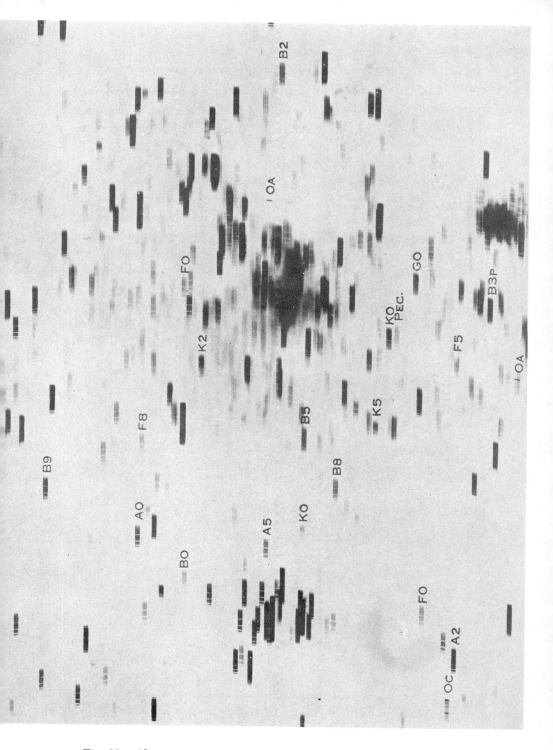

Fig. 93. Objective-prism spectogram of the region around η Carinae, taken about 1900 at Arequipa, Peru, with an 8-in. telescope. (*Harvard Observatory; courtesy* Sky and Telescope)

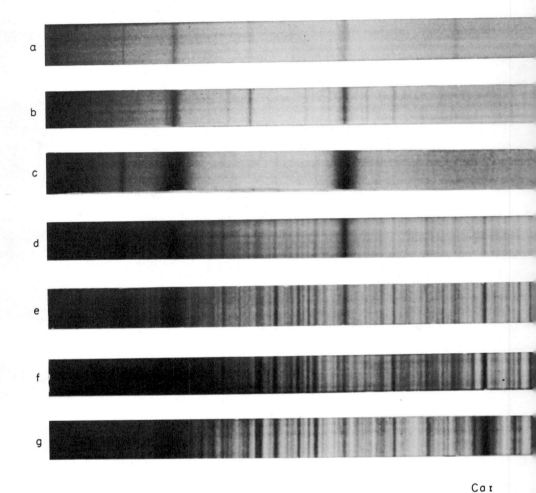

Ca II   H + Ca II   H$_\delta$

a

b

c

d

e

f

g

Ca I

Fig. 94.   Representative stellar spectra. (*Lick Observatory*)

stellar spectroscopy. With single-minded purpose, Miss A. J. Cannon, an associate of Pickering, classified the spectra of almost 400,000 stars photographed with instruments that were modest in size and optical performance even at the time she began her work. This classification was evaluated in 1935 by three of the leading astrophysicists of our time: H. N. Russell of Princeton and C. Payne-Gaposchkin and D. H. Menzel of Harvard Observatory:

Hγ

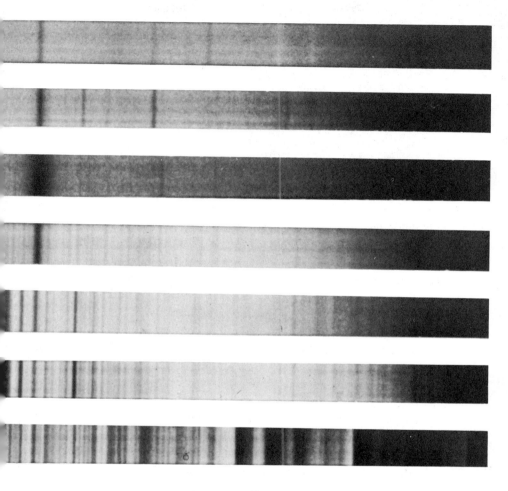

Ti O

The Harvard system is the product of the experience of a group, headed by Pickering and Miss Cannon, who have looked at a greater number of different stellar spectra than any other group; from this standpoint alone it must be recognized as having a maximum representativeness. . . . Multifarious as these criteria [of placing the spectra in convenient pigeonholes] are, they express the most conspicuous features from type to type. It is doubtful whether more outstanding bases for classification could be selected.[1][2]

After nearly 50 years, every astrophysicist still relies heavily upon *The*

Fig. 95. Miss A. J. Cannon (right) and Mrs. C. Payne–Gaposchkin. (*Courtesy* Sky and Telescope)

Henry Draper Catalogue, its more recent Harvard extensions, and several other catalogues built on the Harvard system of classification—such as the Bergedorf and Potsdam volumes, or the lists of stellar spectra from Upsala, Sweden, and other observatories. In the light of the success the Harvard classification still enjoys today, we must recognize the wisdom of the two observatory directors, E. C. Pickering and H. Shapley, who withstood the temptation to embark upon new, and in some respects more exciting, astronomical ventures and did not lose sight of their goal: providing as complete a history of the sky as possible. No other institution was prepared to carry out this vast program of routine classification—a project whose character, typical of astronomy, is unknown in the other physical sciences.

It was recognized early in the Harvard work that spectral classes O, B, A, F, G, K, M, R, N, and S represent a temperature classification, although the criteria were developed without any preconceived physical ideas. A theoretical explanation was not provided until the work of M. N. Saha in 1920 (discussed in the next chapter, together with a more detailed description of the Harvard sequence, the temperature estimates and identification of the principal spectral lines). Discussing spectral classification, the American astronomer R. H. Curtiss noted:

... Lockyer's genera are in vertical sequence with the Harvard classes as rearranged by Miss Cannon. Lockyer reached that order through his search for a temperature sequence based on studies of laboratory and solar atmospheric spectra. Harvard observers came to it as a result of an attempt to classify spectra, as Secchi has done, according to colors and distinctive characteristics, beginning with the simpler spectra. It may, therefore, be considered accidental that the Harvard order proved to be a temperature sequence of valuable physical significance. If it had not, some modification of Lockyer's classification would probably have been in use today.[13]

TWO-DIMENSIONAL CLASSIFICATION

Recognition of Luminosity Differences

When the *Draper Catalogue* was being created, astronomers were not yet aware of the tremendous differences in the luminosities of stars that have the same Draper classes.

Although Lockyer had introduced a second dimension to his classification, his criteria did not prove to be correlated directly with any physical condition. Miss A. C. Maury of Harvard, while preparing part of the *Draper Catalogue,* had noticed conspicuous differences in the widths of the spectral lines and denoted them by the letters *a, b,* and *c,* referring to broad, intermediate, and narrow lines, respectively. Miss Maury also noted that:

Certain stars, such as alpha Cygni and delta C[anis] Ma[joris] have spectra in which the majority of the lines though probably identical in position with lines belonging to the solar spectrum, differ greatly in intensity, while others apparently are not represented in the solar spectrum. . . .[14]

She indicated that there appear to be no differences in relative intensities of lines in the *a* and *b* divisions, while

. . . division *c* is distinguished by the strongly defined character of its lines and it seems that stars of this division must differ more decidedly in constitution from those of division *a* than is the case with those in division *b.*[15]

Although Miss Cannon classified a much larger number of stars, Miss Maury's classification in some respects is superior because, by recognizing the *c*-characteristic, she added a second parameter to the existing system of classification. This practice, however, was not continued in *The Henry Draper Catalogue.*

The importance of the differences noticed by Miss Maury was recognized clearly by E. Hertzsprung in 1905. Since the distances of only a few stars in Miss Maury's list were known, Hertzsprung used a statistical

Fig. 96.   Miss A. C. Maury. (*Courtesy Mrs. C. Payne–Gaposchkin*)

The H lines are very much weaker in the spectrum of the supergiant β Ori than in that of the main sequence star β Per. The absolute magnitude effect for the ratio He I 4471: Mg II 4481 (at B3–B5) is now no longer marked.

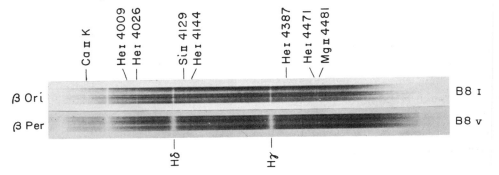

At class B8 the He I series λλ 4387, 4144, 4009 has become much fainter than at B5. The Si II blend at λ 4129 is stronger relative to He I 4144 than in the same luminosity class at B5. In β Per the K line is approximately equal in intensity to λ 4026

Eastman Process

Fig. 97. Differences in the spectra of a "*c*-star" and an "*a*-star," referred to as supergiant and dwarf. (*From W. W. Morgan, P. C. Keenan, and E. Kellman.* An Atlas of Spectral Classification, *Chicago, University of Chicago Press, 1943, Plate 17*)

method employing proper motions to allow for differences in brightness, and adjusting them to represent the star's apparent proper motion (reduced proper motion) at a distance at which it would appear of zero magnitude. Hertzsprung found that *c*-characteristic stars have extremely small reduced proper motions, implying great distance and hence great absolute luminosity. He estimated that the *c*-characteristic stars are at least as bright as the Orion stars, which are very luminous bodies now classified O, and resembling those in the Trapezium of Orion. The two groups could not be distinguished among the stars of spectral type A, or earlier, but the differences increased toward the later spectral types.

Hertzsprung next tried to account for the fact that two stars of apparently similar spectral class and mass, such as γ Leonis and 70 Ophiuchi, differ by at least 5.75 mag in absolute brightness. He observed that if surface brightnesses of the two stars were the same, as would be inferred from

Fig. 98. E. Hertzsprung (left) at the Moscow meeting of the International Astronomical Union in 1958. (*Photograph by B. J. Bok; courtesy* Sky and Telescope)

the fact that their colors were similar, γ Leonis should have a density 3,000 times smaller than 70 Ophiuchi and either must be at an earlier stage of development or represent a parallel series. Hertzsprung believed the latter to be the case. He also concluded that the absolute brightness of most stars decreases with redness, and that the bright c stars are relatively rare per volume of space.

At about the same time, H. N. Russell was engaged in the photographic determination of stellar parallaxes and, hence, of absolute stellar brightnesses. Russell concluded in 1910 that progressive differences in absolute brightness and proper motion are correlated with spectral type. He discussed the bearing of his results on stellar evolution as follows:

It is well known that a contracting gaseous mass must rise in temperature until it becomes so dense that the gas laws no longer hold approximately for its central portions. After this the dense nucleus offers an increasing resistance to further compression, the loss of heat by radiation increases relative to the gain by shrinkage, the temperature reaches a maximum and then falls.

Before the maximum temperature is reached, the surface-brightness increases as the diameter diminishes, and it is not obvious whether the total light-emission rises or falls; but after the star begins to cool, diameter and temperature diminish together, and the decrease in luminosity must be rapid.

There can be little doubt that the faint stars of large proper motion . . . are in the latter condition. The very rapid decrease of light with increasing redness, and the extremely small luminosity of the reddest stars, in spite of the fairly considerable masses of those which can be investigated, are distinctive marks of stars in the late stage of evolution, past their prime, and in some cases verging toward extinction.

If it is assumed that most of the stars which do not surpass the Sun in luminosity . . . are in these later stages of evolution, the peculiarities of their distribution with respect to spectral type are immediately explained.

It should be especially noticed that, on the above hypothesis, there ought to be two kinds of red stars (i.e. of stars of low surface temperature) one in an early stage of evolution, of increasing temperature, small density, large diameter, and considerable total luminosity, and the other of decreasing temperature, great density, and very small luminosity. The reddest stars among the first class would be in the earliest stages of evolution; in the second class, in the latest. Practically all the red stars visible to the naked eye must belong to the first class—as is shown by their small proper-motions, and in some cases by direct measurements of parallax (as for Aldebaran and Antares) which prove that their actual luminosity is much greater than the Sun's. [16]

While Russell in his first paper seems to have been unaware of Hertzsprung's work, in his second discussion, also published in 1910, he refers

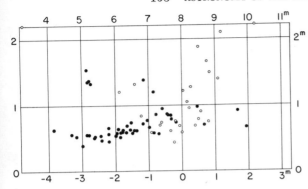

Fig. 99.   Magnitude-color index diagram for stars in the Hyades cluster, by E. Hertzsprung. (*From* Potsdam Astrophysical Observatory Publications, *XXII, 1911, P. 29*)

to Hertzsprung's results as providing additional evidence for his theory. His interpretation of similar material, however, differed from Hertzsprung's, since Russell thought in terms of one continuous series of development, while Hertzsprung suggested two collateral series. According to Russell the

... fundamental concept [of his own theory] is similar to that underlying Lockyer's classification—from which, however, it differs radically as regards the criteria for distinguishing rising and falling temperatures.[17]

Hertzsprung-Russell Diagram

In 1911 Hertzsprung plotted a diagram of apparent magnitudes against color indexes for the stars in the Pleiades and Hyades clusters. He concluded that all stars in the Pleiades and almost all in the Hyades belong to the so-called main sequence, in which stars become redder with decreasing brightness. In addition, he found a few very bright, yellow stars in the Hyades. In the diagram, the abscissae are the apparent magnitude (top) or the absolute photographic magnitude (bottom), the latter corresponding to a parallax of 1″, that is, a distance 10 times smaller than in the customary definition of absolute magnitude. The ordinate is the color index. Dots denote physical members of the Hyades, open circles other stars in the same region of the sky. Note that this diagram should be turned through 90° to correspond to that of Russell in Fig. 100. In 1913, Russell plotted the absolute magnitudes against spectral types of all stars of known parallax. This type of diagram is now known as the Hertzsprung-Russell, or H-R diagram.

Russell first discussed his plot and its significance at the meeting of the Royal Astronomical Society on June 13, 1913. With slight changes, he spoke on the same subject at the meeting of American Astronomical Society in Atlanta, Georgia, on December 30, 1913. The diagram distinctly shows the clustering of representative points along the diagonal line (the

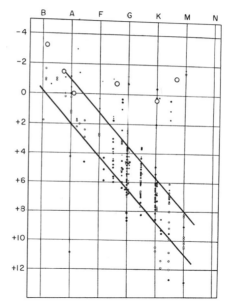

Fig. 100. Absolute magnitude-spectral type diagram by H. N. Russell. (*From* Popular Astronomy, *XXII, 1914, P. 285*)

main sequence) and the horizontal line (the giant sequence), with less numerous, extremely bright supergiants (Hertzsprung's c stars) above the giant sequence. The single point in the lower left-hand corner, the faint companion of the double star 40 Eridani, though it later proved to be very significant, was disregarded because its "... spectrum is very doubtful."[18]

While most astronomers agreed at this time that the spectral sequence was determined by changes in the surface temperatures of stars, there was no general agreement on the causes of luminosity differences. Russell showed that they must result from variance in density (and hence, in surface area) rather than from differences in mass or surface brightness (as already suggested in Hertzsprung's paper in 1905). He formulated his ideas on stellar evolution as follows:

Of all the propositions, more or less debatable, which may be made

Fig. 101. H. N. Russell (left) and H. K. Sen. (*R. E. Cox; courtesy* Sky and Telescope)

regarding stellar evolution, there is probably none that would command more general acceptance than this:—that as a star grows older, it contracts. Indeed, since contraction converts potential energy of gravitation into heat, which is transferred by radiation to cooler bodies it appears from thermodynamic principles that the general trend of change must in the long run be in this direction. It is conceivable that at some particular epoch in a star's history there might be so rapid an evolution of energy, for example—of a radio-active nature—that it temporarily surpassed the loss by radiation, and led to an expansion against gravity; but this would be at most a passing stage in its career and it would still be true in the long run that the order of increasing density is the order of advancing evolution.

If now we arrange the stars which we have been studying in such an order, we must begin with the giant stars of Class M, follow the series of giant stars, in the reverse order from that in which the spectra are usually placed, up to A and B, and then, with density still increasing, though at a slower rate, proceed down the series of dwarf stars in the usual order of the spectral classes, past the Sun, to those red stars (again of Class M), which are the faintest at present known. There can be no doubt at all that this is the order of increasing density; if it is also the order of advancing age, we are led at once back to Lockyer's hypothesis that a star is hottest near the middle of its history and that the redder stars fall into two groups, one of rising and the other of falling temperature. The giant stars then represent successive stages in the heating up of a body, and must be more primitive the redder they are; the dwarf stars represent successive stages in its later cooling, and the reddest of these are the farthest advanced. We have no longer two separate series to deal with, but, a single one, beginning and ending with Class M, and with Class B in the middle —all the intervening classes being represented, in inverse order, in each half of the sequence.[19]

Russell's evolutionary scheme thus presented the available evidence in an extremely simple and straightforward manner. While his deductions regarding the density and temperature factors in stellar spectra were later confirmed, his interpretation of the H-R diagram and his theory of stellar evolution had to be drastically revised. The problems involved are so complex that, before proceeding with these topics, a more thorough discussion of the theories of stellar atmospheres, the interpretation of stellar spectra, and stellar structure is required; these subjects will be taken up in the next three chapters. In the meantime, however, the technical aspects of other refinements in spectral classification will be discussed.

Spectroscopic Parallaxes

With the large differences in luminosity established, it was natural to ask if these could be inferred in any way from an examination of stellar spectra. This possibility was expressed very strongly by Hertzsprung as early as 1911:

> If we could only determine the absolute luminosity of a star from its spectrum, we would be in a position to compute its parallax from the apparent magnitude of the star together with its spectrum. . . .
>
> Strictly speaking, every change of luminosity, whatever its cause may be, should be recognizable in some manner in the spectrum.
>
> The finding of such spectral equivalents of luminosity (distinguishing absolutely bright stars from the normal ones) will therefore be a particularly rewarding task.[20]

Hertzsprung, however, did not pursue the investigation; the task was accomplished instead by W. S. Adams and A. Kohlschütter of Mount Wilson Observatory, in 1914. They apparently were not aware of Hertzsprung's ideas:

> In the course of a study of the spectral classification of stars whose spectra have been photographed for radial velocity determination, some interesting peculiarities have been observed. The stars investigated are of two kinds: first, those of large proper motion with measured parallaxes; second, those of very small proper motion, and hence, in general, of great distance. The apparent magnitudes of the large proper motion, or nearer stars, are somewhat less on the average than those of the small proper motion stars, so that the difference in absolute magnitude must be very great between the two groups.[21]
>
> Certain lines are strong in the spectra of the small proper motion stars, and others in the spectra of large proper motion stars.[22]

The investigation dealt particularly with the phenomenon that "certain . . . spectrum lines are weak in the large proper motion stars, and strong in the small proper motion stars, and conversely."[23] Adams and Kohlschütter selected a number of spectral lines whose ratios differed in the small and large proper-motion stars and thus made possible an estimate of their absolute magnitudes. They found that "the use of the relative intensities of these lines gives results for absolute magnitudes in satisfactory agreement with those derived from parallaxes and proper motions."[24] These criteria were purely empirical; the theoretical explanation awaited the theories of astronomical spectroscopy developed in the 1920's.

This pioneering work was followed by a long list of "spectroscopic parallaxes" of several thousand stars, mostly with metallic lines. There were also a number of papers on the spectroscopic parallaxes of different types of stars, such as the Canadian astronomer A. V. Douglas' work on the A-type stars and reports by several observers of southern stars.

MK Classification System

In about 1930, W. W. Morgan at the Yerkes Observatory became interested in the spectra of A-type stars, and in the course of this work he grew concerned with the differences between absorption lines of stars belonging to the same spectral class in the Draper system. Thus he was led to invent a two-dimensional system of classification that, in a sense, represents an improvement over the method proposed by Miss Maury.

This classification, usually referred to as the "MK System," rests on an *Atlas of Stellar Spectra*[25] that consists of individual prints. It was distributed only to a few of the world's major observatories. However, Morgan and the American astronomers P. C. Keenan and E. Kellman compiled a monograph[26] that listed the names of the stars and the MK classification symbols so that astronomers are able to obtain their own standard spectra and use them to interpolate the spectral types of stars not observed at Yerkes. Those mainly responsible for the Yerkes system (in addition to Morgan, Keenan, and Kellman) are N. Roman and W. P. Bidelman; all have made major contributions to the problem of classification during the past 20 years.

The principal value of the Yerkes system is in its application to studies of galactic structure. Its usefulness was demonstrated dramatically at the Cleveland meeting of the American Astronomical Society in December, 1952, when Morgan announced the discovery of two and possibly three spiral arms of the Milky Way in the vicinity of the sun. The spiral arms detected by Morgan, however, are not entirely consistent with those detected by means of the 21-cm emission line of hydrogen (see P. 430).

Morgan's criteria are entirely empirical. But he began immediately to develop a two-dimensional classification. The stars thus were arranged, not in a linear sequence, but in a rectangular pattern of pigeonholes, like mailboxes at a post office. He used designations to represent the stars as dwarfs, giants, and so forth, on the second coordinate, as follows:

Ia   Most luminous supergiants
Ib   Less luminous supergiants
II   Bright giants
III   Normal giants
IV   Subgiants
V   Main sequence stars

An example of the Yerkes classification is shown in Fig. 97. The vast majority of stars fit into this two-dimensional scheme. The Yerkes classification has the following principal values:

1. It is general: that is, not limited to a few regions of the H-R diagram.

2. The classification represents a gradual process of refinement over many years and is based upon uniform material obtained with the same instrument and similar photographic emulsions.

3. Purely empirical in its criteria, the purpose yet was to locate, as precisely as possible, each star within the H-R diagram—from the absorption and emission features of its spectrum alone.

4. It has been applied to all the brighter stars (but not to nearly the extent of the Draper catalogues), and therefore gives us a statistically significant sample of the Milky Way.

5. Using spectra of small dispersion (125 A/mm at 4340 A), the Yerkes system avoided difficulties arising from the rotational and turbulence effects of line broadening.

6. It is limited in its essential features to stars of Population I,* and does not attempt to compromise the differences that are known to exist between the spectra of stars of *Populations I and II* (see Chap. XIII).

It must be emphasized again that the Yerkes system was developed to aid in probing the Milky Way by establishing reliable criteria of stellar spectroscopic distances. More or less as a by-product, this same method is the best for pursuing Secchi's original goal: "to see if the composition of the stars is as varied as the stars are innumerable."[27]

Astrophysicists with Secchi's interests have not produced a classification developed especially for their purposes, although there have been a few isolated efforts. For instance, in 1933, O. Struve tried to refine the astrophysical classification of the hottest stars. This effort proved its value in a recent study of pulsating stars, of which β Canis Majoris is a prototype, by D. H. McNamara of Brigham Young University. Keenan similarly has improved the classification of the carbon stars.

It has been stated by Russell, Mrs. Payne-Gaposchkin, and Menzel that "If ever we develop a theory sufficiently exact and elastic to account for all of the features of stellar spectra, classification will be either unnecessary or will evolve into a shorthand listing of the parameters necessary to define the exact solution of the problem."[28] This ultimate aim can be approached by astrophysicists only asymptotically—and classifications are intended as aids.

---

* Population I stars are essentially those represented in the original H-R diagram; they are young. A different type of H-R diagram was plotted by W. Baade from a study of stars in globular clusters and in the central regions of galaxies; these stars are usually referred to as Population II stars and are old (see P. 278 for a more complete discussion).

QUANTITATIVE METHODS OF
SPECTRAL CLASSIFICATION

Most recent investigations, especially those with small-dispersion instruments, depend upon the MK classification, but this system involves compromises between criteria that are slightly discordant. Hence two new systems of spectral classification have been invented, the one mainly by D. Chalonge at the Astrophysical Institute in Paris, the other by B. Strömgren, while he was at the Yerkes and McDonald Observatories. Both classification methods are continuous. They depend upon measurements of certain parameters, on photographs in Chalonge's system and by means of photoelectric photometers and narrow-band filters in Strömgren's system.

The approach of Chalonge and his collaborators depends upon photographic observations of the spectra of stars, principally in the ultraviolet region. They use a powerful quartz spectrograph in which the plateholder is driven by a motor around a pivot located along the axis of the spectrum, at a fixed distance from the shortwave end of the exposure. The purpose of this arrangement is to increase the effective exposure in the ultraviolet region, where the light of most stars is weak. The spectra appear wedge-

Fig. 102.   Parameters of spectral classification used by Chalonge. (*Charles Fehrenbach, in* Encyclopedia of Physics, *ed. S. Flügge, Berlin, Springer Verlag, 1958, 50*)

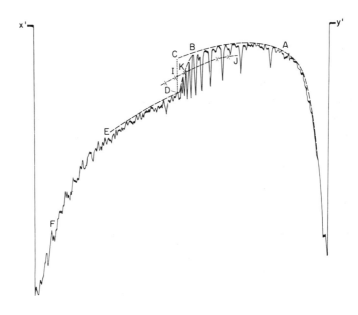

shaped, the band of continuous light being narrower in the ultraviolet than in the blue region.

The Paris spectra record approximately uniform intensities along the entire wavelength range to which the plate is sensitive. Three fundamental quantities are measured in each spectrum. Two of these are illustrated in Fig. 102, which shows a microphotometer tracing of a stellar spectrum; that is, a record of the intensity distribution in the spectrum obtained by scanning it with a photoelectric cell. The dashed line drawn across the tops of the "wiggles" indicates the intensity of the continuous spectrum and the wedge-shaped wiggles are the absorption lines. The amount of the *Balmer jump** is marked by the line CD; this is the first quantity. The second is the wavelength, λ_1, of the point K, which is located halfway between D, where the continuous Balmer absorption is complete, and the point B, where it has not yet started.

The third quantity is the usual spectrophotometric gradient, ϕ, which in effect measures the slope of the energy curve of the star on the red side of the point B. The quantity ϕ therefore, is closely related to the color index and to the spectrophotometric temperature of the star, which is derived by fitting a theoretical Planck curve to the observed energy curve of the star.

Both D and λ_1 can be measured accurately from the microphotometer curves. They are independent of interstellar reddening, which is a source of uncertainty in those spectral classifications that rest mostly upon measures of the color index. This is because dust particles in interstellar space scatter blue light more than red, and hence make stars appear redder. Both quantities can be obtained from spectrograms of very small dispersion (about 250 A/mm), which are easier to obtain than those of the dispersion required in the MK classification.

The Chalonge method is limited to stars in which the hydrogen lines and the Balmer jump are sufficiently marked to show on the plates. In other words, the method is good only for spectral types earlier than about G0. The precision the French astronomers have reached is as good as, or possibly better than, that obtained in the MK classification.

In order to illustrate the relations between the French system and the MK types and luminosity classes, Chalonge and L. Divan have prepared a plaster-of-Paris model (illustrated in Fig. 103). The horizontal coordinates are λ_1 (along the front) and D (from front to back). The vertical

---

* The drop in the intensity of the continuous spectrum to the violet of 3646 A, representing the energy absorbed when electrons originally in the second level of the hydrogen atom are ionized—see Chap. XI.

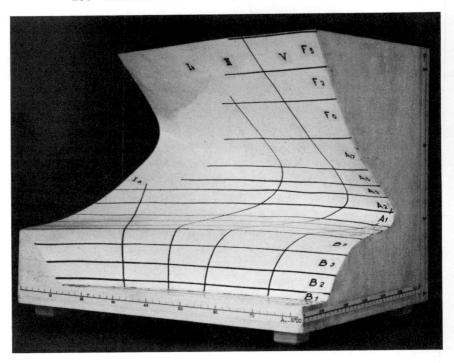

Fig. 103.   Plaster-of-Paris model, by Chalonge and Mlle. Divan, illustrating the relationship between the French system and the MK system.

coordinate is the spectrophotometric gradient ϕ, which measures the temperature. The hot stars are at the bottom, the cooler stars at the top. The black lines on the surface show the conversion of the French into the MK system. The peculiar curving of the surface is caused by the fact that the Balmer jump first increases with diminishing temperature and then decreases (because hydrogen absorption is strongest in spectral class A).

When using this model, astronomers must take into account the fact that the spectrophotometric gradient depends upon interstellar reddening; therefore, for distant stars, the measured values of ϕ must be corrected for interstellar absorption. It should be remembered also that the MK classification applies only to Population I stars; the conversion curves have to be used with caution for Population II objects.

Nevertheless, Chalonge's model already has led to some interesting results with regard to Population II stars. One of Chalonge's associates, Mlle. A. M. Fringant, recently investigated the spectrum of the famous galactic cluster-type variable, RR Lyrae. She found that when the three

Chalonge parameters are plotted in the model, the representative points of RR Lyrae fall consistently below the surface. In other words, this Population II star cannot be represented by the surface; its gradient is always smaller than would correspond to the surface as defined by Population I stars with similar values of D and λ_1.

Exactly the same tendency is exhibited by the Population II subdwarfs (stars falling slightly below the main sequence) studied by Chalonge, with his associates J. Berger, Mlle. R. Canavaggia, and Mlle. Fringant. Again, these stars fall below the surface of the model and are, therefore, bluer than normal stars.

The principal advantage of Chalonge's method is its strong dependence on the properties of the hydrogen atom. It should be possible, to use this scheme in investigations of many problems involving spectral types—such as the interpretation of the H-R diagram, the relation between the ages of the stars and their hydrogen abundances, and so on.

The most recent practical application of Chalonge's procedure is J. Berger's investigation of the spectra of the components of visual double stars. The principal parameters of Chalonge's classification were adopted for a few comparison stars, the information being based upon earlier observations, so that the intensities of the continuous spectrum at different wavelengths could be measured with respect to the already known comparison stars. The results are consistent with the theory of stellar evolution, according to which a visual double star's more massive component always is more advanced in evolutionary characteristics than the less massive component is.

The second of the new methods for quantitative spectral classification is B. Strömgren's. In principle, his investigations are quite similar to Chalonge's, but while the latter uses spectrograms, the former directly examines the light of each star with a photoelectric photometer. Various wavelengths are isolated by interference filters and compared. A two-dimensional classification is established for B, A, and F stars based on measures of the strength of the hydrogen-beta ($H\beta$) absorption line and of the Balmer jump.

Strömgren calibrated his method by measuring about 100 stars for which Morgan classes and luminosity types were known. He can classify to about 0.02 spectral class. This exceeds all previous methods by so much that it constitutes a new epoch in astrophysics. Similarly, the absolute magnitudes of the stars to which this method applies are obtained with a probable error of only about 0.2 mag from a single observation.

For cool stars of type K, similar work with other criteria has been accomplished at the Copenhagen Observatory by K. Gyldenkaerne, with satisfactory results.

At the Nashville meeting of the American Astronomical Society in December, 1953, Strömgren described another advance in observing techniques: simultaneous photoelectric photometry with photon counters of three narrow wavelength regions (Hβ and two comparison regions). A spectrum is produced, by the Coudé spectrograph of the 82-in. McDonald Observatory reflector, and slits are used to select the three narrow regions. Strömgren pointed out that while the interference-filter method used with the 82-in. reflector yields high precision down to about mag 12, the method of simultaneous measures extends the range down to mag 14. For equal precision, the gain over the photographic method is about 4 mag when the photoelectric accumulation time is equal to the photographic exposure time.

XI

STELLAR ATMOSPHERES
& SPECTROSCOPY

AS STRESSED before, the study of the stars necessarily began with the sun, since it is the only star whose surface can be
observed in detail. Thus, the early concepts of stellar atmosphere and of
the origin of stellar spectra were based primarily upon observations of
the sun. With minor modifications, these ideas were then applied to
other stars.

CLOUDY VERSUS GASEOUS ATMOSPHERES

An excellent description of the solar atmosphere as visualized
around 1900 is found in C. A. Young's *The Sun:*

The picture [Fig. 104] is an ideal section through the center, the black
disk represents the inner nucleus, which is not accessible to observation,
its nature and constitution being a mere matter of inference. The white
ring surrounding it is the photosphere, or shell of incandescent cloud
which forms the visible surface. The depth, or thickness, of this shell is
quite unknown; it may be many times thicker than represented, or possibly
somewhat thinner. Nor is it certain whether it is separated from the inner
core by a definite surface, or whether, on the other hand, there is no distinct boundary between them.

The outer surface of the photosphere, however, is certainly pretty
sharply defined, though very irregular, rising at points into faculae, and
depressed at others in spots, as shown in the figure.

Immediately above this lies the so-called "reversing stratum," in which
Fraunhofer lines originate. It is to be noted, however, that the gases which

Fig. 104. Cross-section of part of the sun, by C. A. Young. (*From* The Sun, *New York, 1895, P. 326*)

Size of Moon's Orbit

compose this stratum do not merely overlie the photosphere, but they also fill the interspaces between the photospheric clouds, forming the atmosphere in which they float, and an attempt has been made to indicate this fact in the diagram.

Above the "reversing stratum" lies the scarlet chromosphere, with prominences of various forms and dimensions rising high above the solar surface; and over, and embracing all, is the coronal atmosphere and the mysterious radiance of the clouds, rifts, and streamers, fading gradually into the outer darkness.[1]

The mechanism of absorption-line formation and the nature of the chromosphere were described by Young as follows:

At the upper surface of the photosphere . . . and all through it, indeed, the uncondensed gases are dark as compared with the droplets and crystals which make up the photospheric clouds. Here the pressure and temperature are lowered, so that the vapors give out no longer a continuous but a bright-line spectrum, whenever we get a chance to see them, against a nonluminous background; and, when the intenser light from the liquid and solid particles of the photosphere shines through these vapors, they rob it of the corresponding rays, and produce for us the familiar dark-lined spectrum of ordinary sunlight.

On the outer surface, exposed to the cold of space, the rapid radiation would certainly produce the condensation and precipitation into luminous clouds of such vapors as had a boiling-point higher than that of the cooling surface. These clouds would float in an atmosphere saturated with the vapors from which they were formed, and also containing such other vapors as were not condensed, and thus the peculiarities of the solar spectrum would result. On the other hand, the permanent gases, like hydrogen—those not subject to condensation into the liquid form under the solar conditions—would rise to higher elevations than the others, and form above the photosphere just such a chromosphere as we observe.[2]

This explanation of the origin of the absorption spectrum was consonant with Kirchhoff's *laws of radiation.** But by 1913, A. Fowler wrote in a review on "Solar and Stellar Photospheres" that still "... the chemistry and physics of the photosphere remain a mystery."[3]

It had been established that the solar photosphere's temperature is 6,000°; hence all known terrestrial substances would evaporate. From examination of solar and stellar spectra many lines were identified with terrestrial elements whose spectra had been observed in the laboratory. By 1900 most of the elements found on the earth had been identified, and a chemical uniformity in the universe seemed to exist. Thus it seemed unlikely that any substance not observed on the earth could be very abundant in the stars, and the existence of some unknown process allowing precipitation at high temperatures seemed a more likely, even though not a very satisfactory, alternative.

Since a gas under high pressure also can produce a continuous spectrum, C. G. Abbot of the Astrophysical Observatory of the Smithsonian Institution suggested in 1911 that the photosphere need not contain solids or liquids, but might be entirely gaseous. The gradually increasing opacity of the atmosphere, due to scattering of light, might produce the appearance of a sharp boundary. However, the sharpness of the Fraunhofer lines in the solar spectrum seemed to contradict this theory. Fowler noted that:

> The change of state of a gas from that which gives a continuous spectrum to that giving sharp lines (such as occur in the reversing layer) must be a gradual one, and in place of sharply defined lines we should expect lines of much greater complexity.[4]

He concluded:

> It will be gathered that we have still a good deal to learn as to the nature of the solar and stellar photospheres, or of the equivalent radiating

---

* The laws of spectrum analysis, formulated by the German chemist G. Kirchhoff in the middle of the 19th century may be summarized as follows: A continuous spectrum is produced by a glowing solid, liquid, or gas under high pressure; emission-line spectrum, by a glowing gas under low pressure; absorption-line spectrum, by a continuous source with cooler gases at low pressure between the source and the observer.

regions. Most observers of solar phenomena will doubtless continue to regard the photosphere as an actual cloudlike surface, and further progress in our knowledge of its constitution would seem to depend upon advances in physics.[5]

Actually, A. Schuster and K. Schwarzschild already had discussed a theory of the atmosphere and of the origin of the absorption spectrum that more closely resembles the modern view. This theory, however, was not accepted generally at that time because their investigations involved a number of assumptions that could not be adequately substantiated theoretically. In two investigations (1902 and 1905), Schuster suggested that in a star's outer layer, radiation coming from the inside is partly absorbed by the atoms and then reemitted in an isotropic manner in the same wavelength (process of scattering) but at the same time a part of the radiation from the interior is absorbed by the atoms and then reemitted in all wavelengths in accordance with Planck's law (process of pure absorption). In principle, it is possible to distinguish between the two processes by observations of the disk of a star such as the sun. At the limb, the line of sight passes through a great thickness of gas at a relatively low temperature, so that any absorption line produced by the process of pure absorption should produce line depths that are essentially the same as the background radiation of the continuous spectrum; that it, the absorption lines should disappear at the limb. In the case of pure scattering, the process involved is the same, regardless of the distance from the center of the disk; therefore, absorption lines produced by this mechanism should be the same both at the limb and at the center of the disk. In reality, both processes are present (see P. 215).

In 1906, Schwarzschild introduced the concept of the *radiative equilibrium* of the atmosphere: Energy transported by upward and downward streams (convection) in the atmosphere is negligible compared to the energy transported by radiation. He did not consider a cloudy photosphere at all, but showed that the density of the atmosphere decreases so rapidly as it extends outward that the solar limb should appear quite sharp. He also derived a density and temperature for the solar atmosphere at which a cloudy photosphere is extremely unlikely to occur.

In 1924, a thorough review of the concept of the photosphere and reversing layer was presented by H. N. Russell and the American astronomer J.Q. Stewart:

The results . . . are all consistent with the following conception of the solar atmosphere. At the top is a deep layer, the chromosphere, in which the gases are held up by radiation pressure acting on individual atoms. The pressure and density in the layer increase slowly downward (as gravity somewhat overbalances radiation pressure) and the pressure at its base may be of the order of 10^{-7} atmospheres, or 0.0001 mm of mercury. Below this level, gravity is predominant in the equilibrium, and the pressure increases rapidly with depth—the temperature remaining nearly constant, and not far from 5000°, so long as the gases are transparent. This region is the reversing layer. When the pressure reaches 0.01 atmosphere, the general absorption begins to render the gas hazy. This opacity increases greatly with the pressure, and the reversing layer passes, by a fairly rapid transition, into the photosphere, which on the scale in which we have to study it resembles an opaque mass. As soon as the opacity becomes important the temperature rises in accordance with the theory of radiative equilibrium as developed by Schwarzschild and Eddington. The observed effective photospheric temperature is a mean value for the layers from which radiation escapes to us.

In the reversing layer, with a temperature near 5,000°, and a mean molecular weight probably of about 20 the pressure and density must change tenfold for a change in depth of approximately 40 km. The assumption of an increase of density by the factor 10^5 between the chromosphere and photosphere leads to a depth of 200 km for the layer. A rough calculation . . . indicates that fully 80% of the light originating at this depth should escape from the sun, and practically none of that from 50 km lower. The transition to the photosphere is therefore rapid enough to give the observed sharp limb of the sun in accordance with Abbot's explanation and yet gradual enough to account for the change in brightness toward the limb, as shown in detail by Lindblad and Milne. . . .

Spectroscopically, the upper chromosphere should be responsible for the bright lines visible at the limb with small instruments, and for the dark central cores of the hydrogen and calcium lines in the ordinary spectrum. The flash spectrum probably arises both from the lower chromosphere and upper reversing layer. The stronger Fraunhofer lines should be absorbed mainly in the upper parts of the reversing layer—the lower and denser part accounting for the wings of the dense lines, for the fainter lines . . . and for the band spectra, both in spots and on the disc. All these deductions appear to be in excellent agreement with observations, and most of them are not new.[6]

Astronomers soon recognized, however, that the crude approximation of a sharp boundary—the photosphere—between a star's completely opaque inner layer and the transparent reversing layer did not adequately explain all the observed features of absorption line profiles. A more sophisticated approximation was required, one that discarded altogether the concept of a photosphere and introduced a measure of the absorption of continuous radiation throughout the stellar atmosphere. The quantity involved is defined as the *continuous absorption coefficient*. Depending upon the nature of the investigation, this quantity is a measure of the fraction of continuous radiation absorbed at a certain wavelength per unit distance of depth, or per unit mass in the atmosphere. In the latter case, the quantity is referred to as the *mass absorption coefficient*. Perhaps the most illuminating discussion of the theoretical problem involving the production of absorption lines was published by A. S. Eddington, the English theoretical astrophysicist who contributed more to theoretical advances in astrophysics than any other astronomer during the first half of the twentieth century[7]; this publication is much too technical to be reviewed here.

ANALYSIS OF STELLAR SPECTRA

These advances in the theory of stellar atmospheres were made possible mainly by the great advances in atomic theory, particularly the 1913 theory of the Danish physicist N. Bohr. The quantum hypothesis, proposed by the German physicist Max Planck in 1901, according to which radiation energy is emitted or absorbed in indivisible bundles or units called *quanta*, had accounted for the appearance of sharp spectral lines.

The British physicist Lord Ernest Rutherford in 1911 had developed a model of the atom as having a small, relatively massive, and positively charged nucleus with negatively charged electrons revolving around it in circular or elliptical orbits. Bohr combined the essential elements of both of these conceptions in his model of the atom, forming the basis of the so-called *classical theory of the atom*.

According to Bohr, electrons can maintain only certain orbits, each of which corresponds to a particular amount of energy. Hence electrons are more often referred to as being in certain energy states. In an undisturbed atom, all the electrons possess a minimal amount of energy. If energy corresponding to the difference between two states is supplied (either as radiant energy or the kinetic energy of collision), an electron can "jump" to a higher state (and the atom is said to be "excited"). After an average interval of 10^{-8} sec, by emitting the same amount of energy (either at once or in several steps, if the original jump was not between two neighboring levels), it returns to its original state. If enough energy is provided to overcome the force of attraction of the nucleus, the electron can leave the atom altogether, and the latter becomes then ionized. The Bohr theory was a contribution which gave new impetus to many phases in the study of stellar atmospheres.

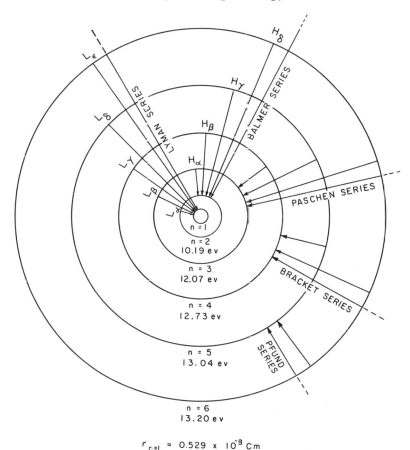

$$r_{n=1} = 0.529 \times 10^{-8} \; Cm$$

Fig. 105.   Schematic diagram of the various electronic shells of a hydrogen atom, according to Bohr's theory. (*From* Elementary Astronomy, *New York, Oxford University Press, 1959, Fig. 17.1*)

The Mechanism of Line Formation

Regarding the mechanism of line production in stellar atmospheres, it was found that absorption lines arising from the atom's lowest energy level, the *ground level*, usually involve an energy jump to an excited level with a subsequent emission at about the same frequency (this is essentially the process of pure scattering). On the other hand, when a line is produced by an electron jump from one excited level to a level of still greater excitation, or when a process of ionization takes place whereby the electron is temporarily removed from the ion, the subsequent emissions more often are distributed among many energy states—a process that would in effect resemble that of pure absorption.

Why are any absorption lines produced when an electron jump associated with the absorption of a quantum of energy is followed immediately by an emission of an equivalent quantum? In the case of a scattering atmosphere, the answer is found in the fact that the emitted radiation usually does not occur in the direction of the original path of the quantum, but is distributed isotropically when many atoms are involved. In addition to this phenomenon, the temperature of the solar reversing layer is lower than the temperature of the photosphere, so that in the case of both scattering and pure absorption an absorption line is produced.

The sun is the only star for which accurate measurements of absorption-line profiles (or contours) can be made in an attempt to distinguish between the two processes. Relatively less accurate results come from the study of certain eclipsing binaries in which a faint large component gradually occults a bright but small component (Algol, U Cephei, and others). R. O. Redman attempted in 1936 to distinguish between pure absorption and pure scattering in a study of the spectra of U Cephei obtained at Victoria during those phases of the binary orbit when only a very narrow crescent of the eclipsed star remains visible. His conclusions were that "... in the principal star of U Cephei ... the hydrogen Balmer lines behave as though they vanish at the limb ...";[8] a process of pure absorption is indicated. However, later studies of U Cephei at the McDonald Observatory showed that the physical phenomena were much more complicated than those considered by Redman. While the He (helium) I lines confirm Redman's conclusions, the Ca II lines* become more conspicuous as totality is approached; this challenges the hypothesis that pure absorption is predominantly responsible for the formation of lines in the principal star.

Saha's Excitation and Ionization Theory

The most important application of Bohr's theory to astrophysics is the work of M. N. Saha during the years 1920–1921. He considered the state of excitation and ionization in stellar atmospheres to be functions of the temperature and the pressure of the atmosphere. (According to B. Strömgren, Bohr also had considered this problem in an unpublished investigation.)

Saha first considered the sun's spectrum:

There is "a priori" no reason why in the sun certain elements should be favored to the exclusion of others. On the contrary, it seems natural to

---

* I refers to a neutral atom, II refers to the first stage of ionization: that is, one electron has been lost by the atom, III to a doubly ionized atom, and so on.

Fig. 106.   M. N. Saha.   (*Courtesy*
Sky and Telescope*)

infer that the sun is composed of the same elements as the earth, and contains all the 92 elements known to the chemists on the earth. . . .[9]

He explained:

The view which is urged in the present paper is that the varying records of different elements in the Fraunhofer spectrum may be regarded as arising from the varying response of these elements with regard to the stimulus existing in the sun. The stimulus existing in the sun is the same for all elements, viz., that arising from a temperature of about 7,500°K, but owing to different internal structure, elements will respond in a varying degree to this stimulus.[10]

In the course of developing the theory, particularly as it applies to an interpretation of the spectrum of the solar chromosphere, Saha also found ". . . that pressure has a very great influence on the degree of ionization, which does not seem to have been anticipated."[11] In a gas, the ionized atoms and the liberated free electrons move about at random, so that occasionally a free electron may approach an ionized atom and be captured by it. After a sufficiently long interval, an equilibrium that will depend greatly upon the pressure of the gas will be established between the number of processes of ionization and the number of captures. When the pressure is low, the distances between the individual particles are great. Processes of collision will occur at relatively long intervals, while processes of ionization, depending only upon the intensity of the light from the deeper layers of the star, are independent of the pressure. Hence ionization will be favored at low pressures and will be retarded when the pressures are great.

The differences in spectra of stars of very different luminosities (observed by Miss Maury and Hertzsprung) and the criteria for estimating absolute brightnesses (developed by Adams and Kohlschütter) thus were attributed mainly to differences in density. Other contributing factors such as turbulence were discovered later. The pressure in the atmospheres of the luminous supergiants and giants is much lower than in the atmospheres of main-sequence stars, and hence a greater degree of ionization is attained. The lines of ionized elements are strengthened, while those of neutral elements (or those of a lower ionization level) are reduced in intensity.

In many respects, Saha's work on ionization was built upon the foundation laid by Lockyer, who had recognized the distinction between the arc and the spark spectra of the elements, but whose personal unpopularity among many of the leading American scientists probably prevented his many constructive ideas from bearing those fruits they surely promised. It also is interesting to note that Saha first submitted a paper embodying his theories to the *Astrophysical Journal*, whose editor rejected it. His theory was published finally in *The Philosophical Magazine;* the next editor of the *Astrophysical Journal* found Saha's manuscript in a box containing the rejected papers of a number of other astronomers who later achieved international fame, together with many articles that were worthless.

Spectral Sequence

Saha employed his theory to explain the spectral sequence. He provided a theoretical basis for the ideas suggested by earlier workers on more intuitive grounds:

> ... We are not justified in speaking of a star as a hydrogen, helium or carbon star, thereby suggesting that these elements form the chief ingredients in the chemical composition of the star. The proper conclusion would be that under the stimulus prevailing in the star, the particular element or elements are excited to radiation of their characteristic lines, while other elements are either ionized or the stimulus is too weak to excite the lines by which we can detect the element. ...[12]

The work thus corroborates Russell's view that the continuous variation of spectral types is mainly due to the varying values of the temperature of the stellar atmosphere, and the classification B, A, F, G, K, M, which has been adopted by the Harvard astrophysicists, as the result of long years of study and observation, are therefore seen to acquire a new physical significance.[13]

The current identification of the main characteristics of the Harvard sequence and its physical significance are given by the following table adapted from *Elementary Astronomy* by O. Struve, B. Lynds, and H. Pillans:[14]

Table 3.

MAIN CHARACTERISTICS OF THE HARVARD SEQUENCE

Class	Temperature in degrees K	Spectral Features°
O	50,000°K	Lines of highly ionized atoms: He II, Si IV, N III, etc.; H weak; occasionally weak emission of some He II and N III lines.
BO	25,000	He II absent; He I strong (maximum at B 2); Si III and O II present; H stronger.
AO	11,000	H at maximum; He I absent; Mg II and Si II strong; Fe II, Ti II weak; Ca II weak.
FO	7,600	H weaker; Ca II strong; Fe II, Cr II, etc., about equal to Fe I, Cr I, etc.
GO	6,000	Resembles the sun; Ca II at maximum; very rich atomic spectrum because of large number of lines of Fe I, and of other neutral elements; molecular bands of CH present.
KO	5,100	H relatively weak; neutral atomic lines all very strong; molecular bands stronger.
MO	3,600	Neutral lines very strong; bands of TiO present but rather weak.
R and N	3,060	Molecular bands of CN, CH, and C_2 strong; TiO absent; line spectrum resembles that of K or M stars.
S	3,000	Molecular bands of ZrO, YO, and LaO, which are not present in other types, are strong; lines of neutral atoms are strong, including those of Zr and Tc.

Figure 107 is a graphical representation of how the strength of absorption lines varies with spectral class for some of the more common elements.

Russell commented in 1922 upon the importance of Saha's theory as follows:

The principles of the ionization theory will evidently be of great importance throughout the whole field of astrophysics and Dr. Saha has made an application of the highest interest to the question of the physical meaning of the sequence of stellar spectra. . . . The possibilities of the new method appear to be very great. To utilize it fully, years of work will be

* The abbreviations above signify the following elements, found alone or in compounds: helium (He), silicon (Si), nitrogen (N), hydrogen (H), oxygen (O), iron (Fe), titanium (Ti), chromium (Cr), calcium (Ca), yttrium (Y), lanthanum (La), zirconium (Zr), technetium (Tc).

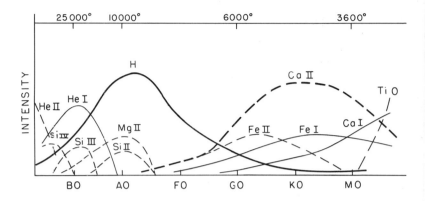

Fig. 107. Intensities of absorption lines in the spectral sequence, after L. H. Aller. (*From* Elementary Astronomy, *New York, Oxford University Press, 1959, Fig. 25.2*)

required to study the behavior of the elements . . . in the stars, in laboratory spectra and by direct measurement of ionization, but the prospect of increase of our knowledge, both of atoms and of stars, as a result of such researches makes it urgently desirable that they should be carried out.[15]

In accordance with this prediction, after the pioneering work of Saha the investigations of stellar spectra proceeded along several lines. Rapid progress was made in the identification of spectral lines. Many factors responsible for the differences in the contours of absorption lines were investigated. One of these, the rotation of stars, will be discussed here. A complete discussion of the causes of line broadening will be found in the Appendix, P. 475. All of the preliminary steps finally enabled astrophysicists to attack the most important problem, that of abundances of elements in stellar atmospheres.

Most of the theoretical work stimulated by Saha on the ionization and excitation of atoms in stellar atmospheres was, in the 1920's and 1930's, produced by R. H. Fowler and E. A. Milne in England, by Russell in America, and by Unsöld in Germany. But nearly all of the observational basis, upon which the theory rested, was contained in the Harvard catalogues of stellar spectra. Clearly, what was needed was a closer integration of the observational and theoretical efforts. This was accomplished by Cecilia H. Payne (now Mrs. Payne-Gaposchkin), a former student of Milne, who went to Harvard and there wrote her famous book *Stellar Atmospheres*,[16] for which she was awarded the degree of Ph.D. from Radcliffe College. It is undoubtedly the most brilliant Ph.D. thesis ever written in astronomy. It was published at the right time and contained the right kind of information to stimulate many new investigations. A further effort along similar lines by the same author appeared in 1930 under the title *The Stars of High Luminosity*.[17]

Line Identification

The identification of stellar and solar absorption lines was facilitated greatly by theoretical studies and laboratory investigations of atomic structure and energy levels. Thus many previously unidentified lines were attributed to known chemical elements in different stages of excitation and ionization. It was, for example, possible to predict the wavelengths of many faint iron lines never observed in the laboratory but that coincide with very faint lines in the solar spectrum.

The best-known triumphs in the field of line identification are those solving the puzzles of the strong green emission lines in the spectra of gaseous nebulae and the very strong emission lines observed in the solar corona. No such lines had been discovered in chemical laboratories. Hence astronomers referred to *nebulium* as the source of the green lines in gaseous nebulae and to *coronium* as the source of the lines of the solar corona. Many papers incorrectly attributed the nebulium or coronium lines to complicated atomic spectra, such as those of argon, possessing a large number of spectral lines in the optical region so that approximate coincidences could easily be found without thereby proving the real source of the astronomical emission lines.

The riddle of the spectral lines of nebulium was solved in 1927 by I. S. Bowen, who at that time was a member of the physics department of the California Institute of Technology. Bowen had observed the spectra of many light sources of high excitation and ionization. He was inspired to attack the problem of nebulium when he was reading Russell, Dugan, and Stewart's textbook *Astronomy*,* in which the authors had concluded:

> Until the lines in question have been produced in the laboratory it is of course impossible to say just what atoms are responsible for them; but it is now practically certain that they must be due not to atoms of unknown kinds but to atoms of known kinds shining under unfamiliar conditions.[18]

Russell, Dugan, and Stewart also remarked:

* This textbook, subtitled "A Revision of Young's Manual of Astronomy," was a thorough revision, in Volume I, of a standard textbook written by C. A. Young, the famous solar astrophysicist of Princeton; Volume II was almost completely rewritten and embodied the ideas of Russell. The book was revised around 1940 and, in spite of the fact that it is outdated in many aspects, it is still one of the most comprehensive and lucid textbooks on astronomy.

The suggestion is tempting that the nebular lines may be emitted only in gas of very low density. (This would happen, for example, if it took a relatively long time as atomic events go for an atom to get into the right state to emit them, and if a collision with another atom in this interval prevented the completion of the process).[19]

Bowen pursued this suggestion further as follows:

An atom in an excited state may give out its energy and return to a lower state either by radiating this energy or by transferring it to another atom through a collision of the second kind. If the mean life of the excited state before spontaneous emission is very long, as in the case of a metastable state,* and if the mean time between impacts is short (in the most rarefied terrestrial sources this is never more than $\frac{1}{1000}$ sec) practically all of the atoms will return by the second process and no radiation will take place. In the nebulae, however, where the mean time between impacts is estimated at from 10^4 to 10^5 sec, the first process may predominate even in the case of jumps from metastable levels. This suggests at once that jumps from metastable states may be the source of lines appearing in nebulae but not in terrestrial sources.[20]

The lines originating in metastable levels under these conditions are usually referred to as *forbidden* lines, in contrast to the *permitted* lines observed in the laboratory. Bowen compared the theoretically derived wavelengths of forbidden lines of elements expected to be present in gaseous nebulae with the observed wavelengths of the nebulium lines, and in this manner attributed the most conspicuous nebulium lines to forbidden transitions of singly and doubly ionized oxygen (O II and O III) and ionized nitrogen (N II).

Many attempts were made subsequently to identify in a similar man-

* An excited state, lasting for as long as a few seconds, from which an atom cannot under laboratory conditions pass directly to the normal state by emitting radiation.

Fig. 108. Spectrum of the Orion Nebula, with the principal emission lines identified. Square brackets denote forbidden lines.

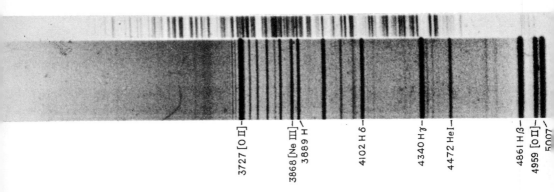

3727 [O II]—
3868 [Ne III]—
3889 H—
4102 H δ—
4340 H γ—
4472 He I—
4861 H β—
4959 [O II]—
5007

ner the emission lines in the solar corona, but no one succeeded until 1941. The German astronomer W. Grotrian at this time noticed that the wavelengths of two coronal lines correspond to forbidden transitions of Fe X and Fe XI. Such a high state of ionization requires a much higher temperature in the solar corona (see P. 137) than had been believed possible, and hence had not been considered before. Grotrian's finding led B. Edlén of Sweden to investigate the spectra of other transitions of highly ionized atoms, and after two coincidences with forbidden transitions of Ca XII and Ca XIII were found, he commented:

This fact increased the probability that the coincidences did not happen by chance and that the whole coronal spectrum might consist of "forbidden lines" analogous to those of the gaseous nebulae but from atoms much more highly ionized than had previously been considered at all.[21]

Edlén and others have identified most coronal lines with forbidden transitions of very highly ionized atoms of common chemical elements. The strongest line (at λ 5,303 A) is due to Fe XIV, the three next strongest to Fe XIII.

Even today, however, many spectral lines in absorption in stellar atmospheres and in emission in gaseous nebulae remain unidentified. Thus in the revision of Rowland's tables of solar lines* currently being prepared at the National Bureau of Standards by Mrs. C. Moore-Sitterly and her co-workers, about 30 per cent of the lines, most of them faint ones, remain unidentified. No one, however, now believes that chemical elements not known on the earth exist in stellar atmospheres or in nebulae.

Most of the unidentified lines in the sun and in the stars are produced by molecules rather than by atoms. The spectra of molecules usually form a number of band systems. A *band* is essentially a group of lines having certain common properties, for example, the "Swan bands" of the carbon molecule obtained by J. G. Phillips. The bands of some molecules are quite distinct and are separated from others by varying intervals in wavelength. Most of these bands, such as those of titanium oxide, have been studied extensively in the laboratory and the resulting comparison samples have been used for identification in stellar spectra. (Note the complicated bands on the high-dispersion spectrogram obtained with the Coudé spectrograph of the Lick Observatory in Fig. 111, as compared to

---

* An atlas of the solar spectrum and table giving precise wavelengths and approximate intensities of about 14,000 lines, published between 1886 and 1895 by the American physicist H. A. Rowland. The original atlas and its revision in 1928 have formed the basis of investigations of the solar spectrum.

the appearance of the same bands in Fig. 110). Other molecules have exceedingly complex band structures, in which two or more bands appear in the same wavelength region. Many of these bands have not been investigated adequately in the laboratory, because it is difficult to assign each specific line to a particular band. Some progress in this field has been made in the past few years by J. G. Phillips, L. Brewer, and F. A. Jenkins, among others, at the University of California. Phillips utilizes a high-speed electronic computer to classify the bands automatically and to reject those lines that do not for one reason or another belong to a particular band. This work, still in progress, will undoubtedly serve as a source for the identification of band lines in stellar spectra.

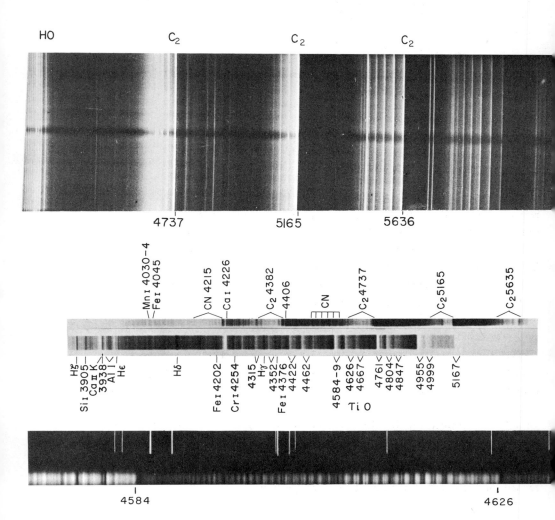

Stellar Rotation

Whenever a great advance is made in a scientific field, a number of phenomena usually are found that are not accounted for by the new theory but come into prominence after the more essential features of the observational data have been explained satisfactorily by the theory. Thus after the factors responsible for the general features of stellar spectra were elucidated and many absorption lines were identified, some astronomers turned to the many individual differences among the intensities and, particularly, the shapes (or contours) of the absorption lines not accounted for by Saha's theory.

While most of the absorption lines in the solar spectrum are narrow, many stars exhibit ill-defined, broad lines. For example, the hydrogen lines in the hotter stars, especially in those of class A, are often several hundred angstroms wide; the lines of ionized calcium H and K are extremely strong and broad in stars of intermediate and late classes (also in the sun), and in many stars of classes O, B, A, and F the lines of iron, titanium, helium, silicon, and other elements are diffuse.

A number of the causes of spectral line broadening have been identified and will be discussed in the Appendix. The discussion here will be confined to one factor, stellar rotation, the recognition of which also has led to important consequences in cosmological theories (see Chap. IX, P. 173).

The existence of stellar rotation was discovered by F. Schlesinger (1909) of Yale University in the spectra of two eclipsing binaries, δ Librae and λ Tauri, whose measured radial velocities indicated a positive excess beyond the expected velocity just before mid-eclipse, while after mid-eclipse the departure was found to be negative. Schlesinger's dis-

Fig. 109 (Top).   Laboratory spectrum, showing the structure of the "Swan bands" of the carbon molecule. (*Courtesy J. G. Phillips, Leuschner Observatory, University of California*)

Fig. 110 (Center).   Spectra of (top) HD 52432 and *o* Ceti showing molecular bands with a much lower dispersion than in Fig. 109. (*From* An Atlas of Spectral Classification, *Chicago, 1943, Plate 54*)

Fig. 111 (Bottom).   TiO bands in *o* Ceti, near maximum light, obtained with the Coudé spectrograph of the 120-in. telescope. (*Lick Observatory*)

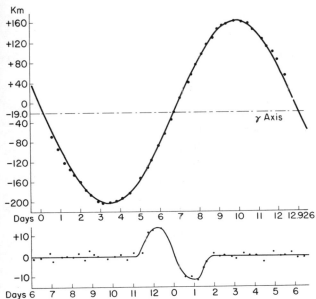

Fig. 112. Rotation effect in the velocity curve of the principal component of β Lyrae. (*R. A. Rossiter, from* Publications of the Observatory of the University of Michigan, V, *1933,* P. 88)

covery remained almost unknown until 1924, when, at the University of Michigan, R. A. Rossiter made a detailed study of the spectra of the eclipsing binary β Lyrae, and D. B. McLaughlin, that of Algol. (In the diagram of the rotational curve of the principal component of β Lyrae, (a) is the velocity curve, based upon large dots only; (b) residuals from the velocity curve. The curve exhibiting the rotational effect is based upon the small dots in the top figure.) Also W. S. Adams and A. H. Joy (1919) in a study of the short-period spectroscopic binary W Ursae Majoris found that:

. . . the unusual character of the spectral lines is due partly to the rapid change in velocity during even our shortest exposures but mainly to the rotational effect in each star, which may cause a difference in velocity in the line of sight of as much as 240 km/sec between the two limbs of the star.[22]

In the late 1920's, G. A. Shajn in the Soviet Union and O. Struve in America (their collaboration was by mail) were impressed by the fact that stars of similar spectral type and luminosity often possess markedly different spectra: In some stars the same spectral lines are broad and diffuse, while in others they are as sharp and as narrow as in the Fraunhofer spectrum of the sun. They investigated the broadening of spectral lines and the decrease in the depth of the lines, both of which had been predicted in the case of rotation, and applied the method to a statistical discussion of spectroscopic binaries. They concluded that: "The existence of fast rotation in spectroscopic binaries of short period seems thus to be established beyond any doubt."[23]

But the possibility existed that such rapid rotations occurred only in binary stars, perhaps because tidal forces produced synchronization of axial rotation and orbital revolution. Because the sun has a very slow axial rotation (only about 2 km/sec at its equator), most astrophysicists still believed that the rotation of all other stars was probably also small.

Struve had in 1923, in his Ph.D. thesis, concluded that:

"The wide lines in stellar spectra, chiefly of type A, could possibly be explained by rotation. The periods of rotation, as derived from the width of the lines, do not appear improbable . . . ,"[24]

but he did not at that time attempt a detailed analysis of the line profiles.

C. T. Elvey applied Shajn's and Struve's method to a study of single stars and found that there are, in fact, many stars whose equatorial rotational velocities are several hundred kilometers per second. A striking example is the bright star Altair whose spectral type resembles that of Vega. In the former, the lines are broad and shallow—"dish-shaped," as Elvey called them; in the spectrum of Vega the same lines are fairly narrow. In the figure the profiles of the absorption line of Mg II at 4481 A are shown at the bottom, where the percentage of absorption is plotted against distance from the center of the line.

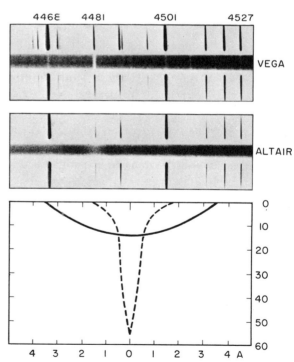

Fig. 113. Differences in the widths of absorption lines in Vega and Altair. (*Yerkes Observatory*)

Table 4.

EQUATORIAL VELOCITIES OF STELLAR ROTATIONS[25]

ROTATIONS	PERCENTAGE OF STARS BY SPECTRAL TYPES					
(km/sec)	Oe,Be*	O, B	A	F0–F2	F5–F8	G,K,M
0–50	0	21	22	30	80	100
50–100	0	51	24	50	20	0
100–150	0	20	22	15	0	0
150–200	1	6	22	4	0	0
200–250	3	2	9	1	0	0
250–300	18	0	1	0	0	0
300–500	78	0	0	0	0	0

Later statistical investigations, principally by Christine Westgate at Yerkes, have shown that the measured values of the rotational component of the velocity in line of sight range from 0 to about 250 km/sec and may occasionally be as large as 400 km/sec or even more. A correlation of rotational velocity with spectral type, shown in Table 4, was found by Struve and Elvey in 1931. The O, B, A, and early F stars frequently have large rotational velocities, while in late F and later types, rapid rotation occurs only in close spectroscopic binaries. It has also been found that no giants or supergiants have large rotational velocities.

Abundances of Elements

An important line of study resulted from the recognition that while the changes in the spectra along the spectral sequence are controlled primarily by the temperature and pressure of the atmosphere, the relative intensities of the lines of different elements in a spectrum depend also upon the abundances of the elements.

The first extensive investigation of the solar spectrum was carried out by Russell in 1929. His most important result was the establishment of the fact that abundance of hydrogen is much greater than had been thought possible. Russell learned this with the aid of D. H. Menzel's observations of the flash spectrum and concluded that ". . . . the solar atmosphere contains 60 parts of hydrogen (by volume), 2 of helium, 2 of oxygen, 1 of metallic vapors, and 0.8 of free electrons practically all of which come from the ionization of the metals."[26] (Figure 114 shows the abundances of the elements in the sun, from a later investigation by A. Unsöld, and in meteorites. The ordinate in the top figure is the number of atoms, while

---

* Oe,Be denote O and B stars, the spectra of which also contain emission lines (e), attributed to a gaseous shell formed due to the rapid rotation.

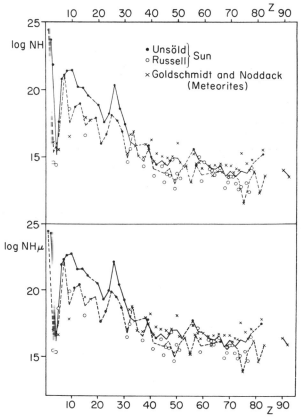

Fig. 114. The abundances of the elements in the sun and in meteorites. (*A. Unsöld*, from Zeitschrift für Astrophysik, *XXIV, 1948, P. 326*)

in the lower figure the numbers have been multiplied by atomic masses. The abscissa is the atomic number.)

A few years earlier Mrs. Payne-Gaposchkin had been the first to compare (in her Ph.D. thesis, mentioned on P. 220) the abundances of elements in a number of stars. She had concluded that the relative abundances are constant and do not differ from those observed in the sun. Several other studies confirmed her results, and there came a period when astronomers began talking about the *cosmic abundance scale* of the universe; that is, the relative abundances of the elements were believed to be the same in all stars. Perhaps this was a reaction to the incorrect views held prior to the publication of Saha's work.

Only two exceptions to the rule were recognized. A branching of the spectral sequence occurs for late-type stars (see Table 3). The majority of the cool stars belong to classes K and M, in which titanium oxide bands are conspicuous. In R- and N-type stars, bands of carbon and of cyanogen are strong, while in S-type stars zirconium oxide bands are found. In 1934, from an extensive quantitative analysis, Russell concluded that: "The predicted properties of stars with an excess of carbon over oxygen closely resemble those of classes R and N...."[27]

This observation confirmed an idea suggested first by R. H. Curtiss several years earlier and described in the Russell, Dugan, and Stewart textbook as follows:

At these low temperatures, chemical compounds can form, as the band spectra prove. If the carbon bands are due to some unoxidized carbon compound (as now appears to be very probable), they should disappear in an oxidizing atmosphere, while titanium oxide should be formed. In a reducing atmosphere titanium oxide should disappear and the carbon bands appear. The difference between the two main branches of the sequence may therefore correspond to this familiar chemical distinction.[28]

In 1930, C. S. Beals of the Dominion Astrophysical Observatory, recognized two groups among the Wolf-Rayet stars (a small number of stars having very strong and very broad emission lines, discussed in Chap. XVI): those that have particularly intense emission lines of nitrogen and those that show almost no nitrogen emission lines but have very strong carbon and oxygen emission lines. All three elements are in high stages of ionization. Until about a decade ago, astronomers were influenced by Beals' work, and it was almost universally believed that there were real abundance differences, one group containing larger amounts of nitrogen, the other larger amounts of carbon and oxygen.

Fig. 115.   Spectra of two Wolf-Rayet stars and two comparison stars. WN indicates the nitrogen sequence, WC the carbon sequence. (*From An Atlas of Spectral Classification, Chicago, 1943, Plate 2*)

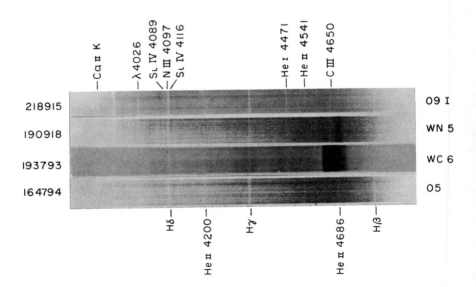

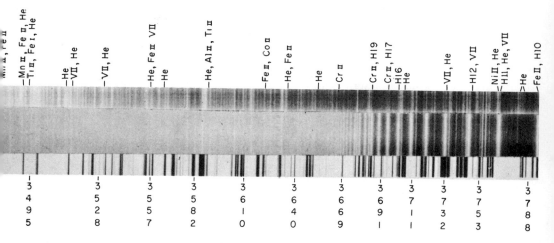

Fig. 116.   The spectra of *v* Sagittarii and *α* Cygni. (*J. L. Greenstein*, *from* Astrophysical Journal, *XCI, 1940, Plate 4*)

This interpretation was criticized in 1958 by A. B. Underhill at Victoria, who presented convincing arguments in favor of an interpretation in terms of temperature differences. There has been no criticism of Russell's conclusions regarding the late-type branching of the spectral sequence, but it is not at all certain that such differences in the abundances of certain elements cannot be explained also in terms of more elaborate versions of Saha's theory of ionization.

It is, however, quite certain that peculiar spectroscopic features found within the last two decades in a number of stars can be explained only in terms of abnormal abundances of some elements. For example, in 1940 J. L. Greenstein noted that the star *v* Sagittarii has very weak lines of hydrogen and relatively strong lines of various metals and other elements, and that this very striking effect clearly demonstrates a deficiency of hydrogen in the star's atmosphere. (In Fig. 116 note the weakness of the hydrogen absorption lines and the complete absence of the Balmer discontinuity at λ 3647 A in the spectrum of *v* Sagittarii).

In 1952, a symposium on the cosmic abundances of the chemical elements in stars was held in Rome. This was probably the first occasion on which the problem of differences in chemical composition, not of isolated groups of stars, but as a general phenomenon, was discussed formally by an international group of scientists. During the last decade, great emphasis has been placed upon this problem by several leading stellar spectroscopists, especially J. L. Greenstein and G. Wallerstein in the United States and A. Boyarchuk in the Soviet Union.

It is now clear that there is no such thing as a cosmic abundance scale. The abundances of the elements in the sun are quite well known. Many stars, especially those located on the main sequence of the H-R diagram, have approximately similar chemical abundances, but stars that are not now on the main sequence often show striking differences in the abundances of the elements. It must be recognized, however, that the evidence discussed here pertains only to the outermost layers of a star. Indirect methods of investigating a star's internal structure provide us with information concerning differences in the abundances of the elements in the deep interiors.

Moreover, there is strong evidence that in certain close binary stars gaseous material from the surface of one (or both) components may be expelled into space or may be captured by the other component, thus leaving exposed a previously unobservable layer that conceivably could reflect the abundances of the elements in a region of the star that did not originally form its reversing layer.

Knowledge of the chemical abundances from stellar spectra is far from complete; astronomers are studying these differences and interpreting them in terms of evolutionary processes that may continue for periods ranging from a few million years (in the case of very massive stars) up to periods of several billions of years (in the case of stars of small mass). The details of the evolutionary processes now believed to exist will be discussed in more detail in the next two chapters. It will suffice to state here that star formation is believed to go on continuously in the universe; that is, stars are born from condensations of interstellar matter. Nuclear processes are known to occur in stars and be the source of stellar energy. A number of possible nuclear reactions, depending principally on temperature, have been studied.

One of stellar spectroscopy's most perplexing problems is the occasional presence of strong absorption lines of technetium in the spectra of certain late-type stars. P. W. Merrill of Mount Wilson is principally responsible for the discovery of these lines in 1952 and the subsequent study of their behavior. Technetium is known from physical studies to be unstable; its most stable isotope has a lifetime of less than a million years. Isotopes are forms of the same element having different atomic weights but the same atomic number and the same number of electrons. Hence it might be expected that, because of the nuclear processes in stellar interiors, technetium would disappear rapidly—as, for example, it has disappeared from the sun's atmosphere. No one knows exactly why its spectral lines are so strong in certain stars. Merrill commented on the problem as follows:

It is surprising to find an unstable element in the stars. Either (1) a stable isotope actually exists although not yet found on earth, or (2) S-type stars somehow produce technetium as they go along; or (3) S-type stars represent a comparatively transient phase of stellar existence.[29]

The second alternative was preferred by M. E. and G. R. Burbidge of the University of California, formerly of Yerkes Observatory, who have carried out extensive investigations of nuclear processes in stars. They suggested that on the surfaces of the stars there may exist nuclear processes that from time to time replenish the atmospheric abundances of technetium and also of such light elements as lithium.

The problem of the great strength of the lithium lines in certain stellar spectra, especially those of the T Tauri stars (irregular variable stars named after T Tauri, the prototype of the group, usually associated with nebulae and believed to be in an early stage of stellar evolution, as will be shown in Chap. XIII, P. 275), was discussed in 1960 by G. Herbig of the Lick Observatory. Herbig pointed out that the abundance of lithium in T Tauri stars closely resembles its abundance on the earth and in meteorites, while its abundance in the reversing layer of the sun is smaller by several orders of magnitude. He concludes that the planetary and T Tauri abundance of lithium actually may represent the original abundance of this element in the Milky Way, while in the sun and in other stars much of the lithium may have been lost because of nuclear transformation. On the other hand, W. K. Bonsack of the California Institute of Technology and J. L. Greenstein have advanced the hypothesis that the high abundance of lithium in T Tauri stars and other similar objects is a consequence of nuclear phenomena on stellar surfaces—phenomena that are not occurring on the sun's surface or on the surfaces of many other main-sequence stars.

There is another strange result, this one based mainly on A. McKellar's work. He found that there are appreciable differences in the intensities of the absorption bands involving the same atomic constituents but differing in their isotopes. For example, D. H. Menzel had estimated in 1930 that the ratio of C^{12}/C^{13} is not more than 10 in the atmospheres of N-type stars, while the terrestrial ratio is about 90. McKellar's large-scale investigation of 1948 confirmed this result. Some mild doubts about McKellar's original interpretations were raised when it became apparent that not only the intensities of atomic lines, but also the intensities of molecular absorption bands could be modified greatly by the phenomenon of atmospheric turbulence.

Equally sensational is the high abundance of the light isotope of helium (He^3) in the star 3 Centauri A, according to a 1961 study by J. L. Greenstein, W. L. W. Sargent of England and J. Jugaku of Japan. As a rule, the wavelengths of the spectral lines of different isotopes of the same element differ by only a very small fraction of an angstrom. Hence, many astronomers undoubtedly have examined this star's spectrum without realizing that its helium lines are not produced by the common isotope He^4 but by the terrestrially rare isotope He^3. The Burbridges had searched for isotope shifts of helium lines in other stars without having reached positive results. Only accurate measurements of the wavelengths of the most highly displaced (about 0.3 A) isotope line will enable astronomers to distinguish among different isotopes.

It is not yet possible to explain such differences, because He^3 does not appear as a probable end product in a chain of nuclear reactions. However, it is certain that as the periodic table of elements becomes more and more complicated, so also does knowledge of the composition of stellar atmospheres. Twelve years ago, astronomers were certain of only occasional differences in composition, and some of them had not been verified. At present it must be realized that not only the nuclear reactions in stellar interiors, but presumably also nuclear processes on the surfaces of the stars, account for measurable differences in the abundances of the elements and their isotopes.

Chromospheres

The preceding discussion was confined to the spectra formed principally in the star's reversing layer, above which lies the more tenuous and more extensive layer, the chromosphere (see P. 213). In solar-type stars, the chromosphere cannot be observed separately. Except in some eclipsing binaries, the spectrum is formed by the entire star's integrated light, and its reversing layer and chromosphere combine to produce the set of absorption lines that is representative mostly of the reversing layer, but may to a small extent result from chromospheric absorption.

Only in very large giant and supergiant stars are the reversing layers of such great extent that appreciable fractions of their chromospheres are seen projected against the background of the night sky, instead of against the background of the star's photosphere. Such extended chromospheres would be expected to produce emission lines. Giant and subgiant stars with slow rotations would have their chromospheric emission lines at the same wavelengths as the absorption lines cf the reversing layer, except for those chromospheric lines that do not correspond to underlying absorption lines and are then seen superposed upon the star's continuous spectrum. It is probable that the undisplaced emission lines of ionized calcium in late-type giants and supergiants and the undisplaced emission lines of permitted and forbidden iron transitions are of chromospheric origin. In the case of the ionized calcium lines, these emission lines normally are seen as central reversals in the broad absorption profiles of the usual Fraunhofer lines. In many instances, the Ca II emission lines are not as sharp and narrow as would be expected from the natural broadening that results from the finite width of the energy levels (this phenomenon usually is referred to as "radiation damping" in the classical physical theory of an atom).

An important investigation of the chromospheric emission lines of Ca II in many stellar spectra of late type was completed at the Mount Wilson and Palomar Observatories by O. C. Wilson and M. K. V. Bappu in 1957. They showed that a very close correlation exists between the broadening of the emission lines and the absolute magnitudes of the stars. In fact, Wilson and other astronomers, mainly at Mount Wilson, have used this luminosity criterion extensively for the determination of accurate stellar spectroscopic parallaxes. (In the figure intrinsic brightness increases from top to bottom, with a total spread of more than a million times. The central, light emission feature in the lines of ionized calcium grows wider as luminosity increases). Not much theoretical work has been done toward an explanation of the broadening of the emission lines and the frequent occurrence of double emission components of unequal strength. It is reasonable to believe that turbulent motions in stellar atmospheres, combined with systematic motions of expansion or contraction and the simultaneous process of absorption in the chromosphere, may account for them.

The extraordinary size of the chromosphere, or shell, of a supergiant star was demonstrated by A. J. Deutsch of Mount Wilson Observatory in the case of α Herculis, which was known to be a binary, consisting of an M5 supergiant and a G0 giant companion, about 4.7″ distant. In 1956, Deutsch noticed that the companion is a *single-line spectroscopic binary* (a close binary with components of dissimilar luminosity; see P. 291) and inferred that the system contains a third star of about spectral type A3. The most curious feature of the spectrograms is the presence in both spectra of relatively narrow absorption lines of Ca I (particularly at

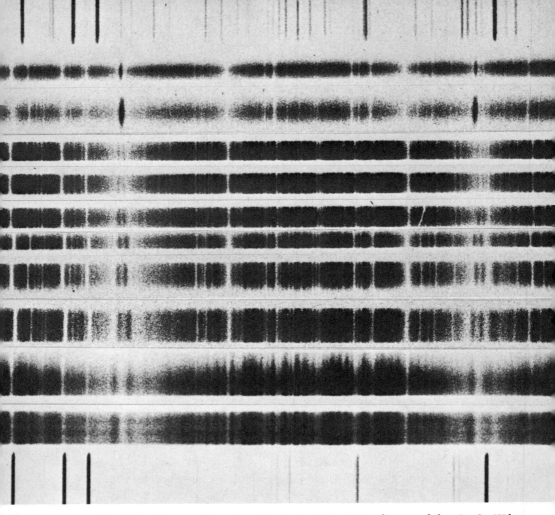

Fig. 117. Spectra illustrating the luminosity criteria discovered by O. C. Wilson. (*Mount Wilson and Palomar Observatories*)

λ 4,227 A) and other lines of constant velocity that do not share the orbital motion of the close pair. From his consideration of the velocities and intensities of these and other absorption lines in the spectra of both the M5 star and the close pair, Deutsch attributes the narrow lines to an enormous chromosphere extending from the M5 supergiant to a distance at least as great as that of the companion, at 700 a.u. or possibly even greater. Deutsch attributes the ionization in the shell to the A3 star. In the figure the large ring indicates the probable extent of the chromosphere of α Herculis. The diameter of the red supergiant star is greatly exaggerated.

The entire shell expands radially from the M star with a velocity of the order of 10 km/sec. From these data, Deutsch inferred that the M star is losing mass at the rate of at least 3×10^{-8} solar masses per year.

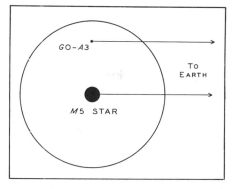

Fig. 118. The system of α Herculis.
(*Courtesy* Sky and Telescope)

It is important to realize that although the velocity of recession from the surface of the M star is lower than the velocity of escape at a distance of one stellar radius, this discussion is concerned not with the velocity of escape at the stellar photosphere, but with the velocity of escape at a great distance from the star: A relatively small radial velocity away from the center of the star might be sufficient to propel the gas to infinity. Even this argument is not necessarily significant; there are many other cases of gaseous matter being ejected from a star into interstellar space at relatively low velocities, either as a consequence of radiation pressure or because of the high pressure of a hot mass of gas expanding into the relatively cold and very tenuous interstellar gas.

Mass Loss and Stellar Generations

Deutsch has questioned whether the loss of mass by supergiant, M-type stars might suffice to replenish the interstellar medium and prevent its exhaustion as a consequence of star formation. This problem has not been solved completely, but an answer is required before it can be confidently assumed that the interstellar gas is being enriched continuously by heavy elements that are formed in the interiors of very old stars, such as the M-type supergiants whose internal temperatures are sufficiently high to produce highly energetic nuclear reactions that lead to the formation of heavy elements. Deutsch's conclusion in 1961 was that the supergiant M stars alone will not significantly affect the physical properties of the interstellar medium, and that even if there is a sufficient mass loss from ordinary M-type giants, the discrepancy between the amount lost

Fig. 119. Coudé spectra, taken by A. J. Deutsch with the 200-in. Hale telescope (I) and the 100-in. Hooker telescope (II and III) of α Herculis. Spectra I and II are of the spectroscopic binary, III of the red supergiant. (*Mount Wilson and Palomar Observatories; courtesy* Sky and Telescope)

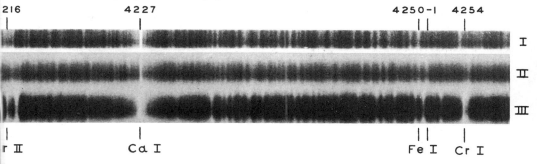

by the stars and the amount of gas required for evolutionary processes involves a factor of several hundred. It is now known, however, that many
other stars also lose mass, and this phenomenon undoubtedly exists in the
P Cygni stars, the Wolf-Rayet stars, the novae and supernovae, and perhaps even in young stars now undergoing contraction. Attempts have
been made, for example, by L. Biermann, to estimate the total amount of
interstellar gas created per unit time as a result of ejection from all stars
of the Milky Way. This estimate is necessarily highly speculative, and it
cannot serve yet as a reliable basis for theories of different generations of
star formation.

Thus, on the one hand, from the study of the physical properties of
the stars there is fairly convincing evidence that (a) the oldest stars in
the Milky Way were formed in a gaseous medium consisting mostly of
hydrogen with an almost negligible addition of heavy elements, and (b)
stars of later generations (for example, those now in the process of formation) contain a relatively greater fraction of metals. On the other hand, it
is nothing more than supposition that an appreciable percentage of the
present interstellar gas was at one time located in the deep interiors of
different kinds of stars, and that, therefore, the ejected material, which is
now thoroughly mixed with the remnants of the original medium, contains a greater percentage of heavy elements than the original medium did.

A self-consistent hypothesis of star formation has been formulated by
W. A. Fowler, of the California Institute of Technology, F. Hoyle, J. L.
Greenstein, and G. R. Burbidge, among others. According to their theory,
before any star was formed in the Milky Way the gas consisted entirely of
hydrogen. Hence stars of very great age were formed of pure hydrogen,
and only those nuclear reactions that could occur in a hot hydrogen gas
sphere produced certain heavy elements, but by no means all of the
elements of the periodic table. In order to explain the abundances of the
heavy elements present in the stars, it is necessary to introduce the concept of different stellar generations. According to this theory, the oldest
known stars—those occurring in certain globular clusters, whose spectra
show weak metallic lines—were formed in an early generation, the sun
represents a much later generation, and presumably stars now being
formed represent an even later generation. However, as noted before, the
several steps in the reasoning that led to this hypothesis still are not confirmed by observation. Moreover, several unexplained differences in the
abundances of the elements in certain stars do not fit readily into this
hypothesis.

XII

STELLAR STRUCTURE

IN THE SECOND HALF of the 19th century, the American scientist J. Homer Lane and the German physicist A. Ritter considered the problem of the internal constitution of the stars. All later investigations, however, have been based on the 1907 book *Gaskugeln* ("Gaseous Spheres") by the German astrophysicist R. Emden[1] In the United States, the principal, perhaps the only, early investigator of the theory of stellar structure and evolution was H. N. Russell of Princeton University (his early theories were discussed in Chap. X, P. 200). At the same time, the Englishmen A. S. Eddington and J. H. Jeans vigorously discussed the same problems. Even though their results were often in disagreement, it is surprising to realize how much information could be obtained concerning a star's structure without any knowledge of the physical processes that create the energies pouring out from the stellar photospheres as electromagnetic radiation (also referred to as ether waves).

A number of Eddington's papers, written after 1916 and included and extended in his 1926 book, *The Internal Constitution of the Stars,* greatly

Fig. 120. R. Emden. (*Courtesy of K. Emden*)

advanced the theory of stellar structure and indicated the principal physical processes occurring in stellar interiors. In the introduction to his book, Eddington defined the problem as follows:

We do not study the interior of a star merely out of curiosity as to the extraordinary conditions prevailing there. It appears that an understanding of the mechanism of the interior throws light on the external manifestations of the star, and the whole theory is ultimately brought into contact with observation. At least that is the goal which we keep in view. . . .

How is T [temperature], or equivalently the rate of outflow of radiation determined by the mass and radius of the star? That is the central problem of this book.[2]

ADVANCES IN THE THEORY OF STELLAR INTERIORS

Energy Transport in Stars

In most of the earlier work, especially in Lane's, the energy transport from the star's center to its outer layers was believed to occur as a result of convection. The hypothesis was reasonable, since it was applicable to the earth's atmosphere and resulted in a first approach to the study of stellar interiors. Eddington, on the contrary, found that the transport of heat inside a star cannot be explained as a result of convection currents, but rather occurs primarily by radiation. He, therefore, introduced into the study of stellar interiors the concept of radiative equilibrium that already had been adopted by another English astronomer, R. A. Sampson, in 1894, but that could not be fully developed without further progress in the field of thermodynamics. As discussed in Chapter XI, P. 212, K. Schwarzschild had shown in 1906 that in the case of stellar atmospheres the heat and light is passed through the atmosphere of a star by radiation rather than by convection. Hence Eddington concluded ". . . our task is to apply the same principle to the interior of the sun and stars."[3]

In the introductory chapter of his book, Eddington gave the following description of the inside of a star:

The inside of a star is a hurly-burly of atoms, electrons and aether

Fig. 121. A. S. Eddington.

waves. We have to call to aid the most recent discoveries of atomic physics to follow the intricacies of the dance. We started to explore the inside of a star; we soon find ourselves exploring the inside of an atom. Try to picture the tumult! Dishevelled atoms tear along at 50 miles a second with only a few tatters left of their elaborate cloaks of electrons torn from them in the scrimmage. The lost electrons are speeding a hundred times faster to find new resting-places. Look out! There is nearly a collision as an electron approaches an atomic nucleus; but putting on speed it sweeps round it in a sharp curve. A thousand narrow shaves happen to the electron in 10^{-10} second; sometimes there is a side-slip at the curve, but the electron still goes on with increased or decreased energy. Then comes a worse slip than usual; the electron is fairly caught and attached to the atom, and its career of freedom is at an end. But only for an instant. Barely has the atom arranged the new scalp on its girdle when a quantum of aether waves runs into it. With a great explosion the electron is off again for further adventures. Elsewhere two of the atoms are meeting full tilt and rebounding, with further disaster to their scant remains of vesture.

As we watch the scene we ask ourselves: Can this be the stately drama of stellar evolution? It is more like the jolly crockery-smashing turn of a music-hall. The knockabout comedy of atomic physics is not very considerate towards our aesthetic ideals; but it is all a question of time-scale. The motions of the electrons are as harmonious as those of the stars but in a different scale of space and time, and the music of the spheres is being played on a keyboard 50 octaves higher. To recover this elegance we must slow down the action, or alternatively accelerate our own wits; just as the slow-motion film resolves the lusty blows of the prize-fighter into movements of extreme grace—and insipidity.

And what is the result of all this bustle? Very little. Unless we have in mind an extremely long stretch of time the general state of the star remains steady. Just as many atoms are repaired as are smashed; just as many bundles of radiation are sent out as are absorbed; just as many electrons are captured as are exploded away. The atoms and the electrons for all their hurry never get anywhere; they only change places. The aether waves are the only part of the population which do actually accomplish something; although apparently darting about in all directions without purpose they do in spite of themselves make a slow general progress outwards. This flow would if uncompensated lead to a gradual change in the whole state of the star, very slow but yet, we believe, too fast to accord with observational evidence. It is therefore necessary to assume that subatomic energy of some kind is liberated within the star, so as to replenish the store of radiant energy.[4]

Radiation Pressure

Eddington was much impressed by the fact that while stars differ greatly in brightness, density, and physical conditions, they differ relatively little in mass. In 1926, the extreme range of stellar masses known was between about $\frac{1}{6}$ and 100 times that of the sun. Since then the upper limit has been reduced somewhat and, according to a recent study by M. Schwarzschild and R. Härm, it may be only 65 solar masses. The smallest stellar masses known at the present time are about $\frac{1}{100}$ that of the sun (or about 10 times the mass of Jupiter). In order to explain the small range in stellar masses, Eddington developed the theory of radiation pressure: Any point in the interior of a star experiences gas and radiation pressure directed radially outward, while the force of gravity compensates for the outward force and keeps the star in equilibrium. The radiation pressure is proportional to the fourth power of the temperature. Thus even in the outer layers of a star where the temperature is 1 million degrees, radiation pressure amounts to about 2,500 atmospheres. In the deep interior of a star, where the temperature may be 10 million degrees, the radiation pressure would be roughly 25 million atmospheres.

Eddington concluded that the radiation pressure inside a star of a mass of about 100 times that of the sun, or 2×10^{35} gm, is high enough to offset the internal gravitation that holds the star together. In Eddington's words: "The force of gravitation collects together nebulous and chaotic material; the force of radiation pressure chops it off into suitably sized lumps."[5]

Mass-Luminosity Relation: Discovery and Theory

Another line of investigation pursued by Eddington was concerned with the relationship between masses and luminosities of stars. In the early years of the present century, a number of stellar masses had been derived from the study of spectroscopic and visual binaries, and in 1911 J. Halm at the Cape Observatory in South Africa suggested that a correlation exists between the absolute magnitudes of the stars and their masses. He combined the previously known correlation between spectral class and luminosity and the apparent correlation between mass and spectral class, which he found from a study of the work of W. W. Campbell on spectroscopic binaries and Russell on visual binaries. This "mass-luminosity relation" was further treated by Russell in 1913 and by E. Hertzsprung in 1918. In 1924, Eddington rediscussed the observational data and presented a diagram showing the mass-luminosity relation together with a theoretical explanation. The theory was based on the *law of perfect gases.*

---

* A theoretical relationship between the volume, pressure, and temperature of a gas which may be written as $PV = nkT$ where P=pressure, V=volume, n=number of molecules, T=temperature (absolute), and k=Boltzmann's constant (the ratio of a molecule's mean total energy to its absolute temperature).

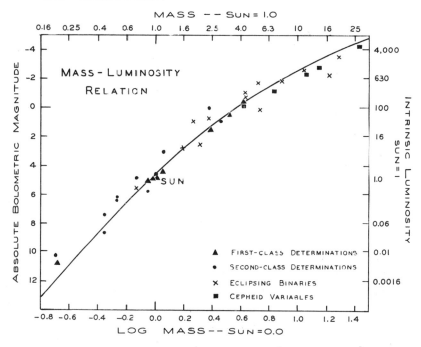

Fig. 122.   Diagram of the mass-luminosity relation by A. S. Eddington.
(*From* Monthly Notices of the Royal Astronomical Society, *LXXXIV,*
1924, Plate 8; courtesy Sky and Telescope)

Hence it was supposed to apply only to giant stars. However, in order to
estimate how far the dwarf or main-sequence stars deviate from the conditions of a perfect gas, Eddington included some in his diagram and
found that they too conformed to the theoretical mass-luminosity relation.
(In the diagram the different symbols refer to differing methods of mass
determination. The triangles are the most trustworthy values). This was
an entirely unexpected result and led to the following conclusions:

More than half of the stars used in the comparison are dwarf stars.
The agreement of their absolute magnitudes with the predicted magnitudes for gaseous stars is in conflict with the current view that they are
too dense to follow the laws of a perfect gas, and that their low luminosity
is attributable to deviation from gas-laws. According to the present results
their low luminosity is fully accounted for by their comparatively smaller
mass without appeal to any other physical difference.

The current expectation that between density 0.1 and 1 the compressibility of a star will fall off rapidly, as compared with the compressibility
of a perfect gas, appears to rest on a false analogy between stellar ions
and atoms at ordinary temperature. Owing to the high ionization, stellar
atoms have only about $\frac{1}{100,000}$ of the bulk of the ordinary atoms and

failure of the laws of a perfect gas is not to be expected till a density 100,000 times higher is reached.[6]

Eddington's last conclusion brought to the foreground another problem—the "white dwarf" stars for which densities of this order of magnitude had been inferred; a slight digression is necessary to review the history of these stars, the best known of which is Sirius B, the companion of the brightest star on the celestial sphere, Sirius.

White Dwarfs

The distance of Sirius, determined by trigonometric parallax measurements, is equal to 8.7 light-years. It also has a fairly rapid proper motion at right angles to the line of sight, amounting on the average to slightly more than 1″ per year. In 1844, F. W. Bessel, at Königsberg Observatory in Prussia, found that the motion of Sirius is slightly irregular and that it describes a wavy path on the celestial sphere. This led to the conclusion that Sirius is really a double star, and the bright star's irregular motion is the result of orbital movement around the center of gravity of a system in which the companion could not be detected. It was referred to, therefore, as a "dark star" and was, according to Eddington, the first "invisible star" to be definitely recognized. The heavy curve (a) in Fig. 123 shows the sinusoidal motion of the primary star, the thin curve represents the motion of the white dwarf companion, and the dashed curve the motion of the center of gravity of the system; (b) shows the apparent orbits of the two components around their common center of gravity; and (c) is the apparent orbit of the companion about the primary. Nineteen years after Bessel's discovery, the American telescope manufacturer Alvan Clark, while testing a new telescope objective made by him for the Dearborn Observatory of Northwestern University in Evanston, Illinois, noticed the faint companion, which since then has been observed regularly. The

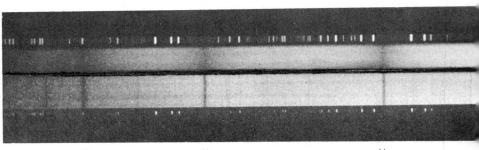

H_ϵ $\qquad$ H_δ $\qquad$ H_γ

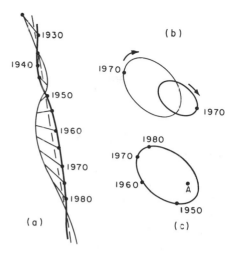

Fig. 123. The visual orbit of Sirius. (*From* Elementary Astronomy, *New York, 1959, Fig. 29.2*)

period of the system is about 50 years, and the mass of the companion is approximately equal to that of the sun, but it is several hundred times fainter. If the brightness of the companion were about $\frac{1}{360}$ that of the sun and if its surface temperature were equal to the sun's, the companion's surface would have to be $\frac{1}{360}$ of the surface and the radius (the square root of this value) about $\frac{1}{20}$ of the sun's radius. However, W. S. Adams found in 1914 that the spectrum of the companion resembles that of Sirius. Hence its surface brightness is greater than that of the sun and the surface area and radius are even smaller than estimated above. This implies an enormous density, and according to Eddington:

The message of the Companion of Sirius when it was decoded ran: "I am composed of material 3,000 times denser than anything you have come across; a ton of my material would be a little nugget that you could put in a matchbox." What reply can one make to such a message? The reply which most of us made in 1914 was—"Shut up. Don't talk nonsense."[7]

Although more is known about the physical properties of Sirius B than about any other white dwarf, another star of this type, 40 Eridani B, apparently was the first one to be recognized. Its message also was disregarded.

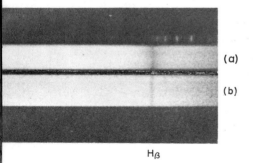

(a)

(b)

H_β

Fig. 124. Spectra of (a) a white dwarf, 40 Eridani B, and (b) a B9 supergiant, σ Cygni. (*Lick Observatory*)

Russell has recollected a visit to the Harvard Observatory in 1910, during which the star 40 Eridani B was discussed:

The first person who knew of the existence of white dwarfs was Mrs. Fleming; the next two, an hour or two later, Professor E. C. Pickering and I. With characteristic generosity, Pickering had volunteered to have the spectra of the stars which I had observed for parallax looked up on the Harvard plates. All those of faint absolute magnitude turned out to be of class G or later. Moved with curiosity I asked him about the companion of 40 Eridani. Characteristically again, he telephoned to Mrs. Fleming who reported within an hour or so that it was of class A. I saw enough of the physical implication of this to be puzzled and expressed some concern. Pickering smiled and said, "It is just such discrepancies which lead to the increase of our knowledge." Never was the soundness of his judgment better illustrated.[8]

It also is interesting to note that 40 Eridani B does appear in Russell's original spectrum-luminosity diagram (see Fig. 100), presenting an apparent exception to the usual stellar characteristics and not accounted for by his evolutionary theory. Russell apparently was not certain at that time of its exceptional characteristics, since he brushed it aside with the comment that the spectral type was very uncertain.

Eddington's investigations in 1924, however, made the strange stories of Sirius B and 40 Eridani B appear more plausible; they might represent matter in a state of compression where normal gas laws no longer apply. An independent check of the density of these stars was suggested by Eddington and attempted by Adams.

In the early part of the present century, Albert Einstein had predicted that the radiation of a certain wavelength emitted by a heavy body would be observed at a slightly longer wavelength by an observer located on a body of smaller mass. This so-called "gravitational redshift," in the case of a ray of light emitted by the sun, amounts to about $\frac{1}{100}$ A. If this redshift were interpreted as a consequence of radial motion, the sun would be observed as though it had a recessional velocity of 0.6 km/sec. Actually, of course, there is no recession, but astronomers have found it convenient to express the gravitational redshift in terms of kilometers per second rather than in angstrom units. Einstein's prediction also indicated that the relativity redshift is proportional to the mass of the emitting star and inversely proportional to its radius. Thus, for a white dwarf having a mass equal to that of the sun but a radius $\frac{1}{50}$ of the sun's, the gravitational redshift would be expected to be about 50 times greater than the sun's, or about 30 km/sec.

In order to verify the existence of a large gravitational redshift, it is necessary to have some reference point for the determination of the white dwarf's true radial velocity. This requirement is met in the case of those white dwarfs that are members of binary systems: the companions of Sirius and of 40 Eridani. Although a fairly large number of white dwarfs are now known, it is impossible to separate their gravitational redshifts from their Doppler displacements, the latter being caused by the relative motion of the white dwarf with respect to the sun.

In the case of Sirius B, Eddington predicted in 1924 that the gravitational redshift would be 20 km/sec, and Adams found a mean value of 21 km/sec. According to Adams: "The results may be considered, therefore, as affording direct evidence from stellar spectra for the validity of the third test of relativity, and for the remarkable densities predicted by Eddington for the dwarf stars of early type of spectrum."[9]

More recent attempts to measure the radial velocity of Sirius B, principally by G. P. Kuiper, have thrown some doubt upon the exact value found by both Adams and J. H. Moore, at the Lick Observatory. The difficulty in the earlier spectroscopic observations arose from the scattered light of the bright component of Sirius, which caused a blending of the spectral lines belonging to the companion with the spectral lines of scattered light from the primary star.

During the past 25 years, the apparent elliptical orbit carried the companion into the immediate vicinity of the primary star, and no recent measurements of the redshift of Sirius B have been published. At present the distance between the primary star and white dwarf companion is increasing, and will be about 11" around 1970. Further attempts will be made then to repeat the measurements of Adams and Moore.

According to D. M. Popper, the gravitational redshift of 40 Eridani B is +21 km/sec. The value predicted on the basis of general relativity, +17 km/sec, is within the uncertainties of the measurements and of the adopted mass and radius of this white dwarf.

About 100 white dwarfs are known now (many of them were discovered by W. J. Luyten, in the course of a systematic study of stellar proper motions and apparent magnitudes), but their relative frequency is much greater than this number would imply. Since all of them are of low absolute magnitude, they can be detected only at small distances from the sun. White dwarfs are of particular interest to astrophysicists, because of the peculiar conditions in their interiors implied by the enormous densities, and also because they have come to be regarded as the end products of stellar evolution.

Mass-Luminosity Relation: Recent Investigations

A more recent discussion of the mass-luminosity relation was presented by Kuiper in 1938. His diagram, shown in Fig. 125, is still being used extensively. (The abscissa is the logarithm of the mass.) Kuiper included in his discussion the so-called Trumpler stars (indicated by crosses in the upper righthand corner). Their masses had been derived by R. J. Trumpler, not from Kepler's third law, but from the tendency of bright O-type stars in clusters to show velocities of recession exceeding those of the fainter stars in the clusters. Trumpler interpreted these as gravitational effects similar to the gravitational redshifts of the white dwarfs.

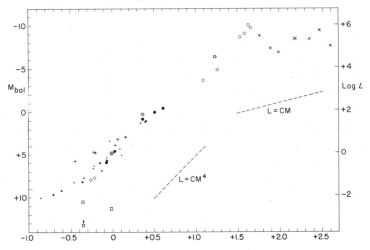

Fig. 125. Diagram of the mass-luminosity relation by G. P. Kuiper. (*From* Astrophysical Journal, *LXXXVIII, 1938, p. 489*)

The observational data used by Trumpler are beyond criticism, but an interpretation in terms of a relativity redshift has been questioned by O. Struve, among others. The spectra of the Trumpler O-type stars closely resemble the spectra of binary stars of similar spectral types, for which masses of 50 times that of the sun have been derived, using Kepler's third law. According to Trumpler's interpretation, the masses turn out to be several hundred times, and in a few cases even a thousand times, greater than that of the sun. It is improbable that such very large masses exist. Hence it appears likely that the redshifts of the O-type stars in galactic clusters are produced by mass motion in the atmospheres of these stars or by a real tendency of the O-type stars to show radial motions of recession with respect to the cluster as a whole.

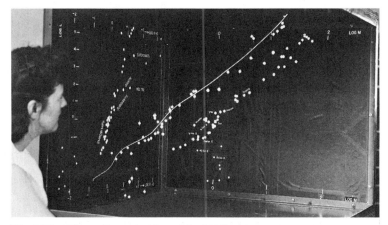

Fig. 126.　Three-dimensional model of stellar parameters.

Figure 126 represents a three-dimensional model in which the principal parameters of each star are shown by means of suspended beads. The wavy line shows the distribution of the representative points of a small sample of stars with respect to luminosity (log L), radius (log R), and mass (log M). The projection of the beads upon the (log L–log R) plane is, in principle, identical with the conventional H-R diagram.*

The projection of the beads upon the (log M–log L) plane is the conventional mass-luminosity relation. In the figure, the Trumpler stars were omitted. The white dwarfs are located near the bottom of the H-R and the mass-luminosity planes.

As is the case with the H-R diagram, the apparent clustering of representative points along the mass-luminosity band is probably a result of the rates of stellar evolution. Most stars tend to vary but slightly in luminosity and mass while they are located on the main sequence of the H-R diagram and on the band represented by the mass-luminosity relation.

During the 1920's and 1930's, most astronomers believed that this relation may be regarded as applying to all stars of different characteristics except the white dwarfs. However, there has been a tendency in recent years to question this conclusion, and the number of stars that appear to violate the mass-luminosity relation is steadily increasing; some examples will be given in Chap. XIV.

Equation of State of a Perfect Gas

Eddington's realization that because of the high ionization in stellar interiors, the law of perfect gases can be used for all stars except the

---

* In the original diagram, the abscissa is usually the spectral type, or surface temperature, of the star; the radius may be found from the relation of $L = 4\pi R^2 \sigma T^4$, where σ is the constant of Stefan's law and T is the surface temperature. *Stefan's law*, $E = \sigma T^4$, states that the amount of heat radiated per second from each square cm by a black body, E, is proportional to the fourth power of its absolute temperature. This diagram is frequently referred to as the "Russell diagram."

white dwarfs, greatly facilitated further study of stellar structure. As mentioned on P. 242, the so-called equation of state of a perfect gas usually is given as the product of the pressure and the volume, being equal to the temperature times a numerical constant. In astronomical calculations, the equation of state is rewritten in a slightly different form: The pressure equals a numerical constant times the density times the temperature divided by the mean weight of a gaseous particle. The pressure given by the equation of state is that of the gas itself. If radiation pressure is not negligible, its effect must be added to that of the gas pressure. Since the stars remain approximately constant in their physical properties over long intervals of time, it is clear that the various layers inside the star adjust themselves in such a manner that at every point the inward force of gravitation is exactly equal to the outward force of gas and radiation pressure. However, in order to calculate the distribution of temperature and density within a star, it is necessary to know the opacity of the gas at each point, because it is this opacity that prevents the radiation from freely flowing outward.

Eddington himself, and numerous theoreticians in more recent years, have calculated the opacities and the average particle weights that apply to each layer. However, it was not known until Russell's work in 1929 (discussed in Chap. XI), that the solar gas is almost entirely hydrogen. Eddington, therefore, made the incorrect assumption that the mean-particle mass is approximately 2, while in the case of pure hydrogen the average mass of a proton and an electron is ½. The helium atom, which has a mass of 4 and two electrons, if fully ionized would produce an average particle mass of ⅓. At the present time, it is customary to adopt the percentages of hydrogen (X), of helium (Y), and of all other heavier atoms as $100-X-Y$, and to carry out the necessary calculations with these assumed values. The results of the calculations then are compared with the actual properties of the stars, and if they are found to be in disagreement, other assumptions are made concerning the abundances of the chemical elements.

REVISION OF RUSSELL'S THEORY OF STELLAR EVOLUTION

As discussed in Chap. X on P. 200 Russell had in 1913 presented a theory of stellar evolution that quite adequately explained all the observational facts known at that time, and it was generally accepted by astronomers. The subsequent theoretical investigations discussed above contradicted several of his assumptions. In addition, it was becoming increasingly clear that the energy of contraction, postulated as the only source of energy by Russell, did not account for stellar radiation throughout the lifetimes of the stars. In 1925, Russell reviewed the implications of these facts in his article "The Problem of Stellar Evolution," which stated:

The great problem of the evolution of the stars may be attacked along two main lines. We may study the properties of the stars themselves, as revealed by observation, and find orderly sequences among them; or we may analyze, on general physical principles, the constitution of a mass of gravitating matter, and the probable sequence of its changes.

Advances on these two fronts have shown a certain tendency to alternation. Lockyer's conception of stars of rising and falling temperature was based mainly on general physical considerations. The recognition of the sequences of giant and dwarf stars lent strong support to this theory, and—as the present writer showed some eleven years ago—a great mass of observed details fits in with remarkable completeness with the idea that the stars rise in temperature until the gas in their interior becomes compressible only with difficulty, and then cool down again.

More recently, progress has been mainly on the theoretical side, and has been very rapid. Among the milestones on the way may be noted the application of the theory of radiative equilibrium to the internal constitution of the stars, the appreciation of the fundamental importance of radiation pressure in this equilibrium, and of ionization in making the mean molecular weight low and almost independent of chemical composition—then, recently, the development of rational, rather than empirical, expressions for the elusive opacity-constant, and the recognition that the dismembered atoms inside the stars are so small that even at enormous densities the material must behave like a perfect gas. Several investigators—Jeans, Kramers, Eggert—have contributed to this field but much the largest share is Eddington's.

Meanwhile, observation has established conclusive evidence—with the joint help of astronomy, physics, chemistry, geology, and biology—that the life of the sun must be enormously long, and that the stars must have within themselves some vast store of potential energy of hitherto unimagined extent. These new developments must obviously lead to changes in the theory of stellar evolution to which reference was made above. One frank, but not unfriendly critic recently characterized these changes as "sudden death." The writer—remembering Mark Twain's response to the rumour of his own demise—believes that in this case, too, the reports have been "greatly exaggerated."

On one point there can be no possible doubt. The feature of the older theory which assumed a fall of internal temperature in the denser dwarf stars owing to the close-packing of the atoms must be finally abandoned. Eddington's argument is conclusive and it is clear that the low surface temperatures of these stars must be ascribed, not to low internal temperatures, but to the increase in opacity with density, which prevents the heat from leaking out quickly to the surface.[10]

As the foregoing quotation indicates, Russell's ideas concerning the interpretation of the H-R diagram had undergone a drastic change since 1913. In the textbook *Astronomy*, mentioned on P. 221, he said the following:

Recent advances (the recognition that stellar energy must come not from contraction but from some unknown source, the development of the theory of stellar luminosity, and, over all, Eddington's recognition, in 1924, that the ionized gas inside a star must be almost indefinitely compressible) have greatly changed the aspect of the problem. Progress is still rapid, and the best theory that can be advanced at present may be radically altered within a very few years. With this warning it may be appropriate to proceed to a discussion of the situation as it presents itself in 1926.[11]

Two main problems discussed in *Astronomy* are the facts that: (1) The so-called main sequence is a fairly broad band and not a narrow line; (2) The giant stars depart greatly from the main sequence.

With regard to the former, Russell argued that on general grounds the rate of energy generation measured in ergs per second per gram of stellar material "may be supposed to vary with the temperatures, density and composition of the gas."[12] If all stars belonging to the main sequence had the same chemical composition, the rates of energy generation would depend only upon their temperature and density. Although the H-R diagram in its conventional form records the star's absolute visual magnitude as the ordinate and the surface temperature as the abscissa, the diagram, in principle, could be converted into another similar diagram in which the two coordinates are the mean density and the mean temperature. Hence, if the chemical composition were the same for all stars, they would define an infinitely narrow line sloping from the upper left to the lower right side of the H-R diagram. Russell stated:

This is emphatically not the case, and from this fact the important conclusion may be drawn that the rate of generation of heat, at points where the pressure and temperature are the same, is different in different stars. The stars cannot therefore all contain the same proportion of "active matter"—or of the various kinds of it which may exist. They must differ in composition.[13]

Although this conclusion adequately explained the width of the main sequence, it did not account for the giant sequence in the H-R diagram that is represented by a wide band in which the most luminous stars are the reddest and in which the yellow stars are of considerably lower luminosity.

It is therefore reasonable to suppose that a second process of generation of heat, at the expense of a different kind of active matter, and at a rate varying in a different manner with temperature and density, takes place in these stars.[14]

In order to account for the two kinds of active matter, Russell adopted the words "dwarf stuff" for the main-sequence stars and "giant stuff" for the sequence of the giants.

Figure 127 is adapted from Russell's book; a star of large mass is indicated by the solid line, one of small mass by the dashed line. A star's evolutionary path depends on the proportion of active material present and on the relative amounts of giant stuff and dwarf stuff. In the simplest case discussed here, the active material (consisting both of giant and dwarf stuff) constitutes a small fraction of the star's mass, so that all through its history the mass, and hence its absolute magnitude, will be nearly the same. A star of large mass first contracts until it reaches the right-hand side of the giant sequence band. It then crosses the band, and in doing so exhausts most of its giant stuff. When the star's evolutionary track emerges from the giant sequence, it continues to contract in accordance with Helmholtz's theory until it reaches the right-hand side of the main-sequence band. At this point, dwarf stuff provides energy and the star continues moving across the main sequence until the dwarf stuff has been exhausted. Finally,

. . . contraction would become more rapid, the diameter would diminish to a very small value and finally the density would become so great

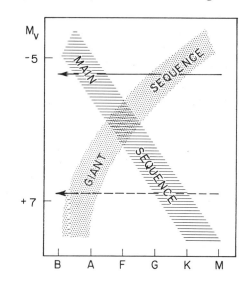

Fig. 127. Schematic evolutionary tracks of a star of large mass (solid line) and of small mass (dashed line), adapted from Russell.

that even the greatly ionized atoms would be almost in contact and no further contraction would be possible. The temperature would then fall, internally and externally, and the star's career, so far as we can trace it in imagination, would be at an end.[15]

The evolutionary track of a star of small mass also would carry its representative point across the diagram from right to left. It first would enter the main sequence where dwarf stuff would furnish the energy. After emerging from the main-sequence band, the star would continue contracting until its representative point reaches the right edge of the hypothetical "giant-stuff band." While passing through this band, the star would be a white dwarf. "As before, the final stage would come when the density precluded further contraction. . . ."[16]

Russell also has discussed several alternative evolutionary tracks in the H-R diagram for stars containing large amounts of active matter and involving considerable mass losses during their evolutionary history. The evolution then becomes considerably more complicated. Since Russell did not know in 1926 that nuclear reactions cause only a very minute loss of mass, he had to allow for the possibility that a considerable mass loss occurred in both the giant-sequence and the main-sequence stages of the evolution. This would cause the evolutionary tracks of both stars to incline downward, while the representative point is in one of the two bands.

Russell's theory predicts, in accordance with the observations, that there should be large numbers of stars in the long-lived states—that is, in those regions of the diagram where either giant stuff or dwarf stuff is being consumed. These stages are represented by the giant band, the main-sequence band, and the region of white dwarfs. "Stars which would be represented by points on other parts of the diagram [where the Helmholtz contraction is the only source of energy] should be rare, but there is no reason why some should not be found."[17]

In accordance with the observations, it is predicted that giants evolve more rapidly than main-sequence stars. The former are, therefore, relatively less numerous than the latter. A B-type star would be formed only after it has used up substantially all of its giant stuff before drawing upon its dwarf stuff. A white dwarf must have exhausted all of its dwarf stuff.

In conclusion, Russell wrote as follows:

It should be emphasized once more, in conclusion, that the scheme of stellar evolution sketched in the preceding pages is *tentative*. It accounts for most of the observed facts, but is far from resting on the solid basis of general physics that underlies the theories of stellar atmospheres and stellar luminosity. Other and quite different theories have been suggested;

for example, Jeans has accounted for many of the facts on the hypothesis that the rate of generation of energy is independent of the temperature. The final theory, when it comes, may be very different; but if nothing should be set down here except what is firmly established, the subject of stellar evolution could not be discussed at all.[18]

Russell's theory of giant stuff and dwarf stuff never was widely accepted by astronomers, but his insistence upon discussing evolutionary tracks in the H-R diagram has been followed by all the more recent investigators, as will be seen in the next chapter. In this respect, his influence has been overwhelming. Russell and his followers were inspired by an analogy suggested by William Herschel:

Following an analogy suggested by Herschel, suppose that an intelligent observer, who had never before seen a tree, were permitted an hour's walk in a forest. During that space he would not see a single leaf unfold; yet he could find sprouting seeds, small saplings, young, full-grown, and decrepit trees, and fallen trunks moldering back into earth, and in that brief hour he might form a correct idea of the life history of a tree.
In the same manner our task is to take the various types and classes of stars with whose properties we have become familiar, and arrange them in some rational scheme of evolution—some orderly sequence of development.[19]

It shall be seen later that there is now some hope of discovering evolutionary processes in individual stars from the study of the changes in periods of pulsating variables. It is also necessary to recognize that catastrophic phenomena, such as the explosions of novae and supernovae, represent significant stages in the evolution of individual stars.

SOURCES OF STELLAR ENERGY

The main problem in Russell's work, and in that of all astrophysicists concerned with stellar structure and evolution in the 1920's and 1930's, was the unknown source of stellar energy. It was agreed generally that energy is derived from transformation of mass into energy, according to Einstein's law: $E = mc^2$, where E is the amount of energy released, m is the mass transformed, and c is the velocity of light. However, the actual process involved was not known, and the possibilities were well described by Eddington in his book *Stars and Atoms* in 1927:

No supply of any importance is found until we come to consider the electrons and atomic nuclei; here a reasonable amount can be released by regrouping the protons and electrons in the atomic nuclei (transmutation of elements), and a much greater amount by annihilating them.

Transmutation of the elements—so long the dream of the alchemist—is realized in the transformation of radioactive substances. Uranium turns slowly into a mixture of lead and helium. But none of the known radioactive processes liberate anything like enough energy to maintain the sun's heat. The only important release of energy by transmutation occurs at the very beginning of the evolution of the element.

We must start with hydrogen. The hydrogen atom consists simply of a positive and negative charge, a proton for the nucleus plus a planet electron. Let us call its mass 1. Four hydrogen atoms will make a helium atom. If the mass of the helium atom were exactly 4, that would show that all the energy of the hydrogen atoms remained in the helium atom. But actually the mass is 3.97; so that energy of mass 0.03 must have escaped during the formation of helium from hydrogen. By annihilating 4 grammes of hydrogen we should have released 4 grammes of energy. Either process might be used to furnish the sun's heat. . . .

The view that the energy of a star is derived by the building up of other elements from hydrogen has the great advantage that there is no doubt about the possibility of the process; whereas we have no evidence that the annihilation of matter can occur in Nature. . . . To my mind the *existence* of helium is the best evidence we could desire of the possibility of the *formation* of helium. The four protons and two electrons constituting its nucleus must have been assembled at some time and place; and why not in the stars? . . . I am aware that many critics consider the conditions in the stars not sufficiently extreme to bring about the transmutation—the stars are not hot enough. The critics lay themselves open to an obvious retort; we tell them to go and find *a hotter place*.

But here the advantage seems to end. There are many astronomical indications that the hypothesis attributing the energy of the stars to the transmutation of hydrogen is unsatisfactory. . . . There is considerable evidence that as a star grows older it gets rid of a large fraction of the matter which originally constituted it, and apparently this can only be contrived by the annihilation of the matter. The evidence, however, is not very coherent, and I do not think we are in a position to come to a definite decision. On the whole the hypothesis of annihilation of matter seems the more promising. . . .

The phrase "annihilation of matter" sounds like something supernatural. We do not yet know whether it can occur naturally or not, but there is no obvious obstacle. The ultimate constituents of matter are minute positive charges and negative charges which we may picture as centres of opposite kinds of strain in the ether. If these could be persuaded to run together they would cancel out, leaving nothing except a splash in the ether which spreads out as an electromagnetic wave carrying off the energy released by the undoing of the strain. The amount of this energy is amazingly large; by annihilating a single drop of water we should be supplied with 200 horsepower for a year. . . .[20]

. . . *If an individual star is to progress any part of the way down the main series it must lose mass.* We can put the same inference in a more general way. Now that it has been found that luminosity depends mainly on mass, there can be no important evolution of faint stars from bright stars unless the stars lose a considerable part of their mass. . . . It is this result which has caused the hypothesis of annihilation of matter to be seriously considered.[21]

But it is now known that no significant mass loss need occur during stellar evolution, except possibly in its last stages. As research into stellar structure and nuclear processes progressed, the alternative rejected by Eddington—namely, the transmutation of elements—was shown to be the source of stellar energy. Many astronomers and physicists, among them T. G. Cowling in England, R. deR. Atkinson at Rutgers University in New Jersey, C. F. von Weizsäcker, and G. Gamow contributed significantly to the final solution by German-born H. A. Bethe of Cornell University in 1939. Bethe showed that the most important source of energy in ordinary stars is the so-called "carbon-nitrogen cycle," in which carbon and nitrogen serve as catalysts for the conversion of four hydrogen atoms into one helium atom. This process was found to account satisfactorily for the rate of the sun's energy generation, if its central temperature were 18.5 million degrees, an estimate that agreed with the temperature of 19 million degrees calculated from Eddington's theory of stellar structure.

Other processes have been suggested since, as mentioned in the preceding chapter. J. L. Greenstein, W. A. Fowler, G. R. Burbidge, and E. M. Burbidge particularly have discussed a number of nuclear reactions that may take place under different conditions in stellar interiors, and occasionally in the surface layers, and thus may account for the formation of all the chemical elements in the stars. The more recent work on stellar structure has been contributed mainly by S. Chandrasekhar, M. Schwarzschild, F. Hoyle, and others. Current views on stellar evolution, based upon their studies, will be discussed in the next chapter.

Fig. 128.   S. Chandrasekhar.

XIII

H-R DIAGRAMS &
STELLAR EVOLUTION

AS MENTIONED on P. 255 in the preceding chapter, the evolutionary history of stars is usually discussed in terms of their "evolutionary tracks" in the H-R diagrams, which show the changes in the basic parameters as a function of time. It is necessary, therefore, to discuss in more detail the characteristics of observational H-R diagrams.

Perhaps the most complete H-R diagram, including all stars for which the surface temperature and the visual absolute magnitude are known, is that constructed by W. Gyllenberg at the Lund Observatory in Sweden. It shows the same characteristics detected by Russell in the original H-R diagram (see Fig. 100): namely, that the vast majority of the stars fall upon the diagonal branch, known as the main sequence, and that there is a wide scattering of representative points belonging to stars of high luminosity and a considerable range in surface temperature (this group includes the *giants* and *supergiants*). A smaller number of stars, often called *subgiants,* fall in the section of the diagram between the main sequence and the giants. Relatively few stars are found in the Gyllenberg diagram below the main sequence. Those near the lower edge of the main sequence usually are designated *subdwarfs.* The few points at absolute visual magnitudes between +10 and +15 are the *white dwarfs.*

Because of the high luminosity of the giants, the supergiants, and the very hot stars in the upper part of the main sequence, observational selection tends to favor them when the H-R diagram is based upon all available data. The diagram does not give a correct estimate of the relative

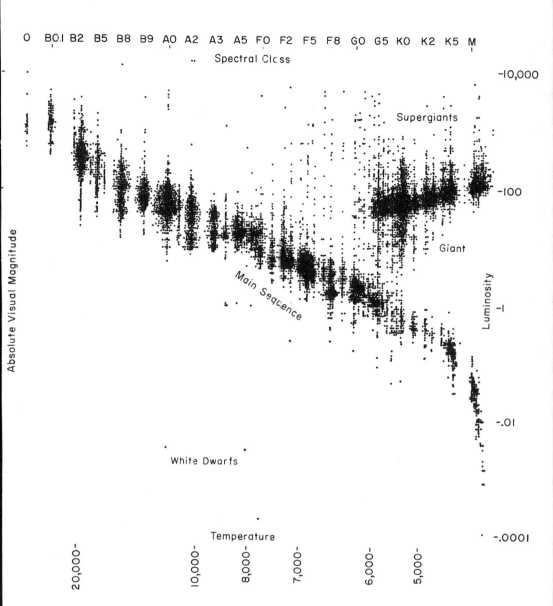

Fig. 129. The H-R diagram for stars accessible to observation with modern telescopes, prepared by W. Gyllenberg, Lund Observatory, Sweden.

numbers of stars in its different parts. In order to avoid difficulties of selection, H-R diagrams that limit the data to all stars within distances of 5 to 10 parsecs from the sun have been made. (Figs. 130 and 131; luminosity is expressed in terms of the sun.) These diagrams clearly show (a) that when a small volume of space in the vicinity of the sun is considered,

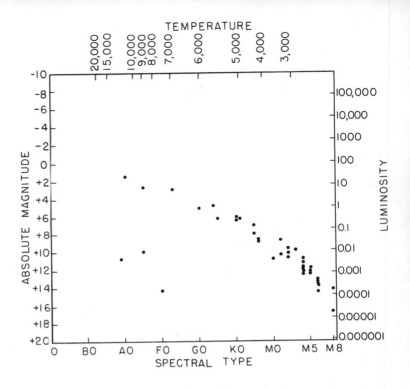

Fig. 130. The H-R diagram for stars less than 5 parsecs distant from the sun, as given by P. van de Kamp in 1953. (*From* Elementary Astronomy, *New York, 1959, fig. 25.6*)

Fig. 131. The H-R diagram for stars less than 10 parsecs distant from the sun. (*From* Elementary Astronomy, *New York, 1959, fig. 25.7*)

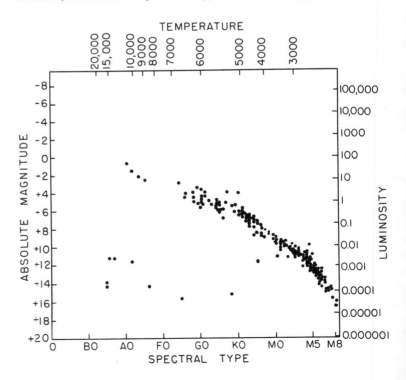

the stars are most numerous at the lower end of the main sequence, and (b) that the white dwarfs are relatively numerous while the giants and supergiants are extremely rare.

It will be noticed from the H-R diagrams for stars at distances no greater than 5 to 10 parsecs that the representative points of the main sequence do not fall upon a continuous line. Rather, they show an appreciable amount of scatter, amounting to perhaps 1 or even 2 mag. Some of this scatter is the result of uncertainties in the determinations of the stellar distances that are required for the computation of the visual absolute magnitudes. However, the investigations of Kuiper and many other astronomers have shown that, even after allowing for the uncertainties of the absolute magnitudes, there remains on the main sequence a dispersion of 1 mag. Thus a fairly wide band, rather than a narrow line, is involved.

In order to examine this problem more thoroughly, in the 1930's O. Heckmann, then in Göttingen and now at the Bergedorf Observatory in Germany, and others, started investigating the H-R diagrams of certain galactic star clusters.

H-R DIAGRAMS OF GALACTIC STAR CLUSTERS

Since the individual stars of a cluster are all at approximately the same distances from us, it is not necessary to determine their absolute magnitudes: The H-R diagram may be constructed by plotting the visual apparent magnitudes as the ordinate and the surface temperature, or its equivalent, the star's color index (see P. 80) as the abscissa. Two modern H-R diagrams, often called *color-luminosity arrays*, by H. L. Johnson

Fig. 132.   (Left) The color-luminosity array of the Pleiades, according to H. L. Johnson and W. W. Morgan. (*From* Elementary Astronomy, *New York, 1959, fig. 26.5*)
Fig. 133.   (Right) The color-luminosity array of Praesepe, according to H. L. Johnson. (*From* Elementary Astronomy, *New York, 1959, fig. 26.6*)

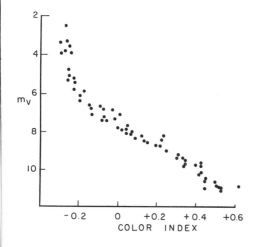

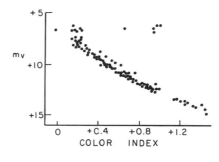

and W. W. Morgan for the Pleiades and by H. L. Johnson for the cluster of Praesepe are shown in Figs. 132 and 133. The representative points of both clusters define a fairly narrow band as the main sequence, with a smaller dispersion than those attained when the stars are picked at random. The dispersions of the color-luminosity arrays of clusters are reduced still further when allowance is made for the fact that some cluster members are double stars.

A superposition of color-luminosity arrays for different star clusters may be used to determine their relative distances from the sun and to display real differences in the main sequences of different clusters. It will be noticed that while the cluster of Praesepe ends on the left-hand side approximately at color index 0, the main sequence of the Pleiades extends almost to color index -0.3. Praesepe has a few stars of large color index and high apparent magnitude (about $+6$); there are no such giant stars in the Pleiades. In both clusters, the upper ends of the main sequences tend to curve steeply upward at the top.

Independently of these investigations R. J. Trumpler, first at the Allegheny Observatory and later at the Lick Observatory, began investigating the properties of galactic star clusters. He studied a large number of clusters, and his observations constitute the main basis for the present theory of stellar evolution. Trumpler's own conclusions, published in 1925, provide an excellent summary of the state of knowledge at that time:

The distribution of spectral types in open clusters varies essentially along two lines. On the one hand we find great differences in the proportion of cluster stars that fall on the giant branch (F-M). In class I we shall include clusters in which the giant branch is entirely missing or cases in which there are so few scattered stars falling within its limits that it must remain doubtful whether they are physical members or background stars. Class 2 comprises the clusters which show a marked crowding of stars along the giant branch although their number may still be small compared with that of the dwarf stars. There is not quite sufficient evidence yet for the establishment of a third class in which the yellow and red giant stars are very numerous and form the most important constituents of the cluster.

The dwarf series, as defined above, on the other hand, while always present does not always extend equally far in the direction of the hotter spectral types. We shall designate with b those clusters in which the dwarf branch reaches up to the spectral classes B0–B5. Clusters of class a contain no types of higher temperature than B8, while those of class f are entirely composed of stars with spectral types F0–M. A priori we might expect, the existence of all possible combinations of 1 and 2 with b, a, f; so far, however, only the following four were found to be represented:

Fig. 134.   The double cluster in Perseus. (*Yerkes Observatory*)

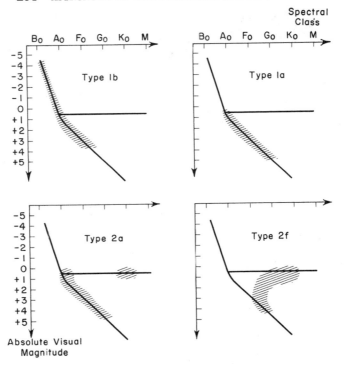

Fig. 135.   Magnitude–spectral class diagrams of four cluster types, by R. J. Trumpler. (*From* Publications of the Astronomical Society of the Pacific, *XXXVII, 1925, p. 315; courtesy* Sky and Telescope)

1 *b*: The brightest cluster stars of Type B0–B5, including occasionally an O-type star. The fainter stars are closely crowding around the dwarf branch, tracing it continuously down to the instrumental limit. Giant stars A5–M are entirely missing or very rare. . . .

1 *a*: The brightest cluster stars are of class B8–A5; the fainter stars follow the dwarf branch closely. No stars of class B0–B5 are present and no or very few giant stars. . . .

2 *a*: The brighter cluster stars are scattered along the giant branch from B8 to K, the fainter stars follow the dwarf branch from B8 toward F and G. In general the giant branch is not uniformly represented but shows a concentration at G5–K0; around class A, where the giant and dwarf branches meet the stars are numerous and pretty much scattered. Often there is even a marked gap in the giant branch between A and G making the G5–K0 giants appear as an isolated group. The dwarf branch is continuous. . . .

2 *f*: No stars of classes B or A are present. The brighter stars follow the giant branch from K to F, which turns somewhat down to reach the F dwarf stage; the points are rather widely scattered at this point and the fainter stars seem to follow the dwarf branch from F0–G.

The magnitude-spectral class diagrams characteristic for these four types are illustrated in Figure 135. The full lines drawn are the axes of the giant and dwarf branches (Hertzsprung-Russell diagram) while the shaded areas mark the regions covered by the plotted cluster stars. The four types are somewhat arbitrarily selected, in reality there is a gradual transition between them.[1]

Trumpler listed the Pleiades cluster and the double cluster in Perseus as typical examples of class 1 *b*, and the Praesepe as class 2 *a*. His classification of star clusters has been confirmed by later studies, but his ideas concerning the evolution of the clusters have been greatly modified.

It is important to realize that at that time a star's evolution was believed to proceed from the red giants to the left, and then downward along the main sequence in the H-R diagram. From the study of 52 star clusters Trumpler concluded that:

There seems to be another factor besides age playing a role in determining the type of a cluster. This second argument may be furnished by the original mass of the cluster members. In other words, a cluster containing very massive stars follows a different course of evolution than a cluster consisting of small masses. . . .

As a whole, the spectroscopic observations are in good agreement with the hypothesis that all stars of a cluster originate at the same time or within a limited period, that the stars differ in original mass and run through their evolutionary course with different speed. If these views are correct we are led to the conclusion that the open clusters are already of considerable age; otherwise we would not find the dwarf branch so well formed in all cases, nor could we explain the general scarcity or total absence of yellow and red giant stars.[2]

Most recent investigators have disregarded Trumpler's second argument of difference between masses of various cluster types. Somewhat arbitrarily, they have assumed that each cluster has approximately the same proportions of stars of different initial masses. However, there is real evidence, especially from the work of M. Roberts and H. F. Weaver at the University of California, that the lower parts of the main sequences of clusters often have entirely different frequencies. Some clusters consist mainly of massive stars, and observational limitations in classifying their fainter members do not suffice to explain the low abundance of stars of small mass. Other clusters have long main-sequence bands, but in most of them the abundances of stars of small mass is lower than those of similar stars chosen at random in the Milky Way. There is as yet no clear understanding of the processes that lead to the formation of many stars of small mass in some clusters while in others stars of large mass are most frequent.

Shortly after Trumpler's investigations, a major reversal occurred in the ideas regarding the evolutionary path of a star in the H-R diagram. It led to the modern concept of evolution from the main sequence toward the giant branch. This implies that the galactic clusters are relatively young groups of stars.

While Trumpler was investigating the observable properties of the members of star clusters, B. Strömgren took the first tentative steps toward developing a theory of stellar evolution. He began with stars located on the main sequence and followed their properties during the early stages of hydrogen exhaustion in their inner parts; that is, he assumed that stellar energy was derived from conversion of hydrogen, even though the exact process was not known. According to Strömgren, the stars would move to the right side and upward in the H-R diagram—from the main sequence toward the giant branch—and the slope of the evolutionary track would depend upon the hydrogen content of the star.

In this connection, it must be stressed that, particularly at this time, theoretical work actually followed observation; that is, attempts were made to find a plausible process that, in the course of a star's evolution, would result in the observed distribution of stars in the H-R diagram.

Kuiper combined Trumpler's observational results and Strömgren's theoretical studies and published them in the *Astrophysical Journal* in 1937.[3] Kuiper's plot of Trumpler's observations of the surface temperatures and absolute magnitudes of stars in several galactic clusters (see Fig. 136; the abscissas are logarithms of the effective temperature; the ordinates are absolute bolometric magnitudes) is the first of a long series of similar diagrams obtained for different clusters.

The interpretation of Fig. 136 depends upon the reasonable assumption that, although clusters probably differ in age, the stars within a single cluster are more nearly of the same age. The figure clearly shows that the sequences of the stars almost coincide at the lower right-hand corner, but diverge conspicuously toward the top. For example, the clusters associated with the stars 12 Monocerotis (No. 1) and S Monocerotis (No. 2) extend toward the upper left corner of the diagram, while the Coma cluster, in Coma Berenices (No. 13) and the cluster NGC 752 (No. 14) show a sharp bend at temperatures below 10,000°.

The various sequences in the figure agree approximately with Strömgren's lines of constant hydrogen content. Kuiper, therefore, suggested that clusters such as 1 and 2 in the diagram consist of hydrogen-rich stars, while the brighter stars in clusters 13 and 14 contain less hydrogen. (It should be emphasized that in 1937 the nuclear processes of hydrogen con-

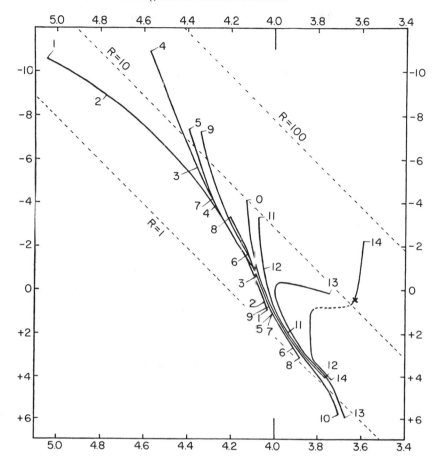

Fig. 136.   H-R diagrams for several clusters, by G. P. Kuiper. (*From* Astrophysical Journal, *LXXXVI, 1937, p. 185*)

version into helium were not known.) In Kuiper's words:

Three otherwise unexplained observational results follow at once from [the hypothesis that the typical spectral sequences in galactic clusters found by Trumpler represent lines of constant hydrogen content in the Hertzsprung-Russell diagram]. . . .

a) Ordinary giants do not occur in a cluster that contains O or early B stars. This mutual exclusion apparently results from the large difference in composition between the two groups mentioned.

b) The spectrum-luminosity arrays of clusters show less scatter than the array for stars in general. Either only a narrow main sequence is present or a main sequence plus a few giants. In the latter case the giants fall between narrow limits in the diagram. We may express this fact by saying that the stars in a cluster seem to form a one-parameter family. Our hy-

Fig. 137. G. P. Kuiper.

pothesis identifies this parameter with the mass, not with a relation between mass and hydrogen content.

c) The main sequences for various clusters differ in shape. In many clusters the brightest stars are abnormally bright for their spectral type. This very remarkable phenomenon was found by Trumpler to occur quite frequently, but it is absent in other clusters. No other than "racial" differences between the clusters can explain such results.[4]

The latest and most reliable calculation of cluster data is contained in the diagram by A. Sandage of Mount Wilson and Palomar Observatories. It can be seen from this diagram that the lower parts of the main sequences of all galactic clusters coincide to within the errors with which the distances of the clusters have been determined by various methods. The upper ends of the main sequences diverge rather strikingly. This phenomenon has been explained, in accordance with Strömgren's and Kuiper's ideas, as the result of the evolution of massive and luminous stars, roughly along horizontal tracks toward the right side of the diagram, from the original "zero-age" main sequence*. This explanation implies that the rapidly evolving stars of each cluster gradually become giants or even supergiants. It is based implicitly upon the previously mentioned assumption that different galactic star clusters have different ages, but that the member stars of any one cluster are all approximately of the same age.

A significant advance in our knowledge of galactic star clusters has come from the study of the youngest clusters: for example, NGC 2264. The first indication that the main sequences of very young clusters might differ considerably from the zero-age main sequence was obtained by P. P. Parenago from his elaborate study of the stars of the Orion nebula association. The hottest, and therefore the most massive, stars of this association lie on the main sequence, but the less massive cool stars fall distinctly above the zero-age main sequence. M. F. Walker investigated this anomaly for several very young clusters. (In the diagram the heavy line

---

* The term "zero-age" is somewhat misleading. It does not imply that the stars were "born" when on the main sequence. It represents a convenient but arbitrary zero point in time.

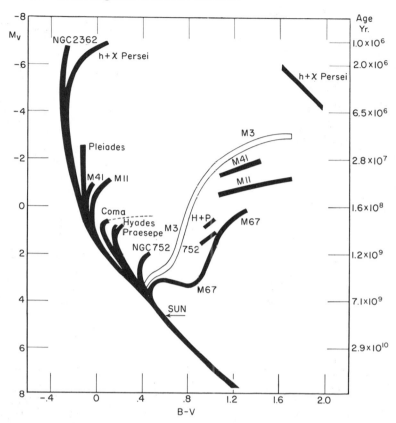

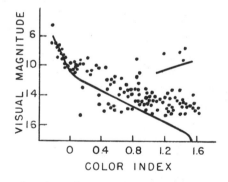

Fig. 138. Superposition of color-luminosity arrays of several galactic clusters and of one globular cluster (M 3), by A. Sandage. (*From* Astrophysical Journal, *CXXV, 1957, p. 436*)

Fig. 139. The color-luminosity array of the young galactic cluster (NGC 2264), according to M. F. Walker. (*From* Elementary Astronomy, *New York, 1959, fig. 26.14*)

represents the normal main sequence, the short line is the normal giant branch.) He concluded that these clusters are only a few million years old, and that the less massive stars have not reached the main sequence. They are, therefore, on the right side in the H-R diagram and represent stars in the stage of Kelvin (or Helmholtz) contraction.

It is now universally accepted that the formation of stars in a cluster occupies only a relatively short interval of time, compared to the age of the cluster as a whole. This conclusion resulted in a simplification in the interpretation of the H-R diagram. In recent years, there has been much discussion concerning the location of the low-mass stars of young clusters observed by Walker and others, because their locations in the H-R diagram do not correspond exactly to theoretical predictions made on the assumption of uniform age for all of these stars.

Some of the large scatter of the representative points in Walker's color-luminosity array for NGC 2264 undoubtedly is caused by stars that are not cluster members, but happen to lie in the sky within the geometrical confines of the solid angle occupied by the cluster. There also is a strong probability that the assumption of uniform age for all members is only approximately true; for example, all astronomers accept the hypothesis that while stars are now being formed in the Orion nebula, other stars in the nebula were formed some millions of years ago. Since all stars of a cluster were not formed at exactly the same time, the interval of formation in a younger cluster, such as the Orion association, represents a much larger fraction of the cluster's total age than in an older group, such as Praesepe. One must admit that the simplification of uniform age was unexpected and that the far-reaching deductions based upon it will require some revision, if it should be proved that a cluster's member stars are formed during an interval of time comparable to the age of the cluster itself.

THEORETICAL EVOLUTIONARY TRACKS IN THE H-R DIAGRAM

At present, on the basis of observations, four stages of a star's evolution can be traced in the H-R diagram. The following summary is based essentially upon the discussions that took place at a symposium on stellar populations at the Vatican Observatory in 1957, and represents, in part, G. Herbig's interpretation of the more detailed papers that were presented in Rome.

1. The stage of the Kelvin contraction, from right to left (Table 5).

Fig. 140.   Nebulosity in Monoceros (outer southern region of NGC 2264), photographed in red light. (© 1957, *National Geographic Society–Palomar Observatory*)

Table 5.

THE DURATION OF KELVIN CONTRACTION

3×10^4 years for B0	stars of mass 20 $\odot$
2×10^6 years for A0	stars of mass 3
5×10^7 years for dG2*	stars of mass 1
2×10^8 years for dK5	stars of mass 0.6
$\sim$ † 10^9 years for dM5	stars of mass 0.2

* "d" preceding the spectral type denotes dwarf stars. The giants and dwarfs are not clearly separated at B 0 and A 0. $\odot$ denotes the sun.

† $\sim$ means "about."

It is reasonable to believe that, for stars $\frac{1}{10}$ the mass of the sun, the contraction stage may last several billion years. The star first becomes visible as a small opaque globule of gas and dust that can be seen projected against the luminous background of an emission nebula. According to B. J. Bok, some of the smallest globules have radii of about 10^{12} km, or about 1 million times the sun's. The mass may be anywhere between about 100 solar masses and 0.01 solar mass. The globule is sufficiently compact to retain its identity over long intervals of time. It will not be disrupted by the tidal forces of the Milky Way as a whole or by those of the neighboring stars and nebulae. Therefore, contraction occurs as a result of self-gravitation, and the temperature gradually rises. For a long interval, presumably, the protostar is invisible, because it does not radiate enough light to be recorded visually or by means of photographs; yet its size is too small to be resolved as a globule.

Most modern workers have considered the evolution of a contracting protostar to begin at some arbitrary point in the H-R diagram the location of which depends mainly upon mass. As seen from Table 5, the contraction proceeds rapidly in the case of massive stars and very slowly in the case of stars of small mass. The evolutionary tracks during this stage—as computed by L. G. Henyey, R. D. Levee, and R. LeLevier at the University of California—for stars between masses 0.65 that of the sun and 2.29 that of the sun are shown in Fig. 142.

It is sometimes convenient to plot the evolutionary tracks, not in the conventional H-R diagram, but in another diagram in which the ordinate is the logarithm of the radius of the star, expressed in units of the solar

Fig. 141.   NGC 2237, nebula in Monoceros, photographed in red light with the 48-in. Schmidt telescope. (*Mount Wilson and Palomar Observatories*)

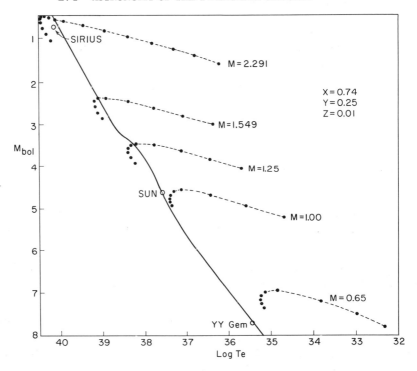

Fig. 142. Theoretical evolutionary tracks for stars of different masses during the pre–main sequence stage, according to L. G. Henyey, R. LeLevier, and R. D. Levee. (*Publications of the Astronomical Society of the Pacific, LXVII, 1955, p. 156*)

Fig. 143. Evolutionary tracks for stars of different masses during the pre–main sequence stage, according to G. Herbig. (*From* Advances in Astronomy and Astrophysics, *ed. Z Kopal, vol. 1, New York, Academic Press, 1962*)

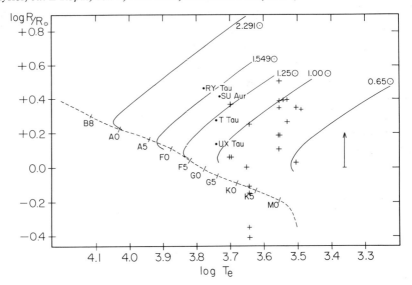

radius. This has been done by G. Herbig for stars of the same range of masses as included in Fig. 142. The evolutionary tracks are shown by the slanting lines, while the main sequence is indicated by the dotted line. The terminal spectral types are those indicated along the main sequence. Herbig's diagram also shows a number of T Tauri variable stars (indicated by solid points and crosses) that have not reached the main sequence yet, and are believed from other observations still to be undergoing contraction. The vertical arrows represent the displacement of the plotted points that would result if the visual absorption were increased by 1 mag.

In 1961, S. S. Huang investigated the distribution of the pre–main sequence stars in the H-R diagram. His computations show that the number of contracting stars of small mass must be very great, and that most of them have maximum energy radiation in the infrared region. He has suggested, therefore, that a greater effort should be made in the search for infrared stars—a type of investigation started in the 1930's by C. Hetzler at the Yerkes Observatory. Unfortunately, little has been done in this field during the past 10 years.

2. The "stable" main-sequence stage, during which the star remains very close to what is often designated as the "zero-age" main seqeunce. The duration of this stage is shown in Table 6.

Table 6.

DURATION OF THE STABLE MAIN-SEQUENCE STAGE

$\sim 10^7$	years for	B 0	stars of mass 20 ⊙
$\sim 5 \times 10^8$	years for	A 0	stars of mass 3
$\sim 10^{10}$	years for	dG 2	stars of mass 1
$\sim 10^{11}$	years for	dK 5	stars of mass 0.6
$\sim 10^{12}$	years for	dM 5	stars of mass 0.2

Although these time intervals are very uncertain, they are all about 100 or 1,000 times longer than the first stages.

During the second stage, nuclear reactions converting hydrogen into helium occur in the deep interior of the star, at temperatures of about 20 million degrees.

3. The fairly rapid stage of exhaustion of hydrogen fuel in the stellar interiors. As the hydrogen in the star's core is converted into helium, the tracks move from left to right, slowly at first, and then more rapidly, until the star becomes a relatively cool giant. The exhaustion of hydrogen is believed to cause a contraction of the inner core (now consisting entirely of helium), which, in turn, leads to adjustments of the outside layers,

which begin to expand and become cooler at the surface while the central temperature increases. At maximum brightness, the star may have an internal temperature of about 10^8 degrees and a helium core of about 50 per cent of the star's mass. It has been suggested that, under these conditions, helium may be synthesized into heavier elements.

While time intervals for the entire stage are too uncertain, something about them may be inferred from the initial theoretical tracks computed by various persons. Thus from Strömgren's work it may be estimated that a star of about $10\odot$ would move from B0 to B2 in roughly 2×10^7 years, and to B4 or B5 in another 2×10^7 years. The third stage, though probably somewhat shorter than the second, appears to be considerably longer than the first.

From an examination of the duration of the three stages, the following conclusions may be drawn:

Fig. 144.   Schematic drawing of the probable evolutionary track of a star having mass slightly greater than the sun, according to B. J. Bok. (*From* The Astronomer's Universe, *New York, Cambridge University Press, 1958, p. 87; courtesy* Sky and Telescope)

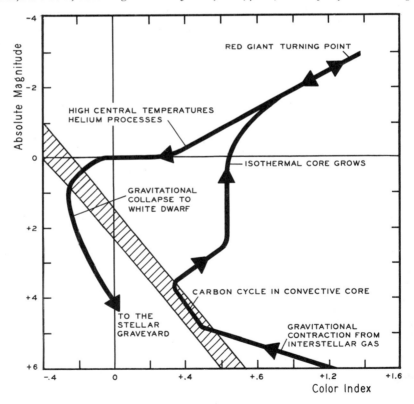

a. The great majority of stars whose masses are greater than $1\odot$ are close to the zero-age main sequence.

b. Most of the fairly massive stars that lie slightly to the right of the main sequence must be in the third or fourth stages of evolution. Only very few massive stars can be expected in the first stage.

c. Among the stars of small mass ($<1\odot$), many may still be in the first stage.

d. Stars of the smallest known masses ($0.1\odot$ and less) may not have had time to reach the main sequence and may all be in the first stage.

4. In the fourth stage, the track runs again from right to left, crosses the main sequence, and then perhaps dips rapidly downward through the region occupied by the novae and nuclei of planetary nebulae into the domain of the white dwarfs. Again, even good guesses of the time intervals cannot be made. It seems from general principles, however, that they must be fairly short, since they involve rapidly acting processes of contraction and nuclear reactions at very high temperatures. The number of stars observable in this stage is small, but apparently they can be separated by spectroscopic means from stars in the second and early-third stages.

The estimates given for the ages of different stars, of course, are not determined by observations, but rather are based upon theoretical conclusions made several years ago. According to Hoyle, among others, these ages probably will have to be increased by a factor of 2. They do, though, represent the relative ages of stars of different masses, and this is all that can be expected on the basis of available observational material.

STELLAR POPULATIONS

The observational H-R diagrams for stars in the neighborhood of the sun and in galactic clusters are all similar to Russell's original diagram. However, H. Shapley, the first student of Russell at Princeton and later director of the Harvard College Observatory investigated the apparent magnitudes of stars in globular clusters. Beginning in about 1915 while he was at the Mount Wilson Observatory, Shapley found that their H-R diagrams differ drastically from that presented by Russell. (The globular clusters are compact groups of stars in the galaxy, containing on the average several hundred thousand stars [see Fig. 199], differing from the loosely grouped and less populous galactic clusters also in their spatial distribution, as will be discussed in Chap. XIX on P. 413.)

Shapley's work was not appreciated fully even at the time of the publication of his book *Star Clusters*.[5] About 15 years later, W. Baade was led independently to the revolutionary concept of two kinds of stellar populations in the Milky Way and other galaxies. This theory was formulated after success in resolving the stars in the nucleus of the Andromeda galaxy and in several elliptical galaxies (discussed in Chap. XX, P. 450).

Baade described as Population I all those single stars and galactic star clusters whose H-R diagrams approximately resemble Russell's early H-R diagram. Population II was used to describe stars in globular clusters, in the nuclei of spiral galaxies, in elliptical galaxies, and those of very large motion in the Milky Way, such as the pulsating variable stars of the RR Lyrae type, cepheid variables of the W Virginis type, and several more. In Fig. 145 the shaded areas are ordinary H-R diagrams—Population I; the hatched areas, H-R diagrams of stars in globular clusters—Population II.

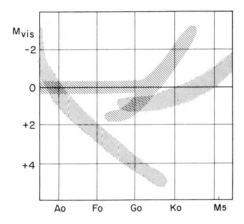

Fig. 145. H-R diagrams of the two stellar populations, according to W. Baade. (*From* Astrophysical Journal, *C, 1944, p. 143*)

The globular star clusters, as was reported before Baade's work, are almost completely devoid of gas and dust and hence star formation does not occur in them at the present time. Baade therefore concluded that all Population II stars are old as compared with Population I stars.

Baade's attempt to divide the stars of the Milky Way into two distinct populations represented only a crude and admittedly very superficial recognition of an important feature of the Milky Way. The sun is located very close to the galactic plane and participates in the phenomenon of galactic rotation (see P. 425) with an angular velocity that is representative of the whole mass of Population I stars. Yet from the sun's properties, its age was known to be at least 5 billion years and conceivably more. Baade never felt quite happy when he was asked about the designation of the sun as a Population I star. The sun's kinematic properties placed it, according to Baade, within Population I, but its age resembled more nearly the stars of Population II.

However, Baade's hypothesis of the two stellar populations did break the ground and lead to further investigations. His work has been described as "naive" by several distinguished Soviet astronomers, but it did force astronomers to explore the problem of star populations in greater detail.

One of the best reviews of the history of the two populations and an evaluation of Baade's early attempts is given in Shapley's article in 1949, "A Half-Century of Globular Clusters":

Much attention has been paid in the past two or three years to the question of types of stellar population. It is of interest to note briefly the contribution of globular clusters to the population problem, and to observe how slowly sometimes we grasp the significance of dissonant observational material.

. . . [the color-luminosity array in Messier 13] was published in 1915. It was such a surprising result, this evidence that the giant red stars were much brighter than the giant blue stars in the globular cluster Messier 13, that attention was called at once to the contrast between this color-luminosity diagram and the one that prevailed for stars around the sun, and for the open clusters like the Hyades. It was noted that the difference must have a bearing on the evolution of stars; but just what that bearing may be was as obscure then as it is now.

To test the generality of the Messier 13 color-magnitude array, careful studies were made of three other globular clusters. . . . In all of them the same phenomenon appeared. For all of them Russell's "reversed seven" diagram, applicable to stars of the solar neighborhood, is distorted, so far as the giant stars are concerned. Every globular cluster tested shows the absolute luminosity brightening with increasing color.

Curiously enough, the anomaly attracted little attention from observers or interpreters, even after Lundmark and others had noted the structural and color similarities of globular clusters, spheroidal galaxies, and the nuclei of spirals. . . . In a thorough examination of the color-luminosity diagram [ten Bruggencate, of Göttingen, Germany, about a dozen years later] rediscussed my material and again called attention to the two types of population. Meanwhile, Trumpler had proposed his classification of galactic clusters and showed from his extensive studies of the spectra in these open systems that the color-luminosity arrays were not like those of the globular clusters. . . .

Quite independently of any consideration of the population type in globular clusters, Oort discussed in 1926 the properties of galactic stars of high velocity, and noted that such stars could be differentiated in several characteristics from stars in general. The globular clusters of course were known to have high velocities, but they were not directly associated with high velocities galactic stars, except possibly with the galactic cluster-type Cepheids. Several of us pointed out, as mentioned above, the similarity of globular clusters with the nuclei of spirals and with the spheroidal galaxies. It was generally assumed that the stellar content was similar, and by analogy similar to the content of the nucleus of our own galactic system which the Harvard and Mount Wilson workers had shown is also very rich in cluster-type Cepheids.

Such is briefly the history of the color-luminosity anomaly, but it took the dramatic resolution of the nucleus and the companions of the Andromeda Nebula by Baade with the 100-inch reflector, and his calling attention to velocity differences as well as the differing color-magnitude arrays, to make astronomers "population sensitive."

It may turn out that we are over optimistic in assigning star assemblages to only two distinct populations. The data on velocities are somewhat ambiguous, suggesting perhaps several population types, or perhaps a continuum with maxima. The luminosity discriminant appears, however, to be clear and positive. But if the two-population concept plays only the same part in studies of stellar evolution as the two-star streams of Kapteyn played in analysis of galactic structure, it will have been sufficiently fruitful.[6]

At the end of the Vatican symposium referred to on P. 271, J. H. Oort presented a summary of the discussions, and first pointed out that the appearance of a star depended mainly on two parameters: total mass and chemical composition of the medium from which it was formed. He then pointed out that it is now possible to distinguish five different kinds of populations:

Halo Population II
Intermediate Population II
Disk Population
Intermediate Population I
Extreme Population I

Halo Population II is represented mainly by the globular clusters. The Intermediate Population II may be composed of old stars in a fairly flattened system involving RR Lyrae variables and others. Stars concentrated close to the galactic plane but perhaps not limited to the spiral arms are representative of the old Disk Population. The Intermediate and the Extreme Population I are massive hot stars, which appear to be associated with the gas and dust clouds of the Milky Way, occurring predominantly in the spiral arms. Other objects, such as planetary nebulae and high-velocity stars, can be identified with one or the other of these intermediate

Fig. 146. Participants at the Symposium on Stellar Populations held at the Vatican Observatory, May 20–26, 1957. Left to right—*Back Row:* E. E. Salpeter, Cornell University; B. Strömgren, Princeton Institute for Advanced Study; L. Spitzer, Jr., Princeton University Observatory; W. A. Fowler, California Institute of Technology; A. D. Thackeray, Pretoria, South Africa; Mme. V. Préobrajensky, Chef du Secretariat; P. Treanor, Vatican. *Center Row:* J. J. Nassau, Cleveland, Ohio; D. Chalonge, Paris Observatory; M. Schwarzschild, Princeton University Observatory; A. Blaauw, Groningen; O. Heckmann, Hamburg–Bergedorf; F. Hoyle, Cambridge, England; W. W. Morgan, Yerkes Observatory; G. H. Herbig, Lick Observatory; A. R. Sandage, Mount Wilson Observatory. *Front Row:* P. Salviucci, Pontifical Academy; B. Lindblad, Stockholm Observatory; J. H. Oort, Leiden Observatory; W. Baade, Mount Wilson Observatory; D. J. K. O'Connell, Vatican Observatory; G. Armellini, Rome; G. Lemaître, Louvain, Belgium; H. A. Brück, Dublin. (*Courtesy Pontifical Academy of Sciences– Vatican Observatory*)

groups. Table 7 represents a summary of the data presented by Oort in 1957.

Most of the quantities listed in this table can be understood easily. The average distance of the particular group above or below the galactic plane is represented by z. It will be seen that the oldest stars—those of the Halo Population II—have the largest value of z, while the Extreme Population I objects—composed of gas, supergiants, and T Tauri stars—are confined to the galactic plane within approximately 100–200 parsecs. Thus the distinction between the various population groups resembles the subsystems of the Milky Way—groups of stars with characteristic spatial distribution and velocity of galactic rotation, first considered by the Swedish astronomer B. Lindblad and discussed in Chap. XIX on P. 420.

Table 7.

STELLAR POPULATIONS[7]

POPULATION	HALO POPULATION II	INTERMEDIATE POPULATION II	DISK POPULATION		INTERMEDIATE POPULATION I	EXTREME POPULATION I
Some Typical Members	*Subdwarfs; Globular Clusters; RR Lyrae Variables with Periods > 0$\overset{d}{.}$3*	*High Velocity F-M; Long-Period Variables*	*Planetary Nebulae; Bright Red Giants; Novae*	*Weak-Line Stars*	*Strong-Line Stars; A Stars; Me Dwarfs*	*Gas Supergiants T Tauri Stars*
z (parsecs)	2,000	700	450	300	160	120
Z (km/sec)	75	25	18	15	10	8
Axial ratio	2	5	~ 25	?	?	100
Concentration toward center	strong	strong	strong	?	little	little
Distribution	smooth	smooth	smooth	?	patchy, spiral arms	extremely patchy spiral arms
Z_{he} (Schwarzschild)	0.003	0.01	—	0.02	0.03	0.04
Age (10^9 years)	6	6.0–5.0	5	1.5–5	0.1–1.5	0.1
Total Mass ($10^9 \odot$)	16		47	5	5	2

Clearly, departure from a spherical distribution implies rapid galactic rotation. There is also a strong correlation between the population groups and the velocities at right angles to the galactic plane. Halo Population II objects have average Z velocities of 75 km/sec, while Extreme Population I objects have velocities of only 8 km/sec. The quantity Z_{he} gives the total mass density of elements heavier than helium expressed in the hydrogen density as unit. These quantities have been taken from the work of M. Schwarzschild. They are smallest for the oldest stars—0.003, and largest for the youngest stars, 0.04. This implies that most recently formed stellar objects were produced out of a medium of interstellar gas and dust already enriched in heavy elements. These elements probably were produced in stellar interiors and expelled by the oldest stars while they were giants, or before they adjusted themselves to the white-dwarf stage. According to Oort, the ages of the stars range from 6×10^9 years, for the oldest, to less than 10^9 years, for the youngest. The total mass of the galactic system is the sum of the quantities of the last line of the table. Although these quantities may not be exact, they reflect the views previously held that Extreme Population I stars contribute only 2×10^9 solar masses and that the largest part of the mass of the Milky Way is composed of stars of the Disk Population and of Intermediate Population II. Although the details given in Table 7 undoubtedly will be changed as a result of future investigations, there is every reason to believe that the general character of the populations represents the fact that there is no sudden break between Population I and II. Rather, they merge gradually from one extreme to the other. Stars probably are being formed now at a much slower rate than was the case some billions of years ago, because a large part of the original gas and dust already has been exhausted as a result of previous star formation.

XIV

DOUBLE STARS

AFTER BECOMING familiar with the general properties of stars and their evolution, it is interesting to consider several special types of stars. The study of these has provided new insights into many problems, but also presented a number of puzzling questions, some of which still remain unanswered. Three broad groups will be described: the *double stars* (or *binary stars*), the *pulsating variable stars,* and the *exploding stars.*

The first group comprises all those "physical pairs" of stars in relative orbital motion due to their mutual gravitational attraction. By extending this definition further, the group includes also multiple stars—triple, quadruple, and so on. The multiple stars usually contain close binaries; that is, triple stars often consist of a close binary with a distant companion, quadruple stars of two close binaries, and so forth. Systems in which the distances between all components are of the same order of magnitude, such as the Trapezium of Orion, which consists of six stars, are not gravitationally stable, and the stars gradually move away from each other.

The pulsating stars, discussed in Chap. XV, vary more or less regularly in radius and temperature, and hence also in brightness. The exploding stars, such as supernovae, novae, and several related groups will be considered in Chap. XVI. These show sudden great increases in brightness, caused by rapid expansion of their outer layers that are ultimately detached from the star in the form of gaseous shells.

Binary stars can be broadly subdivided into three groups: *visual, eclipsing*, and *spectroscopic* binaries. Visual double stars can be separated either through visual observation or on a photographic plate. Eclipsing binaries show periodic variations in brightness when one component of a pair whose orbital plane lies nearly along the line of sight is obscured by the other. Spectroscopic binaries are detected from the periodic variation of the Doppler displacements of their spectral lines.

THE DISCOVERY OF DOUBLE STARS

Visual Double Stars

A few visual double stars can be resolved with the naked eye and were, of course, known long before the beginning of the 20th century. A famous example is the pair in Ursa Major—Mizar and Alcor. Mizar itself was resolved into two stars by the Italian G. B. Riccioli more than 300 years ago. This was the first telescopic discovery of a double star. Riccioli's discovery also showed that the Mizar-Alcor system consists of at least three stars.

The first systematic search of visual double stars was made at the end of the 18th century by William Herschel. He showed that most of these were physical pairs, rather than stars close to the same line of sight but distant from each other in space. His work was continued, and new meth-

Fig. 147.   The apparent orbit of the visual double star ξ Ursae Majoris. The crosses represent observations made between 1822 and 1899; the circles are positions measured from 1900 to 1955. (*From* Elementary Astronomy, *New York, 1959, fig. 29.1*)

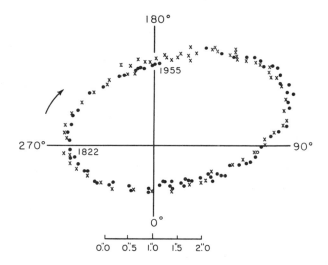

Fig. 148.   S. W. Burnham.

ods of observation were introduced in the early 19th century by F. G. W. Struve.

The most famous 20th-century discoverer of visual double stars is S. W. Burnham, originally an amateur astronomer. His profession was that of a court reporter in Chicago, except for the 4 years he served on the staff of the Lick Observatory. Burnham made his early discoveries with a 6-in. refractor in his backyard, but later had access to some of the best telescopes in the United States. When Burnham started his observations, almost all visual double stars were believed to have been discovered. According to O. J. Eggen, after Burnham had published his first 180 discoveries, the Reverend Mr. T. W. Webb of England, another amateur astronomer, wrote him:

> It will hardly be possible for you to go on for any great length of time as you have begun, because the number of such objects is not interminable, and every fresh discovery means one less to be made; still, what you have already done is so much more than any man now living has accomplished, that your high position as an observer is fully secured.[1]

Burnham discovered 1,340 new visual double stars and in 1894 was awarded the Royal Astronomical Society Gold Medal for his contributions to double-star astronomy. In order to make it easier to determine whether a particular double star had been discovered previously, he started early in his career to prepare a catalogue containing data on all known double stars. After many frustrations and delays, the *General Catalogue of Double Stars within 121° of the North Pole*, containing 13,665 pairs, was published in 1906.[2]

A large number of more difficult binary systems were discovered by R. G. Aitken and W. J. Hussey at the Lick Observatory and by R. T. A. Innes, Dutch-born W. H. van den Bos, and W. S. Finsen at the Union Observatory in South Africa. In 1932 Aitken published his *New General Catalogue of Double Stars within 120° of the North Pole*[3] and a catalogue of southern double stars was published at about the same time by Innes.[4] An entirely new index catalogue covering the whole sky is now in preparation at the Lick Observatory, under the supervision of H. M. Jeffers; it will contain approximately 53,000 pairs.

The total number of pairs in Aitken's catalogue was 17,180, but many of Burnham's wide pairs were omitted by Aitken, who had adopted criteria depending on the combined apparent magnitude of the binary and the angular separation of the components. The upper limits adopted by Aitken are of necessity somewhat indefinite, because they do not permit us to distinguish clearly between physical and optical doubles. However, he reasoned that, for any assumed upper limit of linear separation, the angular separation will be largest for the brightest stars since they are, on the average, closest to the sun. Thus, the limits he adopted range from 400″ for binaries of apparent magnitude +1.0 to 6″ for apparent magnitude +10.0.

The minimum separation at which a visual double star can be resolved is about 0″.1. If a binary, with an orbital semimajor axis of 0″.1, whose component stars are dwarfs of spectral type M (of a surface temperature of about 3,000°) and of apparent magnitude +9.0 is considered, the H-R diagram shows that the visual absolute magnitudes of the stars are +10 each, implying a distance of about 6 parsecs. In this case, the separation in linear units would be 0.6 a.u. Most visual binaries have separations greater than about 1 a.u. For this separation two stars, each having one-half of the mass of the sun, would have an orbital period of 1 year. The periods of most visual binaries are tens or hundreds of years.

There is actually no well-defined upper limit for the periods of binaries or semi-major axes of their orbits. However, in widely separated pairs, even the most massive stars would experience only a small gravitational pull, and the measurements of their relative positions in the sky might not show a detectable amount of curvature. Pairs of stars located at about the same distance from the sun and having equal proper motions and radial velocities (within errors of measurement) are often referred to as *astrometric binaries*. Famous examples are the system consisting of Proxima Centauri and the close visual double star α Centauri—which are so widely separated that the orbital period is probably millions of years—and the pair BD+4°4048 discovered by G. Van Biesbroeck in 1944.[*]

These very widely separated, common-motion stars can be referred to as binaries. They may also be considered as remnants of clusters of stars formed in one initial cloud of interstellar gas and now retaining the cloud's original motions without giving observational evidence of orbital

[*] The fainter stars are usually designated by a catalogue number. Thus, BD refers to the *Bonner Durchmusterung* ("Bonn Catalogue") compiled by Argelander and published in 1863,[5] accompanied by a detailed celestial atlas. The stars are listed in zones of 1° in declination; BD+4°4048 is the 4048th star between declination +4° and +5°.

motion, or of perturbations arising from the gravitation of other stars or cloud complexes. For example, the T Tauri variables have been shown in recent years by G. Herbig to move together in roughly parallel paths within the cloud of obscuring matter in which they were formed. On the other hand, the most recent discoveries of visual binaries, especially by G. P. Kuiper at the Lick and Yerkes Observatories, have brought to attention a number of very close pairs in rapid orbital motion. For example, the binary known as $BD-8°4352$ has an orbital period of only 1.7 years.

Eclipsing Double Stars

The light variation of the eclipsing double stars also has been known for centuries. The first systematic study of Algol, one of the best-known eclipsing binaries, was started by the English amateur astronomer J. Goodricke at the end of the 18th century. He found that the light changes could be explained in terms of eclipses of a bright star by a dark companion, both revolving around each other in an orbit whose plane is nearly perpendicular to the plane of the sky. This theory was confirmed from accurate photometric studies by E. C. Pickering in 1880. Pickering also devised methods by which valuable information about the system, such as the radii of the stars in terms of their separation, can be derived from an accurate light curve. A more complete theory of light variation was developed by Russell and Shapley in 1912. Substantial additions to the theory were made in 1950 by J. E. Merrill at Princeton University, who published a set of tables facilitating the numerical work[6] and in 1959 by Z. Kopal in his book *Close Binary Stars.*[7]

About 20 eclipsing binaries were known in 1900, but many more were detected after the invention of more accurate methods of observation, such as the selenium cell and the photoelectric cell discussed in Chap. V, Pp. 80-85. The first star extensively observed by Stebbins with the selenium cell was Algol; he succeeded in detecting a shallow secondary eclipse and determined ". . . that the companion, far from being dark, gives off more light than our sun, and in addition is much brighter on the side which is turned toward the primary."[*][8]

Actually, there is no observational evidence of eclipses being caused by dark bodies, and the depths and shapes of the minima of the light curves depend primarily on the relative brightnesses of the two stars, on the ratio of their radii, and on the inclination of the orbit to the line of sight.

[*] *Primary eclipse* refers to the occultation of the hotter component by the cooler, producing the greater loss of light of the system. During *secondary eclipse,* the cooler component is obscured by the hotter one.

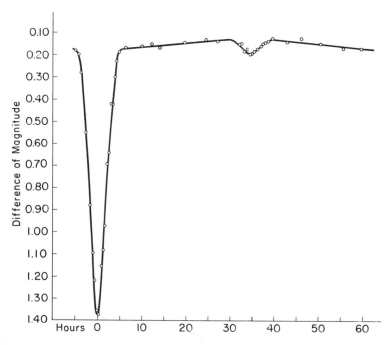

Fig. 149.   Light curve of Algol by J. Stebbins. (*Astrophysical Journal, XXXII, 1910,* P. 213)

Spectroscopic Double Stars

In 1889, while inspecting objective-prism spectrograms used in the preparation of the *Draper Catalogue of Stellar Spectra*, E. C. Pickering noticed that the spectral lines of the brighter component of Mizar sometimes appeared double, sometimes single. Pickering suggested that this effect was produced by the relative motion of two stars revolving around each other. In Fig. 150, the diagram on the left is of the orbits of the two components around the common center of gravity; on the right are the velocity curves of the two components. The maximum separation of the spectral lines corresponds to the times when both components move parallel to our line of sight, one approaching and the other receding. The lines coincide, then, when the stars move perpendicularly to the line of sight. Thus, the Mizar-Alcor system was shown to consist of at least four stars. A few months later, H. C. Vogel observed periodic shifts of spectral lines of Algol, thus confirming the eclipse theory. Only one set of lines, however, was observed in the spectrum of Algol, the companion being too faint for its spectrum to be recorded. Most of the spectroscopic binaries now known are of this latter, so-called single-line type.

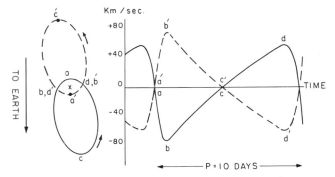

Fig. 150.   The spectroscopic binary ζ Ursae Majoris. (*From* Elementary Astronomy, *New York, 1959, fig. 29.3*)

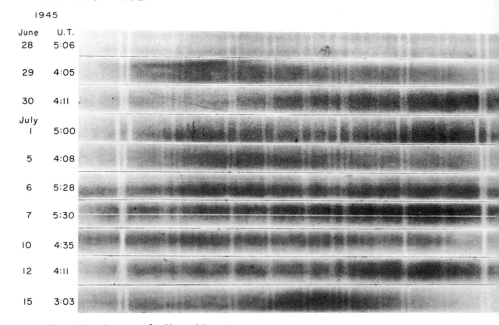

Fig. 151.   Spectra of ζ Ursae Majoris.

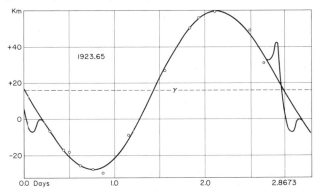

Fig. 152.   Velocity curve of the bright component of Algol by D. B. McLaughlin. Rotation effect superimposed on the velocity curve. (*From* Publications of the Michigan University Observatory, VI, 1934, P. 13, fig. 2)

More than 50 spectroscopic binaries were known by 1900. The number increased very rapidly at first, since at the beginning of this century every star varying periodically in radial velocity was classified as a binary. It was finally realized that in many cases the radial-velocity variation of apparently single-line spectroscopic binaries was actually produced by stellar pulsations (discussed in Chap. XV). The latest catalogue of spectroscopic binary orbits prepared at the Lick Observatory lists 480 systems with known orbital elements.[9] More than a thousand additional stars are identified as spectroscopic binaries in R. E. Wilson's *General Catalogue of Stellar Radial Velocities*, published in 1953.[10]

One of the best-known multiple systems, the sextuple in Castor, contains all three types of binaries. In addition to the visual double star, consisting of two blue stars, Castor A and Castor B, a faint distant companion, Castor C, whose visual magnitude is about +10, shares the proper motion of the bright pair and is thus a physical member of the group. In 1896, A. A. Belopolsky at Pulkovo Observatory found that the fainter of the two blue stars (Castor B) is a single-line spectroscopic binary with a period of 2.9 days, while at the Lick Observatory H. D. Curtis discovered in 1904 that the bright blue star (Castor A) is also a single-line spectroscopic binary with a period of 9.2 days. K. A. Strand has fixed the period of the visual double pair at 380 years. That the faint red companion is also a spectroscopic binary was found by A. H. Joy and R. F. Sanford of Mount Wilson Observatory, who determined the period of this close pair of stars as 0.81 day. The orbital plane is almost exactly in the line of sight; consequently, there are two eclipses in every cycle of 19.5 hr (Castor C is known to photometric observers as YY Geminorum). The spectrum

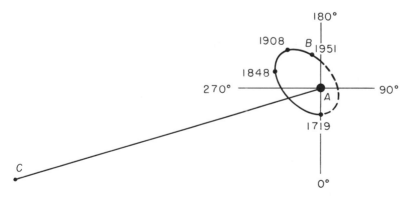

Fig. 153.   The multiple system of Castor (α Geminorum). (*From* Elementary Astronomy, *New York, 1959, fig. 29.10*)

of each of its components is visible, and this fact indicates that the two stars are very nearly equal in brightness, and presumably also in color, size, and mass.

Observational Selection Factors

It should be stressed that the distinction between the different kinds of binaries is based on methods of observation, and different selection factors are introduced. In the case of the visual binaries, observational selection favors the discovery of systems that are relatively close to the sun and those in which the distances between the components are large. The planes of the orbits of eclipsing binaries must be oriented almost exactly in the line of sight. The probability of discovering an eclipsing system is increased if the conditions are such as to favor the production of deep eclipses, and if the binaries have a short period. In the case of spectroscopic binaries, astronomers discover only those systems whose orbits are oriented at a considerable angle from the plane of the sky. There is a definite preference for the discovery of those systems that have large masses and whose orbits are eccentric (elongated), since both of these factors increase the observed range in radial velocity. If all binary systems were alike in their physical characteristics, it would make no difference whether they were discovered by the visual, the spectroscopic, or the photometric method. But binary systems do not all have the same physical properties and hence any statistical discussion of the frequency and of other aspects of binary stars becomes very complex.

FREQUENCY OF DOUBLE STARS

Kuiper has pointed out that the percentage of binaries or multiple stars among the nearest stars to the sun is at least 50 per cent. C. E. Worley of the Lick Observatory has remarked in a recent summary that among the 30 nearest stars, 13 are multiples having a total of 29 components; also, among the 30 brightest stars in the sky, 15 are multiple and contribute 41 stars, while only 15 are apparently single. From a statistical study of the probable error distribution of radial velocities, R. M. Petrie, director of the Dominion Astrophysical Observatory, has estimated recently

... that about one half of the stars, in the samples studied, vary in radial velocity.... Presumably most of the variable-velocity stars are spectroscopic binaries. The results therefore supply additional evidence that double stars constitute an important fraction of the stellar population.[11]

ORIGIN OF DOUBLE STARS

At the beginning of the present century, most astronomers believed that all double stars originated as a result of the process of fission in a single, rapidly rotating star—a theory particularly advocated by Jeans. It soon became apparent that this explanation could not be used in the case of widely separated visual binaries; but there remained the possibility that spectroscopic binaries might still be the result of fission. In recent years, serious objections have been raised against even this application of the fission theory, and most astronomers are inclined to believe that binary stars of all types originated, as single stars and star clusters do, through the gravitational condensation of interstellar gas and dust. As discussed in Chap. XII, P. 242, A. S. Eddington showed that as a result of radiation pressure, stellar masses are limited to no more than about 100 times that of the sun. Hence an interstellar cloud having a mass of thousands or hundreds of thousands of solar masses of necessity must condense into a large number of separate stars. In this way, a star cluster would be formed, or in the case of a relatively less massive cloud, a multiple star or a double star.

More recently, P. Ledoux, and in 1958 M. Schwarzschild and R. Härm, have shown that pulsational instability must disrupt any star whose mass is greater than about $65\odot$. The latter authors have asked the observers to answer three pertinent questions:

1. Is there any fully trustworthy evidence of stellar masses greater than $65\odot$? J. Sahade of La Plata Observatory, Argentina, has shown that there is, in fact, no such evidence; but several binaries (HD 47129, also known as Plaskett's star, and UW Canis Majoris) are close to this limit and *may* even exceed it.

2. Do the most massive stars now known indicate a P Cygni–type outflow of gas? (see P. 357) The answer for both binaries is yes.

3. Do they pulsate with periods of $\frac{1}{3}$ to $\frac{1}{2}$ day? Plaskett's binary is certainly variable, although there are no eclipses. The most recent photoelectric observers, K. D. Abhyankar and H. Spinrad, searched for irregular variations that could perhaps be correlated with irregular changes in the spectrum. We do not know whether there are weak but strictly periodic pulsations.

The study of binary stars can be discussed from many viewpoints. Close spectroscopic and eclipsing systems often present many interesting and puzzling problems. However, of particular importance is the fact that several astrophysical quantities can be derived only from an investigation of double stars. For example, the binary stars offer the only direct means of determining stellar masses, and this is one of the most important lines of investigation.

STELLAR MASSES

Determination of Mass

Kepler's third law in its more general form states that the product of the total mass of the binary times the square of the orbital period is equal to the cube of the semimajor axis. If the period is expressed in years and the semimajor axis in astronomical units, the sum of the masses of the two components will be expressed in units of solar mass. For example, in the case of Sirius,

Period $= 50$ years   Semimajor axis of orbit $= 20$ a.u.

$$M_A + M_B = \frac{20^3}{50^2} = 3.2 \odot.$$

Without additional observations, the result gives only the sum of the masses in terms of the sun's mass. In order to determine each separately, the ratio of the masses must be known. In the case of a visual binary, this requires some knowledge of the orbital motion of each component with respect to a set of distant comparison stars, whose individual motions can be neglected. Thus if the orbit is circular, and the mass ratio is $2:1$, the heavier component will describe a circle whose radius is one-half that of the circle described by the star of smaller mass. In the case of Sirius, the position of the center of gravity, and hence the mass ratio, is known.

$$\frac{M_A}{M_B} = 2 \qquad M_A = 2\,M\odot \qquad M_B = M\odot.$$

In spectroscopic binaries in which both components are sufficiently bright to register their spectral lines, the mass ratio is found directly from the amplitudes of the velocity curves of the two components. However, for a spectroscopic binary, the inclination of the orbital plane to the line of sight cannot be determined unless the binary shows eclipses, in which case the orbital plane is very close to the line of sight. In a visual binary, the orbital inclination can be determined except for its sign, plus or minus. The latter ambiguity can be resolved in only very few exceptional cases.

Despite this difficulty, Finsen and others have shown fairly conclusively that the distribution of the orbital planes of the visual binaries is a random one: There is no detectable tendency for the planes to be in any way related to the central plane of the Milky Way. This is of great cosmogonic interest, because it seems to imply that while the large-scale motions of the interstellar gas are essentially circular in the plane of the Milky Way, any tendency of this sort was lost within the small-scale turbulent motions of cells of interstellar gas producing the binary systems.

Deviations from the Mass-Luminosity Relationship

The most important statistical result based on the determination of binary masses is the mass-luminosity relation discussed in Chap. XII. As was mentioned, deviations from this relationship are being recognized now, and the system of β Lyrae is a conspicuous example.

In a 1941 investigation, G. P. Kuiper and O. Struve began their line of reasoning with the fact that the invisible companion of this famous eclipsing system must be less luminous than the bright primary star whose periodic eclipses by the invisible companion occur at intervals of 12.9 days. At this time, the mass-luminosity relationship was believed to hold true for all stars (except the white dwarfs). The inevitable result was that the bright member of the pair also is the more massive member, and from its orbital velocity a mass of about 75 solar masses was obtained through the use of Kepler's third law. This large mass in turn implied that the absolute visual magnitude of the bright star is about -7. More recent work, especially by H. Abt of the Kitt Peak National Observatory, has shown that the close binary is associated with a distant visual companion whose spectrum is normal and whose absolute magnitude is undoubtedly consistent with its spectral type, B5. Thus from the visual companion the distance of β Lyrae and its true visual absolute magnitude can be determined. The result is about -3.5. A value of the same order also was found from a study of the pressure-broadened lines of hydrogen and helium. If the problem is now reversed and a visual magnitude of -3.5 and a mass that is consistent with this absolute magnitude from the mass-luminosity relation is adopted for the brighter member of β Lyrae, it is necessary to conclude that the invisible companion is actually the more massive star in the system. It therefore strongly violates the mass-luminosity curve.

There are a dozen or more binary systems in which similar discrepancies have been found. Another example, VV Puppis, will be discussed on Pp. 301-302. Most of these binaries show unusual spectroscopic features, but it may not be permissible to conclude that all stars having apparently fairly normal spectra obey the mass-luminosity relation. Good examples are the so-called W Ursae Majoris eclipsing variables that usually show two sets of spectral lines whose velocity amplitudes indicate mass ratios of 2:1 or even 3:1. Yet, the two members of each system are of approximately the same brightness, because the spectral lines of both components are similar in intensity. Thus there is a large group of binaries in which the dynamical data show large differences in mass while the photometric data, interpreted with the help of the mass-luminosity relation, indicate that the stars are similar in mass.

The Most Massive Star Known

As has already been stated, the most massive star known at the present time, HD 47129, was found by J. S. Plaskett in 1922. (Its catalogue number is 47129 in *The Henry Draper Catalogue*.) It consists of two hot stars of spectral type O8 and has a period of 14.4 days. The orbital motion of the primary with respect to the common center of gravity is about 200 km/sec. No eclipses have been observed, so that the inclination of the orbit is not known, but it probably is in the vicinity of 90°, departing from that value just enough to prevent the observation of eclipses. The masses were thought to be 75 times that of the sun for each component but may be only 65. These are close to the theoretical limit of stability, and it is therefore of interest that Plaskett's star appears highly unstable and shows a number of very peculiar features. The spectral lines of both components are seen in the spectra. However, the radial velocity of the center of gravity as determined separately from the two components differs by about 100 km/sec: The stronger is best represented by a value of +25 km/sec, while the secondary component gives about −75 km/sec. The difference is far greater that can be attributed to errors of measurement or a difference in gravitational redshift. Hence, there can be no doubt, especially from the work of the Indian astronomer K. D. Abhyankar done in 1959 while at the University of California, that at least one of the velocity curves, probably that of the more massive but fainter component, is distorted. These effects, caused by the motion of gaseous streams, have been observed in some other spectroscopic and eclipsing binaries, such as β Scorpii.

In the drawing of the velocity curve of β Scorpii the velocities of the center of mass of the system (α_1 and α_2), as determined separately from the velocity curves of the primary and the secondary, differ by about 40 km/sec.

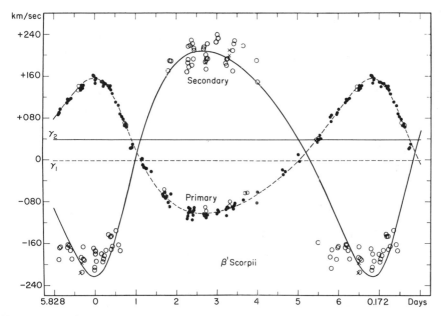

Fig. 154.   Velocity curve of β Scorpii, by K. D. Abhyankar. (*From* Astrophysical Journal Supplement, *IV, 1959, P. 163, fig. 1*)

The Least Massive Stars Known

Equally interesting is the search for stars having the smallest known mass (see Chap. VI, P. 112). In a few visual binaries, the presence of a very faint companion may be inferred from the wavy form of the apparent orbit. The most famous object of low mass is the invisible companion of one of the two stars that comprise the binary system 61 Cygni. The two astronomers who have investigated extensively the system of 61 Cygni are Dutch-born K. A. Strand, now at the United States Naval Observatory, and A. N. Deutsch of the Pulkovo Observatory. Their results are essentially the same. The mass of the companion is 0.008 the mass of the sun and the period is 4.8 years.

Two other stars of small mass are (1) the invisible companion of Lalande 21185 (a star in the list published by the French astronomer J. J. de Lalande in 1801), for which Miss S. L. Lippincott, also at the Sproul Observatory, found a period of about 8 years and a mass of about 0.01; and (2) ϵ Eridani, for which in 1961 F. D. Drake and Miss E. Gundermann at the National Radio Astronomy Observatory computed an orbit on the basis of measurements made by van de Kamp. The results indicated the presence of an invisible companion to ϵ Eridani whose mass may be only 0.006 times that of the sun.

As long ago as the mid-1930's, H. N. Russell expressed the opinion that stars whose masses are 10 times that of Jupiter might represent a type of object intermediate between a real planet and a normal self-luminous star. It is thus reasonable to believe that there is no sharp demarcation between planets and stars, but that very large and massive planets may emit radiation from their interiors that, in most cases, is undetectable with existing telescopes. Whether such stars of very small mass exist only as companions of more massive stars, or whether they also occur as single objects in the galaxy, is not known.

DENSITY DISTRIBUTION WITHIN STARS

While binary stars provide a unique means of determining stellar masses, even more remarkable is the fact that in some cases the distribution of density within the stars also can be derived, even though the two stars cannot be observed separately.

Many eclipsing binaries of short period vary in brightness at times other than the eclipse phases. In some cases, the two maxima of the light variation are curved, and greatest brightness occurs twice each period halfway between *mid-eclipses.*° This phenomenon was explained by Russell as a consequence of tidal deformation, the projected image of each star being circular only at the two mid-eclipses and elongated along the line of centers. It is usually sufficient to assume that the tidal deformation of the two components is similar, and that each is in effect an ellipsoid of rotation.

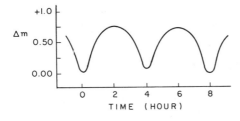

Fig. 155. The light curve of W Ursae Majoris. (*From* Elementary Astronomy, *New York, 1959, fig. 29.8*)

While the force of gravitation of a spherical body may be assumed to originate in its center, no such assumption can be made in the case of a distorted body. The effect of the gravitational pull depends not only upon the shape of the star, but also upon the distribution of matter within it. The most interesting consequence of this is the phenomenon known as the

° The deepest point of the light curve.

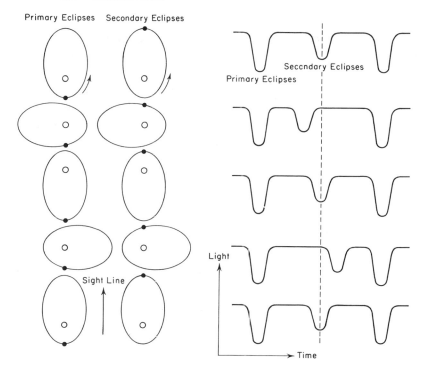

Fig. 156. Rotation of the line of apsides of a binary. Left: changing orientations of the orbit; right: corresponding changes of the light curves. (*M. Johnson, from* Quarterly Journal of the Royal Astronomical Society, *II, 1961, Pp. 10 and 11*)

rotation of the *line of apsides.*[*] The elliptical orbit slowly rotates in its own plane so that the major axis gradually changes its orientation. For example, if at any given time the major axis coincides with the line of sight, the two eclipses occur at equal intervals. Due to the rotation of the line of apsides, after an interval of many years the major axis may assume an orientation at right angles to the line of sight. In this case, the intervals between primary and secondary eclipses will differ noticeably from the interval between the secondary and the next primary eclipse. From these observed effects, the shape of the stars and the density distribution within them can be derived.

The same effect of the rotation of the line of apsides also has been discovered from the study of velocity curves of spectroscopic binaries obtained at intervals of some tens of years. The most famous example is the eclipsing spectroscopic binary Y Cygni, whose orbital period is 3 days and

[*] The major axis of the orbit indefinitely extended in both directions.

whose period of the rotation of the line of apsides is 46 years. The light variation of Y Cygni was discovered in 1886, and in 1900 N. Dunér suggested from the observed changes of the light curve that "... a force has been brought to light which causes the line of apsides to assume all possible positions in the orbital plane in a space of about 40 years."[12] In 1928, when Russell first developed the theory of rotation of the lines of apsides, Y Cygni was still the only star in which the effect had been definitely established, but a number of similar cases have since been found.

CHANGES IN PERIOD AND EVOLUTIONARY PROCESSES

During the past half-century, astronomers also have been searching assiduously for changes in the periods of binaries that might indicate evolutionary processes taking place in the stars. Visual binaries with their long periods offer no hope for detecting such transformations. However, there are a number of spectroscopic and eclipsing binaries whose periods vary more or less drastically. The best-known case is that of β Lyrae, whose period has been increasing gradually at an average rate of about 9 sec/year. There is some indication that the rate of this increase is gradually diminishing. Since β Lyrae is known to expel a considerable amount of mass in the form of streams producing conspicuous violet-displaced absorption lines immediately after primary mid-eclipse, it is reasonable to attribute the increase in period to loss of mass in the system.

There have been many theoretical studies in the field of celestial mechanics concerning the manner in which the period of a binary is affected by its loss of mass. An application of the hypothesis developed by Huang in 1956 to β Lyrae indicated that the system loses mass at the rate of approximately 10^{22} gm/sec. However, the theory is quite complicated and depends critically upon the manner in which the mass is expelled. In the case of β Lyrae, the hot stream of gas moves with an outward velocity of a few hundred kilometers per second. This is probably not sufficient to overcome the system's force of gravity. The observations do show that β Lyrae is immersed in a vast, roughly symmetrical expanding shell that produces violet-shifted absorption lines of hydrogen and helium. In the schematic diagram the component stars are represented by hatching, and their orbital velocities are shown. The inner dashed line, passing through the Lagrangian point, L_1, marks a stability limit for the two components. The outer dashed curve, passing through the Lagrangian

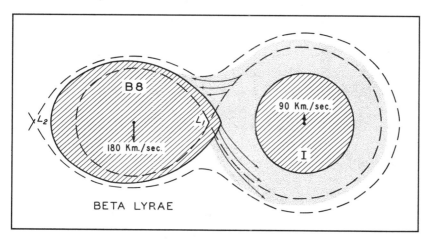

Fig. 157.   Schematic diagram of β Lyrae. (*Courtesy* Sky and Telescope)

point L_2, represents a limit of stability for the system as a whole. The velocity of recession appears to increase with distance from the binary's center of gravity. This phenomenon resembles that of the expanding shells of Wolf-Rayet stars, P Cygni stars, and novae discussed in Chap. XVI. The physical mechanism involved must be gas pressure of the hot ionized material expanding into the tenuous and cold interstellar medium.

UNUSUAL STARS

VV Puppis

An interesting example, illustrating the complexity of the problems encountered in the study of some double stars, is the binary of shortest-known orbital period, VV Puppis, which was discovered as an eclipsing binary by H. van Gent, of Leiden Observatory, on plates taken in South Africa. The period inferred from the eclipses is 100 min. Subsequent photometric investigations made between 1931 and 1950 by a number of astronomers have led to the following conclusions, summarized by G. Herbig in 1960:

1. The mean period of 100 min. has remained constant during an interval of about 157,000 cycles. However, individual photometric maxima often deviate conspicuously from the predicted times.

2. The light curve during the eclipse is unsymmetrical, the descent from maximum light to minimum light being much more rapid than the subsequent recovery.

3. The mean brightness of VV Puppis undergoes conspicuous changes: The star was bright in 1928 when its apparent magnitude at minimum was +14.4; in 1948 the star was too faint for visual identification by J. H. Oort and W. A. Hiltner, who used the McDonald 82-in. reflector; observations at Pretoria in 1948–1949 indicated an apparent magnitude of +17 at minimum; and in 1958 Herbig found an apparent magnitude of +15.5 at minimum.

4. Observers at Pretoria in 1948 to 1949 were at times unable to see any variation in the 100-min period, the apparent magnitude once remaining at about 17 for as long as 18 days.

In 1958, Herbig succeeded in recording the spectrum of VV Puppis with a low-dispersion spectrograph attached to the 36-in. Crossley reflector of the Lick Observatory. Superposed upon the continuous spectrum are strong emission lines of hydrogen and ionized helium, whose total change in radial velocity is almost 1,000 km/sec. The velocity curve is slightly unsymmetrical, and the emission lines of only one component have been observed. According to Herbig, VV Puppis resembles several other known binaries, such as Nova Herculis of 1934 (also designated as DQ Herculis), V 751 Cygni, UX Ursae Majoris, and SS Cygni. The absolute visual magnitude of UX Ursae Majoris and VV Puppis is about +7, yet the level of excitation in the emission spectrum of VV Puppis is similar to that of an O-type star. If the entire surface of the brighter component of VV Puppis radiates uniformly, its radius is about 40,000 km. However, Herbig suggests that only a restricted area of the stellar surface resembles the radiation of an O-type star, and in this case its radius could well be somewhat greater. The low luminosity of the system has been well established by Herbig. The mass of the invisible companion must be at least 0.6 solar mass. It is, however, possible that the two stars have equal masses, of about two or three solar masses, but in this case both stars must be "grossly underluminous for their masses, by as much as 5 magnitudes in the case of the primary and even more for the secondary."[13] Both stars may be white dwarfs or may be on the way to becoming white dwarfs.

Antares

A remarkable phenomenon has been found in the spectrum of the visual binary α Scorpii (Antares). The brighter component of apparent visual mag +1 is an M-type supergiant, whose diameter has been measured by means of an optical Michelson interferometer as about 290 times that of the sun. The diameter was also calculated from its surface temperature of 3,000° and known luminosity of about 390 times that of the sun. By this method the radius of the star is about 175 times the sun's, or $175 \times 7 \times 10^5$ km $\sim 1.2 \times 10^8$ km: equal to ~ 1 a.u. About 3″ away on the celestial sphere is a faint B-type star of apparent mag +6, the two constituting a physical pair. At its known distance from us, the corresponding projected separation between the two stars is about 550 a.u.

In 1937, O. C. Wilson and R. F. Sanford at the Mount Wilson Observatory found that the spectrum of the B-type companion of Antares showed emission lines of forbidden Fe II (see P. 222), in addition to the usual blue continuous spectrum with broad and shallow absorption lines of hydrogen, helium, and other elements. Spectrographic observations made in 1940 with the McDonald 82-in. reflector confirmed the existence of the emission lines. Several exposures were made by O. Struve without trailing the image of the B-type star on the slit of the spectrograph, which was oriented at right angles to the line joining the two component stars. Extensive tests indicated that the narrow emission lines of iron extend 1″ or 2″ beyond the "tremor" disk of the B star.

This 1″ or 2″ extension, which on the spectrogram has the appearance of fairly narrow arrowlike features on both sides of the edges of the stellar spectrum, could not be explained by faulty guiding and the consequent contamination of the spectrum by ordinary star light. It must have originated in a small nebulosity surrounding the B star that remains invisible to the eye when the binary system is examined visually. The existence of this nebulosity, whose diameter is about 5″, is inferred from the emission lines.

Attempts to find the forbidden emission lines of Fe II in the immediate vicinity of the M-type supergiant failed. It is possible, however, that an iron-rich extended chromosphere surrounding the M star and extending to distances greater than that of the secondary (3″), but with emission lines excited only in the immediate vicinity of the hot B star, produces the observed extension of the emission features. The most recent spectroscopic observations of Antares made by A. J. Deutsch with the 200-in. Hale telescope in 1960 revealed more complex features in the spectra of both stars. His results indicate that the radial velocity of the bright M-type component varies irregularly with a mean value of 3.2 km/sec. However, the strongest absorption lines originating in the ground states of Na I, Ca I, Cr I, and Sr II give a radial velocity of −15 km/sec, which suggests an outflow of gas from the entire star, a phenomenon that Deutsch has also found to be present in other late-type supergiant stars.

The broad absorption lines of the B-type component indicate a radial velocity of $+3.0$ km/sec. The shallow appearance of the absorption lines shows that this star rotates rapidly around an axis that cannot be close to the line of sight. In addition to those absorption lines characteristic of a normal main-sequence B-type star, Deutsch found a number of sharp absorption lines of Ti II in the ultraviolet region of the spectrum near λ 3300 A. Radial velocities derived from the latter are about -18 km/sec (within the observational errors of the -15 km/sec velocity given by the strongest absorption lines of Na I, Ca I, Cr I and Sr II in the spectrum of the M star) and they are therefore probably produced in the same vast nebulosity that produces the expanding shell of gas moving radially away from the M-type component.

The ionized calcium lines H and K consist of two components each. The weaker of these components, with a radial velocity of -6 km/sec, is probably due to interstellar absorption and is produced by the ionized calcium atoms along the entire path between α Scorpii and the earth (see Chap. XVII, P. 374). The stronger component of ionized calcium gives a radial velocity of about -18 km/sec, and is thus probably produced in the vicinity of the binary system.

According to Deutsch, the emission lines of forbidden Fe II produced in the small nebulosity are tilted when the slit is held stationary along the line joining the two stars. These lines are sharper on the east side of the B-component than on the west side, where they appear double. The component appearing on both sides of the B-type star has a velocity of $+3$ km/sec, while the other, seen only on the west side, gives a velocity of -4.5 km/sec. The tilted appearance of the emission lines might be explained as a consequence of rotation of the small nebulosity around the B-type component, but there is as yet no physical explanation for the apparent duplicity of the lines on the west side.

Deutsch also found that the spectrum of the B star has emission lines of ionized silicon sharper than those of forbidden Fe II and showing no trace of duplicity. The radial velocity, as measured from the ionized silicon lines, agrees with the radial velocity of the B-type star. Their sharpness rules out the possibility that they are produced in the reversing layer of the BStar. Since the lines do not extend beyond the edge of the stellar spectrum (as the forbidden Fe II lines do) when the image of the star is held stationary on the slit, they must be attributed to the inner part of the small nebulosity whose rotation—if it exists at all—is very much smaller than the axial rotation of the star itself. The forbidden Fe II lines probably originate in the outer parts of this nebulosity.

It is strange that the nebulosity around the B-type component shows only emission lines of iron and silicon, but not those of hydrogen. The enormous abundance of hydrogen in all known gaseous nebulae and the conditions of excitation and ionization resulting from the radiation of a B-type star would render it almost inexplicable for a gas of normal composition to show only the iron and silicon lines in emission. This gave rise to the hypothesis that the material in the vicinity of Antares is metal rich, in turn leading to the supposition that the envelope may be composed of solid substances, such as meteors that have become vaporized and are excited by the radiation of the hot B-type star. This hypothesis is admittedly improbable and may have to be abandoned in the light of future work.

Epsilon Aurigae

The history of the eclipsing binary ε Aurigae is in many respects the history of astrophysics since the beginning of the 20th century. Its orbital period of 27.1 years was determined by the German astronomer H. Ludendorff of Potsdam soon after an eclipse in 1900–1902, which lasted almost 2 years and caused the apparent visual magnitude of the star to drop from its normal brightness of +3.4 to −4.2. Yet, even in 1905, Miss Clerke wondered "whether future minima will honor the cheques of calculations as they fall due," and, "whether epsilon Aurigae may still evade the law of order that it has temporarily obeyed."[14]

Astronomers had to wait until the star again declined in brightness in 1928–1930, and thus gave added force to another comment by Miss Clerke:

Should Dr. Ludendorff's regularization of them [the unusual pair of objects constituting this star] be verified by future observation, their 27-year period will be by far the longest that can be ascribed to any form of stellar light change, and it will be quite important to correlate with it, if possible, the star's period of orbital revolution. There is perhaps no object in the heavens of more pregnant interest than this spectroscopic binary.[15]

About 1900, systematic spectrographic observations of ε Aurigae began to be made at the Potsdam and the Yerkes observatories. The first spectrum obtained at Yerkes was exposed by E. B. Frost on November 29, 1900. Since that date, frequent observations have been made at several observatories, and the last eclipse of the system in 1955–1957 was thoroughly observed by means of the Coudé spectrograph of the 100-in. telescope at Mount Wilson.

The results of the earlier spectrographic observations indicated a velocity curve with a total range of about 32 km/sec and an unsymmetrical shape, implying a somewhat elongated orbit. In 1901, Ludendorff noticed that the absorption lines of ε Aurigae—produced in the atmosphere of an F-type supergiant—were greatly strengthened during the eclipse and in some cases seemed to be unsymmetrical. During the next eclipse, 1928–1930, with better spectrographic facilities, the asymmetries of the absorption lines and their enhanced intensities were recorded by Frost, Struve, and Elvey at Yerkes. Several high-dispersion spectrograms also were obtained by Adams and Sanford at Mount Wilson Observatory during this eclipse, and they noticed that a few of the stronger absorption lines were double during the partial phase between about November 15, 1929, and February 5, 1930. A similar doubling of the lines was observed during the partial eclipse preceding mid-eclipse in September and October of 1955.

The partial phases last 192 days each. The brightness of the star remains constant during the 330-day total phase of the eclipse, except for minor fluctuations. From the duration of the partial and total phases, it became apparent that the eclipsing body must be very large. However, no physical interpretation of this binary system was attempted until in 1937 Kuiper, B. Strömgren, and Struve published a joint article in the *Astrophysical Journal;*[16] the top diagram of Figure 158 indicates their results.

The observers were faced with the fact that the light curve appears to have a flat minimum, 0.8 mag below the normal brightness of the system. Yet during this interval, the spectrum of the eclipsed star remains visible. The spectral lines, normally seen outside of eclipse, are also seen during the phase of totality. Photographic and photovisual observations gave the same depth of the minimum. Hence the eclipse had to be either annular (as was later suggested by Russian-born S. Gaposchkin of Harvard Observatory), or produced by a partially transparent but very large object passing in front of the bright F-type supergiant.

Outside of eclipse, no absorption lines of the companion are seen. In 1937, the three Yerkes astronomers, probably independently of one another, arrived at the same conclusion: The large eclipsing body—referred to as the I star—consists of a very tenuous mass of gas whose bulk is partly transparent to optical light. The ultraviolet radiation of the F-type supergiant causes ionization in a thin layer of the large gaseous body exposed to that radiation. The nature of this ionized layer was thought to be analogous to the ionosphere of the earth, which is produced by the ionizing effect of sunlight in the outer fringes of the earth's atmosphere. In this manner, the optical depth within the crescentlike layer of the invisible

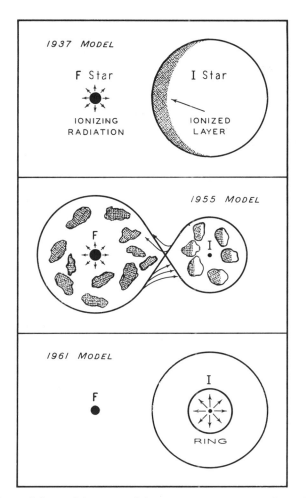

Fig. 158. Three of the models proposed for ε Aurigae. (*Courtesy* Sky and Telescope)

star remains very nearly constant throughout the duration of the 330-day phase of constant minimum brightness. Strömgren's theoretical calculation of absorption produced by the scattering of free electrons within the ionized layer appeared to account for all the observational facts.

Despite its apparent success, the 1937 model of ε Aurigae was criticized on different grounds by several astronomers. In Germany, E. Schönberg and B. Jung suggested that the continuous opacity of the free electrons would be insufficient to produce the observed depth of the minimum of ε Aurigae. Hence they attributed the opacity to fairly large solid particles occupying a volume similar to that found in the 1937 model— about 3,000 times the size of the sun. A similar hypothesis was proposed in 1954 by Z. Kopal, who also attributed the opacity to solid particles, but who assumed that these particles form a ring around the unknown companion star.

Kuiper in 1937 had inferred that the I star has a surface temperature of approximately 1,000°. However, subsequent attempts to discover its radiation, which should be most conspicuous at long wavelengths, by P. B. Fellgett and Kuiper produced negative results. There is no convincing indication in the spectrum of the system of an infrared or red excess of radiation.

In 1954, S. Gaposchkin suggested that the eclipse of ε Aurigae is annular, and that the shape of the light curve could be explained by attributing to the F star, as well as to the I star, surface brightness distributions that would correspond to a radius of more than 1,000 solar radii for the F supergiant and about 500 solar radii for its companion. The asymmetries of the absorption lines during the partial phases of the eclipse, and the occasional doubling of these lines, were attributed by Gaposchkin to the usual rotational asymmetry observed during the partial eclipses of other binary systems. However, certain spectroscopic features observed both in the partial phases of the eclipse and during the constant minimum render this explanation probably untenable.

Still another criticism of the 1937 model was recognized at the very start of the work at Yerkes. The I star, with its surface temperature of 1,000°, was believed to pass in front of the F-type supergiant. During the eclipse, the rays of the F star must pass not only through the thin ionized crescent in which electron scattering occurs, but also through the deeper regions of the I star, in which molecular bands and atomic lines not seen in the light of the F supergiant would have been expected.

An important spectroscopic feature of ε Aurigae during the eclipse is the conspicuous weakness of certain lines: for example, ionized magnesium at 4481 A, neutral iron at 4260 A, and a few others. These lines are not noticeably enhanced during the eclipse, which clearly indicates the presence of what is called the *effect of diluted radiation:* An absorption line that has as its lower energy state the ground level of an atom or one of its metastable levels can be very strong, even though the source of the exciting radiation is located at a great distance from the gas. Absorption lines whose lower energy states are not metastable are greatly weakened when the source of the radiation subtends only a small solid angle, as seen from the absorbing gas. This phenomenon was well known in 1955, and its presence during the eclipse of ε Aurigae unmistakably proves that the absorbing gas of the I star is located far from the surface of the F-type supergiant.

In order to explain these phenomena, Struve proposed in 1955 that there is no infrared star in the system, but that the companion is an invisible star of small dimensions that never eclipses the F-type supergiant and is never occulted by the latter. This unknown star is surrounded by a vast complex of clouds moving with different velocities and in different directions. Within each cloud, a thin layer exposed to the light of the F supergiant is ionized (in accordance with the earlier views of Strömgren). In order to explain the doubling of the lines during the two partial phases of the eclipse, Struve assumed that the F supergiant is also surrounded by a very large complex of clouds and that a gas stream carries matter from the I star to the F star during the first partial eclipse. Another stream of gas, originating in the clouds surrounding the F supergiant, accounts for the negative radial velocities of the component absorption lines in the second partial stage of the eclipse. The physical nature of the companion star remained unknown, but it was tentatively assumed to be a cool star of small size whose own radiation is insufficient to produce any observable effects outside of or during an eclipse.

In 1954 R. P. Kraft of the University of California in Berkeley analyzed several high-dispersion spectrograms of ϵ Aurigae and confirmed the effect of diluted radiation within the mass of gas that stands in front of the F-type supergiant during the eclipse. He was able to measure the degree of ionization in the occulting gas by comparing the intensities of absorption lines of neutral and ionized iron. If there were no dilution effect, the usual ionization equation of M. N. Saha would have enabled Kraft to determine the number of free electrons per cubic centimeter. In this case, however, in order to compute the number of electrons, he had to know both the temperature of the F star and the dilution factor of its radiation: that is, the fraction of the sky occupied by the disk of the F star as seen from the gas. For this factor, he used Strömgren's 1937 estimate of 10^{-4}, corresponding to a 1.8-degree diameter of the F supergiant as seen from the surface of the I star.

On this basis, Kraft calculated that the electron density was only 10^8 electrons per cubic centimeter in the occulting gas. However, it is known that about 10^{11} electrons would be needed to make the gas opaque enough to account for the 0.8 mag depth of the eclipse. In order to overcome this difficulty, Strömgren suggested to Kraft that the opacity of the I star could be caused by negative hydrogen ions (hydrogen atoms with an extra electron attached to each). This hypothesis eliminated electron scattering and made it possible to account for the observed drop in brightness of the system.

The latest contribution to the study of ϵ Aurigae is that of the Italian astronomer Miss M. Hack in 1961. She pointed out that the absorption coefficient of the negative hydrogen ions is not independent of the wavelength and that the depth of the minimum at wavelengths 6280 and 3960 should differ by 0.06 mag—a quantity that she believed to be easily detectable. Photoelectric measurements, however, have failed to show it. She favored electron scattering as the mechanism of continuous absorption, but she was then faced with the problem of reconciling Kraft's electron density of 10^8 free electrons/cm^3 and the required density of 10^{11} electrons/cm^3 that is required to account for the observed minimum.

Miss Hack actually succeeded in determining the dilution factor from measurements of the line profiles of absorption lines having metastable and nonmetastable lower levels. The resulting value, about 0.1, is the so-called physical dilution factor, rather than the geometrical dilution factor calculated by Strömgren. The difference between these two factors becomes important when the absorbing mass of gas is fairly dense. In this case, the geometrical dilution factor loses its significance because the gas itself is a source of radiation and affects all the atomic transitions within it. The physical dilution factor is usually greater numerically than the geometrical factor. (By definition the dilution factor may have any value between zero and $+1$.) Thus, in the case of ϵ Aurigae, if the results of Miss Hack are correct—and there is no reason to doubt them—the physical dilution factor is about 1,000 times greater than that estimated from geometrical considerations.

Almost all the free electrons are produced by ultraviolet radiation. If the F star is the source of this radiation, its ultraviolet continuous spectrum must be about a thousand times brighter than would be expected from a black body having the same temperature, about 7,000° K. Hence, if electron scattering is really the cause of the occultation, the large number of electrons per cubic centimeter must be due to some nearby hot source other than the F star. Miss Hack therefore suggested that the ionization of the occulting gases in ϵ Aurigae is produced by the I star, whose temperature she believes may be about 20,000° and whose radius may be approximately 10^{12} cm or $\frac{1}{10}$ of the radius of the F supergiant. The radius of the occulting shell is approximately 10^{14} cm and the distance between the centers of the two stars is twice the latter value, or 2×10^{14} cm. The small but hot star would be about 2 mag fainter than the F-type supergiant at all accessible wavelengths, and hence would be unobservable as a separate source by any known method.

There remains the problem of the constant minimum brightness in the light-curve of ϵ Aurigae during 330 days of the two-year eclipse. This difficulty apparently could be overcome by assuming that the occulting gas constitutes a ring in the equatorial plane of the I star with an inner radius of the order of 10^{13} cm. The electron density turns out to be of the order of 10^{11} electrons/cm^3 on this assumption.

If the nebulous ring rotated around the I star with the proper Keplerian velocity, the displacements of the absorption lines at the beginning and at the end of the eclipse would be 30 km/sec, or approximately the observed value. It would, therefore, not be necessary to introduce the somewhat arbitrary assumption of two streams that was used in the 1955 model.

The rotating gaseous ring is believed to consist of separate clouds whose radial velocities may depart appreciably from the circular velocities. This might explain the irregular fluctuations in the radial velocities of the shell lines, but not the irregular variations in the radial velocity and brightness of the F-type supergiant. Undoubtedly, the latter possesses an extended chromospheric envelope very much like the one proposed in the 1955 model.

The model of ε Aurigae proposed by Miss Hack is, as she notes, not unlike several other long-period spectroscopic binaries, such as 31 Cygni, 32 Cygni, ζ Aurigae, and VV Cephei. Each of these systems consists of a massive star of late spectral type and a hotter, less massive star. The accompanying chart (Fig. 159) shows the location of the members of all five systems on the H-R diagram. For each system, circles representing the individual components are labeled with their masses, the sun's mass being taken as unity. The similarity of these binaries is very striking. In each case, the more massive component (toward the right in the diagram)

Fig. 159.   ε Aurigae (1961 model) compared with four other eclipsing binaries of long period. (*Courtesy* Sky and Telescope)

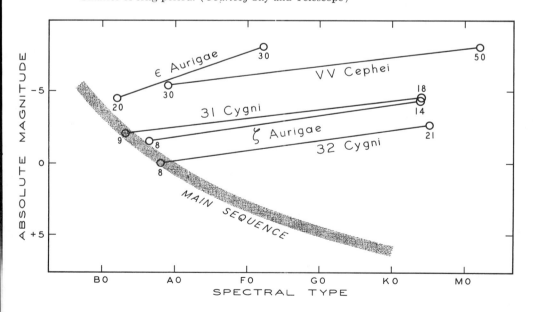

has apparently evolved farther from the main sequence than its less massive companion.

The question often has been asked but never completely answered: Are other types of peculiar stars in reality binaries that cannot be resolved spectroscopically and that do not show eclipses? According to R. P. Kraft, there is an indication that some and perhaps all mild novae explosions occur in binary systems. It also has been suggested that the remarkable spectra of Wolf-Rayet stars (discussed in Chap. XVI) occur in binary systems, but this has been criticized by A. B. Underhill. It would not be surprising if it is found that some mild explosions in a binary system component produce an observable change of the physical parameters of its companion, but these are all questions that cannot be answered definitely.

XV

PULSATING

VARIABLE STARS

A NUMBER OF stars that vary periodically in brightness and in radial velocity puzzled astronomers at the beginning of this century. The light variations of the first-known representative of this type δ Cephei (prototype of the group of cepheid variable stars), had been discovered in 1784 by the English amateur John Goodricke. δ Cephei varies in brightness by almost 1 mag in a period of 5.37 days, the rise to maximum being much steeper than the decline. A clue to its nature seemed to have been provided in 1894, when Belopolsky discovered that the radial velocity of δ Cephei also varies in the same period, suggesting that it is a spectroscopic binary. The second spectrum was not observed in δ Cephei or any other cepheid star, but a less luminous companion was suspected. However, as Miss A. Clerke aptly commented in *Problems of Astrophysics,* "no more curious spectroscopic discovery has been made than that of the binary nature of short-period variables."[1] The curious part was that maximum radial velocity almost coincides with minimum light. Hence the light variation cannot be caused by eclipses, since at the time of eclipse the companion should be moving perpendicular to the line of sight and have a velocity roughly midway between maximum and minimum. A good account of the following period is given by the Norwegian astrophysicist S. Rosseland in his book *The Pulsation Theory of Variable Stars:*

Eclipses were not considered as a cause of variability. In fact, K.

Schwarzschild found in 1899 that the changes in luminosity of cepheids are accompanied by changes in effective temperature, suggesting that the variability is a temperature effect. Most astronomers thought such temperature effects likely to arise from tidal influences. Thus Eddie suggested that tidal effects at periastron caused a conflagration, responsible for the increase in brightness. Roberts thought that at periastron the dark companion is made visible by reflected light. H. D. Curtis developed the idea of a resisting medium which makes the companion hot on the front side at the time of periastron. Duncan developed a variant of this hypothesis that brought in varying absorption in the atmosphere of the primary star.... These attempts met with so little success, however, that the binary hypothesis was finally abandoned, and the variability was ascribed to intrinsic causes, operating in a single star.[2]

R. Emden in 1906 and F. R. Moulton in 1909 suggested variation in the form of a single star of constant volume, the form changing from a prolate to an oblate ellipsoid of revolution. The main problem this theory created was that the period of radial-velocity variation should be twice that of light variation, rather than of equal length.

THE PULSATION THEORY

In 1879, even before the variation in radial velocity was known, A. Ritter had considered radial pulsations: that is, the periodic expansion and contraction of a star. He had conceived a perfectly homogeneous star, and even though this is far from the actual case, had derived a relation between density and period of pulsation that remarkably closely approximates the observations. His ideas, however, were not pursued further by other astronomers until 1914, when the conclusive death blow for the binary hypothesis and a suggestion of a more plausible hypothesis came from Shapley's work.

Shapley considered Russell and Hertzsprung's conclusions that the cepheids have large absolute brightnesses and reasoned that if they were comparable in surface brightness to the sun, they must have volumes between 15,000 and 20,000 times that of the sun. Shapley concluded that "interpreted as spectroscopic binaries these giant stars move in orbits whose apparent radii average less than $\frac{1}{10}$ of the radii of the stars themselves."[3] He suggested that

... In the face of all these difficulties it seems appropriate to abandon completely the attempts to interpret Cepheids on the basis of a binary-star system ... the explanation that appears to promise the simplest solution of most, if not all, of the Cepheid phenomena is found on the rather vague

conception of periodic pulsations in the masses of isolated stars. The
vagueness of the hypothesis lies chiefly in our lack of knowledge of the
internal structure of stellar bodies. . . .[4]

During the next few years, the concept of pulsations was discussed and
developed in some detail by Eddington, and was later refined by other
astronomers. Figure 160 shows a series of variations of δ Cephei. The
continuous line at the top is the observed light curve; the dashed line
indicates what the light curve would be if there were no change in the
star's radius. The 2nd curve shows variation in temperature; the 3rd
curve variation in spectral type; the 4th, change in radial velocity; and
the 5th the change in radius of the star. The abscissa is the phase expressed in fraction of the period.

Fig. 160.   Variations of δ Cephei, according to W. Becker. (*From* Elementary Astronomy, *New York, 1959, fig. 30.3*)

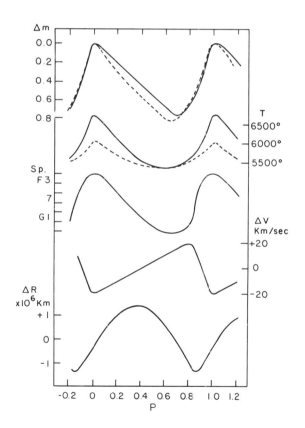

The accepted theory of stellar structure leads to the expectation that the highest temperature would occur at the time of greatest compression (smallest radius) of the star. This would be the time when the gases are at rest (zero radial velocity) on the descending branch of the velocity curve, because just before the stage of greatest compression the gases are still rushing toward the center of the star, away from the observer. In reality, however, maximum temperature occurs when the star has the greatest velocity of approach, a fact that was not anticipated in the simple pulsating model. M. Schwarzschild in 1938 suggested that the star's deep interior pulsates in the manner predicted by this theory, but that in its outermost regions the elements of gas do not all vibrate in unison, causing a lag in the light curve by the observed amount.

It has been shown by the pulsation theory that it is entirely possible that, when for some unknown reason the balance between the gravitational attraction of the star upon its outer layers is disturbed, the star may periodically expand and contract with a period related to the mean density of the entire star. Recent investigations have shown that in a general way all pulsating variable stars obey the fundamental relation

$$\underset{\text{(period) (density)}}{P^2 \quad \times \quad \rho} = \text{Constant.}$$

This theoretical result resembles the relation between the frequency of a vibrating string and its tension. A better analogy is that of an underwater explosion. The explosion causes a gaseous bubble to expand rapidly, more than is consistent with the condition of equilibrium that would require the gas pressure to be balanced exactly with the inward water pressure. This expansion continues until the pressure of the water stops it and causes the bubble to contract. In doing so, the bubble contracts to a smaller volume than is demanded for equilibrium, and thereafter the process repeats itself with a constant period.

When one observes a gaseous bubble produced at a great depth, the outside pressure of the water is very great and the period of the pulsation is short. As the bubble rises toward the surface, the water pressure diminishes and the period of pulsation gradually increases. In the case of a pulsating star, one is not concerned, of course, with the pressure of an outside medium. However, the star has a large gravitational force, and this, in effect, replaces the pressure of the water in the underwater explosion.

The relation between the period and the density in effect implies that for stars of low average density the period of pulsation must be longer than for stars of high average density. A giant star like δ Cephei has a mean density 4×10^{-4} that of the sun (which is of the order of 1.4 ×

the density of water). The period of pulsation of δ Cephei is 5.37 days, and the square of the period is approximately 29. Hence the product of the square of the period times the mean density is roughly $\frac{1}{100}$, and this fixes the constant of the relation. If one should wish then to predict the period of pulsation for a star of solar density, this constant, 0.01 would be divided by the ratio of the densities of δ Cephei and the sun, 4×10^{-4}, and this would give the square of the period of the solar-type pulsating star. The square root then would be 2 hr. (But, of course, the sun does not actually pulsate.)

All pulsating stars whose periods are of the order of days, or even hundreds of days, then, must have exceedingly low mean densities. On the other hand, those that have pulsation periods shorter than 2 hr must have larger mean densities than that of the sun. The shortest period of pulsation known at the present time is that of the former Nova Herculis, which exploded in 1934 and is now known to be a spectroscopic binary with a period of about 4.5 hr. One of the two component stars pulsates with a period of 71 sec, according to observations made by M. F. Walker in 1955 and 1956. The average density of this star, therefore, must be many times greater than that of the sun, and there is every reason to believe that it resembles the white dwarfs in density and perhaps in other respects.

It should be recognized, however, that the concept "mean density" is somewhat vague. At a star's extreme edge, the density is exceedingly low; near its center, the density may be many times greater than that of water. It therefore cannot be expected that the theoretical relation will apply with the same value of the constant for all types of variable stars whose internal density distribution may differ greatly from one group to another. It really is not known which part of the star is pulsating and, therefore, whether the average value of the density should be computed for the star as a whole or for only the inner compact nucleus. Hence the theoretical relation gives only a rough approximation if the constant is assumed to be the same for all types of stars. It is much more reasonable to apply the relation separately for different groups of variables.

There is as yet no knowledge of any periods of pulsation shorter than that of Nova Herculis, because observational techniques are limited by the interval of time required to accumulate a sufficient number of photons from the variable star to determine a precise value of its apparent brightness. In principle, there is no reason why periods of pulsation should not be a few seconds in duration. That, according to the theoretical relation, would occur in stars whose mean densities are about a million times that of water. On the other hand, the longest periods reasonably attributable to the effect of pulsations are about 300 days, implying a density about 10^{-7} that of the sun.

STATISTICS OF PULSATING VARIABLES

Between these limits, several thousand stars are known at the present time. While their light variations in all cases can be attributed to some mode of pulsation, there are large variations among different groups of pulsating stars in their lengths of period, spectral classes, absolute luminosities, spatial distribution, and other properties. Several criteria of classification can be and have been used. A considerable confusion exists regarding even the naming of the different groups; this is particularly apparent in any historical discussion, since the nomenclature has changed as new properties have been discovered and the groupings have been shifted and rearranged.

Thus, since the RR Lyrae stars were the first short-period variables recognized and were found in considerable numbers in globular clusters, they often were referred to as "cluster-type" or "short-period" variables. For a long time, no distinction between ordinary cepheids and W Virginis stars was made, and all of them were called "cepheids." Now they often are described also as "classical," "type I" or "galactic" cepheids and "type II" cepheids, respectively.

Many characteristics of variable stars are associated with the length of period, and the relative frequencies of different periods are shown in Fig. 161. The upper part of the figure shows the observed numbers, the lower part is approximately corrected for volume surveyed. Both horizontal and vertical spacings are logarithmic. Broken curves in the lower figure show the domains of variable stars of several types. A number of relationships between periods and physical properties are known for several groups of variable stars—for example, period-luminosity and period-spectrum relationships. Table 8 lists the principal groups of variable stars and some of their properties. Fig. 162 shows that pulsating variable stars occur in different parts of the H-R diagram. The location of the variable stars in the H-R diagram is important, since a certain range in spectrum and luminosity is associated with each group, most of them being located in the upper part of the diagram. An important distinction is provided by the membership in either Population I (horizontally shaded area) or Population II (vertically shaded area), representing stars of different ages and having different spatial distributions. The main features of the H-R

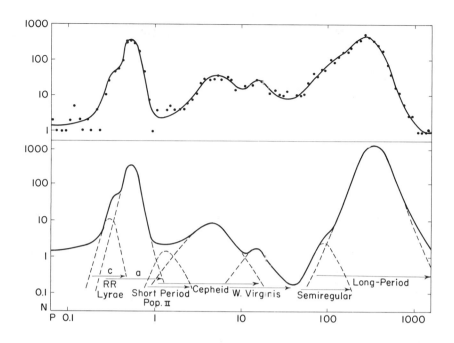

Fig. 161.   Numbers of variable stars known in 1950, according to C. Payne-Gaposch-kin. (*From* Variable Stars and Galactic Structure, *University of London, 1954, P. 17*)

Fig. 162.   The H-R diagram for intrinsic variables. (*From* Elementary Astronomy, *New York, 1959, fig. 30.2*)

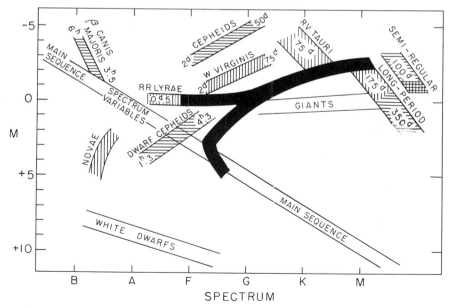

Table 8.

PRINCIPAL GROUPS OF PULSATING VARIABLE STARS[5]

Type of Variable	Characteristic Period	Characteristic Amplitude (mag)	Characteristic Spectrum	Distribution	Characteristic Absolute Magnitude
β Canis Majoris	4^h	0.1	B	In spiral arms	−3
Dwarf Cepheid	3^h	1	A and F	In spiral arms	+2
RR Lyrae or Cluster	12^h	1	A and F	In halo and near nucleus	0
Classical Cepheid	7^d	1	F and G	In spiral arms	−3
W Virginis	15^d	1	F and G	In halo and near nucleus	−2
RV Tauri	75^d	2	G and K	In halo and near nucleus	−2
Short long-period	175^d	5	M	In halo and near nucleus	−1
Long long-period	350^d	6	M	In spiral arms	0
Semi-regular	100^d	1	M	In spiral arms, in halo, and in nucleus	−2

diagrams of Population I and II are indicated in the diagram by the white and black bands, respectively.

We do not know why in the course of a star's evolution it at times acquires the ability to pulsate with one or more periods, while at other times it remains constant in size. Much work has been and is being done to discover multiple periodicities in such variables as RR Lyrae. Some of the most remarkable results have been obtained by the Dutch astronomer T. H. Walraven, in the case of SX Phoenicis, by the French astronomer A. M. Fringant and the Hungarian L. Detre, in the case of RR Lyrae. Apparently, when a star begins to pulsate it does so not only in one mode, but also in one or more overtones. This produces the phenomenon of beats if the amplitudes in light or in radial velocity are of the same order of magnitude.

For a detailed discussion of the different groups of pulsating variable stars, the reader is referred to any of the recent textbooks listed in the Bibliography. This discussion will be confined to two important problems, regarding which significant information has been derived from the study of pulsating stars: namely, the period-luminosity relation of cepheid variables, which provides the basic yardstick of cosmic distances; and the changes in periods of the β Canis Majoris stars, which provide almost the only hope of detecting evolutionary changes in single stars.

PERIOD-LUMINOSITY RELATION OF CEPHEIDS

Discovery

The remarkable and extremely useful period-luminosity relation resulted from the discovery in 1912 by Miss H. S. Leavitt of Harvard that a group of variable stars in the Small Magellanic Cloud show a correlation between their periods and apparent brightnesses. The Magellanic Clouds, the two closest to the Milky Way galaxies, were already believed to be fairly distant. Thus Miss Leavitt suggested that: "Since the variables are probably at nearly the same distance from the Earth, their periods are apparently associated with their actual emission of light, as determined by their mass, density and surface brightness."[6] Although Miss Leavitt noticed that "they resemble the variables found in globular clusters, diminishing slowly in brightness, remaining near minimum for the greater part of time, and increasing very rapidly to a brief maximum,"[7] she did not identify these variables with cepheids, nor did she try to estimate their absolute brightnesses. E. Hertzsprung soon showed that they are similar to cepheids and made the first attempt to calibrate Miss Leavitt's

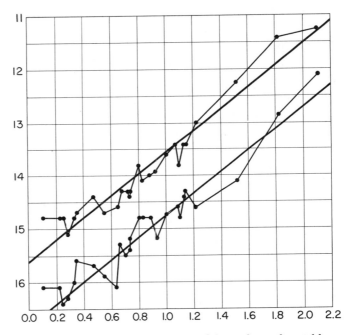

Fig. 163.   The relation between magnitudes and logarithms of variable star periods in the Small Magellanic Cloud, by Miss H. S. Leavitt. The two lines indicate maximum and minimum brightness. (Harvard College Observatory Circular, *173, 1912, P. 3*)

relation in absolute magnitude. Hertzsprung suggested that a method is thus given to find the distances of individual cepheid stars, once the period and apparent magnitude are known and the absolute magnitude can be estimated from the period-luminosity relation. Shapley was the first to make extensive use of this method in deriving the distances of the globular clusters and hence an estimate of the size of the galaxy (as discussed in Chap. XIX, P. 415). In the course of this early work, Shapley redetermined the zero point of the period-luminosity relation.

The Calibration of the Period-Luminosity Relation by Shapley

If the distance of a single cepheid variable star in the Milky Way system could be measured trigonometrically, and if the amount of interstellar absorption between us and this variable star could be estimated, an immediate determination of the zero point would be possible. Unfortunately, even the brightest of the cepheid variables are so far away that ordinary trigonometric parallaxes are useless. Nor is there any indirect method available of the kind astronomers use when they take advantage

Fig. 164.   The Magellanic Clouds, photographed by T. Houck with a
3-in. lens at the South African Station of the Harvard Observatory. The
bright star near the top is α Eridani; the starlike image to the right of the
small Cloud is the globular cluster 47 Tucanae, a member of our galaxy.

of a special type of star occurring as a member of a visual binary system. Cepheid variables do not occur among moving clusters of stars, such as the Hyades, nor among other galactic clusters, such as the Pleiades, for which the distances can be estimated with the help of the H-R diagram. Only the difficult method of statistically estimating the distances of certain groups of galactic cepheids remains, with the help of their radial velocities and proper motions.

The apparent angular motions of bright cepheid variables have been determined from accurate measures of their positions in the sky extending over hundreds of years. For the same stars, radial velocities have been determined from measures of the Doppler shifts of their spectral lines. An individual cepheid, however, may be moving only at right angles to the line of vision, thus having large proper motion and no radial velocity with respect to the earth. Another star could be moving entirely along the line of sight, and would then have no detectable proper motion, or tangential velocity. It is not possible to determine in the case of an individual star whether a small proper motion results from an actual small velocity at right angles to the line of sight, or whether the motion seems small because the star is very far away. But if the problem is considered statistically, the motions may be assumed to be at random, the radial component being as large as the tangential. The radial and linear tangential values may roughly be equated. On this basis, the measured radial velocity should be approximately a measure of the star's linear motion, while the angular proper motion should be a measure of this same velocity as seen from the distance between the earth and the star. Thus, if a star of large radial velocity has a small proper motion, its distance must be relatively great; stars of larger proper motion must be nearer. It is important to realize that if, over a large statistical sample of stellar data, the similarity of the radial and tangential velocities is granted, relatively reliable statistical parallaxes may be obtained.

In this manner, Shapley set the zero point of his famous period-luminosity curve. The abscissa has the same meaning as in the period-luminosity relation of Miss Leavitt, but the ordinate now represents the intrinsic, or absolute, photographic magnitudes of the variable star half-way between maximum and minimum light. This diagram, therefore, gave a means of determining the individual distances of the cepheid variable stars once their periods were observed.

To illustrate the use of the cepheid period-luminosity relation, the observation of a variable star whose apparent magnitude, halfway between maximum and minimum light, is +8.2 may be assumed. After a

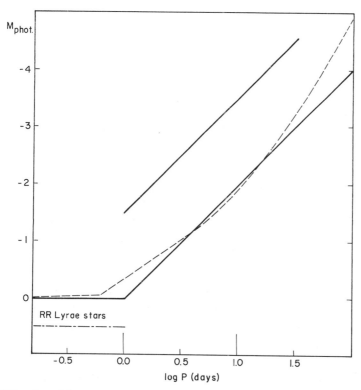

Fig. 165. Period-luminosity relation for RR Lyrae stars and cepheids. The dashed line indicates Shapley's diagram, the solid lines Baade's (the top line applies to type I cepheids, the bottom one to type II), and the dotted line is the correction suggested recently for RR Lyrae variables.

series of observations, it is found that the period is 10 days. Taking the logarithm of the period, namely 1.0, and using Shapley's diagram, the ordinate scale shows that the absolute magnitude of the variable is −1.8. The star thus appears 10 mag fainter when actually observed on a photographic plate than if it were located at the standard absolute magnitude distance of 10 parsecs or 33 light-years. A difference of 10 in magnitude corresponds to a ratio in light of 10,000. Since light intensity diminishes with the square of the distance, the real distance of this variable is 100 times greater than 10 parsecs, and is thus equal to 1,000 parsecs.

It is now known that interstellar absorption tends to make stars look fainter than they otherwise would. A correction to the observed apparent magnitude therefore has to be introduced, allowing for intervening dust and gas, and thus reducing the distance somewhat. This factor was not taken into account in Shapley's early work (discussed in Chap. XIX).

This method is perfectly straightforward, and it was used successfully at Mount Wilson by E. P. Hubble and all of his followers in determining the distances of the nearer galaxies. In these systems, many cepheid variables were discovered, their periods determined, and the rest of the procedure resembled the example worked out in the preceding paragraphs.

Hubble, in 1929, found that cepheids of corresponding period in the Andromeda galaxy are about 4.6 mag fainter than in the Small Magellanic Cloud by using this method. The distance of the Andromeda galaxy then would be 8.5 times greater than the distance of the cloud. Using the value of 106,000 light-years, as determined by Shapley, for the cloud, Hubble set the distance of the Andromeda galaxy as 900,000 light-years.

Except for a relatively minor correction in this figure—bringing it down to 750,000 light-years—due to the small amount of interstellar absorption in the direction of Andromeda, this result remained generally accepted until 1952. Not only that, but all other extragalactic distances were tied to the distance found by Hubble with the help of the cepheid variables. Hence the framework of the metagalactic system rested entirely upon Shapley's zero point of the period-luminosity curve. From the time of the first determination of the period-luminosity curve, numerous attempts were made to revise the original value, and various corrections to Shapley's zero-point determination were indicated. The range covered by these corrections was about 1.5 mag, indicating among other things how difficult it is to derive the zero point accurately.

Shapley himself, however, estimated at one time that the error of the adopted zero point would not exceed a quarter of a magnitude. This prediction, made in 1930, seemingly was confirmed by R. E. Wilson in 1939, when he rederived the zero point on the basis of a large mass of new data on the radial velocities and proper motions of the Milky Way cepheids. His extensive computations "indicated corrections to the photographic period-luminosity curve amounting to 0.0 ±0.2 for the short-period variables, and −0.14 ±0.2 for those of longer period, if we corrected for galactic absorption of 0.85 magnitude per kiloparsec."[8]

The Revision of Zero Point

In Shapley's period-luminosity diagram, the RR Lyrae variables and the classical cepheids form one continuous curve, the former with periods of about one-half day being about 2 mag fainter, intrinsically, than the classical cepheids with 10-day periods. The classical cepheids, on direct photographs of the Andromeda galaxy M 31 taken with the 100-in. Mount Wilson telescope, have apparent magnitudes of 20. The RR Lyrae variables were too faint to be observed with the 100-in., but were predicted to have apparent magnitudes of 22. They should, therefore, have been easily accessible to the 200-in. Hale reflector at Palomar. Yet, at the 1952 meeting of the International Astronomical Union in Rome, Baade stated:

The very first exposures on M 31, taken at the 200-inch telescope, showed at once that something was wrong. Tests had shown that we reach with this instrument . . . stars of $m_{pg} = 22.4$ in an exposure of 30 minutes. Hence we should just reach in such an exposure the cluster-type variables in M 31, at least in their maximum phases. Actually we reach only the brightest stars of population II in M 31 with such an exposure. Since, according to the latest colour-magnitude diagrams of globular clusters, the brightest stars of the population II are photographically about 1.5 mag. brighter than the cluster-type variables we must conclude that the latter are to be found in M 31 at $m_{pg} = 23.9\pm$, and not $m_{pg} = 22.4$ as predicted on the basis of our present zero-points.[9]

The conclusion as reported in the minutes of the meeting was:

. . . that either the zero-point of the classical cepheids or the zero-point of the cluster variables must be in error. Data obtained recently—Sandage's colour—magnitude diagram of M 3—supported the view that the error lay with the zero-point of the classical cepheids, not with the cluster variables. Moreover, the error must be such that our previous estimates of extragalactic distances—not distances within our own Galaxy—were too small by as much as a factor 2. Many notable implications followed immediately from the corrected distances: the globular clusters in M 31 and in our own Galaxy now come out to have closely similar luminosities; and our Galaxy may now come out to be somewhat smaller than M 31. Above all, Hubble's characteristic time scale for the Universe must now be increased from about 1.8×10^9 years to about 3.6×10^9 years.[10]

Thus, the error of 1.5 mag, corresponding to an error in the resulting distances by a factor of 2, in the sense that all distances must be increased by this number, is attributable to the classical cepheids. The curve representing their intrinsic period-luminosity relation should apparently be raised 1.5 mag above that for other cepheid-like pulsating variables, such as the W Virginis stars. Perhaps the best way to make the distinction between the cepheids is to follow Baade in separating them into types I and II, corresponding to his general division of all stellar objects into Populations I and II. The classical, or type I, cepheids are those for which the period-luminosity curve must be raised; that is, they are intrinsically 1.5 mag brighter than type II cepheids of corresponding periods (including W Virginis stars). The cluster-type, or RR Lyrae, variables are of very short period; their luminosities remained unchanged, and they still formed part of the original period-luminosity curve along which the type-II cepheids fall, as shown in the accompanying diagram (Fig. 165).

The type-I cepheids, in the Milky Way and in the distant galaxies, are therefore twice as far away as had been previously assumed. But the distances of the globular clusters and of the Milky Way star clouds in Sagittarius, which have been estimated with the help of the cluster-type variables, remain unaffected. More recently, however, it has appeared that the absolute luminosities of the RR Lyrae stars are smaller than estimated before: +0.5 mag on the average, rather than 0. In 1961, Miss Fringant and J. B. Oke independently obtained a value of +0.8 mag.

Baade's work was confirmed by the independent results of A. D. Thackeray with the 74-in. Radcliffe Observatory reflector in South Africa. At the Rome meeting, he announced that the first cluster-type variables found in the Small Magellanic Cloud have magnitudes of 19. The old period-luminosity relation had predicted a magnitude of 17.4. Again, the use of classical cepheids, with periods of between 1 and 40 days, as a basis for the figures, is at fault. The Magellanic Clouds are twice as distant as had been thought previously.

Also in line with Baade's results are some recent observations of colors and magnitudes of star clusters in the two Magellanic Clouds by S. C. B. Gascoigne and G. Kron, on the basis of work at the Mount Stromlo Observatory in Australia. Some of the clusters they observed are probably globular in kind—yet they have found these clusters about 1.5 mag fainter, intrinsically, than those of the Milky Way. Since the globular clusters are probably all rather similar to one another, the suspicion arose, as in the Mount Wilson work, that the distances of the Magellanic Clouds had been underestimated. Work of a similar nature on the Magellanic Clouds has been carried on at Harvard's southern station, and Shapley sets the revised distance at 150,000 light-years, making their respective diameters 30,000 and 20,000 light-years. This result was announced by Shapley at the December, 1952, meeting of the American Astronomical Society at Amherst College. More recently, the problem of the period-luminosity relation has been investigated by many astronomers, in even more detail, both theoretically and observationally. A summary of the results was presented by A. Sandage at a conference on galaxies held in Santa Barbara, California, in August, 1961. It would appear that there is near unanimity among the active workers in this field now that the zero point of the period-luminosity relation has been determined fairly accurately and is close to Baade's revised value.

The new distance scale helps to reconcile a number of contradictions that had resulted from the previous scale. The observable part of the universe is now so large that a time interval of at least 3.6×10^9 years is required to account for the velocities of the galaxies (see Chap. XX , P. 472)—that is, the expansion began 3,600 million years ago, if we adopt the simple, unsophisticated interpretation of the red-shift phenomenon as a result of an initial (or "big bang") explosion. This new time scale agrees with the radioactive determination of the earth's age and with the evolutionary time scale of the stars. The maximum range of the 200-in. instrument is double what it was thought to be; it sees a billion light-years into space.

Still another consequence of Baade's work was commented upon at the Rome meeting by the French astronomer J. Dufay. Formerly, the diffuse, gaseous emission nebulae in the Milky Way had appeared to be about twice as large as in the Magellanic Clouds and the galaxy NGC 6822. The new distance scale makes these sizes practically identical. The same improvement in relative sizes was found for the stellar associations of blue giant stars that can be identified both in our own and in nearby galaxies—these now seem to follow a standard pattern for size.

The newly established luminosities of the classical cepheids require that they be physically larger, by a factor of 2, and thus less dense, by a factor of 8, than had been assumed previously. This also agrees much better with the theory of stellar pulsations.

The question still remains unanswered: why was the zero point of the classical cepheids in error by as much as 1.5 mag? In Shapley's early work it had not yet been realized that the cluster-type variables belong to Population II (old stars), while most classical cepheids are members of Population I (young stars). Hence, in the earlier discussions there was a tendency to force the period-luminosity relation to form a continuous curve from the shortest periods of 2 hr to the longest periods of 40–50 days.

That the constitutions of Population I and II stars are not the same, and that the zero points for the two groups of variables are independent quantities is now known. The existence of a discontinuity in the period-luminosity relations of the cluster-type variables and of the classical cepheids was recognized by B. V. Kukarkin in 1949. However, after a re-evaluation of the data used by Wilson in 1939, Kukarkin still found a difference of only 2 mag between the 10-day cepheids and the half-day, cluster-type variables. This was the value that had led to the erroneous prediction in the case of the Andromeda galaxy.

It is improbable that errors of measurement in the proper motions or in the radial velocities could have caused so large an error in the mean distances of the Milky Way cepheids. It is true, however, that because these stars are all relatively distant, their proper motions are small, and therefore more difficult to measure satisfactorily against the smaller motions of the background comparison stars on which the measurement of proper motion must depend. The statistical procedure of determining the cepheid distances must be searched further for possible anomalies in cepheid behavior that may make the method inapplicable to these stars. For instance, what is the true radial motion of a cepheid? These stars have fairly large systematic velocities away from the sun, as was found, for example, by the Russian astronomer O. A. Melnikov. There is also some question of whether the mean radial velocity of a pulsating gas bubble really represents the motion of its center of gravity. If all cepheid velocity curves should turn out to be discontinuous, as has been found in the case of RR Lyrae and W Virginis, for example, it would be necessary to argue long and hard as to the star's true velocity.

Another question is whether the cepheids represent peculiar kinds of stars that possess unusual dynamical properties with respect to the sun and its more normal neighbors. Perhaps they form a stream whose motion with respect to the sun is unsymmetrical. The statistical determination of the zero point assumes that there is no such peculiarity of motion; it is possible that the discovery of a spiral structure in the galaxy will result in a modification of the earlier statistical derivations. The cepheid variables of our galaxy may belong to several different arms in the vicinity of the sun, and these arms may not have the same properties of galactic rotation.

β CANIS MAJORIS STARS

About fifteen stars are known to belong to the so-called β Canis Majoris, or β Cephei, group. Their ranges in brightness are as a rule quite small—a few hundredths of a magnitude. Only one β Canis Majoris star, BW Vulpeculae, also known as Petrie's star, has an amplitude in brightness of 0.2 mag. The discovery of variable stars of this type by photometric methods is difficult.

In radial velocity, the β Canis Majoris stars range from a few kilometers per second to several tens of kilometers. Some of them are known to have two or more periodicities with different amplitudes, both in brightness and in radial velocity. For example, β Canis Majoris itself has a period of $6^{h}0^{m}$ and another period of $6^{h}1^{m}$. These two pulsations produce a conspicuous beat phenomenon, and it is from a study of these beats that astronomers have been able to disentangle the multiple periods.

In spectral type, all known β Canis Majoris stars belong to the small interval between about B1 and B3. When plotted in the H-R diagram, they form a conspicuous sequence merging with the main sequence at spectral type B3. The rest lie about 1 mag above the main sequence at spectral types B1 and B2. D. H. McNamara found in 1953 that there is a strong correlation between the average period and the location of the star within the sequence in the H-R diagram. At the bottom of the sequence, spectral type B3, the variable γ Pegasi has a period of 3.4 hr. At the top, spectral type B1, the period is 6^h0^m.

Since the luminosities of the stars, in terms of the luminosity of the sun, can be expressed as a product of the surface area of the star times the light emitted per unit area, it is always possible to enter in the H-R diagram a series of lines representing the loci of equal radius. When the H-R diagram is drawn with the visual absolute magnitude or with the intrinsic luminosity of the star relative to the luminosity of the sun as the ordinate, and with the surface temperature as the abscissa, the lines of equal radius tend to slope gently downward from the upper left of the diagram to the lower right. In this way, it is possible to estimate that a star such as γ Pegasi has a radius five times that of the sun, while a star such as β Canis Majoris has a radius 10 times the sun's. Since the volume of a sphere is proportional to the cube of its radius, the ratio of the volumes is approximately $8:1$ in favor of β Canis Majoris.

No reliable mass determinations have been made for any of the known β Canis Majoris stars, because they do not occur as members of binary systems. However, from the study of binary stars it is possible to assume that the mass of a β Canis Majoris star at the bottom of the sequence is approximately five times the mass of the sun, while the mass of a star at the top of the sequence is approximately 10 times that of the sun. A star's mean density is the ratio of its mass to its volume; hence if β Canis Majoris and γ Pegasi were compared, the ratio of their densities would be approximately $1:4$. The theoretical relation predicts that the ratio of the densities would be inversely proportional to the ratio of the squares of the period. The latter is:

$$\left(\frac{3.5}{6.0}\right)^2 = \frac{1}{3.4}.$$

This is in good agreement with the estimate obtained from the ratio of the densities. Hence it may be concluded that the relation does apply to the β Canis Majoris variables located in different parts of the sequence.

This sequence strongly suggests that the variables recently have evolved away from the main sequence. A few of the stars are known to be members of relatively young associations. Hence the variables are not very old, and therefore are assumed to be evolving along computed evolutionary tracks in the H-R diagram, carrying them roughly horizontally across the sequence and into the region of the giant stars. It is not known why they oscillate when in this particular region of the diagram, but it has been found that as they evolve from left to right they do so over a considerable length of time, because the sequence is not infinitely narrow but shows a spread in surface temperature corresponding to approximately the range between stars of types B1 and B3. Apparently, the variables do not start pulsating until they reach the left edge of the sequence, and they stop pulsating when they emerge at the right-hand side. As they evolve, their surface temperature decreases. Luminosities remain approximately constant, as the masses do. A decrease in surface temperature without a corresponding decrease in luminosity implies that the star increases in radius and that, consequently, its mean density decreases while it passes through the sequence. The increase in period can be estimated from the length of time required to traverse the sequence and from the differences in periods at the ends; it is about 0.04 sec century.

BW Vulpeculae has shown the largest increase, amounting to about 3 sec/century, and several other β Canis Majoris variables have shown smaller increases; as yet, none has been found to have a decreasing period. However, some of the observed increases are much larger than expected, and would imply a much faster rate of evolution than currently estimated. Recent theoretical studies by P. A. Sweet and V. C. Reddish in England also make it appear less likely that the increasing period of β Cephei, roughly 1 sec/century, is the result of evolution. Nevertheless, prolonged studies of the periods of these and other groups do give great promise that ultimately the evolutionary process in a particular star will be discovered.

Although, as mentioned before, it is not known why some stars start pulsating at a particular stage in their evolution, a recent study of the β Canis Majoris variables and of nonvariable B stars by McNamara indicates that rapid axial rotation might prevent a B star from pulsating. He also has extended this argument to other types of variables, such as those resembling δ Scuti.

XVI

EXPLODING STARS

LIGHT VARIATIONS on a much greater scale than those discussed in the preceding chapter are caused by what may be described as stellar explosions—the sudden catastrophic expansion of the outer layers of a star that ultimately become detached from it. This results in a rapid increase of brightness, by as much as 10 to 20 mag. Since many of these stars are too faint to be detected before their outbursts, at one time it was thought that they suddenly began to shine and hence they were called new stars or novae. At the present time the term *nova* is used to describe a milder form of the phenomenon, with a brightness increase of about 10 mag, on the average, while the most spectacular cases, with brightness changes of 15 and even up to 20 mag are referred to as *supernovae*.

S ANDROMEDAE

On August 20, 1885, E. Hartwig observed a star in the central region of the Andromeda galaxy, M 31, that he had not seen previously, although he had been observing on August 7, 10, and 11. In a recent article, S. Gaposchkin reviewed the 1885 observations of the star, later designated S Andromedae, the first supernova known to astronomers. Gaposchkin suggested that the maximum brightness of S Andromedae probably occurred 2 or 3 days before Hartwig's discovery, when it may have reached a visual brightness of $+5.4$ mag, and noted that ". . . Hartwig was the only discoverer who recognized from the first that a new star had appeared in the Andromeda nebula."[1] L. Gully in France, Baroness Podmanidzky in Hungary, and M. Wolf in Germany had noticed the nova, but had not recognized its significance.

According to the best available estimates, the Andromeda galaxy's distance is a million and a half light-years, and the maximum apparent visual magnitude of S Andromedae was +5.4, hence the absolute magnitude of S Andromedae at maximum brightness was −18. The galaxy's integrated brightness, representing as it does the flux of optical radiation from the approximately 200 billion stars in the system, corresponds to an absolute magnitude of about −19.5. Thus, at its maximum brightness S Andromedae emitted optical light at a rate only about four times less than that of all normal stars of M 31.

The sudden appearance of this supernova (the only star resolved within M 31, then believed to be a purely gaseous body) created an enormous amount of interest, not only among astronomers but also among the general public. In 1885, E. B. Frost, who later succeeded Hale as the director of the Yerkes Observatory when Hale went to Mount Wilson, was a senior at Dartmouth. In his autobiography he describes his reactions to S Andromedae, which was believed to represent

. . . the sudden transformation of the nebula into a star along the lines of the theory of Laplace. . . . I was familiar with the appearance of the nebula and was immensely excited over the new phenomenon. Perhaps it was this that led me somewhat definitely to enter the field of astronomy rather than that of physics. I had just passed my nineteenth birthday at this time and had a right to youthful enthusiasm.[2]

Frost continued his account with a description of his school's requirement.

. . . that every senior should deliver before the college an original oration during the course of the year. . . . When my turn came, I had the temerity to choose as my topic this remarkable new star in the Andromeda Nebula.[3]

In 1892, the German astronomer H. von Seeliger developed a theory that figured prominently in the first decades of this century in the arguments about the nature of spiral nebulae. Von Seeliger suggested that a nova outburst is caused by the engulfing of a star by a moving nebulosity.

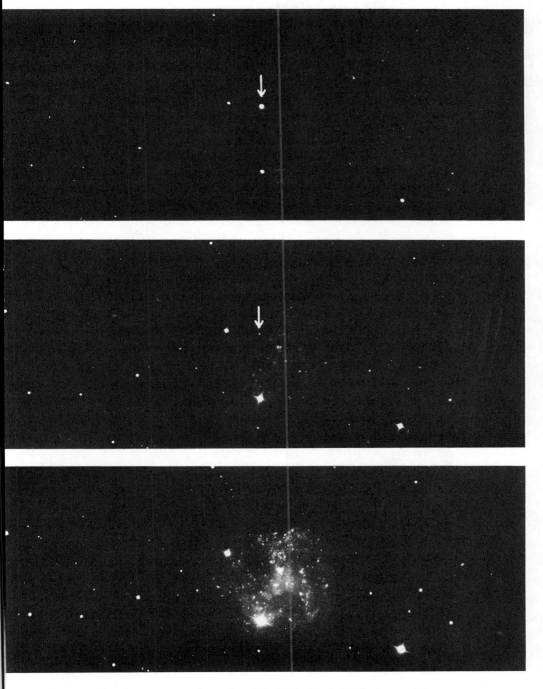

Fig. 166. Supernova in the galaxy IC 4182. (top) 1937, August 23, maximum brightness; (center) 1938, November 24, faint; (bottom) 1942, January 19, too faint to observe. (*Mount Wilson and Palomar Observatories*)

Fig. 167   Ritchey's nova of 1917 in the galaxy NGC 6946. Left, 1917; right, 1933.
(*Yerkes Observatory*)

NOVAE IN GALAXIES AND THE DISTANCE SCALE

Interest in nova outbursts in galaxies was revived in 1917, when G. W. Ritchey at Mount Wilson Observatory accidentally found a nova of apparent mag 15 in the galaxy NGC 6946. This discovery induced Ritchey to examine the Mount Wilson plate collection and he found two relatively faint novae in the Andromeda galaxy M 31. At the same time, H. D. Curtis inspected the direct photographs of galaxies made at Lick with the Crossley 36-in. reflector. Curtis found one nova in galaxy NGC 4227 and two in NGC 4321. Only 2 months after Ritchey's announcement of the nova in NGC 6946, several astronomers had compiled a list of 11 novae in seven galaxies, four of them in M 31. At this time, astronomers were trying to decide whether these galaxies are systems of stars similar to the Milky Way or aggregates of nebulous matter within our galaxy (see Chap. XX).

Since a number of Milky Way novae had been observed, and were believed to attain roughly the same maximum absolute magnitude, an attempt was made, notably by Curtis in 1918, to determine the distances of the galaxies by comparing the apparent maximum brightnesses of novae in the galaxies with those estimated for Milky Way novae. Curtis at first obtained a distance of close to 10 million light-years for M 31, because he had overestimated greatly the distances of galactic novae. Later he decreased the estimate to 500,000, which still indicated that the spirals are extremely distant and are probably galaxies of stars. However, many astronomers doubted these results, because at maximum most novae in M 31 are many magnitudes fainter than S Andromedae. If the fainter novae were similar to those in the Milky Way, and M 31 as distant as Curtis believed it to be, S Andromedae would have attained an absolute magnitude of −16, at that time considered impossibly high. Curtis, however, disregarded S Andromedae in his calculations and suggested that the dispersion in maximum brightnesses of novae may reach at least 10 mag and that "a division into two magnitude classes is not impossible."[4]

Much later, it was established definitely by W. Baade and R. Minkowski that explosive phenomena of nova outbursts fall into several distinct groups: the ordinary novae, which in a large galaxy, such as M 31 or the Milky Way, occur at a rate of a dozen or more per year, and the much less frequent supernovae, such as S Andromedae and a few similarly luminous objects. Baade and Minkowski also have shown that it is possible to distinguish between two kinds of supernovae, which they designate as Type-I and Type-II supernovae.

Fig. 168. Schematic light curve of ordinary nova, after D. B. McLaughlin. (*From C. Payne-Gaposchkin*, Galactic Novae, *New York, John Wiley and Sons, Inc., 1957, P. 17*)

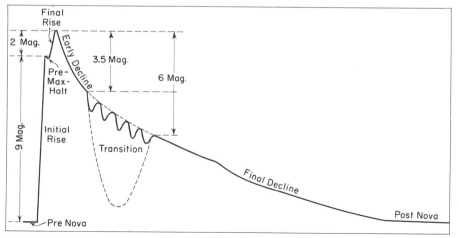

PROPERTIES OF NOVAE AND SUPERNOVAE

Light Curves

Figures 168 and 169 show the schematic light curves of ordinary novae and supernovae. While there are variations in the forms of the individual light curves and in the maximum brightnesses attained, the following general characteristics are observed: (1) Both ordinary novae and supernovae have light curves that are exceedingly steep during the outburst. (2) Maximum brightness usually lasts only for a few days, while the decline in brightness of an ordinary nova may last a few months and of a supernova as long as a year, or even several years. (3) Ordinary novae reach, on the average, an absolute magnitude of about -8; Type-I supernovae, -16; and Type-II supernovae, -14. (4) The light curves of Type-II supernovae are similar to those of ordinary novae, while Type-I supernovae have a much steeper decline in brightness.

All Type-I light curves are very similar, while supernovae of Type II display more variations, both in light curves and in spectra, which led Mrs. Payne-Gaposchkin to suggest that there may be more than two types of supernovae; a similar conclusion has been reached by Swiss-born F. Zwicky of Mount Wilson and Palomar observatories. The similarity in the forms of light curves and in spectral characteristics suggests that Type-II supernovae and ordinary novae represent the same phenomenon, which exists on a larger scale in the Type-II supernovae. The processes involved in a Type-I outburst are not yet understood.

Spectra

Invariably with an ordinary nova, which is bright enough to record its optical spectrum, in the earliest stages of explosion several series of absorption lines strongly displaced toward the violet are found. These violet shifts have been observed in all ordinary novae since the beginning of the century, or perhaps even earlier. The shifts indicate that as a nova

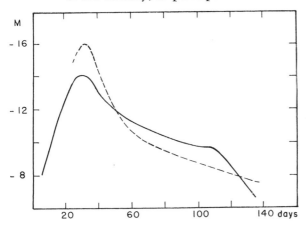

Fig. 169. Schematic light curves of type I (dashed curve) and type II (solid curve) supernovae, after C. Payne-Gaposchkin. The ordinates are absolute magnitudes.

explodes, several consecutive gas shells are blown off into space, thereby rapidly increasing the star's surface area without any drastic change in the temperature of the surface layers. The rapid increase in surface area causes a sudden rise in brightness. Soon after the star has reached maximum brightness, emission lines that undergo progressive changes and show relatively small Doppler shifts appear in the spectrum. However, the lines are broadened greatly as a result of the Doppler motion of surface-layer elements moving radially at different angles to the line of sight. In the later phases of a nova outburst, the spectrum becomes almost entirely one of emission lines, and the star may persist in this stage for many years.

In supernovae, the phenomenon of radial expansion is even more pronounced, and the velocity at the time of outburst may be as high as 10,000 km/sec. The only available spectroscopic data on supernovae come from studies of explosions in galaxies other than our own. Those few objects bright enough to be recorded on small-dispersion spectrograms have yielded little information other than a bewildering superposition of greatly broadened features, few of which have been identified with known atomic lines.

The spectra of Type-I supernovae, described by Minkowski in 1939, appear to consist of overlapping bright lines that have not yet been satisfactorily identified. Type-II supernovae show emission lines of the Balmer series of hydrogen and of several other ionized atoms, such as N III. According to Mrs. Payne-Gaposchkin, the proper classification for the brightest of the extragalactic supernovae, S Andromedae, is not known definitely. Its very high intrinsic luminosity suggests Type I; however, the form of the light curve investigated by Miss D. Hoffleit in the United States in 1939 and by the Soviet astronomer P. P. Parenago in 1949 resembles a Type-II light curve. Mrs. Payne-Gaposchkin states that: "The accounts of the (visually observed) spectrum suggest that it showed bright lines from the first, thus resembling Type I, but it is difficult to identify its features with those of well-observed Type-I spectra."[5] She concludes that "....thus ironically, the brightest supernova of modern times remains an enigma."[6]

Mass Loss

There are several estimates of the amount of mass lost during a nova or supernova explosion. For an ordinary nova, the value usually quoted is roughly 10^{-5} of the original star's mass. For a Type-I supernova the estimates, necessarily uncertain, are between $\frac{1}{100}$ and $\frac{1}{10}$. For a Type-II supernova, the mass lost is somewhere between $\frac{1}{10}$ and $\frac{9}{10}$ of the original star's mass. As discussed in Chap. XIII, it is now believed that the final state in the evolution of a star is that of a white dwarf. S. Chandrasekhar and others have found that no white dwarf can exist with a mass greater than about 1.5 solar masses. It has been suggested, therefore, that nova explosions represent a process that permits a massive star to blow off excess mass, leaving only what is necessary to produce a white dwarf. Type-I supernovae are believed to represent explosions of old stars of Baade's stellar Population II, whose initial masses are not much in excess of 1.5 solar masses. Hence it is understandable that in these supernovae the masses blown off are relatively small compared with the star's initial mass. Type-II supernovae are believed to come from stars of Baade's stellar Population I; most of them are massive, exceeding the sun's mass by factors of between 2 and 65. It is understandable, therefore, that in Type-II supernovae the mass of the remnant may be considerably greater than that of the sun.

In ordinary novae, the mass lost during a single explosion is almost negligible compared to the sun's mass. However, according to the 1934 work of Parenago and Kukarkin, several ordinary novae have been observed to explode at irregular intervals of between 10 and 60 years. The Soviet investigators have shown that there appears to be a correlation between the violence of a nova explosion and the interval between two successive explosions; that is, the more violent explosions occur at less frequent intervals. Since the violence of an explosion is undoubtedly correlated with the amount of mass blown off, it is probable that in the course of several billion years an ordinary nova may undergo tens of thousands of explosions that would allow even a fairly massive star to lose an appreciable fraction of its mass before it settles down as a white dwarf.

SUPERNOVAE IN THE MILKY WAY

The Crab Nebula

After the existence of supernovae had been established, astronomers asked: Is there any evidence of supernovae that have exploded within the structure of the Milky Way? A bright new star—visible in full

Fig. 170. Direct photographs of the Crab Nebula by W. Baade: top, in the light of H-α line; bottom, in green light. (*Mount Wilson and Palomar Observatories*)

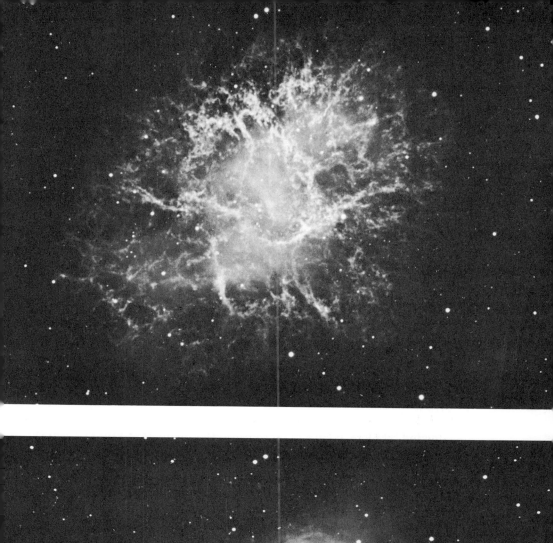

daylight—had been observed by Chinese and Japanese astronomers in the constellation Taurus from July 4, 1054, to April 17, 1056—in the same region of the sky where the Crab Nebula is now located. John C. Duncan's measurements, made at Mount Wilson Observatory in 1921, showed the Crab Nebula to be expanding, at approximately the rate that would have brought it to its present size had the expansion begun 9 centuries before. Evidence relating the nebula and the supernova was reviewed in several articles published in 1942, when N. U. Mayall of the Lick Observatory and J. H. Oort definitely identified the Crab with the remnants of the star of 1054, "which also probably was one of the brightest supernovae on record."[7] The Crab Nebula also has been found to be a strong source of radio emission, and is known as the radio source Taurus A.

Modern observations show that the Crab Nebula consists, in part, of luminous filaments with a bright-line spectrum. These are especially striking on photographs taken in red, Hα light. Much of the light of the Crab comes, however, from a relatively featureless nebulosity that has a continuous spectrum. This amorphous substratum shines in strongly polarized light, as was discovered a few years ago by the Soviet astronomers M. A. Vashakidze and K. I. Dombrovsky, whose results were confirmed and extended by Oort, Baade, and others (in the photographs on Pp. 344-345, the arrows indicate the orientation of the polaroid). The Crab Nebula's polarized light is believed to be synchrotron radiation. Electrons moving at nearly the speed of light are compelled by the nebula's magnetic field to spiral around and along the magnetic lines of force. This spiraling accelerates or decelerates the electrons, which therefore emit completely polarized light of all wavelengths. Fast-moving particles in laboratory synchrotrons have been observed to emit such radiation. Astrophysicists are intensely interested in the details of the processes by which the Crab Nebula's visible and radio radiations are produced.

As with the optical radiation, the nebula's radio emission also should be polarized. In 1957, the Naval Research Laboratory's team of C. H. Mayer, T. P. McCullough, and R. M. Sloanaker, using a 50-ft parabolic receiver at a wavelength of 3.15 cm, found polarization for the Crab of about 7 per cent in a position angle close to 149°. This figure agrees rather well with the over-all value of 9.2 per cent at nearly 160° found in optical measurements by Oort and his associate T. H. Walraven. The optical polarization of a few small spots of the Crab is almost 100 per cent, but in most regions the line of sight penetrates a vast thickness of nebulous material in which the magnetic lines of force are probably not exactly parallel. This factor accounts for a certain amount of depolarization. The beam width of the radio telescopes used is so large that the amount of recorded radiation comes to represent a fairly large part of the entire visible surface.

The supernova of 1054 was so brilliant that the Chinese saw it by daylight for 23 days. Its apparent magnitude may have been −6, which corresponds to an absolute magnitude of −16 at the distance of about 4,000 light-years that has been estimated for the Crab. The Crab Nebula usually is regarded as a typical remnant of a Type-I supernova, while the best-known remnant of a Milky Way Type-II supernova is the radio source Cassiopeia A.

Radio Source Cassiopeia A

This discrete radio source is shown in a clear way on Grote Reber's 1944 radio map of the sky (see Fig. 47), but it was not then recognized as a supernova. It was rediscovered in 1948 by M. Ryle and F. G. Smith in Cambridge, England, and it since has been observed assiduously by many radio astronomers.

Despite its great intensity at radio frequencies, all attempts to identify the discrete radio source with a photographed astronomical object failed until the year 1951, when F. G. Smith obtained an exact determination of its coordinates from observations made with a large radio interferometer. With the help of this position, Baade and Minkowski repeatedly searched direct photographs taken with the 200-in. Hale telescope and found an area of about 4 min of arc (4′) across, which contained some 200 small nebulous fragments and condensations. The center of this area is in close agreement with the center of the radio source. Moreover, Smith's interferometer measurements, and 125-Mc work by R. Hanbury Brown, R. C. Jennison, and M. K. Das Gupta at Jodrell Bank, show that Cassiopeia A is not a point source, but that it seems to be a round spot whose diameter is about 5′.

The nebulosities on the Palomar plates are of two distinct types. The first is composed of sharp, broken bits that can be photographed only in red light; these show no measurable proper motions and have small radial velocities. Their spectra display hydrogen emission lines, along with forbidden lines of neutral oxygen and N II. The second variety consists of more diffuse-looking nebulosities that can be photographed in both blue and red light. Their spectra show no hydrogen, but do show very strong forbidden emission lines of O I and O III. It is likely that the oxygen atoms are excited to shine by collisions with interstellar atoms, rather than by radiation falling on them.

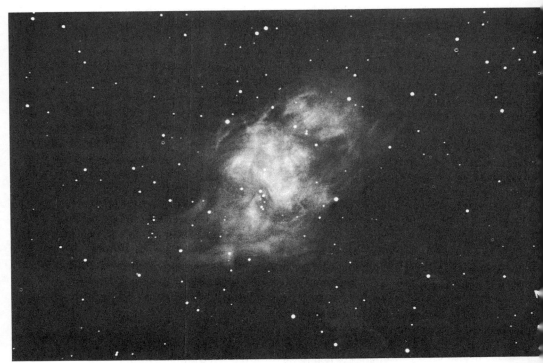

Fig. 171. Direct photographs of the Crab Nebula in polarized light by

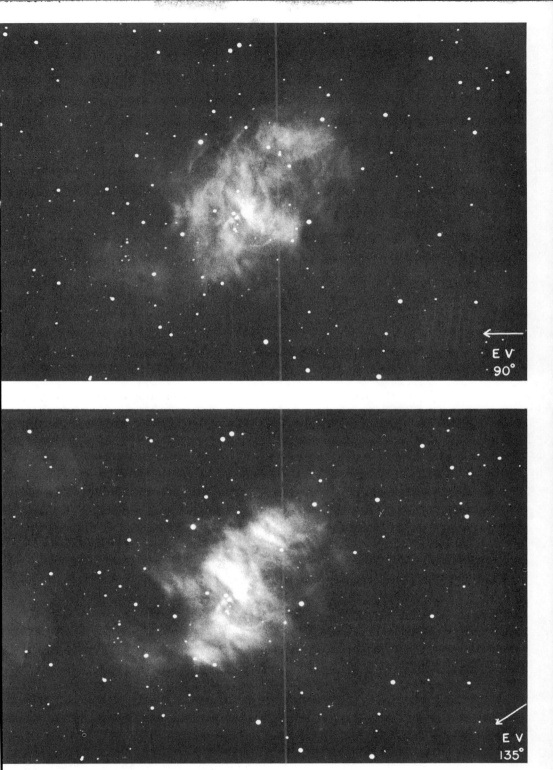

W. Baade. (*Mount Wilson and Palomar Observatories*)

The blue-red nebulosities are remarkable for their enormous radial velocities, ranging between about 6,000 km/sec of recession and 4,000 km/sec of approach. Fig. 172 was drawn by Minkowski to show how the observed radial velocities depend on angular distance from the center of the area. The plot at the left, for the fast-moving, blue-red wisps, indicates that they form a group expanding outward from the center at a rate of about 7,440 km/sec. The second plot, for slow-moving red fragments, shows that they do not participate in the expansion.

The rapidly moving wisps also have large proper motions directed outward from the center. According to Minkowski, the proper motions amount to 0."46/yr at a distance of 118" from the center. If the expansion has been proceeding at a uniform rate, it must have begun about 118/0.46 =256 years ago (around 1700). From the same data, Minkowski estimated the distance of Cassiopeia A, assuming that 7,440 km/sec is also the expansion velocity at right angles to the line of sight. If this velocity produces the angular shift of 0."46/yr, then the distance is 7,440 (4.74 × 0.46) = 3,400 parsecs, or about 11,000 light-years.

From the spectra of the fast-moving nebular fragments, Minkowski and L. H. Aller have estimated that they contain some 1,000–10,000

Fig. 172. Radial velocity measurements for Cassiopeia A, as plotted by R. Minkowski. (*From* Paris Symposium on Radio Astronomy, *ed. R. N. Bracewell, Stanford, Calif., Stanford University Press, 1959, P. 318, Fig. 4; courtesy* Sky and Telescope)

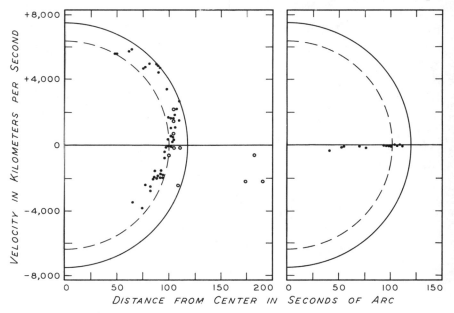

hydrogen atoms/cm^3. Their average density is thus about 10^{-20} gm/cm^3. Since the individual wisps are about $1''$ or $2''$ in diameter, they have volumes of about 4×10^{50} cm^3. Each wisp may contain $4 \times 10^{50} \times 10^{-20} = 4 \times 10^{30}$ gm of matter; all 200 fragments may equal 10^{33} gm— half the sun's mass. Since only a fraction of the shell is visible, the entire exploded material may amount to one or two solar masses.

At the 1958 Paris symposium on radio astronomy, Minkowski told of his conclusions:

There is no longer doubt that the nebulosity is the remnant of a type-II supernova. This is the only type of object for which velocities of expansion of the order of 5,000 km/sec have been reported; a value of 7,500 km/sec is well within the range of possible interpretations. Moreover, no other type of nova or supernova is known to have an ejected mass of the order of 1 solar mass. An ejected mass of this order seems acceptable for the type-II supernova, which as members of Baade's Population I may be very massive stars. At a distance of 3,400 parsecs and with an interstellar absorption of about 6 magnitudes over the center of the nebulosity, the expected apparent brightness of a supernova of type II is about $+5$ magnitudes, too faint to expect discovery of the supernova [when it was at maximum light, about A.D. 1700].[8]

The hypothesis that Cassiopeia A is the remnant of an old supernova was advocated strongly by the Soviet astronomer I. S. Shklovsky, even before Minkowski and Baade reached the same conclusion. However, in his 1956 book on radio astronomy,[9] Shklovsky depended on an earlier and now obsolete estimate of the distance—500 parsecs. Furthermore, he supposed that the nebulosity was formed between 700 and 2,000 years ago, by the outburst of a supernova that attained an apparent magnitude of perhaps -3.5. These inferences led Shklovsky to identify Cassiopeia A with "an unusual star" recorded in ancient Chinese chronicles as appearing in Cassiopeia in March of A.D. 369. The object became invisible in August of the same year. According to K. Lundmark, this was very probably a genuine nova or supernova that became as bright as apparent mag -3. However, the Chinese astronomer Hsi Tse-tsung questions the identification of this star with the radio source, and Shklovsky in a paper in the *Russian Astronomical Journal* accepted Minkowski's age determination.[10]

In Cassiopeia A a bright-line spectrum resulting from excited atoms in the nebula is observed at optical wavelengths. There is no optical synchrotron radiation, but it is reasonable to believe, as Shklovsky and others have shown, that the radio emission is caused, in fact, by the synchrotron effect.

The magnetic field inside the small region of the Milky Way occupied by Cassiopeia A may be approximately uniform, but its electrons have a wide range of velocities and energies. The total flux from Cassiopeia A is the sum of the contributions of all the electrons. This flux is proportional to the volume of the emitting cloud, to a power of the frequency at which observations are made, and to a power of the magnetic-field strength. Shklovsky assumed that the strength of the magnetic field decreases as the nebula expands. At the same time, the energies of all its electrons must decrease. Thus he deduced that the radiation flux is gradually diminishing, at a rate of 2 per cent per year if the nebula is 300 years old.

Measuring this change in flux directly is difficult, but J. W. Findlay is now attempting to do so with a large horn antenna at the National Radio Astronomy Observatory. Meanwhile, Shklovsky has suggested that it would be relatively easy to detect the decay of Cassiopeia A by measuring the ratio of the flux from the constant source Cygnus A (a pair of colliding galaxies) to the flux of the former source. The latest results by J. A. Högbom and J. R. Shakeshaft of the Cavendish Laboratory in England and by D. S. Heeschen and B. L. Meredith of the National Radio Astronomy Observatory (at 1,400 Mc/sec), together with the available earlier observations, indicate a decrease in the ratio of flux of about 1 per cent per year—a slower rate than suggested by Shklovsky.

Frequency of Supernovae in the Milky Way

Shklovsky's extensive historical investigations have led to an interesting hypothesis about the frequency of supernovae explosions. The six or seven supernovae recorded in the Milky Way during the past 2,000 years, he learned, were located fairly close to the sun. Hence he concluded that, although optically bright supernovae have been discovered at a rate of only one per 300 years, there must be a considerable number of supernovae in the Milky Way remaining undetected because they are obscured by heavy clouds of cosmic dust. Supernovae appear in our galaxy, he believes, at an average rate of one in 30 to 60 years.

SUPERNOVAE IN OTHER GALAXIES

Frequency

Most information about the frequency of supernovae explosions in other galaxies rests upon an international search conducted by Zwicky and his associates at the Mount Wilson and Palomar Observatories during the past 25 years. Zwicky presented results of this search at the

AAS (American Astronomical Society) meeting in Mexico City in August, 1960. The total number of supernovae detected in different galaxies was 44. Several different classes of supernovae were found, ranging in absolute magnitudes at maximum brightness from about 10 million to more than a billion times the sun's absolute luminosity. In some of the brighter galaxies, the frequency of supernovae explosions is much greater than one in 300 years. Indeed, in each of the spirals NGC 3184, 4321, and 6946, three supernovae have appeared during the past 60 years. Recent results seem to indicate that frequency of explosion may depend upon the mass and the size of the galaxy. Supernovae explosions apparently are more frequent in large galaxies, such as the Milky Way and M 31, and relatively rare in elliptical galaxies.

Distribution of Supernovae

How are supernovae distributed with regard to their distances from the central regions of each galaxy? Although the nucleus of the Milky Way cannot be observed by optical means, it was investigated thoroughly in 1959 by F. C. Drake with the 85-ft radio telescope at the National Radio Astronomy Observatory. He concluded that there is a small, very dense cluster of stars—a superglobular cluster—in which the density of stars per unit volume is some thousands of times greater than it is in the vicinity of the sun.

A. Lallemand, M. Duchesne, and M. F. Walker at the Lick Observatory observed by optical means the central nucleus of the Andromeda galaxy. They found the radius to be about 7.4 parsecs and the volume to be about 2,000 cubic parsecs. Within this volume, there are about 10 million stars of solar mass approximately. Hence the average star density is about 150,000 times greater than in the spiral arms of the galaxy.

S Andromedae may have exploded within the nucleus of M 31. Of course, there is no information concerning optical observations of supernovae in the nuclear parts of the Milky Way. It is probable, however, that the frequency of outbursts is approximately proportional to the number of stars per unit volume throughout the entire galaxy. This conclusion does not apply necessarily to those spectacular galaxies known to be exceedingly strong emitters of radio waves.

As mentioned in Chap. VI, a normal galaxy is a relatively faint source of radio emission. In exceptional cases, other galaxies may be about 1 million times more luminous in the radio range of frequencies than are the normal galaxies. It is probable that most of this is synchrotron radio emission, and some astronomers have suggested that it may result entirely

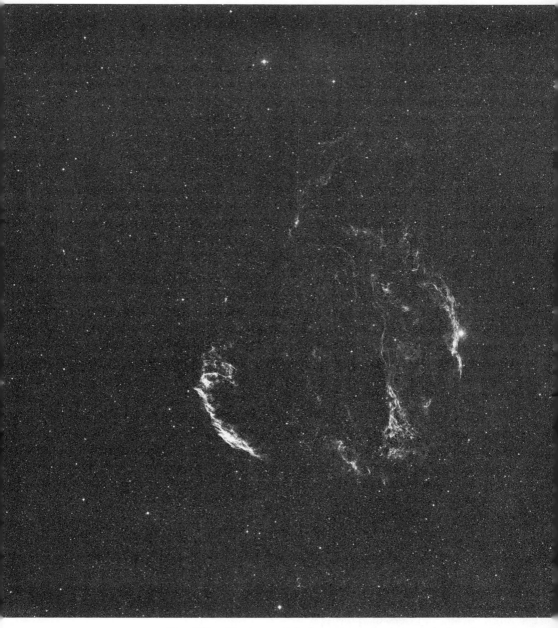

Fig. 173. The Loop Nebula in Cygnus, photographed with the 48-in. Schmidt telescope. (*Mount Wilson and Palomar Observatories*)

from the superposition of a large number of discrete radio sources resembling Milky Way supernova remnants such as the Crab Nebula and Cassiopeia A.

In 1961, G. R. Burbidge suggested that the density of stars in the central nuclei of some galaxies may be much greater than in the Milky Way or in M 31. His article in *Nature*[11] showed that it would not be inconsistent with existing observations to assume that in some galaxies—giant ellipticals or giant spirals—the density of stars may be as great as 10 million/parsec[3], provided that the volume occupied by such a super-globular cluster does not exceed 1 or 2 parsecs in radius. With a density of this magnitude, the distance between two neighboring stars may be only a few hundred astronomical units. A star resembling the sun would be seen from its nearest neighbor at an apparent magnitude of about -14, which is brighter than the full moon as seen from the earth. Because of the stars' gravitational interactions, their individual velocities easily might be 400 km/sec, or even more. Actually, collisions of neighboring stars might occur as frequently as one per year. Burbidge believes that it might be possible to explain the almost simultaneous origin of many supernovae in such a dense cloud of stars by the mechanism of stellar collisions, but he prefers a mechanism that involves the accidental explosion of one supernova within the cloud. A considerable fraction of the emitted radiation would trigger off supernova explosions in neighboring stars. The theory has not been developed fully, but the fundamental idea is attractive, because it involves an element of chance. A supernova exploding in a galaxy's outer regions, where the distance between neighboring stars is 1 parsec on the average, would cause no trigger mechanism; the result would be an isolated supernova remnant with a long-enduring synchrotron source of radio emission and a somewhat shorter-lived optical shell, such as the famous Loop Nebula in Cygnus that may have exploded in the Milky Way tens of thousands of years ago. Since the total number of stars in a galaxy is about 10^{11}, while the density at the center corresponds to about 10^7 stars, isolated supernova explosions that cause no more than a weak emission of synchrotron radio radiation are much more probable. But if a supernova accidentally blows up in the dense nucleus, the trigger mechanism easily could produce a chain of explosions lasting about 150 years. In such a process, a vast amount of highly excited gas would be produced, causing for a relatively short interval an intense emission spectrum of the kind observed in many galaxies by C. K. Seyfert of Vanderbilt University. The radio emission constrained within a fairly small volume by magnetic fields might last for many thousands of years, and would then account for the so-called radio galaxies. In itself, however, Burbidge's discussion does not explain the existence of the large, optically undetectable sources of radio emission often observed on both sides of the galaxy's optical image at distances of hundreds of thousands of parsecs from the center.

I. S. Shklovsky suggested in 1962 that the absolute radio magnitudes of galaxies (observed at 160 Mc/sec), when plotted against the dimension R of the emitting regions, define two distinct sequences: (1) The "main sequence," whose members have values of R similar to the radii of the optical images. For them the radio flux $L \propto R^{2.5}$. At the bottom of this sequence is Sagittarius A, the nucleus of the Milky Way, with $M_r \sim -11$ and $R \sim 10^2$ parsec. (2) The other, "giant" sequence has values of R that are many times larger than the optical images. At the top are Cygnus A and 3C-295, both with $M_r \sim -35$ and R of the order of 100,000 parsecs. At the bottom of this sequence is Centaurus A (NGC 5128), with R even greater than in Cygnus A.

Somehow gas is ejected by galaxies to very great distances. Shklovsky believes this ejection proceeds at a rate of $5\odot$ per year. There are not enough gas and stars in the nuclear regions of any galaxy to sustain this outflow for long. Hence Shklovsky believes that intergalactic gas with $\rho = 10^{-28}$ gm/cm^3 is captured by the galaxy, and is later partly ionized (to produce in emission [O II] λ 3727). The atoms are accelerated by a magnetic field, in accordance with the ideas of the Italian physicist E. Fermi, and become in effect cosmic rays with energies of up to 10^{11} or 10^{12} electron volts.

GALACTIC NOVAE

While the supernovae are more spectacular, the ordinary novae have provided a wealth of information regarding the nova phenomenon. Several novae in our galaxy have been observed in considerable detail; over half a dozen of naked-eye visibility have appeared during this century.

Novae Persei: 1901

The first bright nova of the 20th century—Nova Persei—was discovered in the early morning of February 22, 1901, by the English amateur astronomer Anderson (who also had discovered Nova Aurigae in 1892); it reached its maximum brightness about a day and a half later. When discovered, its visual magnitude was about +3; when photographed 28 hours earlier, its visual magnitude was below +12. At maximum brightness, it reached 0 mag and was one of the brightest stars in the sky.

Extensive observations were begun immediately, and Nova Persei was the first nova observed in the premaximum stage. To the surprise of the observers, it did not exhibit the bright- and dark-line spectrum considered typical of novae; dark lines appeared only after the brightness had started declining. The Doppler displacements of the dark lines then indicated a velocity of expansion of about 1,000 mi/sec for the gas ejected by the nova

Fig. 174.   A direct photograph of Nova Persei (1901), and its shell, photographed with the 200-in. Hale telescope almost 60 years after the outburst. (*Mount Wilson and Palomar Observatories*)

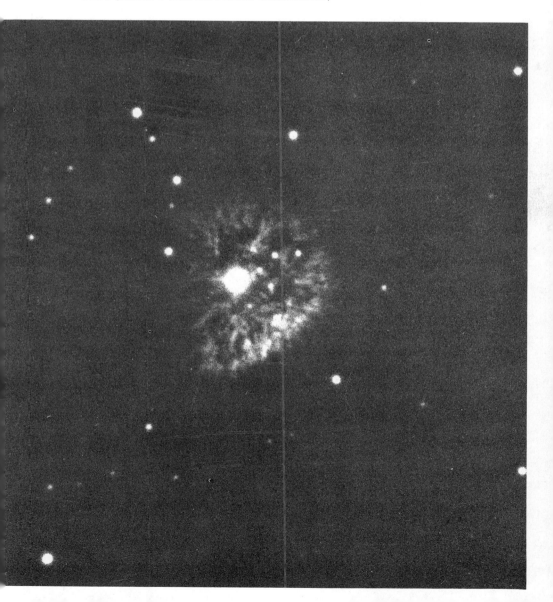

outburst. Toward the end of August, M. Wolf noticed (on a direct photograph) a small nebulous arc surrounding the star; this arc was shown subsequently to be expanding, apparently with a velocity as great as that of light, rather than at 1,000 mi/sec, as determined spectroscopically. Actually, what was observed was the propagation of a light-wave from the nova through a nebula, illuminating its successive layers. The true expanding nebulous shell was discovered by the English astronomer W. H. Steavenson in September, 1916, and later in the same year independently by E. E. Barnard. By 1920, it was shown to be expanding at the expected rate of 1,000 mi/sec.

Nova Aquilae: 1918

The brightest nova of modern times, actually the brightest since Kepler's nova of 1604, was discovered because of its great luminosity by several observers on the night of June 8, 1918, when it was of mag +1; it reached mag −1 the following night. Photographs taken on June 7 showed it as a star of mag 6; those taken on June 5 showed it at its normal brightness, +10.5 mag. The rapid decline started on the second night after discovery. Nova Aquilae is the first nova whose spectrum had been photographed in the pre-outburst stage, when it appeared to be a typical A-type star.

Nova Herculis: 1934

Another famous nova of this century, Nova Herculis, was discovered by the British amateur astronomer Prentice on the morning of December 13, 1934; that morning, the first spectrogram was taken at the Greenwich Observatory. Beginning the following evening, extensive observations were made of its spectrum. From the spectrograms obtained at various observatories, the English astronomers F. J. M. Stratton and W. H. Manning later published an atlas—still the only one covering the day-by-day changes in a nova's spectrum.[12] The light curve of Nova Herculis was peculiar. Four days after it had started fading, it suddenly brightened up again and stayed at about mag +2 for almost 4 months; then it again suddenly faded and subsequently brightened to mag +7 for another year. But probably the most interesting discoveries regarding Nova Herculis are M. F. Walker's (discussed in Chap. XV, P. 317). Walker established that the star is an eclipsing binary, one component of which is a pulsating star of extremely short period.

Fig. 175.   Nova Herculis before and after outburst. (*Yerkes Observato*

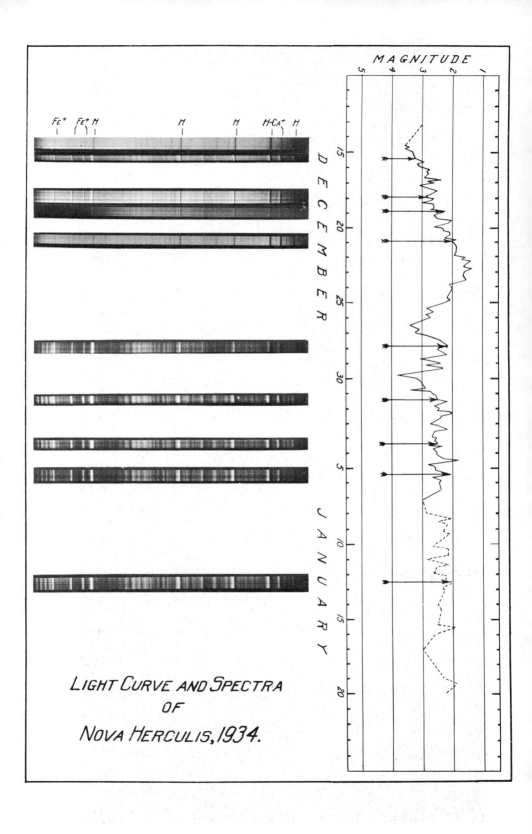

LIGHT CURVE AND SPECTRA
OF
NOVA HERCULIS, 1934.

From the work of R. P. Kraft it is known that most, perhaps all, dwarf novae are members of binary systems. What happens when one component of a close double star suddenly explodes? Apparently, not much. In East Germany P. Ahnert has shown that Nova Herculis was an eclipsing binary before its outburst in 1934. Its period was then 0.1932084 day; it is now 0.1936206 day. This 3½-min increase in period implies a small loss of mass from the system that is quite consistent with what is known from the spectrum.

NOVALIKE OBJECTS

Recurrent Novae

As mentioned before, several novae have been observed on two or more occasions as exploding stars. Thus, T Coronae Borealis first exploded in 1866, then was quiescent, and exploded again 80 years later, when A. J. Deutsch found it as a bright star in the constellation Corona Borealis. There apparently exists a gradual transition between the ordinary novae and the pulsating variable stars, and astronomers have used the designation "recurrent novae" to describe their properties. Some of them are known also as SS Cygni or U Geminorum variables. These are probably binaries and undoubtedly extend to such mild explosive stars at 17 Leporis. Violet-displaced absorption lines are visible at all times in its spectrum, but it displays slightly more violent outbursts at irregular intervals lasting several months. Some of these stars show little or no variation in brightness, but only a change in the Doppler displacements of their absorption lines.

P Cygni Stars

There also may be a connection between the ordinary novae and the P Cygni stars. The latter show strong but not especially broad emission lines with violet-displaced absorption components on a continuous background corresponding to a photosphere of a relatively high temperature. C. S. Beals has listed 69 P Cygni–type stars—11 in the Magellanic clouds.

The past history of P Cygni is most interesting. In 1600, this previously inconspicuous star suddenly increased in brightness until it reached mag +3. It remained at this brightness until 1606, when it began to decline;

ig. 176.   Light curve and spectra of Nova Herculis by D. H. Menzel. (*Courtesy* ky and Telescope)

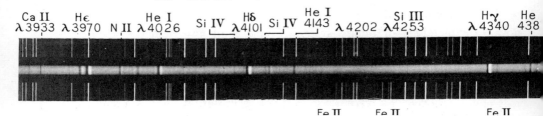

| Ca II λ3933 | Hε λ3970 | N II | He I λ4026 | Si IV | Hδ λ4101 | Si IV | He I 4143 | λ4202 | Si III λ4253 | Hγ λ4340 | He 438 |

Fe II   Fe II   Fe II

Fig. 177. The spectrum of P Cygni, photographed by C. S. Beals.
(*Dominion Astrophysical Observatory*)

it reached mag +6 in 1620. For some years thereafter it was invisible to the unaided eye. But in 1654 it began to brighten again and reached mag +3.5 in 1655, remaining at this brightness for 4 years. By 1715, it had returned to mag +5.2, and with only minor fluctuations has remained at approximately this brightness. This behavior resembles that of a nova. Most other P Cygni stars have shown only small fluctuations in brightness and spectrum.

Beals has estimated that P Cygni is about 1,000 parsecs from the sun and that its absolute magnitude is about −6. The average absolute magnitude of the P Cygni stars is about −4.5, and their surface temperatures lie between 10,000° and 40,000° K.

Wolf-Rayet Stars

Another very interesting group of stars that may be related to the novae is the Wolf-Rayet group. Only about 200 of them are known at the present time. Estimates of their absolute magnitudes range between −4 and −8. The emission lines of the Wolf-Rayet stars are exceedingly broad and in a few cases are connected with violet-displaced absorption borders. The enormous widths of the emission lines formerly were interpreted as an indication that electron scattering in the outer layers of a star's atmosphere might be responsible for the appearance of the emission lines. This interpretation has been dropped in favor of ordinary thermal motions caused by the high temperature of the atmosphere. A few Wolf-Rayet stars belong to galactic star clusters that also contain relatively young O- and B-type stars. Hence, the Wolf-Rayet stars also must be fairly young stars, which perhaps are in the process of contraction. It is possible that the P Cygni stars and the Wolf-Rayet stars are related and that the principal distinction between them is in temperature.

Some of the best-known Wolf-Rayet stars are members of close binary systems. It has been suggested, therefore, that a binary nature is necessary to produce the properties observed in these objects. However, A. B.

Underhill has observed several Wolf-Rayet stars that are apparently single. Although Wolf-Rayet stars and P Cygni stars are subject to small variations in brightness and also eject gas in small amounts into interstellar space, their number is not sufficient to maintain the presently observed amount of interstellar gas and dust out of which new stars are being formed.

XVII

INTERSTELLAR
MATTER

ON NUMEROUS occasions in this volume, references have been made to *interstellar matter* (dust and gas of exceedingly low density distributed throughout the galaxy), and to *galactic nebulae* (higher concentrations of interstellar matter). Even though the existence of galactic nebulae was recognized at the beginning of this century, it took some time to develop an understanding of the physical processes that occur in them, and several links in the theory are still missing, as will be seen in Chap. XVIII. It took, however, the first 30 years of this century to prove even the existence of interstellar matter.

A. S. Eddington once remarked that although astronomers do not know much about interstellar matter, they talk a great deal about it; they are like the guest who refused to sleep in a "haunted" room and who, when asked whether he believed in ghosts, replied: "I do not believe in ghosts, but I am afraid of them." It is probably no exaggeration to say that interstellar matter, particularly in the form of dust, was the ghost that haunted astronomers for many years. Even though it is now believed to consist, on the average, of roughly 1 per cent of dust to 99 per cent of gas, the effects of the latter were not nearly as bothersome, and evidence regarding it accumulated gradually with far less conscious effort and controversy. The real ghost, however, was dust of extremely low density spread roughly uniformly throughout interstellar space.

INTERSTELLAR DUST

Three possible effects of diffuse interstellar matter were investigated at the beginning of this century:

1. *Dispersion:* The velocity of light in the interstellar medium was believed to vary with its wavelength, in analogy to the well-known effect observed in glass and other substances.

2. *Selective absorption:* Fine particles would scatter light of short wavelength more effectively than light of long wavelength, and thus make starlight appear redder than it otherwise would. Selective absorption usually is expressed in terms of *color excess*—the difference between the observed color index of a star and the intrinsic color index corresponding to its spectral type.

3. *General absorption:* A dimming of starlight that would be produced by the combined effect of scattering and absorption of the incident light. Scattering, which produces selective absorption, is also to a large extent responsible for general absorption. The two effects are related, and many attempts have been made to determine their ratio, particularly since it is easier to determine selective than general absorption.

Dispersion

The most promising way of detecting dispersion would seem to be by timing a stellar event, such as an eclipse, from observations in light of different colors.

In 1908, the Russian astronomer G. A. Tikhoff and the French astronomer C. Nordmann found that when certain eclipsing variables are observed in red light, the phase of central eclipse, or minimum light, occurs earlier than when the observations are made in blue light. For Algol (β Persei) the observed lag was 16 min ± 3 min, for λ Tauri 50 min, and for RT Persei 4 min. However, the famous Russian physicist P. Lebedeff pointed out almost immediately after the announcement that the distance of Algol was then believed to be 60 light-years and of RT Persei, 740, yet the nearer star has the greater lag. If interstellar dispersion were responsible for the phenomenon, the dispersion constant would have to be almost 40 times larger in the direction of Algol than in the direction of RT Persei.

Modern determinations give somewhat different distances for the two stars, but Lebedeff's conclusion has been confirmed. Unless the absurd assumption is made that the dispersion constant is entirely different for different stars—even if they are located in the same part of the sky—the Tikhoff-Nordmann phenomenon, if real at all, must be due to some other cause. Lebedeff also pointed out that if properties similar to any known substances are assigned to the interstellar matter causing such dispersion, the light should suffer such great absorption that "through such a medium no appreciable fraction of the light of the sun or of the stars could in any way reach the earth."[1] The unlikely alternative is to assign to the interstellar matter the peculiar property of dispersing light without absorbing any part of it.

Several later investigators obtained a time lag in the opposite sense (that is, longer for RT Persei than for Algol), and in 1917 the absence of dispersion was shown conclusively by Shapley from his observations of variables in globular clusters. These variables are at much greater distances than those considered in the earlier discussions, and Shapley found that "... radiations which differ in wavelength by about 20 per cent, and in amplitude as well, can travel through space for 40,000 years without losing more than 1 or 2 minutes with respect to each other, if indeed there is any difference whatever,"[2] which amounts to velocities that are the same to at least one part in 10^{11}.

Selective Absorption

In 1895, the Dutch astronomer J. C. Kapteyn, particularly famous for his studies of galactic structure, discovered that the average color of stars in the Milky Way belt is bluer than that of those outside it, and suggested that this phenomenon might be caused by selective absorption. This, incidentally, would require that the concentration of intergalactic dust is smaller in the plane of the Milky Way than in higher galactic latitudes: that is, exactly opposite to the true distribution, as will be shown later. After a careful study of star colors in 1904, another Dutch astronomer, W. de Sitter, found the same effect, but he concluded:

Whether this variation of the average colour, as we proceed along the Milky Way, has any relation to the general structure of the galaxy, whether it is caused by real differences in the relative intensity of the different parts of the spectrum, or by a general absorption in one part of the spectrum, whether the stars having the same relative intensity of spectrum are really clustered together in space, or whether the effect is due to selective absorption by intervening cosmical clouds or nebulous masses, these are questions that can be put, but not yet answered.[3]

We know now that the intrinsically blue, hot stars have a much greater tendency to concentrate toward the galactic equator than the cool, red stars do. Hence the Kapteyn phenomenon has no bearing upon the question of selective scattering.

Another line of evidence appeared in 1908 when H. H. Turner, among others, noticed that, to obtain photographic star images of equal densities for successive stellar magnitudes, it was not sufficient to increase the exposure times in the ratio of 2.5 for each step of 1 mag. Indeed, it was found that the ratio of the exposure times is much more nearly 3 than 2.5—even though, by definition, a step of 1 mag signifies an intensity ratio of 2.5. Tikhoff and Turner suggested that selective absorption will make the stars appear redder as their distances become greater. Distant stars are, on the average, faint. Hence faint stars are reddened, and must require relatively longer exposures on the blue-sensitive photographic emulsions—the only ones then used for these observations. Turner summarized the matter thus: "The fact that when the photographic exposure is prolonged in a ratio which ought to give stars fainter by five magnitudes, we only get four visual magnitudes [is an argument in favor of] the scattering of light by small particles in space."[4] As noted in Chap. V, P. 79, this phenomenon was later attributed to reciprocity failure of the photographic emulsion and does not have any relation to interstellar reddening.

At about the same time, a new attack upon the problem became possible with the development of accurate methods of photographic photometry. Miss A. C. Maury had remarked in her work on the spectra of the stars that, among representatives of a single class of spectrum, some are weak in violet light while others are strong. In 1909, Kapteyn examined the available data on star colors and reported that, within narrow groups of spectra, stars that are rich in violet light have large angular proper motions, while those with little violet light have smaller proper motions. Since a star's angular proper motion is a good statistical measure of distance, he concluded that distant stars are reddened by absorption.

However, this conclusion was incorrect, and another interpretation could be given. As a result of observational selection, the stars he examined were, within any given spectral class, all more or less similar in apparent brightness. Hence the distant stars of each group were giants, while the nearby stars were dwarfs.

W. S. Adams and A. Kohlschütter established in 1914 that giants of the same spectral class are deficient in blue light in comparison to the dwarfs, and hence appear redder. Kapteyn had been aware of this possibility. In fact, he commented in his original paper: "The meaning of our result may therefore also be: for stars of the same spectrum, the light of the more luminous objects is relatively weaker in the violet part of the spectrum."[5] However, he disregarded this possibility, as other investigators did, and thought, instead, in terms of scattering of light until Adams and Kohlschütter's investigations showed that ". . . at least a part of the absorption in the violet part of the spectrum of the distant stars must be ascribed, not to scattering of light in space, but to conditions in the stellar atmospheres."[6]

In 1915 and the following years, Shapley investigated the color excesses of stars in distant globular clusters and failed to find measurable values. He remarked that many of these stars are as blue as the bluest stars observed in the galaxy, and that space absorption in the direction of the clusters is entirely negligible. Thus, in 1923, in a paper reviewing the evidence on the absorption of light in interstellar space, the German astronomer H. Kienle could only conclude that the coefficient of selective absorption must be less than 0.1 mag/kiloparsec (kpc), for a wavelength difference of 800 A.

The first conclusive evidence came from the work of R. J. Trumpler, in 1930. This investigation of galactic clusters, (discussed on P. 366) showed that selective absorption is definitely present in the galaxy and amounts on the average to about 0.32 mag/kpc.

The first extensive and accurate investigation of selective absorption was that of color excesses of B-type stars determined photoelectrically by J. Stebbins, C. M. Huffer, and A. E. Whitford. These results show a progressive reddening for the more distant stars. In setting the 82-in. McDonald telescope upon a faint, B-type star, I have often been amazed at the redness of these stars. Their continuous spectra show energy distributions corresponding to some 4,000° or 5,000°, while their absorption lines correspond to a temperature of 20,000°.

Other investigations have been concerned with the energy distribution and colors of stars involved in dense clouds of absorbing matter and the color excesses of distant cepheids and of globular clusters.

General Absorption

The possibility of general absorption was first considered in the 18th and at the beginning of the 19th centuries, on the grounds that an infinite universe with an infinite number of self-luminous stars should cause the entire heavens to be ablaze with light unless there were absorbing matter. Mathematical theory and observational evidence were first used in 1847 by F. G. W. Struve, who obtained conclusive evidence of absorption of about 1 mag/kpc by essentially the same methods that were used at the beginning of this century by H. von Seeliger, Kapteyn, and others. In the course of statistical studies of the distribution of stars in the Milky Way, by methods that will be discussed in more detail on Pp. 411-412 in Chap. XIX, they assumed that stellar density cannot increase with increasing distance from the sun. Thus Kapteyn stated: ". . . as soon as we admit the existence of a somewhat considerable extinction of light, we must at the same time admit a star-density which, at great distances from the sun, increases with enormous rapidity."[7] He derived an upper limit to general absorption of 0.0016 mag/parsec but he believed the actual value to be negligible. Considerably larger values of the absorption coefficient were derived by the American G. C. Comstock of Washburn Observatory in 1904 and in 1917 by J. Halm at the Cape of Good Hope Observatory. The assumptions of the two men differed slightly, and their results were not generally accepted. Most astronomers disregarded the existence of interstellar matter, but the uncertainty of the evidence is clearly shown by Kienle's conclusion that the loss of starlight through absorption must definitely be less than 2 mag/kpc, and that it is probably less than 0.1 mag/kpc.

Conclusive Evidence of Interstellar Absorption

Although fairly conclusive evidence of a general absorption of 0.5 mag/kpc was obtained from the Swedish astronomer C. Schalén's studies made in 1929 of the distribution of early-type stars, the first definite break in astronomical opinion came in 1930 when Trumpler published his results on open star clusters.[8] His work was based upon a series of measurements obtained at the Lick Observatory of the diameters of galactic star clusters.

By observing the spectra of cluster stars and their brightnesses, Trumpler was able to prepare an H-R diagram for each cluster (see Chap. XIII). Physically speaking, the main sequence of one cluster should be rather similar to the main sequence of another (for typical H-R diagrams of clusters see Figs. 132 and 133). But since the distances of two clusters are, in general, not the same, it is necessary to shift the diagrams along the vertical coordinate in order to make the sequences coincide. The dis-

Fig. 178.   R. J. Trumpler. (*Courtesy* *Mrs. H. F. Weaver*)

placement, measured along the vertical coordinate in stellar magnitudes, provides a measure for the relative distances of the two clusters. Distances determined in this manner are affected by absorption. Suppose the vertical shift corresponds to 3 mag; this means that all stars of the brighter cluster are $(2.5)^3 = 15.6$ times as intense as those of the fainter. If there were no absorption, it should be concluded from the inverse-square law that the fainter cluster is $\sqrt{15.6} = 3.9$ times as far away as the brighter cluster. If absorption were present, the real distance would be smaller. Trumpler conceived the idea of measuring the diameters of the clusters, making sure first that he was measuring physically similar objects. If the brighter cluster had a diameter of 15′, the fainter should have a diameter of 15′/3.9 = 3′.9, provided the distances inferred from the H-R diagram are correct.

From a large amount of very homogeneous material, Trumpler found that the diameters of the fainter clusters were systematically too large, and he concluded:

... as none of the observational errors discussed offers a possible explanation of the observed discrepancy there are only two alternatives left; either to admit an actual change in the dimensions of open clusters with increasing distance or to assume the existence of an absorption of light within our stellar system.[9]

Trumpler adopted the latter alternative and derived a value of 0.67 mag/kpc. He warned, however, that:

... if we speak of general absorption this does not mean that it is necessarily uniform throughout the stellar system; the absorbing material may have many local irregularities but must be so distributed that on the average the absorption in magnitudes is approximately proportional to distance.[10]

Trumpler further investigated selective absorption. Large discrepancies between the observed color indices and spectral types in open-star clusters had been known for some time, but were ascribed to dust within the clusters. In order to test the hypothesis of selective interstellar absorption, it was necessary to show that the average color excesses in various clusters depend on their distance; Trumpler found such a correlation.

Since the open star-clusters are greatly concentrated toward the galactic plane, Trumpler's results applied only to this region and he stated:

We are thus led to the conclusion that some general and selective absorption is taking place in our Milky Way system, but that this absorption is confined to a relatively thin layer extending more or less uniformly along the plane of symmetry of the system.[11]

This concentration explained why Shapley had not found any color excesses in globular clusters; most are far above or below the galactic plane. However, absorption was found to affect Shapley's distance estimates of several low-lying clusters.

Recent Investigations of the Amount of Absorption

Among many modern attempts to arrive at the average amount of interstellar absorption per unit distance, one of the most interesting is that of A. H. Joy at Mount Wilson. His method depends upon determinations of radial velocities of cepheid variables and upon the theory of the rotation of our galaxy, predicting that the rotational component of a star's motion in the line of sight must be proportional to the distance from sun.

The method is complicated by the fact that the stars have their own individual motions. These probably are distributed at random, so that if average velocities for groups of cepheid variables are arranged according to apparent magnitude, a series of values should be derived, the ratios of which, after correction for foreshortening, directly give the ratios of the true distances for the various groups. Another estimate of the distance can be derived from the period-luminosity relation of cepheids. If there were no absorption, the two procedures should give identical results. From the departures, which are conspicuous, Joy, and later R. E. Wilson, derived an absorption of about 0.6 mag/kpc.

A second method for determining interstellar absorption depends upon counts of extragalactic objects in different parts of the sky. These distant galaxies are seen through the thickness of absorbing matter in the Milky Way. Their numbers are greatest near the two galactic poles. Near the plane of the galaxy, in the so-called *zone of avoidance*, the absorption is so great that no outer galaxies are seen through it (see Fig. 216). In intermediate galactic latitudes, the absorption is a function of the latitude. For example, at galactic latitude 10°, the absorption is 1.4 mag; at 20°, 0.7 mag; at 30°, 0.50 mag; at 60°, 0.29 mag; and at 90°, 0.25 mag.

The smooth manner in which these values progress has suggested to F. H. Seares of Mount Wilson Observatory that "a widely diffused absorbing stratum extending equally above and below the galactic plane"[12] is being dealt with. The zone of complete avoidance of galaxies, which is irregular in shape, is associated by Seares with the obscuring clouds in the Milky Way that also have a distinctive irregular appearance.

Recent determinations give values of the average absorption coefficient of between 0.4 and 0.85 mag/kpc, but several astronomers have suggested that in the galactic plane it may be as high as 2 and even 2.5 mag/kpc, because the most distant stars used in the determinations are actually in the least-obscured regions. Local regions of heavy obscuration, amounting to as much as 5 mag/kpc, have been found.

An important quantity is the ratio of selective absorption to total absorption. From his consideration of all available data, Seares concludes that:

(1) Total absorption equals 10 times the selective absorption, for the diffuse stratum of interstellar matter.

(2) Total absorption equals 5.7 times the selective absorption, for the dark nebulae of the zone of avoidance.

The latter law corresponds to an absorption coefficient which is proportional to λ^{-1}. According to the law formulated by the English mathematician Lord Rayleigh in the second half of the 19th century, the scattering by molecules, such as occurs in the earth's atmosphere, is proportional to λ^{-4}. The departure from Rayleigh's law in interstellar scattering was first established by Trumpler and was confirmed by O. Struve, P. C. Keenan, and J. A. Hynek. This departure, together with the fact that particles 10^{-3} cm in diameter or larger would block out the star light without scattering it, suggests that the interstellar dust particles must have diameters of about 10^{-5} cm.

The Nature of Interstellar Dust

Many investigations have been concerned with the constitution and origin of interstellar dust. For some time the particles were believed to be metallic, but recent work indicates that they are more probably icelike compounds of the lighter atoms. It also is believed now, particularly from the theoretical investigations of van de Hulst and Oort, that interstellar particles grow by accretion from interstellar gas, instead of originating from meteoric disintegrations, as had been believed earlier.

Polarization

Another effect produced by interstellar dust—the polarization of starlight—was discovered accidentally by the American astronomers W. A. Hiltner and J. S. Hall. Suggestions that the light of ordinary stars may be polarized had been made before, but no observational evidence was available. A revival of interest in this problem arose in 1946 when S. Chandrasekhar predicted a small amount of radial polarization near the limbs of early-type stars caused by the presence of large numbers of free electrons in their atmospheres—a phenomenon originating in the stars, not due to an interstellar medium. The symmetry of the polarization renders this effect unobservable when the light of the entire star is integrated by the photometer. In an eclipsing binary, however, just before totality sets in, a small crescent of the eclipsed star remains visible, and its light should be plane-polarized. In June, 1946, the American astronomer Edith M. Janssen made some promising photographic observations of U Sagittae with the 40-in. telescope at Yerkes, and a few months later Hiltner obtained fairly convincing evidence that a small amount of polarization is present at the limb of the brighter component of RY Persei.

Because of the exceptional importance of this problem (to which repeated attention had been called by Z. Kopal), Hiltner, in collaboration with Hall, then of Amherst College, undertook in August, 1947, a series of observations with a photoelectric photometer attached to the 82-in. reflector of the McDonald Observatory. They selected the Wolf-Rayet eclipsing binary, CQ Cephei, which Hiltner previously had observed spectrographically and photometrically. In a report to the American Philosophical Society in 1947, Hiltner stated that "... evidence was obtained for the presence of polarization of radiation from the limb...."[13] The instrument was unfortunately not reliable, and both observers agreed to rebuild the apparatus in order to eliminate the instrumental errors that had made it difficult to discern the true effect. In subsequent months, Hall, with considerable help from Hiltner, perfected his own polarizing photometer. During the summer of 1948, Hall was unable to resume the work at McDonald (because of his transfer to the United States Naval Observatory), and Hiltner observed alone, with an instrument of his own construction.

This time:

Fairly large polarizations were found but they did not appear to depend on the phase of the binary motion. The possibility of instrumental polarization was considered, of course, but ruled out by control measures on check stars. Similar observations made on a group of Wolf-Rayet... stars in Cygnus showed no appreciable polarization, while two stars in Scutum gave positive results....

We conclude... that the measured polarization does not arise in the atmospheres of these stars but must have been introduced by the intervening interstellar medium. If this conclusion is accepted, a new factor in the study of interstellar clouds is introduced. Further observations are in progress for relating this phenomenon with other observable characteristics of the interstellar medium... the results already at hand indicate that the plane of polarization approximates the plane of the galaxy.[14]

These results were confirmed by Hall, who also found a correlation be-

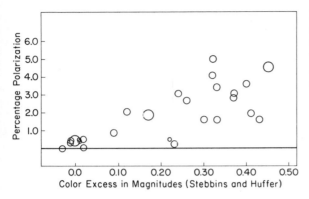

Fig. 179.   Correlation between color excess and percentage of polarization for early-type stars, according to J. S. Hall. (*From* Science, *CIX, 1949, P. 167; courtesy* Sky and Telescope)

tween color excess and polarization in the sense that an increased amount of polarization is accompanied by an increased color excess, while the reverse is not always true.

Thus it appears that the presence of dust is a necessary, but not sufficient, condition for polarization. The dust grains must be slightly elongated, and must have a preferential alignment in one direction. Both of the latter conditions are not always satisfied. In particular, while the grains in one cloud might all have a preferential alignment, if the star light passes through several such clouds, the planes of polarization might not coincide but rather cancel each other out. If the aligning force is parallel to the galactic plane and also is related to the spiral structure, differences in polarization would be expected, depending on whether observations are made along the direction of the spiral arm or perpendicular to it, as has been actually observed when comparing the regions of Cygnus and Cassiopeia. In the diagram of Cassiopeia the coordinates are galactic longtitude and latitude; each line represents a star, the length of the line is proportional to the amount of polarization, and the position angle of the line corresponds to the position angle of the plane of vibration. According to Hiltner:

> . . . the direction of Cassiopeia is nearly perpendicular to the presently identified spiral arms. The particles will, therefore, be aligned in all clouds except for small disturbances caused by the turbulent motions of the clouds. Hence, to a first approximation, the plane of vibration for all stars in Cassiopeia should be similar, and furthermore, the amount of polarization should increase as the number of clouds traversed by the stellar radiation increases. This is observed. In the direction of Cygnus, however, the line of sight is nearly parallel to the axis of the spiral arm in which the sun is located. In other words, the line of sight is nearly parallel to the alignment force. If this were rigidly the case the scattering would be iso-

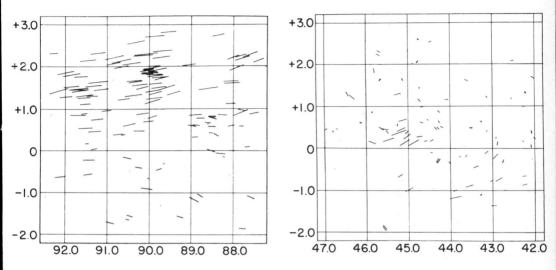

Fig. 180.   (Left) Interstellar polarization in Cassiopeia, according to W. A. Hiltner. (*From* Vistas in Astronomy, ed. A. Beer, London, Pergamon Press, 1956, II, P. 1082)
Fig. 181.   (Right) Interstellar polarization in Cygnus, according to W. A. Hiltner. (*From* Vistas in Astronomy, London, 1956, II, P. 1082)

tropic and no polarization would be observed. However, as seen in Cassiopeia, the lines of force are not strictly parallel and may show significant departures. The particles, although they may be well aligned by the acting force are poorly aligned for producing polarization as seen from the solar system.[16]

In terms of physical theory, interstellar polarization requires a magnetic force that tends to align the elongated particles whose original alignment, if it ever existed, must be disturbed continually by collisions. An interstellar magnetic field approximately parallel to the Milky Way plane of about 10^{-5} gauss might explain the observations, according to a theory by J. L. Greenstein and L. Davis, Jr. There are no direct observational data on polarization other than those obtained by radio astronomers, who have found in the direction of Perseus a field of about 10^{-6} gauss. This work was done at the Nuffield Radio Astronomy Laboratory in Jodrell Bank. Even now, all radio astronomers are not convinced that interstellar polarization really exists. But one of the most competent, J. H. Oort, has expressed the opinion that a small amount of polarization can in fact be observed in several regions of the Milky Way when all instrumental effects (and these can be quite troublesome) are eliminated.

It is regrettable, perhaps, that Hiltner and Hall did not combine their results but published them separately. Apparently their joint observation in August, 1947, was somewhat more convincing to Hall than to Hiltner. But in their subsequent, independent observations they have extended their earlier work in a most remarkable way, and reached substantially the same conclusions. The question of priority, which may still seem important at the present time, no doubt will be submerged soon by the universal recognition this outstanding work deserves. The detection of interstellar polarization always will remain one of the most striking examples of a purely accidental discovery, such as Wilhelm Röntgen's discovery of X rays in 1895. It required exceptional instrumental skill to detect the small variations of the light of a star as the analyzer was turned, but even more important was the quick realization that the effect was completely new and in no way foreshadowed by previous work.

INTERSTELLAR GAS

The Discovery of Interstellar Absorption Lines

While interstellar dust affects the entire spectrum, the absorption by interstellar gas is strictly selective, affecting only light of certain wavelengths. In 1904, the German astronomer J. Hartmann found that the absorption lines of Ca II in the spectrum of the double star δ Orionis fail to take part in the periodic oscillations of the other lines. He eliminated the obvious explanation that the stationary Ca II lines come from a very massive secondary component of the binary system, and concluded that:

We are thus led to the assumption that at some point in space in the line of sight between the sun and δ Orionis there is a cloud which produces that absorption, and which recedes with a velocity of 16 km/sec, in case we admit the further assumption, very probable from the nature of the observed line, that the cloud consists of calcium vapor.[16]

Since that time, other atoms and molecules have been found to originate in interstellar space, among them Na I, Ca I, K I, Ti II, CN, and CH. There are several unidentified absorption lines from interstellar matter that are very prominent in several B-type stars—for example ζ Ophiuchi —and are clearly of interstellar origin. There are also a number of diffuse absorption lines, or bands, that as yet are unidentified, but there is evidence that their intensities are correlated closely with color excess, so that perhaps they are produced by solid crystal-like particles. G. Herbig recently has succeeded in resolving into band lines some of these diffuse interstellar absorption lines, and he has discovered several new ones. Their identification should follow in the near future.

Although supported by V. M. Slipher in 1909, Hartmann's interpretation of the stationary lines was not immediately accepted, and their exact nature remained a puzzle for many years. One complicating factor was the presence of these lines only in the spectra of hot stars (spectral type B 3 or earlier). This misled many astronomers into trying to associate the origin of interstellar lines with the intensity of stellar radiation.

Some astronomers were inclined to associate the stationary calcium lines with gaseous masses located in the immediate vicinity of the stars. For example, O. J. Lee's Ph.D. dissertation at the University of Chicago was based upon a binary orbit of the star α Camelopardalis, whose spectrum has, in addition to very broad and diffuse lines unsuitable for precise measurement, a pair of very sharp calcium lines. Lee thought that the calcium gas was connected with the binary system and that certain unusual features of the velocity curve could be explained in terms of this hypothesis. His work was never confirmed. Later measurers usually have attributed the sharp calcium lines to the interstellar medium, and they have indirectly discarded Lee's theory as untrustworthy. Many years later, Lee still believed that his early measurements were essentially correct and that, therefore, at least a part of the sharp absorption comes from the immediate surroundings of the star.

The correct explanation of the problem was complicated further by the Canadian astronomer R. K. Young's radial velocity measurements of the calcium lines in 12 Lacertae. These measurements indicated different radial velocities in different years, which if correct would not support the hypothesis of the interstellar medium.

In 1924, J. S. Plaskett suggested that the stationary lines are produced by absorption in a widely distributed tenuous cloud of matter enveloping the stars, and that the cloud's calcium atoms would be ionized in the vicinity of the hotter stars. O. Struve, in 1925, attributed the phenomenon of stationary calcium lines to vast clouds that

... show a strong concentration toward the plane of the Milky Way, where they seem to cover practically every square degree in greater or smaller density. The clouds form separate masses which show small but definite systematic motions with respect to the stellar system as a whole. In high galactic latitudes the clouds are scarcer, and it is probable that at least in some directions the line of sight does not encounter any such clouds.

... The stars move in all directions through these clouds, but only the hot stars, of spectral type B 3 or earlier, are capable of exciting and ionizing at a distance the material of which the cloud consists.[17]

Eddington's Theory

Eddington, with his marvelous insight, was able to discard unreliable observational results, and he ignored the work of Lee and of Young. He showed conclusively in 1926 that the gas producing the absorption lines is not associated with the star in whose spectrum they appear, but occurs throughout large interstellar clouds. Moreover, the lines are not produced in the immediate vicinity of the stars. Eddington attributed the absence of stationary lines in spectra later than B3 to: (a) masking by broad stellar lines, which begin to appear at about B3; (b) insufficient radial velocity of late-type stars; and (c) insufficient distance of those late-type stars bright enough to be observed. He showed that, in the vicinity of a hot star, the amount of Ca II actually would decrease because of double ionization, and that the velocities observed by Plaskett would require that a stationary cloud of matter be expelled by the star while the star itself possesses a considerable motion with respect to it.

Eddington also gave the correct explanation for the occurrence of radial-velocity curves of spectroscopic binaries based upon calcium lines that in some cases have a smaller range than the normal stellar absorption lines do. The latter results, obtained by several different observers, were explained by Eddington as a simple phenomenon of the blending of a stellar calcium line with a stationary interstellar line.

It is interesting to note that another now-famous astronomer, B. J. Bok, director of the Mount Stromlo Observatory in Australia and previously a faculty member at Harvard Observatory, started his astronomical career by pointing out to me that I had badly underestimated the signifi-

Fig. 182.   Correlation of interstellar line intensity with distance in spectra photographed with Coudé spectrograph of the 120-in. telescope. (*Lick Observatory*)

Ca II K   CH⁺ 395

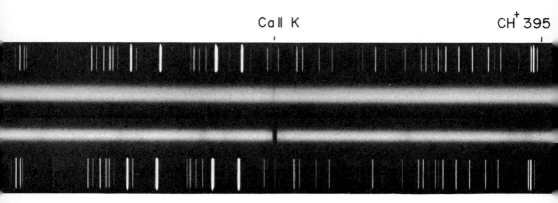

cance of the blending of interstellar and stellar calcium lines.

The absence of stationary lines between the stellar components of the binary star 66 Eridani was an apparent contradiction to Eddington's theory, since relative displacements of the absorption lines of the two components is 220 km/sec at maximum and a stationary line should appear between the stellar lines. Because the distance of 66 Eridani is only about 100 parsecs, Eddington concluded that, "... We must presume then that this distance is insufficient to give detectable absorption."[18]

Apparently no other search for interstellar lines in the spectrum of 66 Eridani has been made. But such lines have been found on high-dispersion spectrograms of several nearer stars. In 1941, T. Dunham, Jr., detected interstellar calcium lines in the spectra of α Virginis and η Ursae Majoris at distances of 53 and 66 parsecs, respectively, and in 1961, at the Palomar Observatory, A. Unsöld and G. Münch found a faint line in the spectrum of α Ophiuchi, at a distance of only 18 parsecs.

Eddington also suggested that in order to test his theory, an attempt should be made to correlate distances of stars and the intensity of the stationary lines. Such a study had already been undertaken by O. Struve, who was able to show that in low galactic latitudes the strength of the interstellar calcium lines increases with the stellar distances up to at least 500 or 600 parsecs from the sun, (see Fig. 182; top, a B3 dwarf star; bottom, a distant supergiant). However, some doubts about Eddington's interpretation were still caused by the sudden disappearance of the interstellar lines at spectral type B3, which seemed too abrupt to be satisfactorily accounted for by blending with stellar lines. It is now known that the disappearance of interstellar lines is much more gradual than at first was believed.

Later studies by Dunham, Struve, and others also proved that the diffuse interstellar gas is mostly hydrogen. While it does not produce ob-

Ca II H

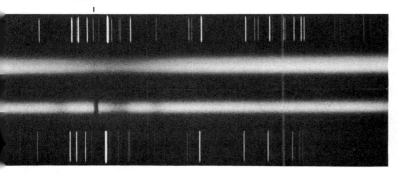

I Scorpii   B3

HD 190603 B1.5 Ia$^+$

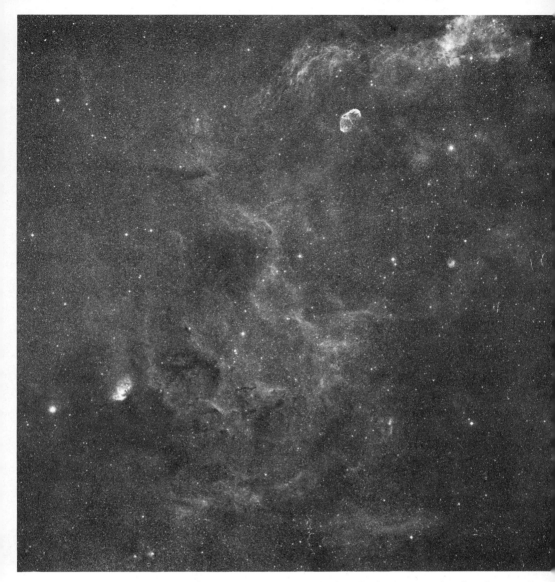

Fig. 183. Gas clouds in Cygnus, photographed with the 48-in. Schmidt telescope. (*Mount Wilson and Palomar Observatories*)

servable Balmer absorption lines, it furnishes enough free electrons to maintain the ionization of the calcium gas at the observed level.

Distribution of Interstellar Gas Clouds

In the early 1930's, astronomers lost sight of the nonuniformity in the distribution of the interstellar gas clouds. However, in 1936 Beals reported that interstellar lines are sometimes multiple, indicating that more than one absorbing cloud lies between us and the star. Subsequently, Adams reported from Mount Wilson that about half of the 300 stars he had observed have double or triple interstellar lines and that in several stars the calcium K line has four components. These observations were used later in Whipple's detailed analysis of the regional character of the clouds. The photograph of multiple interstellar lines shows the K line of Ca II at the left, the H line at the right. The stars from top to bottom are ζ Aurigae, 10 Lacertae, λ Orionis, and κ Orionis.

The multiple structure of an interstellar absorption line is caused by differences in the radial velocities of separate clouds along the line of sight to the star. The individual clouds vary greatly in size, but the average diameter is about 20 or 30 light-years. The number of clouds penetrated by the line of sight is about nine or ten for each 1,000 parsecs from us.

Fig. 184.   Multiple interstellar lines, photographed by W. S. Adams.

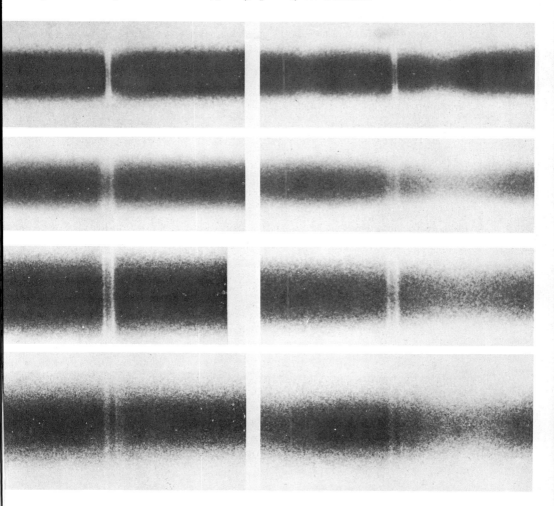

The most important recent studies of interstellar lines are those of G. Münch and H. Zirin. They follow up Adams' 1949 finding that

> ... the radial velocity from individual components in 7 stars exceeds 50 km/sec and reaches nearly 100 km/sec in one case, but the strongest component nearly always gives a low velocity. Double stars and stars close together in position usually show the same structure for the H and K lines, and nearly the same radial velocities.[19]

However, there are indications that high-velocity clouds are smaller than those of low velocity, because neighboring stars occasionally have dissimilar, highly displaced components, while the strong but slightly displaced components are essentially the same.

In 1957, Münch listed the radial velocities and intensities of the interstellar calcium and sodium lines in 112 very distant stars located near the galactic plane and with galactic longitudes between 55° and 160° (in Lacerta, Cassiopeia, Perseus, Auriga, and Orion). The remotest of these stars, some 3,000 parsecs away, usually showed two strong absorption components; one is produced by nearby clouds located in our spiral arm of the Milky Way (the Orion arm), the other by clouds in the next outer arm (the Perseus arm, see P. 432). Occasionally, in addition to these strong components, there are fainter, highly displaced lines, evidently due to small, high-velocity clouds.

In 1961, Münch and Zirin published their observations of interstellar lines in the spectra of two dozen distant O- and B-type stars at high galactic latitudes, ranging from 240 to 2,700 parsecs above and below the galactic plane. The spectra of all these stars show interstellar components; some gas clouds probably occur at 1,000 parsecs from the plane and have velocities of 50 km/sec toward or away from the plane.

This discovery of fast-moving gas clouds at high galactic latitudes is a major advance in astrophysics. Münch and Zirin have attempted to explain the origin of these features and their physical properties:

> ... the rather different appearance of the complex interstellar lines in high galactic latitude stars ... from that observed in stars near the galactic plane. ... In Milky Way stars at distances not greater than, say, 1 kiloparsec from the sun, invariably one strong component, with a small Doppler shift is observed, around which lines with larger shifts may appear with considerably smaller strength. In high galactic latitude stars with complex lines, in contrast, we observe the component with smallest velocity ... [to have a] strength comparable to the others. The difference is, of course, due to the fact that the strong lines in the Milky Way either arise from the partial superposition of a number of weaker lines or are formed in extensive gas masses with considerable internal mass motions.[20]

From the clouds' radial velocities and their present distances above and below the galactic plane, Münch and Zirin estimate lifetimes of 40 million years. High-velocity clouds in low latitudes have much shorter lives, perhaps only a tenth as long. Presumably, they are dispersed by collisions with other clouds and by the drag exerted upon them by the more tenuous gaseous substratum of the Milky Way. But such a cloud, propelled away from the central plane, will encounter very few others after it has attained a distance of a few hundred parsecs above or below the plane. At distances of several thousand parsecs, the probability of collision with another cloud would be very small.

On the other hand, a cloud moving into empty space should be expected to expand fairly rapidly, and would lose its identity in less than 40 million years. Münch and Zirin suggest, therefore, that this expansion is restrained by a highly rarefied but very hot galactic corona, whose pressure is sufficient to overcome the tendency of the relatively dense and cool clouds to grow. (Such a galactic corona had been suggested previously by Lyman Spitzer, Jr.)

With an *electron temperature* (inferred from the velocity distribution of electrons rather than true temperature measurements) of 1,000,000° K and a density of only 0.0005 hydrogen atoms/cm^3, the corona would be too tenuous to be observed in emission with present astronomical techniques and too highly ionized to cause absorption in the currently accessible region of the spectrum. But it could prevent a high-velocity cloud from expanding rapidly.

DENSITY OF INTERSTELLAR MATTER

An indirect method of estimating the density of interstellar matter rests upon Oort's study in 1932 of stellar motions at right angles to the plane of the Milky Way. The motions of the stars in the galactic plane are governed largely by the mass of the galactic nucleus. But the motions across the galactic plane, the Z components, are determined almost wholly by the distribution of mass in the vicinity of the sun. From the observed radial velocities, Oort computes the stars' space motions. The Z components then are analyzed with regard to the stars' distances from the galactic plane. This leads to a determination of the accelerations in the Z coordinate, dependent upon the density of matter in the vicinity of the sun. The data of observation are satisfied best by an average density of 0.092 solar mass/parsec^3, which is equivalent to 6.3×10^{-24} gm/cm^3. Oort found that the luminous stars in the solar neighborhood account for 0.038 solar mass/parsec^3. Hence, the difference, or 0.05 solar mass/parsec^3, must be due to stars too faint to be detected and to diffuse matter in interstellar space. This corresponds to a density of 3×10^{-24} gm/cm^3—the famous Oort limit for the density of interstellar matter. Thus, roughly equal amounts of the mass of the galaxy were believed to be contained in the stars and in interstellar matter. Recent radio observations have shown, however, that the proportion of interstellar matter had been overestimated greatly: It amounts to only 2 per cent, on the average, but may be as high as 10 to 15 per cent in the spiral arms, such as in the solar neighborhood.

XVIII

GALACTIC
NEBULAE

THE DISCUSSION in the preceding chapters was confined to the "ghost that haunted astronomers"—the very tenuous "substratum" of interstellar matter. In a greater concentration, however, interstellar matter makes its presence known quite readily in the form of dark or luminous nebulae. Dark nebulae were discussed briefly in Chap. III in connection with the photographic work of E. E. Barnard and M. Wolf. As a result of both visual and photographic observations, many luminous nebulae such as the Trifid Nebula (Figs. 21 and 22), the Orion Nebula (Fig. 186), the nebulosity in the Pleiades (Fig. 188), and many others were long recognized in the Milky Way. A luminous nebula is produced if a star happens to be situated within or near a cloud of dust and gas, and two types of bright nebulae have been recognized from spectroscopic observations: the emission and reflection nebulae.

BRIGHT GALACTIC NEBULAE

Emission Nebulae

The conspicuous feature of the emission nebulae (the Orion and Trifid nebulae are of this type) is a number of bright emission lines in their spectra (see Fig. 108). These lines were first observed by Huggins in the 19th century. The emission results from ionization of the atoms of gases by hot stars and the subsequent recapture of electrons. The peculiar problems involved in the production of the nebular emission lines and

Fig. 185. The "Horsehead" Nebula, in Orion, photographed in red light with the 200-in. Hale telescope. (*Mount Wilson and Palomar Observatories*)

Fig. 186. The Great Nebula in Orion, photographed with the 100-in. telescope. (*Mount Wilson and Palomar Observatories*)

Fig. 187. Dark and bright nebulae in Ophiuchus and Scorpius; Antares is in the
lower center of the picture.

their identification were discussed in Chap. XI, but it should be repeated here that the nebulae are a more perfect vacuum than can be achieved in any terrestrial laboratory. The spectra of most emission nebulae also contain some reflected starlight.

Reflection Nebulae

The reflection nebulae were discovered by V. M. Slipher, who in 1913 observed the spectrum of the nebulosity in the Pleiades. Instead of the emission lines he had expected to see, he found a continuous spectrum crossed by absorption lines and noticed that: ". . . the whole spectrum is a true copy of that of the brighter stars in the Pleiades."[1] In these nebulosities, the starlight is reflected by small dust particles. Most of them are illuminated by hot, luminous stars that are blue in color. The nebulosities also are blue—perhaps even bluer than the radiating stars themselves, because the very small dust particles that are contained in the clouds tend to make the transmitted starlight redder, and consequently the scattered light of reflection nebulosities appears bluer. Many nebulosities of this type are known: for example, those near ρ Ophiuchi and σ Scorpii.

Immediately after the publication of Slipher's discovery of the reflection character of the nebulae in the Pleiades (especially near the star Merope), E. Hertzsprung reached one of his many brilliant, intuitive conclusions: If the nebula is a white screen, hemispherical in shape, its surface brightness must be the same as the surface brightness of an extrafocal image of the illuminating star whose diameter is made the same as the diameter of the nebula. In the case of the Pleiades, the extrafocal star image is some 4 or 5 mag brighter than the nebula. Hence the latter is not a white screen; either its albedo is much smaller than one, or its particles occupy only a small fraction of the space, or, probably, both effects are present. No true reflection nebula can be whiter than white. But such is the case in the nebula known as B10 (entry 10 in *Barnard's Catalogue*). Hence the latter is a very strange object, and deserves further study.

The Relation between Two Types of Bright Nebulae

The study of bright nebulae was advanced greatly in the 1920's through the work of E. P. Hubble, who first investigated the spectral types of stars associated with nebulae and found that:

. . . stars involved in nebulae having continuous spectra are nearly always of type B1 or later; but stars involved in emission nebulae nearly always have spectra earlier than B1.[2]

This intimate relation between spectral type of nebulae and of involved stars raises a presumption that one is a consequence of the other. It seems more reasonable to place the active agency in the relatively dense and exceedingly hot stars than in the nebulosity, and this leads to the suggestion that nebulosity is made luminous by radiation of some sort from stars in certain physical states. The necessary conditions are confined to certain ranges in stellar spectral type and hence are possibly phenomena of effective temperature. The nebulous material itself must be in a physical state sensitive to the stellar radiation and close enough for the density of radiation to be effective.[3]

Hubble also investigated the luminosity of both types of bright nebulae as functions of their distances from the associated stars and of their luminosities. If the reflection and emission nebulae were identical in composition, the latter should be more luminous than the former. The scattered star light would be the same, but the emission nebulosities would have an additional glow, due to the fluorescence of hydrogen and other atoms. Hubble found that the relationship between the nebula's maximum angular extent and the star's apparent luminosity was identical for both types.

In 1936, O. Struve and H. Story at Yerkes repeated Hubble's work, adding many newly discovered nebulosities and attempting to distinguish between emission and reflection objects. Although Hubble's work in the main was confirmed, there was an indication that the reflection nebulae may be slightly less luminous per unit angular surface than the emission nebulosities are. However, this work has not been confirmed since, and there is still some doubt about the complete interpretation of both types of nebulae.

THE THEORY OF NEBULAR EMISSION LINES

The modern theory of nebular emission lines is based almost entirely upon a truly revolutionary idea advanced by H. Zanstra in the mid-1920's. According to Zanstra, very hot stars emit strong radiation in the ultraviolet region of the spectrum, and every ultraviolet quantum whose energy is greater than that which corresponds to the Lyman limit at λ 912 A (energy required to remove the electron from the ground state of hydrogen) can ionize an interstellar hydrogen atom, producing in each case one free proton and one free electron. When the free electrons recombine with free protons, they do not always fall into the state of lowest

Fig. 188.   Nebulosity surrounding the stars of the Pleiades. (*Yerkes Observator*

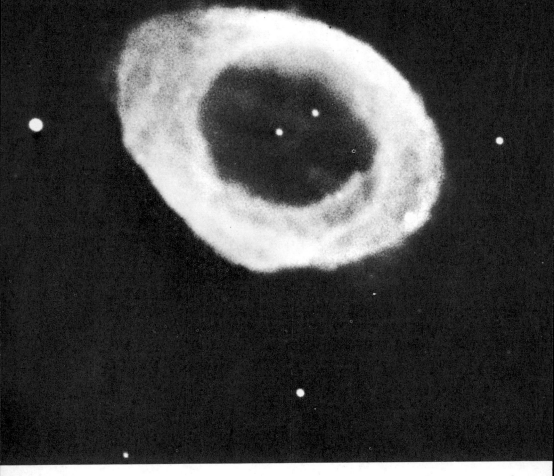

Fig. 189. The "Ring" Nebula, the planetary nebula in Lyra, photographed with the 200-in. Hale telescope. (*Mount Wilson and Palomar Observatories*)

energy, but "cascade" through several intermediate levels, thereby producing emission lines of the entire hydrogen spectrum. The total energy of the absorbed stellar ultraviolet photons must then be equal to the total energy of all the nebular emission lines.

Zanstra summarized his work in his 1961 George Darwin Lecture, "The Gaseous Nebula as a Quantum Counter." He pointed out that the original idea occurred to him and to Menzel at the same time. The theory has been extended greatly by Menzel and several of his associates at Harvard in a long series of articles and by L. H. Aller.

Planetary Nebulae

Zanstra's original purpose was to determine the temperatures of the central stars of planetary nebulae (gaseous shells surrounding certain very hot and presumably old stars). In his words:

> The integrated intensity L of a monochromatic picture from a certain line of the nebula was measured in an arbitrary but true scale, and the same was also done for the intensity per frequency unit of the adjoining star spectrum.[4]

The theory of the hydrogen atom makes it possible to calculate in advance the fraction of original ultraviolet stellar quanta that produces a particular Balmer emission line in the nebula. Since the distance from us to the star is the same as from us to the nebula, the ratio of the two observed quantities gives the temperature of the star, which is regarded as a black body in accordance with Planck's radiation law (see P. 95). In a similar manner, stellar temperatures have been derived from the emission lines of helium and other elements.

When the distances of the stars and their associated nebulae are known from independent studies (Zanstra used L. Berman's distances of several planetary nebulae obtained at the Lick Observatory), Zanstra's theory results in an absolute determination of the total number of ultraviolet quanta emitted per second by the entire star. This, in turn, can be used to determine the central star's size—usually a little less than the sun—and its absolute *bolometric magnitude** because the temperature is already known and hence the amount of energy radiated per unit of surface: 1 cm². Zanstra's result is M (bolometric magnitude) $= -3$. The theory is not entirely free of minor contradictions, and some assumptions are verified only approximately.

One wonders, for example, why any emission lines of He I and He II are produced by recombination if all stellar quanta below the Lyman limit of hydrogen at λ 912 A are used up for the photoelectric ionization (the required energy is supplied by ultraviolet radiation, rather than col-

* Brightness corresponding to the total amount of energy radiated by the star, in all wavelengths.

Fig. 190. Planetary nebula in Aquarius, photographed in red light with the 200-in. Hale telescope. (*Mount Wilson and Palomar Observatories*)

lisions between atoms) of interstellar hydrogen. The ionizing wavelength of He I is at λ 504 and of He II at λ 228. Zanstra suggests that

> ... the most reasonable approximate model for a star seems to be one with a flux per cm^2 corresponding to T_H in the visual region and in the ultraviolet not too far short of λ 912, but with often a strong ultraviolet excess for the region λ < 228 A, this excess being produced at or close to the stellar surface by some mechanism as yet unspecified.

The very sharp discontinuity discovered by Hubble—stars of spectral type earlier than B1 produce emission nebulae, and those later than B1 produce reflection nebulae—suggests, at first glance, that there is a very sharp deficiency in ultraviolet quanta in stars of the later types. But this information is probably not complete because, as discussed above, Hubble's geometrical relation has almost the same constants (Hubble said: "the same total actinic value") for both types of nebulae. It looks almost as though very small scattering dust particles (their diameters are, on the average, 10^{-5} cm) are not formed where the hydrogen ionization predominates.

Oort and others have argued that the ratio of dust and hydrogen is nearly the same in all different galactic clouds. This is not the case in small regions. For example, Struve found that the star σ Scorpii—which is embedded in the large obscuring nebulosity surrounding Antares, ρ Ophiuchi, and several other bright stars—has on one side a fairly conspicuous emission nebula, and on the other side a reflection-type luminous nebula. The spectral type of σ Scorpii is B1. There is also evidence from the Harvard radio-astronomical observations of the neutral hydrogen 21 cm line that the dust-to-gas ratio varies in different regions.

H I and H II Regions

The theory of nebular emission was further developed by B. Strömgren, who recognized that when the nebula is very thin (small optical depth in ultraviolet light), the available number of ultraviolet quanta of the star are exhausted as more and more of them are used up in ionizing interstellar hydrogen atoms. This led to Strömgren's theory of H I and H II regions of interstellar gas. The exhaustion of stellar ultraviolet quanta follows an exponential law, which in turn produces a fairly sharp boundary between the H II region that surrounds the hot star, and the un-ionized H I region on the outside.

To allow for this effect, Strömgren used the Saha ionization formula, to which he added a factor that accounted for the depletion of the ionizing stream of quanta by the atoms in the neighborhood of the exciting star. This factor depends, among other things, upon the density of the interstellar medium and the length of the path traversed by the radiation. He showed that in the immediate vicinity of a star all hydrogen is ionized, and that there is a sudden transition at a certain distance from the star between ionized and neutral hydrogen. Assuming a density of 3 hydrogen atoms/cm^3, Strömgren computed that in the vicinity of a main-sequence O5 star, hydrogen would be ionized to a distance of 67 parsecs. In the case of a B0 star, the ionized region extends to 12 parsecs, and in the vicinity of an A0 star to only 0.2 parsec. An extrapolation of Strömgren's calculations to spectral class G0 indicates that the H II region surrounding the sun would not extend beyond the space occupied by the planetary orbits.

There are still a number of puzzling questions regarding individual nebulae. Before discussing some of these, it will be helpful to consider a type of instrument—the *nebular spectrograph*—that was developed for the study of faint nebulosities.

NEBULAR SPECTROGRAPHS OF THE YERKES AND McDONALD OBSERVATORIES

In 1936, Struve and Elvey at Yerkes (and later at the McDonald Observatory) were interested in determining whether the solar system is embedded in a cloud of luminous hydrogen. This possibility was suggested in part by the proximity to the sun of two very hot stars—γ Velorum and ζ Puppis—whose ultraviolet light could ionize the atoms of hydrogen at a considerable distance. Besides this, there has always been the theory that cosmic clouds of the absorbing kind in Taurus and Orion merge with similar clouds at the opposite side of the sky, in Sagittarius and Ophiuchus. Oort and others had suggested that dark, obscuring dust clouds always are accompanied by clouds of hydrogen atoms.

Properties of the Nebular Spectrographs

The nebular spectrographs invented at Yerkes and McDonald in 1937–1938, while radical departures from the conventional types of instruments, actually represented a revival of the very simple optics employed by the inventors of spectroscopy. The first spectroscopic results in the 19th century were obtained with a slit located at a considerable distance from a prism, and sometimes even without a focusing camera. In the Yerkes and McDonald instruments the collimator was eliminated, and the slit was placed at a great distance from the dispersing unit, so that the light reaching the prism was almost parallel. However, a camera was needed to produce adequate resolution. One reason for omitting the collimator was that, while at McDonald no suitable lens or mirror was available, the Yerkes 40-in. refractor possessed a scale of 10″/mm and a conventional 1cm-long slit would correspond to a scale in the sky of about 100″ and would record, therefore, only a small part of a nebulosity. It was also realized that, because there would be no loss of light either at the collimator's surfaces or due to opacity of glass when a lens is used, fainter objects could be observed than with a conventional slit spectrograph.

The Yerkes nebular spectrograph was immediately put to use by G. Van Biesbroeck, L. G. Henyey, and J. L. Greenstein in photographing the spectra of the nebulosities around γ Cygni, which turned out to be of the emission type. This was true despite the fact that the illuminating, or exciting, star is of spectral type F and normally would be expected to produce only a reflection nebulosity. Van Biesbroeck and Henyey also studied the ultraviolet spectrum of the periodic Comet Encke, in which several new emission lines were discovered.

At McDonald, a small polar head was used to support two plane mirrors. The one used to obtain the spectrogram of a nebulosity was 36 in. long; the width, which could be changed according to the declination, usually was about 1 in. The second, shorter mirror could be tilted in declination to obtain a photograph of a comparison region. Light from the two slit mirrors was reflected toward a circular plane mirror 75 ft away that returned the beam downward along the polar axis. The light then was photographed with a Schmidt camera (employing the same principles as the Schmidt telescope, see P. 55) attached to the polar mount, in front of which was placed a quartz prism. A guiding telescope was used to keep a star in the same position during the entire exposure. And although, strictly speaking, focusing the camera upon the slit rendered the stars and nebulosities slightly out of focus, no serious trouble was encountered as a result of this.

The F/1,[*] 90-mm Schmidt camera used in the McDonald spectrograph had been made by C. H. Nicholson of Duquesne, Illinois, an amateur astronomer. Commercial firms were not acquainted with the properties of Schmidt instruments and were unwilling to undertake their manufacture. The nebular spectrographs had one thin 4-mm glass correcting-plate made of ultraviolet transparent glass, so that the spectrograms extended into the far ultraviolet (to about λ 3100 A).

[*] The *F-number* denotes the ratio of the aperture of the lens or mirror to its focal length.

24-inch Plane Mirror

Diaphragm

Plane Mirror and Slit

Comparison Mirror and Slit

Guiding Telescope

Schmidt Camera and Prism Box

Fig. 191. The 150-ft nebular spectrograph of the McDonald Observatory.

Observational Results

The resulting spectrograms showed the nebulosity's long spectral lines, with the comparison region's shorter spectrum lines on the side. If the entire sky had been uniformly luminous in hydrogen, the two spectra would be similar. Numerous observations were made at McDonald with this instrument, using panchromatic emulsions in order to record the Hα line; in many parts of the Milky Way, emission nebulosities were discovered that had not been known previously. The comparison spectra were taken away from the Milky Way; they recorded essentially no visible hydrogen emission lines. The conclusion, therefore, was that the hydrogen nebulosities are concentrated in and near the plane of the Milky Way. Because of the great length of the slit, corresponding to $1°.5$ in the sky, it was possible to record on one spectrogram not only a small part of the nebulosity but also, in many cases, its full extent. This showed quite clearly the edge where luminous hydrogen ceases to exist and the light from the night sky is seen as merely the result of both air glow and the unresolved background radiation of very faint stars and unresolved galaxies.

There is every reason to believe that protons and free electrons are present everywhere in the Milky Way, and especially inside the solar system. However, whether there is luminous hydrogen surrounding the solar system, or perhaps even within the region of the planets, has not yet been determined.

Nebulosity Surrounding Antares

The red nebulosity surrounding Antares was one of the many nebulosities photographed at McDonald. When these spectra, taken at a distance of about 15′ north of Antares, were matched against the comparison spectrogram taken about 50° farther north, it was seen immediately that the nebula's continuous spectrum is exceedingly strong in the red, but that there is no indication of hydrogen emission lines. Presumably the red nebulosity is of the reflection type, and the light of Antares, which is red in color, is simply scattered by the very small particles of the vast obscuring cloud in the region of Scorpius and Ophiuchus.

In 1938, at an AAS meeting in Ann Arbor, a paper by V. M. Slipher was read that severely criticized the work of the Yerkes and McDonald astronomers. Slipher stated categorically that the nebular spectrograph was strongly affected by out-of-focus star light and that the nebulosity around Antares is blue, not red. The Yerkes astronomers listened in stunned silence; they had thought that their results confirmed and extended Slipher's earlier discoveries, not contradicted them. In a footnote at the end of a paper on luminous nebulosities in the Milky Way, which was published shortly after the meeting, Struve wrote as follows:

We have always emphasized that the Yerkes nebular spectrograph integrated over a region of 16′ diameter, while our present spectrograph integrates over 6′ if focused on the slit or over 0′ if focused on the sky. The fundamental nature of Slipher's early observation has always been recognized by us. The Yerkes observation was for the purpose of showing how the early-type absorption spectrum gradually merges with the general sky spectrum. Had there been conspicuous emission lines in the outer

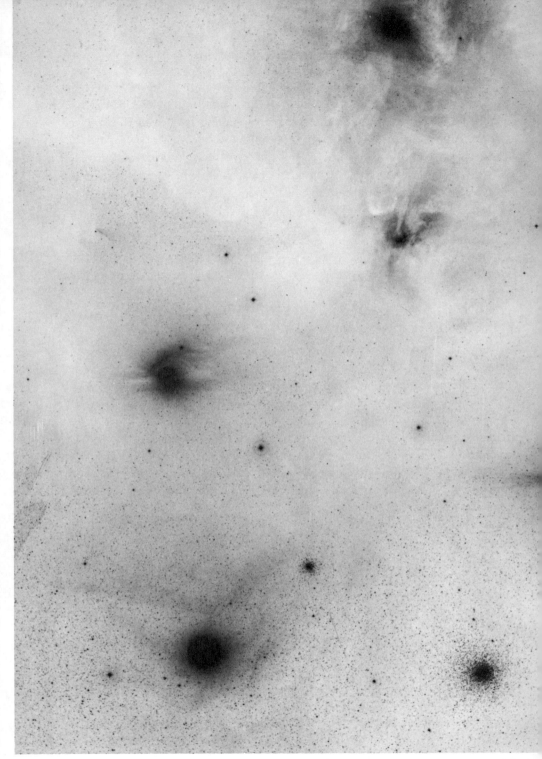

Fig. 192. The region near Antares, in blue light (left) and in red light (right).

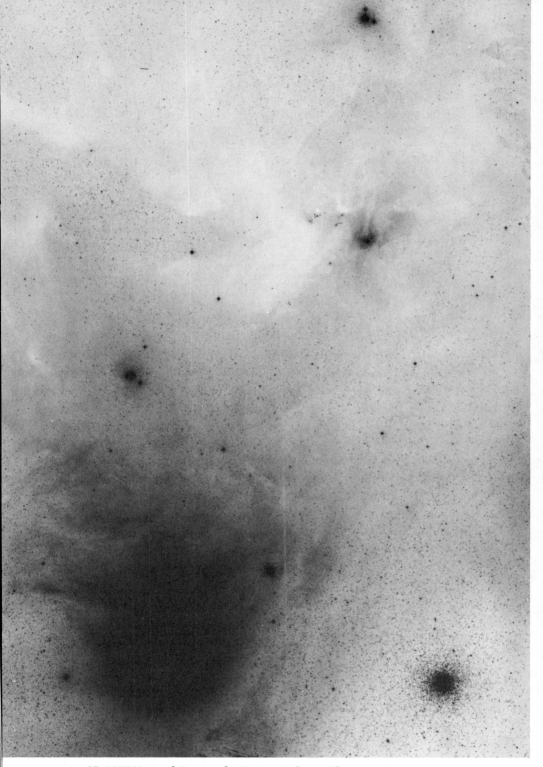

regions, they would have been found on these plates. The contamination by starlight referred to by Slipher is slight, but the blurring of the features of the objects is important and has been fully considered. . . . Dr. Slipher suggested that the nebula north of Antares is not red and is not illuminated by Antares. Our photovisual and photographic observations . . . prove that the nebula is indeed red, compared with nearly all other reflection nebulae. Hence, it is probably illuminated by Antares. There seems to be a tendency for reflection nebulae to be slightly bluer than their respective stars, and this may account for Slipher's observation.[6]

The McDonald observations have been borne out by all later investigations. The red nebula around Antares can be seen on the *National Geographic-Palomar Atlas* charts; it is one of the most conspicuous regions on red photographs.

In 1937, the nebular spectrographs represented a great advance, and a photograph of the McDonald instrument was used as the frontispiece by the Russian astronomer B. A. Vorontsov-Velyaminov in his 1940 book on practical astrophysics.[7] A more accurate method of recording faint hydrogen emission was later developed by B. Strömgren, who used narrow-band filters to isolate Hβ or Hα lines and measured the intensities of these radiations with a photoelectric cell. His method, of course, recorded only the radiation that was passed through the narrow-band filter, not the entire spectrum. Also, even though the nebular spectrograph was an extremely useful instrument in recording faint nebulosities, this does not mean that large optical telescopes have lost their value in nebular research. Because a large reflector's scale is some seconds of arc per millimeter, it can be used to investigate small features within the nebulosities—this cannot be handled by the nebular spectrograph.

DISTRIBUTION OF DARK CLOUDS

As has been shown, the emission nebulosities detectable with modern instruments do not envelop the solar system and are strongly concentrated toward the galactic plane. The same seems to be true of the more conspicuous obscuring nebulosities. Khavtasi at the Burakhan Observatory and Mrs. B. Lynds at the National Radio Astronomy Observatory have shown (in investigations based upon the *Atlas of Dark Nebulae*,[8] prepared by the former, and the Atlas and catalogue, by the latter[9]) that the nearest galactic dark nebulae belong to the local system of the Milky Way—also called *Gould's belt*.* This belt can be understood as a "wrinkle"

* In 1879, B. A. Gould, then the director of the Cordoba Observatory in Argentina, called attention to it and estimated that it contains less than 500 stars.

in the otherwise very flat galactic system defined by the more distant B-type stars. This local cloud or "wrinkle" (because it probably merges continuously with the general galactic system) is inclined by about 20° to the galactic plane, and has a diameter of about 1,000 parsecs. It consists mainly of B-type stars brighter than apparent mag 6, fairly bright A-type stars, diffuse reflection nebulae, and extended dark nebulae. A recent estimate of the mass of this local system is 10^8 solar masses.

In any case, because they have few foreground stars, the most conspicuous dark, obscuring nebulae must be relatively close to the sun. Distance estimates of 100 to 200 parsecs have been published for the nearer ones. In East Germany in 1961, the astronomer W. Wenzel discussed various types of irregular variable stars, including those of the T Tauri (or RW Aurigae) class, which occur in or near conspicuous dark cosmic clouds. He found that they also preferentially lie in or near Gould's belt. In one particular grouping of these variables, associated with what he calls the "Taurus–north dark cloud" (at $\alpha = 4^h25^m$, $\delta = +26°$), he finds a mean distance of 170 parsecs and states that this is the "second" such obscuring cloud, presumably ranking them in terms of distance from the sun. The "first" such cloud, according to the same author, reaches as far as the sun.

Wenzel's findings agree with the often-made supposition that the dark clouds in Taurus (perhaps also those in Orion) and those in the region of Scorpius, Ophiuchus, and Sagittarius form one vast network of large and small clouds, with the sun located somewhere between the two regions. The line joining these regions is directed roughly toward the galactic center and is at right angles to the direction of the spiral arms of the Milky Way. The distances from the sun are roughly 200 parsecs in each direction, and this distance would not conflict with the estimated thickness of a spiral arm of, say, 500 to 1,000 parsecs. But if this concept is correct, it might be expected that some dark clouds have distances much less than 200 parsecs.

An interesting possibility in this respect arises from Mrs. Lynds' discovery of a number of fairly opaque dark clouds at high galactic latitudes; one of them (located at $\alpha = 15^h 37'$; $\delta = -7°$; galactic latitude $+37°$) has a conspicuous, reddish, surface brightness slightly exceeding the normal background surface brightness of the night sky between the resolved stars. This nebulosity, whose surface brightness is uniform over its entire extent, probably is of the reflection type. As yet, there is no spectrum of it. A powerful nebular spectrograph would certainly enable astronomers to determine whether it is a reflection or an emission nebula.

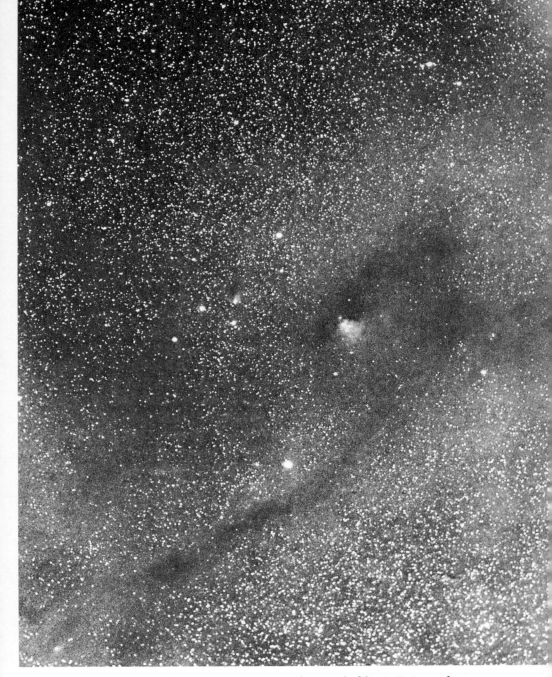

Fig. 193.   Dark nebulosities in Taurus, photographed by E. E. Barnard.

The nebulosity probably derives its light from one or more reddish stars. There are several K-type stars in the vicinity, as projected on the sky, but they seem to be too faint to account for the nebula's surface brightness. Another (unlikely) possibility is Antares, approximately 40°

away, but so intensely luminous in red light that it might produce a background illumination in a cloud of dust particles of high reflectivity. Still another possible answer—one that would be quite sensational—is that this cosmic dust cloud is quite close to the solar system, only a fraction of 1 parsec away.

A crude estimate of a nearby cosmic cloud's surface brightness can be made by supposing that its general reflectivity resembles that of the moon. The apparent magnitude of the full moon is -13, and as seen from the earth it occupies about $\frac{1}{5}$ square degree of the celestial sphere. If instead of the moon there were a complete sphere, 1 a.u. (1.5×10^8 km) in radius, surrounding the sun, the cloud's surface brightness would be the same everywhere—about 5 stars of apparent mag -13, or 10^{10} stars of apparent mag $+10$ per square degree. If the nebulosity is considered as part of a sphere whose radius is not 1 a.u. but 10^5 a.u. (about 0.5 parsec), the surface brightness per square degree would be $10^5 \times 10^5 = 10^{10}$ times smaller: that is, one star of apparent mag 10 per square degree. This is only about 1 per cent of the night sky's unresolved brightness and could not be detected. The cloud would have to be much closer to us, say at a distance of 10^4 a.u., to produce a surface brightness resembling that which has been recorded. Such a cloud would be within the sun's gravitational field (since the nearest star is at a distance of about 1.3 parsecs or almost 3×10^5 a.u.). It presumably would revolve around the sun with a period of approximately 1 million years. Though the evidence is rather unconvincing, it is not entirely impossible that during the formation of the solar system such clouds were produced, as the distant comets were.

A related problem arises in connection with the most opaque dark nebulae in the Milky Way, discovered by Barnard. These are often darker in their central regions than near the edges, even though the latter appear to obscure completely the light of background stars. Thus Barnard described B 216 as "a dark spot in a lane," and Struve found in 1937 that the centers of the obscuring nebulosities are about 0.1 mag darker in surface brightness than the outer parts. Since all features of the Milky Way are overlaid by the diffuse light of the air glow (mostly produced in the earth's atmosphere), the real contrast is considerably greater. According to Struve, this effect can be explained as the result of the illumination of the clouds from all sides by starlight, with a function that favors scattering in the direction of the incident beam. This may be inferred from the sizes of the grains that, as discussed in the preceding chapter, were estimated to be, on the average, 10^{-5} cm.

LUMINOUS RIMS OF NEBULAE

No such explanation can account for the very narrow and luminous rims of dark "elephant trunks" often seen superposed over the more uniform background of an emission nebula. According to Spitzer

> ... many of the bright nebulae are characterized by tongues or "elephant trunks" of obscuring matter extending from the surrounding dark nebulosity into the emitting regions and pointing in the general direction of the exciting star.... A recent analysis by Frieman shows that spikes of this approximate size and shape are a natural result of an assumed expansion of the hot gases in the luminous nebula. When gas is heated and expands, it becomes less dense than the cool clouds which surround the nebula and which are being pushed radially outward.... It was shown by Lord Rayleigh (1899) many years ago that this state of affairs was unstable....[10]

And, any small irregularity in the interface tends to increase.

In an exhaustive study of the luminous rims of emission nebulosities made in 1956, the American astronomer S. Pottash attributed their spectra to "... absorption of light quanta below the Lyman limit (λ 912 A) and the subsequent reemission of a good part of this energy as visible light...."[11] Pottash adopted the Zanstra mechanism and then was able to show that the densities of the gas in rims ranged between 100 and 200 atoms/cm³. Most of the rims are excited by stars of very high surface temperature— roughly 40,000°—and of spectral class O9 or earlier. A typical rim may be located at a distance of 5 parsecs from the exciting star, at the end of a 1-parsec long "elephant trunk," but with a rim-thickness of only 0.04 parsec. The relatively high density of the rims is the result of the expansion of the hot ionized gas into the cool, un-ionized gas beyond. The importance of the expansion phenomena, advanced by Oort in 1946, has been recognized by many astronomers and has produced a plausible explanation for such remarkable optical objects as the great filamentary nebula in Cygnus, the remnant of an ancient supernova (Fig. 173).

VARIABLE NEBULAE

Many problems are presented by several nebulae associated with the T Tauri variable stars. Most of the T Tauri stars are red (with spectral types between about K and M), and they vary in light irregularly. Our knowledge of their physical properties comes principally from the work of A. H. Joy and of G. H. Herbig, who also have studied a few of their associated nebulosities, some of which are variable in brightness and structure. Herbig has investigated especially a nebula associated with T Tauri itself. This faint nebulosity, discovered by F. R. Hind in England in 1852 with a 7-in. refractor, had disappeared completely by 1868. It was rediscovered by Barnard and S. W. Burnham in 1890 at Lick Observatory, when it was just at the limit of visibility of the 36-in. refractor. Once photography was applied, beginning in 1899, unmistakable changes in the nebula were observed, and in about 1920 a different area suddenly began to brighten considerably.

Burnham also noticed a very small, elliptical nebulosity in which T Tauri itself is embedded and that seems to be variable. In the photographs (a) was taken with the Crossley reflector in 1914; (b) the same telescope in 1952, the nebula had become much brighter; (c) a recent picture—taken with the 120-in. reflector—showing the small nebula discovered by Burnham. It appears as a loop extending from the star image at left, and as an extension of the image toward upper right, causing the star to appear noncircular in this picture and in (d) using a longer exposure. The large glow is Hind's nebula. While Hind's nebula shines by reflected light, the small nebula has a bright-line spectrum. Herbig states:

Fig. 194.   Hind's nebula. (*Lick Observatory; courtesy* Sky and Telescope)

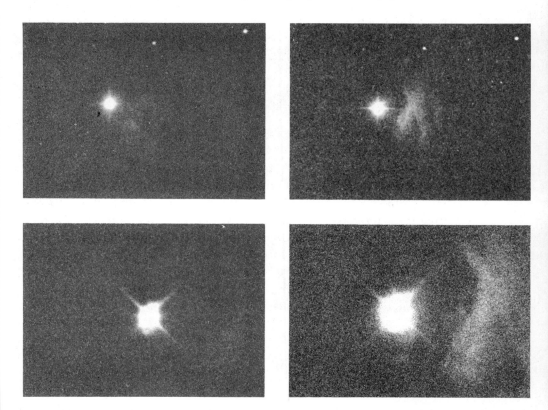

No entirely satisfactory explanation of this anomaly has yet been given. It does show that the near and outer nebulosities at T Tauri are significantly different in physical conditions, for reasons we do not now understand.[12]

The presence of the emission nebulosity is puzzling, particularly because emission lines are normally associated with hot stars, while T Tauri is a cool, red star. Herbig tried to answer the question of what makes these nebulae vary in light:

It seems quite unlikely that the variations are due to the nebulosity having been swept away and then reformed, because the velocities required are improbably large. We cannot blame the light changes of the nebula upon the irregular light-variations that have been observed in the star, for there seems to be little correlation between the two. For example, T Tauri has varied its light to only a minor extent since 1916, but during that time Hind's nebula has greatly increased in brightness. Experience with other somewhat similar nebulae associated with variable stars suggests that these changes are largely ones of variable illumination. It seems likely that the clouds which a century ago were so brightly lit up by T Tauri, were not dissolved about 1861, but rather they disappeared when the shadow of something nearer the star swept across them. We are probably witnessing no more than the play of light and shadow on a relatively fixed curtain of dust clouds. It is tempting to think that the shadows are cast by moving clouds or condensations in the close nebulosity around the star, which seems a natural place for such activity to take place. The changes in brightness of Hind's nebula may therefore be due to variations in T Tauri *as seen from the nebula*, but those variations are probably quite different from the fluctuations of the star that are visible from our direction.[13]

HAGEN'S CLOUDS

One of the most fantastic chapters in the history of 20th-century astronomy deals with Father J. G. Hagen's visual observations of dark cosmic clouds at high galactic latitudes. Hagen, who was the director of the Vatican Observatory, had compiled a general catalogue of bright and dark nebulae, and had started in 1893 to observe the dark nebulae with a modest visual refractor capable of recording the stars down to apparent mag 13. His observations extended over a period of several decades, and were summarized in *Specola Astronomica Vaticana* ("Publications of the Vatican Observatory").[14] Apparently he was convinced that he could "see" in many regions of the sky "objects" that had not been photographed.

There was some confusion among his readers about whether the

Hagen clouds were dark objects that obscure the background field of stars, or faintly luminous patches resembling the emission and reflection nebulosities of the Milky Way. Hagen himself felt that these objects are not the same as Herschel's "dark holes" or the dark dust clouds photographed by Barnard and Wolf.

The best summary of Hagen's work was given by the German astronomers F. Becker and J. Meurers in 1956:

In the years between 1920 and 1930 J. G. Hagen published a series of papers on "cosmic clouds" observed by him with the visual refractor at the Vatican Observatory. He found that the sky background appeared in many places to be covered by a more or less dense gray obscuration, the intensity of which he was able to estimate in a scale of five steps. Step 1 represents a completely black background, step 5 the strongest gray obscuration. Hagen was convinced from the beginning that he was dealing here with interstellar matter, and his conclusion was strengthened by the fact that he was able to observe a considerable number of regions of low star density in the Milky Way; he assigned to them steps 4 and 5. He showed further that the 52 nebular regions described by W. Herschel were identical with the effect that he had observed.[15]

Toward the end of his work, Hagen was joined by Becker and Father G. Stein. Becker and Stein confirmed the existence of a faintly luminous sky background, but substituted in place of Hagen's "cloudy way" (as distinct from the "Milky Way") a fairly uniform tendency for the sky-background surface brightness to appear predominantly at the galactic poles and down to about $\pm 40°$ of galactic latitude. In the meantime, considerable efforts were made to determine whether the Hagen clouds involved obscuration of star light. For example, Shapley reported in 1925 that:

Hagen's dark nebulae are, as Wirtz also concludes, apparently observable phenomena, to be explained not as *obscurations* but as effects of the known distribution of stars brighter than the fifteenth magnitude. The Öpik and Lukk results, for regions of abnormally low star density, are verified; but the extension of star counts on Harvard plates to considerably fainter stars shows that a different and less revolutionary interpretation of the vacancies must be advanced. The stars brighter than the 15th magnitude seem to be distributed much more unevenly than would be expected from elementary considerations of random distribution.[16]

But Hagen and his disciples had insisted that the "dark" clouds at high galactic latitudes are, in fact, faintly luminous, so faint that only very experienced visual observers can "see" them at all, and even photoelectric measurements can be expected to show only the more conspicuous "objects." Becker had suggested several clouds in the vicinity of UW and V Draconis, while Hagen had mentioned an easily observable cloud, of density 4–5 on his scale, extending some 24′ in all directions about X Cancri. In 1933, C. T. Elvey and P. Rudnick observed these regions with the photoelectric photometer at Yerkes and found that near UW Draconis

... the region which Becker gave as density 2–3 was slightly brighter than the region of density 5. The difference, however, is very small, amounting to 0.016 mag ±0.009 mag, or roughly 2 per cent with a probable error of 1 per cent.[17]

If these observations are to be trusted, they indicate that the densest Hagen clouds are darker than the less dense ones—precisely the opposite of what the Vatican observers had concluded.

Even more perplexing were the attempts by K. Haidrich in Vienna to photograph the Hagen clouds. In a long series of articles published (1930–1936) in the *Astronomische Nachrichten* (for which he surprisingly was awarded the second Dorothea Klumpke–Isaac Roberts prize of the French Astronomical Society), he discussed the properties of various sensitized photographic emulsions and reached the conclusion, among others, that at least some of the dark clouds are reddish in color and might be identified with the stationary calcium clouds whose existence had been detected from the "detached" (or interstellar) absorption lines of ionized calcium. Haidrich claimed that he had solved in practice the problem of luminous interstellar calcium clouds, whose photographic detection had thus far not been attempted. To support this contention, he listed a dozen neutral calcium lines in the wavelength region from λ5513 to λ5587A. The emission of these lines, he thought, could produce the reddish glow that his special photographic emulsions had shown.

Despite the high recognition Haidrich had received from the French Astronomical Society, his results were severly criticized by several astronomers, and he defended his conclusions in an article in the *Astronomische Nachrichten* for 1936.[18]. Although his work on the photography of nebulae continued until after the end of World War II, nothing more seems to have been published by him, nor by anyone else, on the calcium emission nebulosities. An indirect evaluation of the reliability of this work may be contained in Becker and Meurers' comment: "Why such objects can be seen but not photographed remains an open question."[19]

It is, however, not so easy to dispose of the Hagen clouds. Becker and Meurers have made a series of visual experiments with several artificial star fields having different star densities and different background surface illuminations. Their results indicate that at least part of the observed effects are "not . . . real, but would be caused by contrast effects due to the increasing star density."[20] At the same time, they believe "that Hagen's observations cannot entirely be attributed to contrast effects, [because] there remain some fields in which Hagen saw strong obscuration in spite of a high star density [and also] fields of low star density in which the sky background has been estimated at 1 or 2 (i.e., very black)."[21]

W. Becker (the brother of F. Becker) pointed out in his book *Sterne und Sternsysteme* ("Stars and Stellar Systems"),[22] that the surface brightness of the night sky between the resolved stars actually might be affected by: (a) the diffuse radiation of unresolved galaxies, which is absorbed in the zone of $\pm 40°$ galactic latitude by real cosmic dust clouds; and (b) the existence of a faintly luminous spherical halo of the kind found in other nearby spiral galaxies, such as M 31, principally by J. Stebbins and A. E. Whitford. The physical properties of these optical halos are not understood fully. There is, however, some indication that the Milky Way and other spiral galaxies are embedded in radio-emitting halos of non-thermal origin resembling the radio emission of the Crab Nebula, as was discussed in Chap. VI, P. 107.

It would seem that astronomers in recent years have shown a tendency to discount the evidence that appeared so convincing to Hagen, F. Becker, and others. The human eye, of course, is exceedingly sensitive to low surface brightnesses. Yet, modern photographs with wide-angle Schmidt telescopes usually show everything that the eye can see, and more. In some respects, visual observations are afflicted by phenomena that are still little understood. For example, the eye's contrast sensitivity changes markedly with its adaptation to darkness. Thus, the structure of the Milky Way is best seen by the unaided eye after it has been adjusted to darkness for 10 to 15 min. Further adaptation to darkness, for an hour or more, renders the entire night sky more luminous, but does not enhance the eye's ability to distinguish structural details of the Milky Way. If anything, it appears to become more submerged within the general luminosity of the night sky. This experience is not mentioned by S. Gaposchkin, who states that "the eye should be exposed to darkness for at least 15 minutes,"[23] and who has recently produced a visual picture of the entire Milky Way as observed in different parts of the earth. There is no indication in Gaposchkin's work of the phenomena reported by Hagen.

XIX

THE MILKY WAY

ALMOST ALL of the objects thus far discussed, including the solar system, single and multiple stars, star clusters, interstellar matter, and dark and luminous nebulae, are now known to belong to one large system: the Milky Way galaxy. If it could be examined from the outside, it would resemble the galaxy M 81 (Fig. 195), and the solar system would be located near the edge of one of the spiral arms. If looked at edgewise, the system would be similar to the galaxy NGC 4594 (Fig. 196), with a somewhat less pronounced central bulge. This picture, however, has emerged only quite recently because astronomers have had to draw their conclusions from observations made from within it. The problem is well described by Mrs. C. Payne-Gaposchkin:

The problem of surveying our own galaxy may be likened to the problem of drawing a map of New York City on the basis of observations made from the intersection of 125th Street and Park Avenue. Although it would be clear to an observer at this spot that the city is a big one, any statement as to its extent and layout would clearly be impossible. London would offer an even better analogy, for the neighborhood is not only congested but foggy.[1]

Progress in surveying the Milky Way can be divided in two main steps: (1) attempts to determine the galaxy's size and shape; and (2) attempts to determine its structural details. The two phases overlap somewhat. Speculations about the structure began before the over-all shape and size of the galaxy were established beyond doubt, but definite progress in the second problem followed the solution of the first.

Fig. 195.   Spiral galaxy, M 81 (type Sb) in Ursa Major, photographed
with the 200-in. Hale telescope. (*Mount Wilson and Palomar Observatories*)

Fig. 196.   Spiral galaxy, NGC 4594 (type Sa/Sb) in Virgo, seen edge on. Photographed with the 200-in. Hale telescope. (*Mount Wilson and Palomar Observatories*)

SIZE AND SHAPE OF MILKY WAY GALAXY

Star Counts and the Kapteyn Universe

The oldest method used in surveying our galaxy is that of star counts, first employed by W. Herschel at the end of the 18th century. He counted stars in different areas of the sky, to successive limits of apparent magnitude and assumed the stars to be of equal luminosity, so that the distances could be estimated directly from their apparent brightnesses; that is, a star 1 mag fainter than another would be $\sqrt{2.512}$ or 1.6 times farther away. If the stars were distributed uniformly in space, the ratio between all stars counted to two successive magnitudes (for example, +6 and +5) would be 4. From the observed ratios, which are smaller than 4 and which decrease gradually as fainter stars are counted, Herschel concluded that the sun was placed near the center of a flattened "stratum of the fixed stars," which extends about five times as far in the plane of the Milky Way as it does in a direction perpendicular to it (that is, the thickness is one-fifth the diameter).

When Herschel's method was revived by H. von Seeliger around the turn of this century, differences in absolute brightnesses were taken into account. Von Seeliger counted in different parts of the sky not only the total number of stars to successive magnitudes, but also the numbers between successive limits of apparent brightnesses. Von Seeliger thus obtained the system's rate of thinning and a model of the galaxy essentially the same as Herschel's.

However, this method alone gave no dimensions. Only after Kapteyn in 1901 determined the average distances of stars between certain limits of apparent brightness from their proper motions did von Seeliger get the first satisfactory estimate of the system's dimensions: a diameter of 23,000 light-years and a thickness of 6,000 light-years. Von Seeliger's mathematical methods later were improved and refined by K. Schwarzschild. The most extensive star counts represented in the *Kapteyn Universe* were made by Kapteyn and his associate P. J. van Rhijn and were based on the so-called *Kapteyn Plan of Selected Areas*. Kapteyn had proposed the Plan in 1906 in order to enlist the cooperation of astronomers in making extensive star counts in 206 areas of the sky and in extending the counts to fainter stars than had previously been attempted. At the same time astronomers were asked to determine the apparent magnitudes, spectral types, proper motions and radial velocities of as many stars in the Selected Areas as were possible.

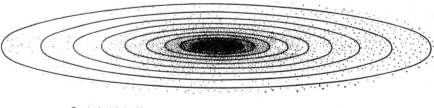

Fig. 197.   J. C. Kapteyn.

The observed quantities in these investigations were the star counts and mean parallaxes; the unknown space distribution depended also on the *luminosity function** and interstellar absorption, both of which were unknown. As discussed in Chap. XVII, P. 365, assuming that the true space density of stars cannot increase at greater distances, both von Seeliger and Kapteyn found the upper limit of absorption to be so small that it could be disregarded. The luminosity function was assumed to be constant and was included, usually as an unknown, in the solution of the problem.

The New Model Proposed by Shapley

The model of the galaxy as derived from star counts was challenged seriously for the first time by Shapley about 1917. He envisaged the galaxy as a flattened, lens-shaped system of stars and nebulae 300,000 light-years in diameter (in the plane of the Milky Way) and 30,000 light-years in thickness, the center of the system being in the direction of the constellation Sagittarius, at a distance of about 50,000 light-years from the sun.

Shapley's conclusions were based on an extensive study of globular clusters. He estimated the direction of the galaxy's center from the peculiar distribution of globular clusters on the celestial sphere. These clusters are found predominantly in one hemisphere of the sky, and one-third of

* Numbers of stars per unit volume in successive intervals of absolute magnitude.

Fig. 198.   The Kapteyn Universe. (*Courtesy* Sky and Telescope)

Scale in Light Years

20,000   16,000   12,000   8,000   4,000   0

Fig. 199. The globular cluster M 13 in Hercules, photographed with the 200-in. Hale telescope. (*Mount Wilson and Palomar Observatories*)

the known globular clusters are in the Sagittarius region, within an área of 2 per cent of the celestial sphere.

The earliest reference to the peculiar distribution of globular clusters and its significance seems to have been by John Herschel, who remarked in the first part of the 19th century that it could not be due to an accidental coincidence. The problem was next pursued in 1909 by the Swedish astronomer K. Bohlin, who considered the globular clusters as a compact group forming our galaxy's central core, the sun as situated just outside it, and the Milky Way clouds as surrounding this "cluster of clusters."

Shapley investigated the distribution of these clusters thoroughly and noted: (1) While most globular clusters are concentrated in the direction of Sagittarius, in the southern hemisphere of the sky, some clusters are found also in the northern hemisphere. Such an effect would be observed if the globular clusters formed an extensive, almost spherical system and

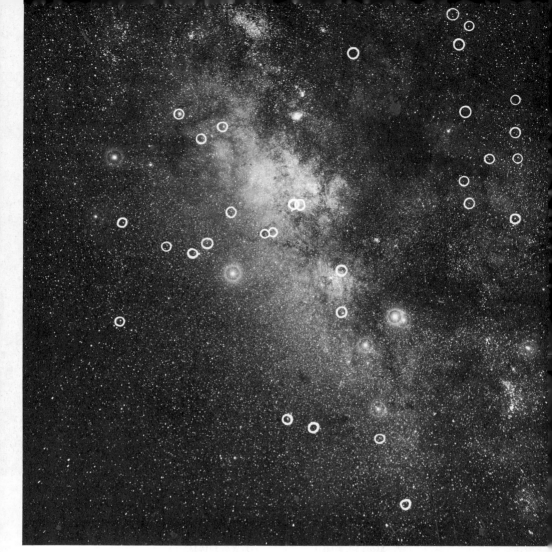

Fig. 200. Globular clusters in the region of Sagittarius (circled), photographed with the 3-in. Ross-Tessar camera at Harvard Observatory's Boyden Station. (*Harvard Observatory; courtesy* Sky and Telescope)

if the sun were located within this system, but far from its center. (2) The globular clusters are distributed symmetrically with respect to the plane of the Milky Way (about as many are found above it as below), and hence the system of globular clusters and the more flattened system of stars and nebulae must be related.

Shapley assumed that the array of globular clusters was of the same extent, in the plane of the Milky Way, as the system of stars and nebulae and concentric with it. Thus the galaxy's extent could be derived if a method were available to measure the distances of the clusters and hence estimate the dimensions of their array.

Since most globular clusters contain RR Lyrae variables, Shapley used the cepheid period-luminosity relation to determine the distances of the nearer ones (see Pp. 321–325). The great globular cluster in Hercules, M 13, was found to be 36,000 light-years away. From a study of the near clusters, Shapley also found that the brightest stars in each are about 2 mag brighter than the RR Lyrae variables. Hence he estimated the distances of the clusters farther away, in which the variables could not be detected, from a comparison of the apparent and absolute magnitudes of their brightest stars.

Even this method could not be applied to the most distant clusters. In the course of the study, Shapley noticed that the true diameters and integrated absolute brightnesses were approximately the same for all clusters. Hence the distance could be derived from comparisons of the apparent and true diameters, or of the integrated brightnesses. In this manner, the distances of even the most remote clusters were estimated up to 220,000 light-years. From his own investigations and those of Kapteyn, von Seeliger, and others, Shapley felt justified in assuming that there is no absorption of light in interstellar space. The model in Fig. 202 essentially follows the one proposed by Shapley, but interstellar absorption has been taken into account and the dimensions reduced accordingly. The large dots denote globular clusters, the small ones high velocity stars. The scale is in parsecs.

Shapley's views were revolutionary at the time they were proposed: The galaxy's estimated size was increased about tenfold, and the sun was assigned a highly eccentric position. These theories were not accepted for some time. Most astronomers continued to support the star-count model. One of its strongest proponents, as well as one of Shapley's most outspoken critics, was H. D. Curtis. In order to present both sides of the argument, a debate between them was arranged on April 26, 1920, at the National Academy of Sciences in Washington, D. C.[*]

Fig. 201.   H. Shapley.

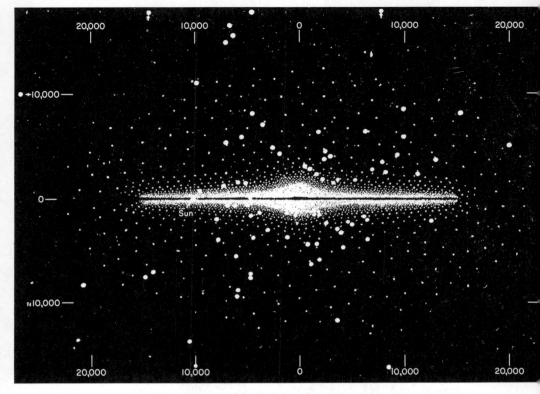

Fig. 202. Model of the Milky Way galaxy by J. S. Plaskett. (*From Popular Astronomy, XLVII, 1939, P. 255*)

The "Great Debate": Part 1

In the debate, both participants supported their conclusions with formidable arrays of observational data that they themselves had secured. Both had carefully scrutinized observations by others and checked their results. Written statements were prepared by both men and exchanged before the meeting. Each had made minor revisions after reading his opponent's views, but neither found it possible to accept the other's principal conclusions.

* They also disagreed and debated about whether the spiral nebulae are other galaxies or relatively small nearby objects (discussed in Chap. XX).

Fig. 203. H. D. Curtis. (*Courtesy Sky and Telescope*)

They did agree, however, on several points: namely, (a) that there is no interstellar absorption, (b) that the *relative* distances of globular clusters as determined by Shapley are correct, and (c) that the stars in the clusters and in remote parts of the Milky Way are not peculiar, but resemble those in the sun's neighborhood.

Relying on these points of agreement, Shapley based his case upon a defense of the distance of 36,000 light-years of M 13. Curtis argued that while the relative distances of the globulars were estimated correctly by Shapley, all the actual distances were exaggerated by a factor of about 10. Hence for M 13, Curtis would have adopted about 3,600 light-years. (Later in the debate he modified this value to 8,000.) To refute this contention, Shapley presented a table[2] contrasting some predicted properties of M 13 for assumed distances of 36,000 and 3,600 light-years respectively (Table 9).

Table 9.

PREDICTED PROPERTIES OF M 13

Property	36,000 light-years	3,600 light-years, or less
1. Mean absolute photographic magnitude of blue stars [of negative color index]	0	+5, or fainter
2. Maximum absolute photographic magnitudes of cluster stars	−1.0 to −2.0	+3.2, or fainter
3. Median absolute photovisual magnitudes of long period cepheids	−2	+3, or fainter
4. Hypothetical annual proper motion [of cluster]	0″004	0″04, or greater

Shapley had found a number of blue stars of mag 15 in M 13, which he identified with ordinary galactic B-type stars. It is now known that this contention was incorrect. There are very few blue stars in globular clusters, and those that may be assigned to spectral classes A and B certainly are not normal young A and B stars, such as are found in the neighborhood of the sun. They are, according to our present view, old stars that have exhausted their internal supply of hydrogen, and have reached spectral type B after passing through the giant and supergiant stages of their evolution. These old B stars do have absolute magnitudes of about 0, and, therefore, seemingly support Shapley's argument. But they are certainly not a demonstration of the "uniformity of conditions and of stellar phenomena naturally prevailing throughout the galactic system,"[3] a postulate adopted at the outset.

Shapley's second point concerned the absolute magnitudes of the brightest member stars in the cluster. He correctly argued that, because of the great distances of the clusters, only the more luminous giants and supergiants could be observed, and not the yellow and red dwarfs. Such stars in the Milky Way have absolute magnitudes of −1. At Mount Wilson, Adams and Shapley had taken low-dispersion spectrograms of some of the brightest stars in M 13, and it seemed reasonable that they were similar to yellow and red giants and supergiants in the sun's neighborhood. If the distance of the cluster were 36,000 light-years, its brightest members would have absolute magnitudes matching their nearby counterparts; if the distance were 3,600 light-years, the absolute magnitudes would be around +3. There was no doubt then, nor is there now, that in this respect Shapley's argument stood the test.

The third criterion for the distance of M 13 involves the period-luminosity relation of cepheid variable stars. This was severely criticized by Curtis, who pointed out that many Milky Way variables, not used in Shapley's calibration of the relation, failed to agree with his curves. Shapley correctly explained that the shape of the curve was known from Miss H. Leavitt's study of the Magellanic Clouds, and that the only important quantity obtained from the Milky Way cepheids was the average absolute magnitude for the entire group.

In 1920, it was impossible to determine reliable distances of individual cepheids, but there could be no serious doubt that the known cepheids and RR Lyrae stars were very luminous objects, with absolute magnitudes ranging between 0 and about −4. An average of −2 for cepheids agreed with a distance of 36,000 light-years, and contradicted Curtis' figure of 3,600, at which the average absolute magnitude would be +3 or fainter.

The last line of argument concerned the motions of clusters. Shapley pointed out that the globular clusters' line-of-sight velocities, as measured from their spectra, were about 150 km/sec. It was reasonable to assume that the average velocity at right angles to the line of sight would be the same. On this basis, the brighter globular clusters should have proper motions of around 0″.04 per year, if they were only 3,600 light-years distant. However, a large body of observations had shown that proper motions of the clusters were much smaller than this; hence their distances must be much greater than 3,600 light-years.

Curtis' criticism of the distance of M 13 derived by Shapley was based, in part, on the incorrect assumption that the yellow and red stars in globular clusters must be dwarfs, resembling the sun in absolute magnitude. This view might have been acceptable if it could have been shown that these clusters are devoid of giants and supergiants, but it ignored the fact that the spectra of the brightest stars indicated high luminosity.

Curtis had strong misgivings about the reliability of distances obtained by means of cepheid variables. In his opinion, ". . . available observational data lend little support to the fact of a period-luminosity relation among galactic Cepheids."[4] His views, in summary:

There are so many assumptions and uncertainties involved that I am most hesitant in attempting to assign a given distance to a given cluster, a hesitancy which is not diminished by a consideration of the following estimates of the distance of M 13. . . .

Shapley, 1915, provisional	100,000 l. y.
Charlier, 1916	170 l. y.
Shapley, 1917	36,000 l. y.
Schouten, 1918	4,300 l. y.
Lundmark, 1920	21,700 l. y.

It should be stated here that Shapley's earlier estimate was merely a provisional assumption for computational illustration, but all are based on modern material, and illustrate the fact that good evidence may frequently be interpreted in different ways.

My own estimate, based on the general considerations outlined earlier in this paper, would be about 8,000 light-years and it would appear to me, at present, that this estimate is perhaps within fifty per cent of the truth.[5]

There can be no doubt, except for both speakers' disregard of the effects of interstellar absorption, that Shapley was more nearly correct than Curtis in the determination of the distances of the globular clusters, although Shapley had overestimated the distance of M 13 by about 50 per cent, principally because he disregarded the effects of interstellar absorption. The latest determination, reported by Helen S. Hogg of Toronto, Canada, in 1959, is approximately 25,000 light-years.

A 1922 paper by Kapteyn and van Rhijn, in which they criticized Shapley's results, was based on star counts in the Selected Areas, and essentially confirmed Kapteyn's earlier model, constructed with a central sun and the Milky Way system of small extent. Kapteyn and van Rhijn believed that the large proper motions of short-period, RR Lyrae variables indicated that they are relatively nearby stars, and hence dwarfs, not giants as Shapley maintained. It was shown later that the short-period variables also possess high radial velocities, and hence their large proper motions result from high space velocities, rather than small distances from the sun. Kapteyn's and van Rhijn's criticism therefore was not valid.

The next clue to the puzzle of the galaxy came from a consideration of the motions of stars, not from direct surveying.

Asymmetry in Stellar Motions

In 1926, the Swedish astronomer B. Lindblad began studying the asymmetrical motions of the "high-velocity stars," that is, stars with velocities in excess of about 60 km/sec. Most stars in the sun's neighborhood have rather small velocities, rarely exceeding 30 km/sec, with a nearly random scatter of directions. However, the motions of all high-velocity stars, many of which are found at high galactic latitudes and which had been observed particularly by J. H. Oort and by G. B. Strömberg at the Mount Wilson Observatory, are directed toward one hemisphere of the sky (see Fig. 204). Lindblad reasoned that while the high-velocity stars cannot belong to the same dynamic system as stars of low velocity because of the asymmetry in their motions, they must be related to the rest of the galaxy, because their motions are symmetrical with respect to the galactic plane. He demonstrated that the observed effect can be explained satisfactorily if (a) the sun and other low-velocity stars have high speeds of rotation around a distant center (and, as a consequence, form a rather flattened system of stars), and (b) the high-velocity stars have much smaller velocities of rotation (and form a more nearly spherical system),

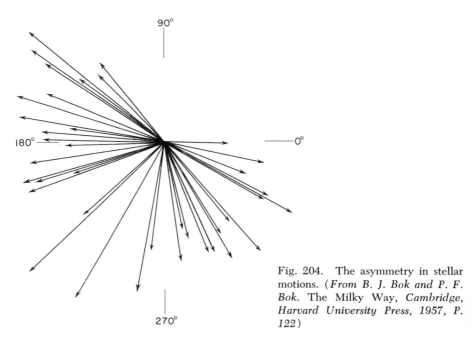

Fig. 204.   The asymmetry in stellar motions. (*From B. J. Bok and P. F. Bok.* The Milky Way, *Cambridge, Harvard University Press, 1957, P. 122*)

Fig. 205. B. Lindblad, H. Spencer Jones, J. H. Oort, and B. Strömgren (left to right) at the dedication of the McDonald Observatory in 1939.

thus lagging behind as the sun overtakes them. In Lindblad's words:

> ... the stellar system may be divided up into a series of subsystems having rotational symmetry around one and the same axis, with different speed of rotation at the same distance from this axis and consequently having different degrees of flattening. The most flattened systems have a high star-density, though decreasing with decreasing speed of rotation; the systems with the highest speed of rotation are assumed to form the Milky Way clouds. In the extreme outer systems the space density of the individuals, stars or globular clusters, is relatively very low. The latter subsystems show, on account of their low speed of rotation a strong asymmetrical drift in velocity nearly at right angles to the radius vector of the big systems when the velocities of the members are measured from a star, like our sun, moving as a member of a Milky Way cloud.
>
> The center of the stellar system should lie in the galactic plane in a direction at right angles to the direction of the asymmetrical drift. This gives nearly galactic longitude 330°, galactic latitude 0°. The direction toward the center of the system of globular clusters according to Shapley is galactic longitude 325°, galactic latitude 0°.[6]

Observational evidence confirming Lindblad's hypothesis was provided about a year later by Oort who, moreover, showed that the galaxy does not rotate as a solid body—rather, the innermost parts rotate fastest, the speed decreasing with distance from the center.

Solid-Body Rotation of the Galaxy

Oort studied the small, systematic effects that, as a consequence of galactic rotation, should be observable in the radial velocities and proper motions of fairly distant stars. He argued that if the system rotated as a solid body ". . . we shall not find any indications of rotation in the radial velocities but the proper motions in galactic longitude should be systematically negative for stars in all longitudes."[7] Such systematic shifts had been discussed before, notably by Charlier, who found an average value of $-0''.0024/yr$. This type of rotation would occur if the mass of the galaxy were distributed fairly uniformly throughout the disk-shaped system. The effect of solid-body rotation of the galaxy as determined from stellar proper motions depends essentially upon measuring the gradual changes in the stars' celestial coordinates, referred to the celestial equator and the vernal equinox (see P. 518). In principle, this coordinate system should make it possible to determine accurately the stars' negative proper motions, principally in the galactic plane. In practice, however, the problem is greatly complicated by the precession of the earth's rotational axis. The non-uniform attraction of the sun, moon, and planets upon the slightly flattened earth causes a conical motion of the axis of rotation of the earth around a line perpendicular to the ecliptic and a shift of the intersection of the equatorial and ecliptic planes, the vernal equinox, westward by 50''/yr. Hence it has been found necessary to derive from the entire material of proper motions the constant of precessions, as well as the angular solid-body rotation of the galaxy.

Differential Rotation of the Galaxy

Oort further argued that if, on the other hand, most of the mass is concentrated near the center, the velocity of rotation* would be more nearly proportional to $1/R^2$ (R = distance from center of galaxy), and differential effects proportional to the distance from the sun would be observed both in the proper motions and in the radial velocities. Figure 206, together with the description thereof, is adopted from R. L. Waterfield's *A Hundred Years of Astronomy:*

* This type of velocity is also referred to as *Keplerian velocity*, since it follows the law proposed by Kepler for planetary motions.

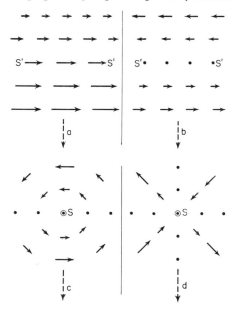

Fig. 206. Differential proper motions and radial velocities. (*From R. L. Waterfield*, A Hundred Years of Astronomy, *New York, The Macmillan Company, 1938, P. 320*)

In each of the four parts of the diagram the centre of the galaxy is supposed to be situated in a direction vertically downwards and at a considerable distance off the page. In (a) the arrows represent the actual velocities of individual stars revolving in five adjacent galactic zones round the distant galactic centre. The middle zone (S'S') is that in which the sun is, while the two upper zones are somewhat further from the galactic center and the two lower zones are somewhat nearer the centre. The lengths of the arrows are proportional to the velocities of revolution and so are greatest in the lowest zones. In (b) the *absolute* velocities have been converted into velocities that are *relative* to the solar zone; hence the stars in the solar zone, which is now looked upon as stationary, become dots, while those in the upper zones which are lagging behind the sun have velocities directed backwards to the left, and those in the lower zones which are gaining on the sun have velocities directed forwards and to the right. In (c) we take the central dot (S) in the solar zone to represent the sun itself, and draw the arrows proportional in length to that part of the velocity of each star relative to the sun which is perpendicular to the line joining the star to the sun—proportional, in fact, to the velocity of its proper motion. It will be seen that the velocity of the proper motion is greatest in the two directions in the sky exactly towards and exactly away from the galactic centre, and falls off gradually to zero in the two perpendicular directions—the directions towards which and away from which the sun in its revolution is travelling. In (d) we again take the dot (S) to represent the sun, but this time we draw the arrows to represent that part of the velocity of each star relative to the sun which is directly towards or away from the sun—to wit the velocity of its radial motion. This last part of the diagram shows that for stars lying directly towards and away from the galactic centre the radial motion is zero; for obviously such stars are neither approaching nor receding from the sun. Again the radial motions are zero for stars situated in the perpendicular direction; for these are revolving in the same zone as the sun, with the same velocity and in the same direction. But in directions intermediate between what we may call the four cardinal points, the radial motions are no longer zero and attain maximal values in four directions inclined to the cardinal points at forty-five degrees; in two of these directions the motion is towards the sun, in the other two it is away from the sun. Another point illustrated by the diagram is that both the radial and proper motions produced in any given direction by galactic rotation increase in velocity in proportion as the distance of the stars from the sun increases; thus in (c) and (d) the arrows get longer the further they are from the sun.[8]

A distribution in radial velocities and proper motions as functions of their galactic longitudes was derived by Oort from statistical studies of several groups of stars located at different distances from the sun. He found that the resulting plots indicated a curve showing two maxima and two minima similar to those shown in Fig. 207.

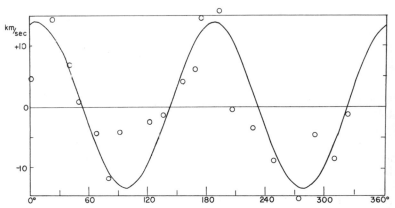

Fig. 207.   Double-wave radial velocity curve, adapted from J. S. Plaskett and J. A. Pearce. The dots are observed mean values.

Oort estimated the velocity of galactic rotation to be 272 km/sec in the neighborhood of the sun, around a center at a distance of 5,100 parsecs. The direction of galactic center derived by Oort closely agreed with that determined by both Shapley and Lindblad. Among the many investigations of the effect of differential galactic rotation, one of the most important is J. S. Plaskett and J. A. Pearce's study at Victoria of the motions of B-type stars in the Milky Way, upon which Fig. 207 is based. The magnitude of the effect of differential rotation they found, about 17 km/sec/kiloparsec, is almost the same as the value first derived by Oort. Since about 1950 numerous investigations of this quantity (now called "Oort's constant A") have been published and there has been a good deal of controversy on this subject. H. Weaver in Berkeley derived a value of the order of 10 or 12 km/sec/kiloparsec, and has vigorously defended it at scientific meetings. The latest result, based on the motions and distances of cepheid variables, by M. Schmidt and R. P. Kraft, in Pasadena, is between 14 and 15 km/sec/kiloparsec.

The random motions of the individual stars in the vicinity of the sun are so large that the double-wave curve could be ascertained only by taking the means for sufficiently large numbers of stars located at approximately the same galactic longitude. The random motions of the interstellar gas clouds in the Milky Way are considerably smaller; hence accurate double-wave curves were obtained by Oort from the measurements of the radial velocities of the interstellar calcium lines in the spectra of early-type stars.

Oort found the amplitudes of these double-wave curves to be considerably smaller than those of the associated stellar velocities. Plaskett and Pearce later found the amplitudes of the radial velocity curves derived from the interstellar lines to be almost exactly one-half that of the amplitudes derived from the radial velocities of the stars. Hence these results also confirmed the hypothesis adopted by earlier workers that the interstellar gas clouds are uniformly distributed through space, in which case the effect of differential galactic rotation for the interstellar lines would be one-half that determined from the associated stars.

It is of some interest that, in an early discussion of the radial velocities of the interstellar calcium lines, Struve plotted the interstellar velocities on a map of the sky and found several distinct regions in which the interstellar velocities tended to be positive, while in other regions they were predominantly negative. He incorrectly attributed these regions of positive and negative velocities to the existence of systematic motions of large aggregates of interstellar gas clouds and did not notice that they essentially represented the double-wave curve demanded by the theory of differential galactic rotation.

Acceptance of Shapley's Model

Lindblad's and Oort's work finally overcame resistance to Shapley's model of the galaxy. The errors in Kapteyn's model were shown to have resulted from two incorrect assumptions: (a) the absence of interstellar absorption and (b) the uniformity of the luminosity function throughout the galaxy; the luminosity function used by Kapteyn applies only to regions relatively close to the sun.

However, until 1930 there were still large discrepancies in the scale of the Milky Way, as estimated by Shapley and Oort: The distance of galactic center determined by Shapley was about three times that calculated by Oort. This difference resulted from the neglect of interstellar absorption by the former and was eliminated only after Trumpler's work. The best values available now are as follows: The distance to galactic center is about 8,300 parsecs, the diameter of the galaxy is between 25,000 and 30,000 parsecs, and the speed of rotation of the galaxy at the distance of the sun from the center is 220 km/sec.

The theory of galactic rotation also explained another problem that had puzzled astronomers since 1904, when Kapteyn discovered two preferential directions in stellar motions. It had been believed almost universally that after stellar motions were corrected for the sun's motion with respect to its neighboring stars (20 km/sec in the direction of Hercules), they were distributed at random. Kapteyn found instead that there were two diametrically opposed preferential directions of motion—more stars move toward the constellations of Orion and Scutum than toward inter-

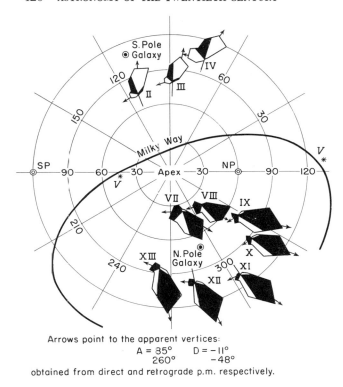

Arrows point to the apparent vertices:

A = 35°   D = −11°
    260°   −48°

obtained from direct and retrograde p.m. respectively.

Fig. 208.   Distribution of the proper motions for a particular region of the sky, as plotted by J. C. Kapteyn. (Report of South African meeting of the British Association in 1905, *Section A, 1905*)

mediate points. Since the line connecting these vertices lies in the plane of the Milky Way, it was suspected that the preferential motions have some connection with galactic structure. Various theories, none of which was quite satisfactory, were devised to account for them. Lindblad correctly explained that the stars probably would experience small perturbations with subsequent departures from strictly circular orbits. Also, these departures would appear more pronounced in the directions toward or away from the center—that is, the directions of preferential motion observed by Kapteyn, rather than in the general direction of rotation.

Detailed Studies of Galactic Rotation

Although in his early work Oort took only differential rotation into account, in his later study of the radial velocities of interstellar hydrogen gas (from radio observations of the 21-cm line) he demonstrated that rotation in the innermost parts of the Milky Way is essentially similar to that of a solid body. Outside of this nucleus, about 3,000 parsecs from the center, there is a gaseous ring (possibly involving a number of stars) that not only rotates around the center but appears to expand in all directions with a velocity of 50 km/sec. The true Keplerian type of motion appears to predominate at distances of 6,000 parsecs from the center and greater.

These complicated motions have not been explained. It has been suggested that the motions of expansion in the 3,000-parsec ring around the galactic center rapidly exhaust the entire central mass of the galaxy. If so, some material should flow into the center, perhaps through the galaxy's polar regions. It is possible, therefore, that there is a vast circulation of gas and stars throughout the Milky Way, the material flowing away from the center in the galactic plane, returning through the outer halo, and falling back into the nucleus by way of the polar regions. Radio-astronomical observations, made principally by Frank Kerr in Australia, however, indicated an inflow, rather than an outflow, of neutral hydrogen gas at high galactic latitudes as observed from the earth. Hence, if the circulation suggested by Oort really exists, it presumably would indicate an outflow at right angles to the plane of the Milky Way at distances from the center that are much greater than 8,000 parsecs.

Because of the transition within the Milky Way between solid-body rotation and Keplerian motion, and because of the complications indicated by the expansion of the 3,000-parsec ring, most recent investigations have been concerned with the curve describing the circular rotational velocity of the Milky Way as a function of the distance from the center, rather than with the change in velocity per unit distance. Such a curve (based on one of Oort's recent discussions) is shown in Fig. 209, together with a similar one, obtained from the observations of the Andromeda galaxy by N. U. Mayall and H. W. Babcock.

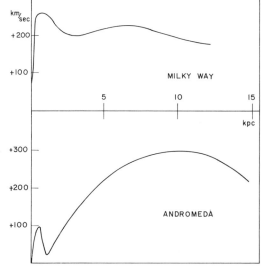

Fig. 209. Rotation of the Milky Way and of the Andromeda galaxy, adapted from the work of G. W. Rougoor and J. H. Oort (Milky Way) and H. W. Babcock and N. U. Mayall (Andromeda).

STRUCTURE OF THE MILKY WAY GALAXY

Views Expressed from 1900 to 1950

As mentioned on P. 408, speculations about the structure of our galaxy started before its size and shape were known. These speculations were concerned particularly with the conspicuous Milky Way belt and its relation to the sun and its neighboring stars. In most earlier work, the Milky Way was considered to be an annular ring of stars or nebulosity surrounding the main system of stars, with the sun roughly centrally placed. The nonuniform appearance of the Milky Way, however, created doubts in some minds, and in 1900 C. Easton suggested that the galaxy may have a spiral form, with the sun eccentrically placed and the center in the direction of Cygnus (see Fig. 210). Easton, however, added:

> I wish to insist upon the fact that Fig. [210] does not pretend to give an even approximate representation of the Milky Way, seen from a point in space situated on its axis. It only indicates in a general way how the stellar accumulations of the Milky Way might be distributed so as to produce the galactic phenomenon, in its general structure and its principal details, as we observe it.[9]

He found that a certain plausibility for his theory was lent by the then-recent recognition of spiral structure in the Andromeda nebula by J. Scheiner and J. E. Keeler's observations of numerous spirals, which indicated "...that the spiral is a much commoner form in the structure of nebulae than has hitherto been supposed."[10] A different concept of the spiral (shown in cross-section in Fig. 211) was envisaged by Eddington in 1914.

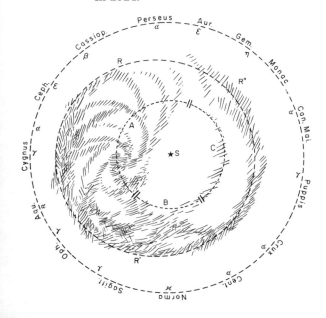

Fig. 210.   Schematic drawing of the structure of the Milky Way by C. Easton. (*From* Astrophysical Journal, XII, 1900, P. 157)

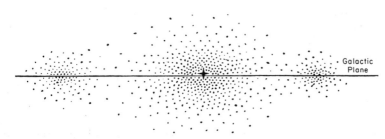

Galactic
Plane

Fig. 211.   Schematic drawing of the Milky Way by A. S. Eddington. (*From* Stellar Movements and the Structure of the Universe, *London, Macmillan and Co., 1914, P. 31*)

It also is interesting to consider Shapley's views regarding the structure of the galaxy. In about 1920, he tried to incorporate the Kapteyn system (the "local cloud") within the framework of the larger galaxy he proposed. In his own words:

The moving Galaxy was visualized as collecting in the course of time subordinate external systems and gradually dismembering and absorbing them. The local cloud was mapped out and described as one of these minor elements, though previously it had been treated as the major part. The Galaxy was considered not a single spiral nebula but rather an organization of many half-digested star clouds and clusters, moving in an extensive stratum of stars and galactic nebulae.[11]

However, about 10 years later, he revised these ideas as follows:

The earlier hypothesis concerning the possible origin and growth of the Galaxy has not been disproved. Nevertheless . . . the interpretation should be amended. . . . Our galactic system, it now appears, is neither a spiral, such as the Andromeda Nebula (Messier 31), nor a single unified discoidal star system, like a Magellanic Cloud on a grand scale; it is rather a super-galaxy—a flattened system of typical galaxies. In mass and population, therefore, the galactic system should be compared with the Coma-Virgo Cloud of bright galaxies, rather than with one of its members. Our local system, a star cloud that is a few thousand light years in diameter, appears to be a galaxy, similar to the Clouds of Magellan or to a typical extra-galactic nebula.[12]

This was essentially speculation without sufficient observational proof, and B. Bok concluded in 1936 that:

In writing a survey of our present knowledge of the distribution of the stars in space, one has to admit that very little is known concerning even the broadest features of galactic structure . . . the eccentric location of the sun in the galactic system is the only well-established fact concerning the structure of our system. . . .

Working models for the galactic system have, at various past stages of development, been of value for the coordination of existing knowledge and the effective planning of future research. Shapley's model in which the local system played the role of an important subsystem, has proved eminently satisfactory for the past twenty years. The time has now come to go one step farther and consider a more detailed working model. Several astronomers have stressed the probable similarity in structural features between the galactic system and some of the larger spiral nebulae. Seares has suggested that our stellar system may well have a structure similar to that of Messier 33, the well-known spiral nebula in Triangulum. Our sun would then be located in one of the spiral knots, at a distance equal to two-thirds of the radius of the nebula from the center.

It is surprising to note how well such a model agrees with the general impression obtained when the Milky Way is viewed from the tropics. . . . Individual stars do not stand out particularly against the brilliant continuous background of the Milky Way in Sagittarius; but the impression is quite different for the Cygnus and Carina clouds, in which a multitude of individual stars is seen projected against a faintly luminous background. The observer in the tropics should not find it difficult to accept as a working model for our Milky Way system one with a distant center in Sagittarius and in which a spiral arm passes from Carina through the sun toward Cygnus.[13]

Observational Evidence During the Last Decade

The first indication that astronomers might be able to trace spiral arms in our galaxy came with Baade's discovery that the luminous stars in the Andromeda galaxy M 31 lie along such arms. Shortly afterward, in 1951, W. W. Morgan and others investigated the distribution in distance of luminous early-type stars along the Milky Way, and the first vestiges of spiral arms became discernible. In recent years, evidence for the existence of these features in the galaxy has come from numerous sources. Optical observations, however, are limited by the all-prevailing haze of interstellar absorption in and near the galactic plane, whereas radio observations, which are unaffected by this obscuration, yield, at present, the clearest pattern.

The large contour map in Fig. 212 represents the spiral structure of the Milky Way as determined from the distribution of neutral hydrogen by means of radio telescopes in the Netherlands and at Sydney, Australia. The sun's position is indicated by the small circle in the upper part of the map, at an assumed distance of 8,200 parsecs from the galactic center, which is labeled C.

The left side of the drawing primarily represents observations made at Sydney. The right side, from about galactic longitude 200° clockwise to 340°, corresponding to the arc of the sky from Canis Major to Sagittarius, is based on Dutch results. Since the methods and equipment used by the

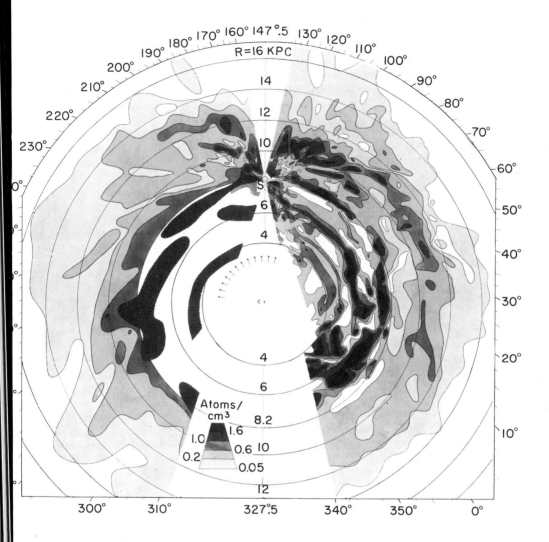

Fig. 212.   The distribution of neutral hydrogen gas in the galactic system, according to J. H. Oort, G. Westerhout, and F. J. Kerr. (*From* Monthly Notices of the Royal Astronomical Society, *CXVIII, 1958, plate 6; courtesy* Sky and Telescope)

two groups were not the same, the structure indicated on the right is more detailed than that at the left. Nevertheless, in the region of overlap the Australian and Dutch observations are in good agreement.

At first glance, the large number of roughly circular arms or branches in this picture seem to be more ragged and irregular than the corresponding features in nearby spirals like M 33 (Fig. 228). However, Oort and his colleagues point out that several arms can be traced for considerable lengths.

The sun appears to be situated near the inner edge of an arm stretching out in the direction of Cygnus, toward longitude 50°, and this can be followed, with some breaks, clockwise to about longitude 340°, where the contour intensities are high. Though this arm is not shown in the direction of the anticenter, between longitudes 135° and 160° (due to limitations of present techniques), it may be supposed that the Cygnus arm extends toward Orion, longitude 160°, and includes the Orion association of hot young stars. The Dutch observers call this entire structure the Orion arm. As one goes clockwise along it, in the direction of galactic rotation, the distance from the center becomes less, decreasing from 8,500 parsecs at longitude 130° to 7,000 parsecs at 340°.

Well outside the sun is a conspicuous formation, the Perseus arm, extending from longitude 130° in Auriga to perhaps 30°. The almost circular shape of this arm is indicated by distances from the center of 10,500 and 10,000 parsecs in these directions, respectively.

Two spiral arms, at least, occur in the direction of the center. One, the Sagittarius arm, lies between 1,000 and 2,000 parsecs from the sun and appears to spiral in toward the center if followed in a clockwise direction. As discussed on P. 427, there is an expanding arm (indicated by the arrows) at about 3,000 parsecs from the center. It has been observed between longitudes 303° and 331°, but it may extend all the way around the center and form a ring. Oort and his associate G. W. Rougoor interpreted radio observations of this arm as indicating a rotational velocity of 200 km/sec, while different parts of the arm move outward at between 30 and 200 km/sec.

This picture of spiral structure is not adhered to by all astronomers. Bok, at Mount Stromlo Observatory, is willing to accept the Perseus and expanding arms, but believes the existence of the Sagittarius and Orion arms is not even tentatively established. He points out the important feature that extends from the sun toward the region of Carina, at longitude 255°, and ties this in with the Cygnus arm on the other side of the sky. As has been noted, Bok suggested this particular feature in 1936 on more speculative grounds. Bok's diagram (Fig. 213) shows his attempt to bring radio and optical data into better agreement. He believes that several short spurs extend outward from the main Carina-Cygnus arm, one toward Orion, one parallel to that spur, and one toward Vela, traceable to a distance of some 1,500 parsecs.

On this basis, the Carina-Cygnus arm would be nearly circular, while

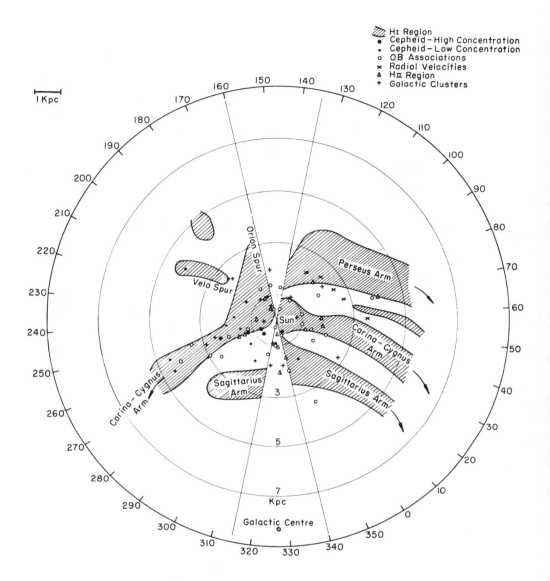

Fig. 213. B. J. Bok's concept of the spiral structure of the Milky Way system within about 5,000 parsecs of the sun. (Observatory, *LXXIX*, 1959, P. 61; *courtesy* Sky and Telescope)

Oort's Orion-Cgynus arm definitely is not. In other words, the latter seems better than the former to fit the idea of the arms spiraling outward from the center. Though the combined radio and optical evidence seems to favor the hypothesis of arms trailing behind as the galaxy spins, Bok points out that there are only slight deviations from circularity and that his model should not be ruled out on this ground.

From the various observations under consideration, the type of spiral represented by the Milky Way system may be inferred. Ours is a relatively large spiral, its ill-defined outer boundary being about 15,000 parsecs from the center. From the number of continuous arms that would be cut by a radius drawn from the center and from the spacings of these arms, Oort and others have inferred that our system resembles the Andromeda galaxy, or M 81, in Ursa Major. The Milky Way is certainly much more compact than the loosely wound spirals M 101 in Ursa Major (Fig. 215) and M 33 in Triangulum, but it does not have such tight spiral arms as the early Sb galaxy NGC 4594. Moreover, the central bulge of our galaxy, though very pronounced, is not comparable to that of NGC 4594, according to Oort, Kerr, and Westerhout. They also have pointed out that another clue is furnished by the over-all fraction of mass in the form of interstellar gas. The percentage of interstellar hydrogen in the Milky Way increases outward from the nucleus. Again, our system seems to be intermediate in type between the Andromeda nebula and M 33, as 2 per cent of the mass of our system is interstellar gas, compared to 0.8 per cent and 4 per cent for the other two respectively.

XX

GALAXIES

THROUGHOUT THIS book, many references have been
made to galaxies that are essentially similar to the Milky Way.
In Chap. XIX this similarity was assumed and an attempt was then made
to infer some properties of the Milky Way from observations of other
galaxies. This view was established beyond doubt only recently, in the
1920's. It was accepted then with considerable difficulty, even though as
early as the 18th century suggestions had been made, on purely philosophical grounds, that there exist in space many systems called "island
universes" that are similar to our galaxy.

The difficulty in determining the nature of galaxies can be attributed
mainly to their enormous distances. Except for a few of the nearer ones,
they appear nebulous even when observed with the largest telescopes.
Indeed, until the late 19th century the many kinds of nebulous objects
seen in telescopes of moderate size—galactic nebulae, planetary nebulae,
unresolved globular clusters, galaxies—were not differentiated each from
the other. By the end of the 19th century, the application of photography
had made some differences apparent. Galactic nebulae, it was learned, are
irregular, of wide variety of form; galaxies have a fairly well-outlined
elliptical shape that sometimes suggests spiral structure. But both groups
still were referred to as "nebulae." Even now, the galaxies often are referred to as "extragalactic nebulae." Prevalent opinion about their nature
was summarized by Miss A. Clerke in 1890:

The question whether nebulae are external galaxies hardly any longer needs discussion. It has been answered by the progress of discovery. No competent thinker, with the whole of the available evidence before him, can now, it is safe to say, maintain any single nebula to be a star system of coordinate rank with the Milky Way. A practical certainty has been attained that the entire contents, stellar and nebular, of the sphere belong to one mighty aggregation. . . .[1]

NATURE OF SPIRAL NEBULAE

Observational Evidence During the First Two Decades

Possible evidence to the contrary was provided in 1899. J. Scheiner found that the Andromeda nebula, M 31, has a solar-type spectrum that he believed indicated M 31 possibly to be a large aggregate of stars similar to the sun. He also hypothesized a basic similarity between our system and M 31: The nuclear part of M 31 might correspond to the complex of stars surrounding the sun; its spiral structure might correspond to the Milky Way clouds.

Interest in the problem was stimulated further by J. E. Keeler's photographs of many nebulae, mostly of spiral structure, taken with the 36-in. Crossley reflector at Lick. His photographs showed that the nebulae are much more numerous than earlier workers had believed (he estimated 120,000 to be within reach of the Crossley reflector). Because of the predominance of spiral form, the word "spirals" was used for many years to denote all the objects now known as "galaxies."

Keeler's observations, however, did not provide any clues to the physical nature of spirals. Most evidence from the many different types of investigations during the next two decades supported the view that spirals are small, nebulous objects within the Milky Way or very close to it.

The spectroscopic observations of Scheiner, while correct, were discounted considerably after V. M. Slipher discovered the reflection spectrum of the nebulosity in the Pleiades (see P. 385), which was definitely known to belong to the Milky Way. According to Slipher:

This observation of the nebula in the Pleiades has suggested to me that the Andromeda nebula and similar spiral nebulae might consist of a central star enveloped and beclouded by fragmentary and disintegrated matter which shines by light supplied by the central sun. This conception is in keeping with spectrograms of the Andromeda nebula made here and with Bohlin's value for its parallax [see below].[2]

Photographic images of the condensations in the spirals appeared to be nebulous, even those taken with the 60-in. Mount Wilson telescope.

Fig. 214.   The Andromeda galaxy, M 31, (type Sb) photographed with the 36-in. Crossley reflector. The satellite galaxy NGC 205 is above, right, and NGC 221 is at the edge of M 31. (*Lick Observatory*)

According to G. W. Ritchey: "All of these [spirals] contain great numbers of soft, starlike condensations which I shall call nebulous stars. They are probably stars in the process of formation."[3] In the 1920's, it was learned that this nebulous appearance had been due to instrumental difficulties (see P. 446).

Seares estimated in 1920 our galaxy's surface brightness, on the basis of the density and luminosity distributions of stars derived by Kapteyn and van Rhijn, and found it to be much smaller than that of the spirals. He concluded that:

This result indicates that spirals differ from the galactic system by being nebulous, or that they must be much larger or composed of more stars or brighter stars.[4]

Since it was assumed generally that if the spirals were galaxies similar to the Milky Way, they would be of roughly comparable size, the first alternative seemed more plausible. The error, of course, stemmed from Kapteyn's underestimation of the size of our galaxy.

Evidence against the "island-universe" theory was furnished also by the English astronomer J. H. Reynolds, who measured the brightness distribution and colors of the spirals and found their outer regions to be bluer than the nuclei. As indicated in Chap. XIX, around 1920 the Milky Way was assumed to be uniform in composition, and hence Reynolds' result could not be explained satisfactorily if the spirals were systems of stars similar to the Milky Way. He remarked:

There is no observational reason why the amorphous nebulosity should be considered as actually a conglomeration of star discs; in fact, all the photographic evidence is against it. . . . It seems safest to adopt for the present an agnostic position as to the real nature of the spiral nebulae; there always is the possibility that they represent formations for which there are no analogies in the galactic system at all. . . . The absorption lines in their spectra may be produced by comparatively cool gases composing the amorphous nebulosity, the hotter nucleus and nebular condensations radiating a continuous spectrum.[5]

The correct explanation of Reynolds' observations came much later, with Baade's discovery of the two stellar populations (see Chap. XIII and later in this chapter).

It was always realized that conclusive proof would be provided by determining the distances of the spirals: distances comparable to the size of the Milky Way would prove them to be parts of it; larger distances would imply their being outside the boundaries of the Milky Way and hence would support the island-universe theory.

From a very extensive series of measurements, in 1907 Bohlin found a trigonometric parallax of the Andromeda nebulae of $0''.171$, implying a distance of 19 light-years. This figure, Lundmark proved later, reflected systematic errors. In 1911, the American physicist F. W. Very derived a distance of 1,600 light-years for the Andromeda nebula from a comparison of the brightnesses of S Andromedae and Nova Persei (see Chap. XVI). It is now known that the former is a supernova and the latter an ordinary nova in the Milky Way.

The most powerful arguments for regarding the spirals as relatively close objects rested upon van Maanen's measurements of the proper motions of certain distinct features he could recognize in several spirals. In 1916, he reported proper motions of $0''.02$ in M 101 all arranged in a roughly circular pattern, and therefore implying a period of rotation of 85 thousand years; he later observed comparable values for several other spirals. It has sometimes been argued that if the spirals were at the large distances required by the island-universe theory, their speeds of rotation would be excessively great: greater than the velocity of light. But the reasoning behind this argument is slightly deceptive. Whatever the rotation period of a galaxy may be—call it P—it means that after an interval of P years the galaxy has completed one full revolution: the distance of the galaxy is not involved. If van Maanen had been right, a proper motion of $0''.02$ per year would be expected, regardless of the distance. Thus, without additional information, van Maanen's measurements do not distinguish between the two hypotheses. This point has not always been appreciated by modern authors. The real question is not the one they have stressed. It is: are the proper motions of $0''.02$ *per year* physically real? We now know that they are not; as we shall see, the real proper motions of rotation must be of the order of $0''.001$ *per century* (not per year!), and this quantity is not yet measurable, even on the best existing photographs.

The first suggestion of much larger distances came from H. D. Curtis (discussed in Chap. XVI, P. 337), who compared the brightnesses of ordinary novae in the Andromeda nebula with those of ordinary novae in the Milky Way and derived a distance of 500,000 light-years. This result indicated that the Andromeda nebula and other spirals are far outside the boundaries of the Milky Way.

Curtis became the principal champion of the island-universe theory. His ideas were criticized by many astronomers, particularly Shapley. The second part of their debate (the first part was discussed in Chap. XIX) was devoted to the status of the spirals.

Fig. 215.   Spiral nebula M 101 (type Sc) in Ursa Major, photographed with the 200-in. Hale telescope. (*Mount Wilson and Palomar Observatories*)

The "Great Debate": Part 2

Curtis tried to defend his belief that "The spirals are not intragalactic objects but island universes like our own galaxy...."[6]; while Shapley believed:

> ... that the evidence ... is opposed to the view that the spirals are galaxies of stars comparable with our own. In fact there appears as yet no reason for modifying the tentative hypothesis that the spirals are not composed of typical stars at all, but are truly nebulous objects.[7]

Shapley relied heavily on the observations of Seares, Reynolds, and particularly of van Maanen, but he also considered novae observed in the Andromeda nebula, as Curtis had done, but interpreted the data differently. Shapley argued that if the spirals were stellar systems resembling the Milky Way in size and structure (assuming the size he had derived—a diameter of 300,000 light-years), they would have to be at enormous distances, roughly 10 million light-years in the case of M 31. But this distance, he maintained, raised a serious inconsistency: The ordinary novae in the Andromeda nebula would have to be much more luminous than the ordinary novae of the Milky Way. Here Shapley reasoned from "the general principle of approximate equality of size for celestial objects of the same class,"[8] an assumption on which both he and Curtis agreed.

Curtis, on the other hand, reminded the audience that Shapley in previous papers had suggested distances of 20,000 light-years for nearby spirals that have angular diameters of 1 or 2 degrees. But the smallest clearly discernible spirals are 5″ across, or less. Hence Curtis argued that, on the above assumption of equality in size, the smallest spirals would be much farther than the nearest ones, about 10 million light-years distant, and far outside the boundaries of the Milky Way postulated by Shapley.

Curtis and Shapley differed also in their interpretation of two other observations:

1. The distribution of spirals: They are not found near the galactic plane, and their numbers increase toward galactic poles. In the figure, the horizontal line 0°—0° represents the central plane of the Milky Way, the north galactic pole is at the top; small dots indicate normal numbers of galaxies per sample; large disks and circles, excesses and deficiencies, respectively; dashes, samples in which no galaxies were found. The blank spaces at the extreme right and left of the diagram represent the southern skies, which cannot be observed from the station at which the survey was made.

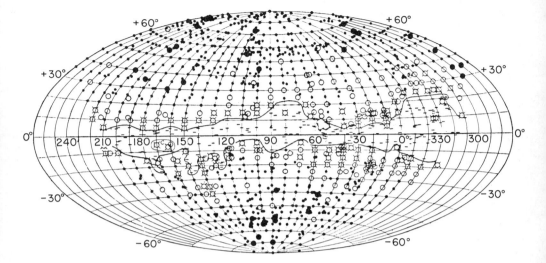

Fig. 216. Apparent distribution of galaxies. (*From* The Realm of the Nebulae, *New Haven, Yale University Press, 1936, P. 62*)

2. The large radial velocities of spirals: Spectroscopic observations Slipher had been conducting at the Lowell Observatory since 1912 indicated that most of the large spirals have substantial velocities of recession (much greater than those observed for other objects).

Shapley assumed that the spirals are probably nearby nebulous objects that do not belong to our galaxy but are scattered more or less uniformly in space, and that only the nearest are bright enough to be seen. He hypothesized that as the Milky Way travels among the spirals in its motion through intergalactic space, it exerts a peculiar repelling force upon them, causing them to move away from its central plane, thus accounting for both the observed distribution and velocities. Curtis, on the other hand, pointed out that many edgewise spirals show peripheral belts of dark, occulting matter and that the Milky Way system probably possesses a similar feature that would obliterate the distant spirals from view, and result in the observed distribution. As for the high velocities, Curtis did not try to correlate them with the much smaller speeds of all galactic objects. High velocity, he proposed, is a property that sets spirals apart from other objects and hence lends support to the separate galaxy theory, since ". . . . such high speeds seem possible for individual galaxies."[9]

Perhaps the most imaginative portion of Curtis' argument is his discussion of the proper motions of spirals:

Should the results of the next quarter-century show close agreement among different observers to the effect that the annual motions of translation or rotation of the spirals equal or exceed 0″.01 in average value, it would seem that the island universe theory must be definitely abandoned.

A motion of 700 km/sec across our line of sight [based on the assumption that the average transverse motions are equal to the average radial motions] will produce the following annual proper motions:

Distance in light-years	Annual proper motion
1,000	0″.48
10,000	.048
100,000	.005
1,000,000	.0005

The older visual observations of the spirals have so large a probable error as to be useless for the determination of proper motions, if small; the available time interval for photographic determinations is less than twenty-five years.

The first proper motion given above should inevitably have been de-

Fig. 217.   Spiral galaxy NGC 4565 (type Sb) in Coma Berenices, seen edge on; photographed with the 120-in. telescope. (*Lick Observatory*)

tected by either visual or photographic methods, from which it seems clear that the spirals cannot be relatively close to us at the poles of our flattened galactic disk. In view of the hazy character of the condensations measured, I consider the trustworthy determination of the second proper motion given above impossible by present methods without a much longer time interval than is at present available; for the third and the fourth, we should need centuries.[10]

This appraisal has met the test of time. The final words on the controversy about the proper motions of spirals were printed in two papers in the *Astrophysical Journal* for 1935, one by Hubble and the other by van Maanen.[11] These made it clear that the proper motions measured on photographs were observational errors.

While Curtis undoubtedly was more nearly correct about the status of the spirals, this could not be proved at the time. As in the first part of their debate, neither convinced the other; nor were other astronomers able to decide definitely between the two points of view. It is interesting to note the conclusions reached by two other astronomers at about the same time.

Views of Eddington and Lundmark

Eddington, who had an exceptionally fine grasp of theoretical developments and whose extraordinary intuition often helped him appraise the value of conflicting observational results, stated:

The distribution of spiral nebulae presents one quite unique feature: they actually shun the galactic regions and preponderate in the neighborhood of the galactic poles. The north galactic pole seems to be a more favoured region than the south. This avoidance of the Milky Way is not absolute; but it represents a very strong tendency.

It must be admitted that direct evidence is entirely lacking as to whether these bodies are within or without the stellar system. Their distribution, so different from that of all other objects, may be considered to show that they have no unity with the rest; but there are other bodies, the stars of Type M for instance, which remain indifferent to galactic influence. Indeed, the mere fact that spiral nebulae shun the galaxy may indicate that they are influenced by it. The alternative view is that, lying altogether outside our system, those that happen to be in low galactic latitudes are blotted out by great tracts of absorbing matter similar to those which form the dark spaces of the Milky Way.

If the spiral nebulae are within the stellar system, we have no notion what their nature may be. That hypothesis leads to a full stop. It is true that according to one theory the solar system was evolved from a spiral nebula, but the term is here used only by a remote analogy . . . The spirals to which we are referring are, at any rate, too vast to give birth to a solar system, nor could they arise from the disruptive approach of two stars; we must at least credit them as capable of generating a star cluster.

If, however, it is assumed that these nebulae are external to the stellar system, that they are in fact systems coequal with our own, we have at least an hypothesis which can be followed up, and may throw some light on the problems that have been before us. For this reason the 'island universe' theory is much to be preferred as a working hypothesis; and its consequences are so helpful as to suggest a distinct probability of its truth.[12]

Lundmark, who in 1920 completed an extensive investigation of globular clusters and spirals, wrote:

The present investigation has given as the main result that the spiral nebulae must be considered as situated at considerable distances from the solar system. Whether they are Jeans' star-producing mechanisms [nebulae in the process of contraction] or remote galaxies is, on the other hand, more difficult to decide. Possibly we might in the present facts see a suggestion that the latter is the case, but the spiral nebulae do not, however, seem to be of such dimensions as those that should be ascribed to the galactic system with regard to Shapley's investigations, and much also speaks against regarding the galaxy as having a structure, analogous to that of spiral nebulae.[13]

Confirmation of the Island-universe Theory

The mystery of spirals was solved principally by Hubble's work at Mount Wilson. He suspected that the nebulous-looking condensations

Fig. 218.   W. S. Adams, J. H. Jeans, and E. P. Hubble at the Mount Wilson Observatory.

Fig. 219.   Region 5′ northeast of the nucleus of M 31, on major axis, showing resolution into stars; photographed in red light with the 120-in. telescope. (*Lick Observatory*)

observed in spirals might result from photographic effects, since in the nuclear regions the condensations are superposed upon a relatively dense, unresolved background. Moreover, in the outer regions, where the background is less conspicuous, various aberrations of the telescope might distort the images. Short exposures made under critical conditions with the 100-in. telescope on the outer regions showed, he reported, "no difference between the photographic images of so-called condensations in M 33 and the images of ordinary galactic stars."[14] However, this fact alone would not prove that the "condensations" are actually stellar images, since they also could have been produced by very compact nebulous regions or by star clusters. More definite proof was provided by the observation of cepheid variables.

Three variable stars in extragalactic nebulae had been recognized by J. C. Duncan in 1922, but the material was insufficient to determine the type of variability. The first variable star in M 31 definitely identified as a cepheid was reported by Hubble at the end of 1923, and several more were identified in M 31 and M 33 soon afterward. In Fig. 220 the photograph on the left was taken with the 100-in. telescope on August 24, 1925, the one on the right on November 26, 1924. Stars Nos. 43 and 44 are irregular variables, the others are cepheids. Variation is conspicuous in Nos. 25, 26, and 30, and is appreciable in 37, 39, 43, and 48. The observed light ranges were the same as those expected from the relations known for cepheids in the Milky Way and in the Magellanic Clouds. (If they were stars within clusters, the light of the variable would be integrated with the light of many stars of constant brightnesses, and hence the relative change in brightness would be smaller. In the drawing of light curves of cepheids in M 31, the vertical scales represent apparent photographic magnitudes, the horizontal scale the period in days).

Hubble's argument rested on three assumptions: (1) The variables are connected with the spirals. (2) There is no serious amount of absorption resulting from amorphous nebulosity in the spirals. (3) The nature of cepheid variation is uniform through the observable portion of the universe. By comparing the mean apparent and absolute magnitudes, Hubble then derived a distance of 900,000 light-years for M 31 and M 33. This distance agreed well with that derived from the maximum brightnesses of novae and hence indicated a diameter of 30,000 light-years for M 31.

These observations settled the long-debated problem. Spirals are vast systems of stars, located at great distances from the Milky Way galaxy. Still, apparently it was difficult for some to believe that the issue had been closed forever. Even as late as 1926 Lundmark wrote:

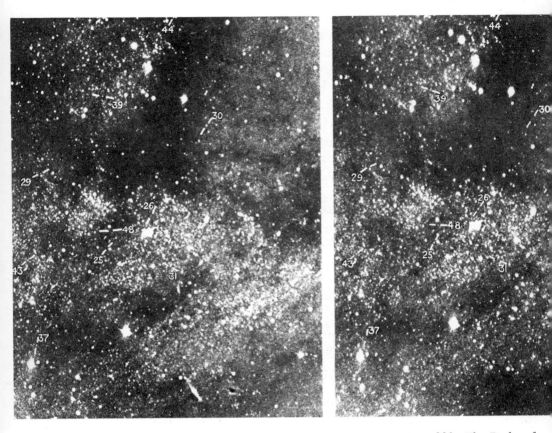

Fig. 220.   Cepheid variables in M 31. (*From E. Hubble,* The Realm of the Nebulae, *New Haven, Yale University Press, 1936, plate 6*)

During the time passed since William Herschel's days the pendulum of astronomical opinion has swung many times as to the conception of the cosmogonical role of the nebulae. On many occasions the evidences have been rather strong in favor of one or the other theory. For the present it seems rather plausible that the island-universe theory has obtained its final confirmation. . . .

Or will the pendulum swing again?[15]

It has not done so.

Hubble's results, however, did not support the argument that the spirals and the Milky Way are of commensurate size, even after 1930 when the discovery of interstellar absorption reduced Shapley's estimate by a factor of about 3 to 100,000 light-years. Actually, Shapley's comment (see P. 429) was an attempt to explain this difference. The answer

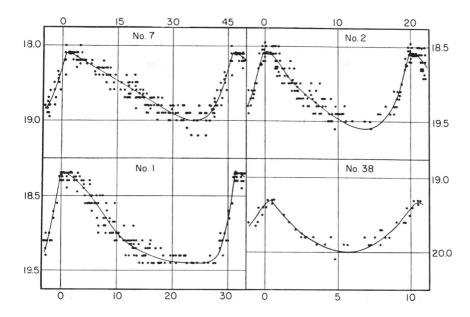

Fig. 221. Light curves of four cepheids in M 31. (*From* The Realm of the Nebulae, *New Haven, 1936, P. 95*)

was provided only after the revision of the period-luminosity relation of cepheids (Chap. XV, P. 327), which established the true distances, and hence linear dimensions, of galaxies. The distance of M 31 is between 1.5 and 2 million light-years, and its size is comparable to that of the Milky Way.

While Hubble had resolved the outer portions of nearby spiral galaxies into stars, the nuclei of the spirals and the elliptical galaxies were not resolved until 1944. It appears that W. Baade, who was born in Germany and had been at Mount Wilson since 1929, had taken out his first citizenship papers before World War II. He lost these papers moving from one house to another, but did not bother to take care of the matter. As a consequence, during the war Baade was declared an "enemy alien" and was restricted to the Mount Wilson–Pasadena area, but he was permitted to continue his work with the 100-in. telescope when many of his colleagues were occupied temporarily with research problems for the government. Baade thus had ample opportunity to use the large telescope

Fig. 222. W. Baade. (*Courtesy* Sky and Telescope)

under exceptionally favorable conditions, the most important of which was the blackout in Los Angeles and neighboring towns.

In 1944 Baade resolved the elliptical galaxies M 32 (NGC 221) and NGC 205 (companions of the Andromeda nebula) into stars, also the central region of M 31 itself, and the elliptical galaxies NGC 147 and NGC 185. He used red-sensitive plates, and these made it possible to increase the contrast between the yellow and red giants and supergiants and the diffuse background radiation from a multitude of stars belonging principally to the main sequence of the H-R diagram.

NGC 147 and NGC 185 are relatively small in size and in mass; their absolute magnitudes were estimated by Baade as −10.3 and −10.6, respectively. Both contain enormous numbers of yellow and red giants whose images resemble those of the faintest Milky Way stars. The images are so densely crowded, even in the outer regions of these galaxies, that it seemed impossible to produce convincing evidence of their existence with ordinary halftone illustrations. Baade therefore requested that actual photographic prints of NGC 185 be used in his paper in the *Astrophysical Journal*,[16] and the editor agreed to this procedure (probably the only time that actual photographic prints have been bound with the text of a printed article).

From a study of these photographs and from similar studies of globular star clusters, Baade constructed the H-R diagram of Population-II stars, discussed in Chap. XIII, on Pp. 277-283.

CLASSIFICATION OF GALAXIES

Hubble's Classification: Original and Revised

After Hubble had settled the basic problem of the nature of galaxies, astronomers became interested in the great variety of their structural features. Many tentative attempts had been made before 1900 to devise a system of classification of objects now known to be outer galaxies, but the first comprehensive classification was devised by Hubble in 1925 (a full description of his work can be found in his book *The Realm of the Nebulae*,[17] which is based upon the Silliman lectures he delivered at Yale in 1935).

Hubble's classification of regular galaxies is best represented by his

Fig. 223.   NGC 147, nebula in Cassiopeia, showing resolution into stars; photographed in red light with the 200-in. Hale telescope. (*Mount Wilson and Palomar Observatories*)

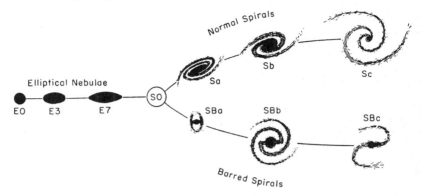

Fig. 224. The sequence of nebular types, by E. Hubble. (*From* The Realm of the Nebulae, New Haven, *1936, fig. 1, P. 45*)

Fig. 225. Types of nebulae, according to E. Hubble. (*From* The Realm of the Nebulae, *New Haven, 1936, Plate 2*)

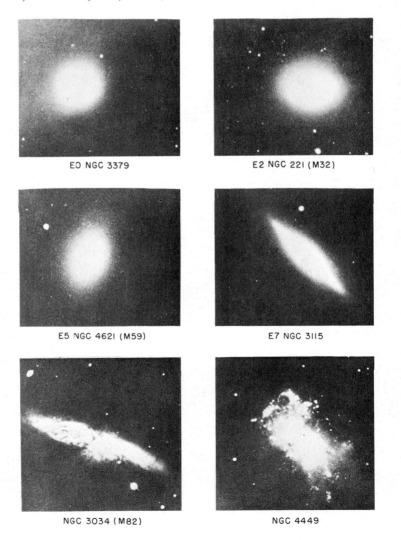

own diagram (see Fig. 224). Although he avoided the implication that his scheme represents an evolutionary sequence, most astronomers were inclined to the view that a normal galaxy first appears as a more or less elliptical spot of luminous matter—presumably unresolved stars—and that in the course of time an approximately spheroidal galaxy (designated by Hubble E0) becomes more and more flattened, ending with a distinctly elliptical galaxy (designated E7). Beyond this point, the galaxies presumably form two divergent sequences: (a) normal spirals with tightly wound arms, designated Sa, which in turn become Sb and Sc spirals; and (b) a parallel sequence that arises at approximately the same time as the Sa, Sb, and Sc spirals but contains luminous bars (designated by Hubble as SBa, SBb, and SBc objects). In addition to these sequences, there are

Fig. 226.   Types of nebulae, according to E. Hubble. (*From* The Realm of the Nebulae, *New Haven, 1936, Plate 1*)

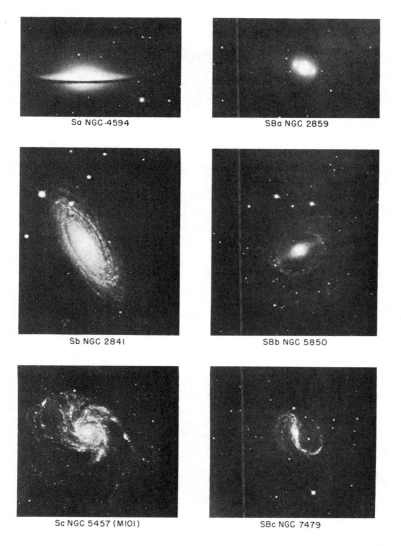

So NGC 4594

SBo NGC 2859

Sb NGC 2841

SBb NGC 5850

Sc NGC 5457 (M101)

SBc NGC 7479

many irregular galaxies, often of very peculiar shape, that could not be fitted into Hubble's scheme of classification. Nevertheless, as W. W. Morgan has remarked in his Russell Lecture, delivered at Nantucket, Massachusetts on June 19, 1961:

> The Hubble classification of galaxies is a remarkable achievement; although it was devised at a time before Baade's great work on stellar populations, its basic value has survived through the spectacular developments of the past quarter-century; and we are still able to perceive quite clearly the genius of its formulator. The progression from elliptical systems at one extreme to little-concentrated spirals at the other represents without any question an arrangement according to some physical property or properties.[18]

As more photographs of galaxies accumulated, Hubble attempted to revise his classification scheme in order to make it more comprehensive,

Fig. 227.   Spiral nebula NGC 2681 (type Sa) in Ursa Major, photographed with the 200-in. Hale telescope. (*Mount Wilson and Palomar Observatories*)

but he was unable to finish this task before his death in 1953. In the *Hubble Atlas of Galaxies*, edited by A. Sandage, Hubble's ideas, found in his notes, are followed as far as possible. Two new types, S0 and SB0, are used ". . . to include objects later than E7 but with no trace of spiral structure,"[19] and other symbols are rearranged as indicated in Table 10.

Table 10.

CLASSIFICATION OF SPIRAL GALAXIES

Old Class	New Class		Old Class	New Class
Sa	{ S0		SBa	SB0
	Sa		SBb	{ SBa
Sb	Sb			SBb
Sc	Sc		SBc	SBc

Sandage stresses the fact that, as in Hubble's original classification, an evolutionary connotation to the sequence of forms is avoided

. . . at least in the presentation of the classification. However, facts deriving from the stellar content of galaxies of different types (Sa, Sb, Sc, etc.) combined with the theory of evolution of individual stars that has developed in recent years, make it clear that the problem of the evolution of galaxies can be approached today on other than speculative terms. . . .[20]

The present view, which is only hinted at here and which must be worked out in detail with the facts marshaled, suggests that a given galaxy begins as an Irr or Sc (SBc). There is much dust and gas available for star formation. Each successive generation of star formation uses up the raw material (dust and gas) until little of that material is left. The differential velocity field in each galaxy (plus perhaps magnetic fields) controls the nature of the spiral arms. When star formation ceases, the arms tighten up . . . and the galaxy evolves into an Sb type. The bright stars die, and are therefore not present to form the lumpy condensations in the arms. They are not replaced by new stars, for the formation of stars has ceased. The faint stars that remain are red and are *not* distributed in spiral arms because random motions have wiped away the separate arm structures. At this stage, the galaxy is an Sa system. When all arms are gone, and no stars are being formed, the system becomes an S0. . . .

The present classification was devised by Hubble before evolutionary hypotheses were ever attempted. So, today, the belief that evolution proceeds from the Sc through the Sb and Sa groups to the S0 does not negate the form in which the classification sequence is given from E through S0 to Sa, Sb, Sc, and Irr. The continuity of the sequence is still present; only the direction of travel is reversed.[21]

Fig. 229.   NGC 7741, a barred spiral galaxy (type SBc) in Pegasus, photographed with the 200-in. Hale telescope. (*Mount Wilson and Palomar Observatories*)

Morgan-Mayall Classification

In 1957 Morgan and Mayall approached the problem of classifying galaxies from a different point of view. Prior to their work, the few spectra of galaxies that had been obtained usually were arranged in accordance with the Harvard classification of stellar spectra, the *Henry Draper Catalogue*. Although it was recognized that a galaxy's spectrum records the integrated light of many stars, usually a single spectral type was assigned to the galaxy as a whole, and this of necessity was a compromise between different criteria. Morgan and Mayall, and later Morgan alone, attempted to distinguish from the spectra what types of stars are most effective in contributing to the integrated light. In the case of very large galaxies, they were able to notice differences between the central nuclei and the outer, less luminous spiral arms or envelopes.

The new classification depends upon one of Hubble's criteria: the

Fig. 228.   Spiral galaxy M 33 (type Sc) in Triangulum, photographed with the 120-in. telescope. (*Lick Observatory*)

degree of central concentration of luminosity. This parameter is correlated with the spectra. In accordance with a suggestion first made by Shapley (and also recognized by Sandage; note last quotation), the order of the progression of types has been reversed from the order adopted by Hubble. The amorphous central regions of spirals similar to M 31 in Andromeda are typical of the K-type stellar population encountered in elliptical galaxies. The outer, fainter regions of M 31 correspond to an earlier spectral type, approximately F. Morgan was able to show from McDonald Observatory spectrograms that the transparent regions in our neighborhood in the direction of the nuclear bulge of the Milky Way correspond to the spectra of K-type stars. Milky Way regions in which obscuring clouds are present have spectra with strong hydrogen lines, and therefore correspond to an earlier spectral type.

A simplified system retaining the major features of the more elaborate Morgan-Mayall classification is presented in Fig. 230. The galaxies are classified into seven groups according to the degree of central concentration, starting with the irregular galaxies, concentration class 1, in which no distinct spiral nucleus is visible, but in which there may be several, irregularly spaced concentrations of hot stars and gas. Next is concentration class 2, in which central condensations of small diameter can be distinguished, while in concentration class 6 the central nuclei are very large and luminous, and the spiral arms are wound tightly and are relatively much less conspicuous than they are in the preceding concentration

Fig. 230.   W. W. Morgan and N. U. Mayall's classification system, in simplified form. (*From* Astrophysical Journal, *CXXXV, 1962, Fig. 1*)

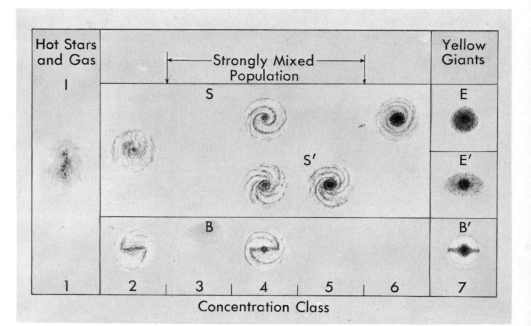

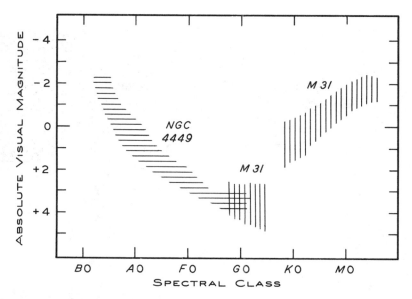

Fig. 231. Hypothetical H-R diagram for the principal contributors to the light of the inner part of M 31 (vertical lines) and of NGC 4449 (horizontal lines). (*From W. W. Morgan and N. U. Mayall,* Publications of the Astronomical Society of the Pacific, *LXIX, 1957, P. 295; courtesy Sky and Telescope*)

classes. The last concentration class, 7, includes various types of ellipticals.

Hubble's distinction between normal and barred spirals is essentially retained. However, among the spirals, Morgan distinguishes between those designated by the letter "S"—in which the central nucleus grows in size, developing brilliant amorphous characteristics in passing from concentration classes 2 to 6—and another sequence of spirals designated by the letter S'—nuclear regions of nearly the same size, which tend to be bounded by ringlike structures. Morgan suggests that the S' sequence begins with concentration class 4 and continues into the ellipticals, which are designated E' and differ conspicuously in appearance from the more nearly spherical galaxies designated E. Concentration class 1 is characterized by high percentages of hot stars and gas, while class 7 derives its light from yellow giants and shows no evidence of gas or dust.

Morgan comments as follows on the relation of his to Hubble's system:

The (S) and (B) sequences resemble those of the Hubble system; however, there are considerable divergences in the case of individual galaxies because of lack of correlation between the appearance of the arm structure and the nuclear region. Since the latter appears to be the most sensitive criterion of the stellar population of the inner parts of a galaxy, the abscissa in [Figure 230] is closely correlated with the spectral type of the inner region.[22]

Fig. 232.   Spiral galaxy M 51 (type Sc) and its companion NGC 5195 (type Irr.),
photographed with the 120-in. telescope. (*Lick Observatory*)

INTERACTING GALAXIES

Many interesting problems are presented by the structural features of *interacting galaxies* (two or more separate galaxies relatively near one another whose structural features are noticeably distorted as a result of a force between them). Some interacting galaxies may be immersed in a common luminous envelope. A relatively near and well-known pair is M 51, which consists of the large spiral NGC 5194 and its elliptical companion NGC 5195 (see Fig. 232). During the past 10 or 12 years, F. Zwicky frequently has discussed a number of interacting galaxies, and an atlas and catalogue, based principally on the *National Geographic-Palomar Atlas*, was published in 1959 by B. A. Vorontsov-Velyaminov of the Sternberg Astronomical Institute in Moscow. This catalogue contains 355 interacting galaxies.

The interacting galaxies of the type of M 51 suggest that new galaxies are being formed out of, or in the immediate vicinity of, already existing (and therefore presumably chronologically older) galaxies. Such newly formed galaxies have been observed on direct photographs and by means of spectrographs, by E. M. Burbidge and G. R. Burbidge. They call attention especially to NGC 244-5, which "certainly, to us, looks like the formation of a new galaxy from intergalactic material in the presence of an already existing one."[23]

Interacting galaxies present a variety of features, the most common being luminous filaments and "tails" extending from one galaxy to the other. Vorontsov-Velyaminov has attempted to discuss the physical properties of the various interactions listed in his atlas. He believes that the narrow and long connecting links and the tails cannot be explained in terms of tidal effects. Thus in the case of a link whose length is 40,000 parsecs, 4×10^8 years would be required for its formation if the velocity of the material were 100 km/sec. However, a dispersion in the velocities of only 10 km/sec would cause the connecting filament to acquire a thickness of several thousand parsecs.

Vorontsov-Velyaminov favors an explanation of the formation of the filaments in terms of gas motion in magnetic fields along the lines of force. Apparently, he says, one galaxy's lines of force may extend all the way toward the companion galaxy, but no attempt is made to provide a physical theory of gas motion within the roughly cylindrical volumes occupied by the filaments. At the same time, Vorontsov-Velyaminov insists that both filaments and tails consist of stars and gas and thus resemble a typical

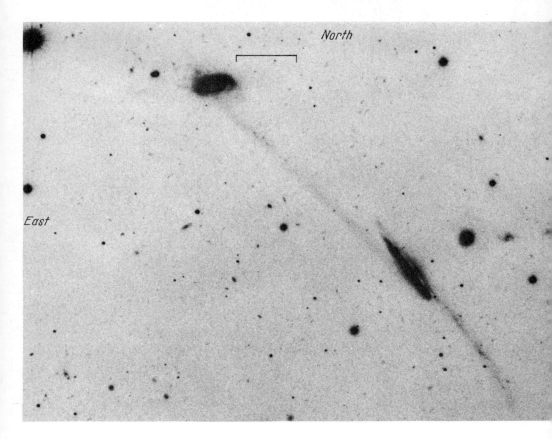

Fig. 233. Tidal disturbances in a pair of neighboring galaxies, photographed by F. Zwicky. (*Mount Wilson and Palomar Observatories*)

galaxy's normal content. He agrees with V. A. Ambarzumian's suggestion that the frequently observed pairs of galaxies experience an otherwise unknown force of repulsion and that even in multiple galaxies the individual components tend to recede from one another.

From measured radial velocities it is not possible to decide unambiguously whether the interacting galaxies are receding from or approaching each other, or whether they constitute pairs revolving in Keplerian orbits around their common center of gravity. In those few instances when radial velocities have been measured for both component galaxies, the differences of about 200 km/sec may not exceed the unavoidable errors of measurement. Even in cases when the measurements are sufficiently accurate, it would be difficult to distinguish between orbital motion, recession, or approach.

A decision must be made, therefore, on grounds other than those contained in the existing catalogues of velocities. From the work of T. L. Page, E. M. Burbidge, and G. R. Burbidge, it appears that relative motions

Fig. 234. A group of five galaxies, "Stephan's quintet," photographed with the 120-in. telescope. (*Lick Observatory*)

of pairs of galaxies give approximately the expected masses, if these differences are interpreted in terms of orbital motion.

Although Vorontsov-Velyaminov discards gravitation as the main force leading to the formation of connecting filaments and tails, it is reasonable to exploit as fully as possible the implications of the theory developed by B. and P. O. Lindblad. The former considered single galaxies, and after a long series of investigations concluded that under certain conditions a flattened galaxy may develop a massive, elliptically shaped ring whose center coincides with the galaxy's center. The line of apsides of the elliptical ring (described by B. Lindblad as a dispersion ring) rotates with an angular velocity that is related in a certain way to the galaxy's angular rotational velocity at the assumed distance from the center. B. Lindblad predicts in some galaxies the formation of several dispersion rings that interact with one another and that possess maxima and minima of density along the ring's circumference. P. O. Lindblad has investigated the gravitational effects causing distortion of the dispersion rings. For example, Fig. 235 stars with three rings at distances of 2, 4, and 6 kiloparsecs from the center. Each mass point in the three rings is assumed to be 6.4×10^7 solar masses. It thus represents a group of stars, rather than a single star. The numerical integrations show how the rings are distorted gradually at different times, beginning with time zero at the upper left of the figure and time 640 million years at the lower right. Toward the end of the sequence, distinct spiral arms which resemble those of the Milky Way and of other galaxies are formed.

P. O. Lindblad also has investigated the motions of particles in the gravitational field of two galaxies. The results are shown in Fig. 236, starting with a particle in a circular orbit 7.2 kiloparsecs from the parent galaxy's center. The other galaxy is assumed to be a mass point approximately similar to the galaxy at the origin of the coordinates. The entire coordinate system rotates in a retrograde direction so that the companion galaxy retains its position in the diagram. The endpoint of the ejected particle occurs at time 2.56×10^9 years. Lindblad remarks that some of the features shown by his computations resemble those actually observed among the galaxies shown in the Vorontsov-Velyaminov atlas.

It should be noted, however, that special conditions and resonance effects are required to produce the spiral arms in a single galaxy, or the long connecting links of pairs of galaxies. Therefore, it is not yet clear

Fig. 235. Development of spiral arms in a galaxy, according to P. Lindblad (*From* Stockholm Obs. Annaler, *XXI, 1960, Pp. 56–58*)

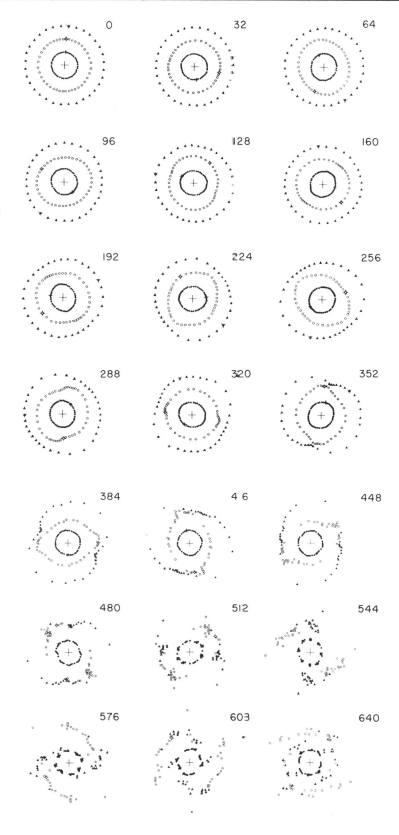

|———|——————→ 10 kpc

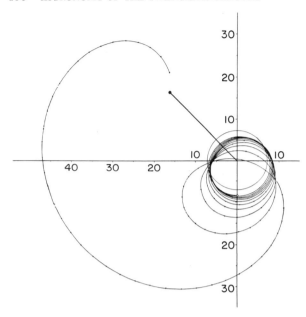

Fig. 236.   Track of a particle in a double galaxy, computed by P. Lindblad. (*From* Stockholm Obs. Annaler, *XXI, 1960, P. 31; courtesy* Sky and Telescope)

whether purely gravitational computations can account for the straight and narrow connecting filaments present in many interacting galaxies. All authors who have discussed this problem agree that there may be physical phenomena that are not observed within the confines of a single galaxy, such as the Milky Way.

THE EXPANDING UNIVERSE

Another extremely important line of investigation has developed from Slipher's discovery of the large radial velocities of galaxies. For about 10 years, Slipher was almost the only astronomer trying to determine the radial motions of galaxies, and he accumulated a list of 41 galaxies, with radial velocities ranging between 300 km/sec of approach to approximately 1,800 km/sec of recession. Slipher's work was continued by M. Humason at Mount Wilson, and later by Mayall at Lick. The latest publication on the redshifts of the extragalactic objects appeared in 1956 under the joint authorship of Humason, Mayall, and Sandage. The work lists the Doppler displacements of 620 galaxies observed at Mount Wilson and Palomar and of 300 galaxies observed at Lick. The largest observed redshift corresponds to a velocity of recession of 61,000 km/sec. By comparing measurements of the same objects, the authors were able to ascertain the degree of precision of their results. They also were able to prove that no serious systematic errors had affected the measurements.

In 1929, Hubble announced a relationship (suggested earlier by the German astronomer C. W. Wirtz and others) between the recessional radial velocities of extragalactic nebulae and their distances, and he concluded that there is a linear relation between these two quantities (now referred to as *Hubble's law*): The increase in recessional velocity amounts to approximately 500 km/sec for an increase in distance of 1 million parsecs. However, Hubble's determination of the distances of galaxies was found to be affected by serious errors. The first and most significant of these arose in connection with the nearby galaxies in which cepheid variables could be identified. When the period-luminosity relation of cepheids was revised, their distances were increased by a factor of about 2. Since the Doppler displacements were not affected by a similar systematic error, an increase in the distance by a factor of 2 resulted in making the Hubble constant equal to one-half the original value: approximately 250 km/sec for every million parsecs.

A further difficulty in determining distances of more remote galaxies arose from Hubble's having identified as very luminous stars certain discrete objects in galaxies that looked like stellar images but that later were found to be either compact gaseous nebulae or clusters of stars. In these galaxies, cepheid variables and RR Lyrae variables could not be resolved, and Hubble had assumed that objects that looked to him like stars were

Fig. 237.   Velocity-distance relation, according to E. Hubble. (*From* The Realm of the Nebulae, *New Haven, 1936, P. 114*)

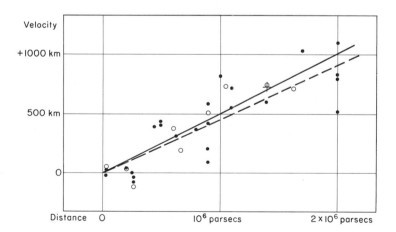

RED-SHIFTS

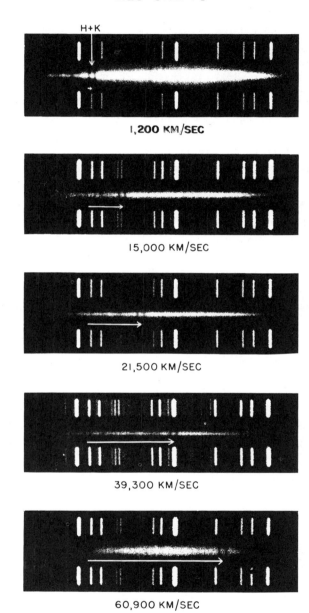

Fig. 238. The spectra of five galaxies, showing redshifts between 1,200 km/sec (23 million light-years distant) and 60,900 km/sec (1 billion light-years distant), photographed by M. L. Humason. (*Mount Wilson and Palomar Observatories*)

similar in absolute magnitude to the brightest supergiants in the Milky Way. Considerable work has been done already to identify real supergiants in galaxies of intermediate distances in order to apply to them absolute magnitudes similar to those of the supergiants of the Milky Way, but the task is not yet complete. It is known, however, that the distances of these galaxies must be increased not by a factor of 2 but perhaps by a factor of 3 or even more—resulting in a Hubble constant some astronomers believe may be as low as 75 km/sec/million parsecs or as large as 175 km/sec/million parsecs.

Thus, the determination of the distances of the more remote galaxies is still in a confused state. The best that can be done at present is to concentrate upon clusters that may contain a thousand or more galaxies within a relatively small volume of space. Since an average nearby cluster of galaxies usually contains all types of galaxies—large spirals, giant ellipticals, ordinary ellipticals, and small, irregular systems—it is reasonable to postulate that the optically brightest four or five galaxies of each cluster may resemble in absolute magnitude the Milky Way, and the largest and most luminous galaxies in our immediate neighborhood, such as the Andromeda galaxy. Their integrated absolute magnitudes are about -19 or -19.5, and these quantities have been used for determining distances of remote clusters of galaxies in which the integrated apparent magnitudes of the four or five brightest galaxies were measured.

Since the exact value of the Hubble constant is not known, and since it is not known whether a real constant independent of the distance is involved, the best that can be done at the present time is to use a compromise value of 100 km/sec/million parsecs. But, even though the exact value of the Hubble constant is not known, the existence of a linear relation between redshift and distance is the most spectacular discovery in astronomy that has been made during the past 60 years.

The observed redshifts usually have been interpreted as velocity effects and have led to the theory of the expanding universe; that is, the recession of galaxies from each other, which tends to increase intergalactic distances. This interpretation depends on the proportionality of the Doppler displacement in wavelength to the wavelength: The proportionality is found to hold in the limited range of the optical spectrum of about 3,000 A.

However, it must be recognized that in most distant galaxies the number of spectral lines suitable for measurement is very small. In most, only the ionized calcium lines K and H, normally at wavelengths of 3,934 and 3,968 A, have been detected. The light that produces a galaxy's spec-

Fig. 239. Cluster of galaxies in Coma Berenices, at a distance of about 40 million light-years, photographed with the 200-in. Hale telescope. The cluster extends beyond the limits of this photograph. (*Mount Wilson and Palomar Observatories*)

trum is the integrated light of many billions of stars, all moving with a random distribution of velocities and causing the spectral lines to be strangely diffuse and affected by the superposition of the light coming from the early- and late-type stars. In addition to the absorption lines, many galaxies show a few more or less conspicuous emission lines, the strongest of which is usually the forbidden line of ionized oxygen at wavelength 3,727 A. Even in those few galaxies in which other emission lines could be measured, the proportionality between wavelength redshift and wavelength cannot be tested accurately.

In 1955, A. E. Lilley and E. F. McClain of the Naval Research Laboratory in Washington, D.C., attempted with a radio telescope to measure the redshift of the hydrogen 21-cm line in the spectrum of the well-known galaxy Cygnus A. Their first results indicated the presence of an absorption line at the precise position expected from the optical measures of the same galaxy's redshift. However, the authors later withdrew their results, because they were unable to confirm the hydrogen absorption line's existence, although they had used a better radio telescope and a more sensitive receiver. Lilley and McClain must be complimented for their frankness in withdrawing their earlier conclusion that "$\Delta\lambda/\lambda$ is constant over an interval of 500,000/1 in the electromagnetic spectrum."[24] They undoubtedly will search again for the 21-cm absorption line in Cygnus A or in other radio galaxies and ultimately will reconfirm the proportionality between $\Delta\lambda$ and λ. Astronomers who had seen the feature attributed to the 21-cm absorption line felt that the evidence clearly supported the original conclusion, and one wonders whether the failure to find this feature at a later date may not represent the discovery of an entirely new phenomenon of a variable absorption feature in Cygnus A.

Although the existence of a 21-cm hydrogen absorption line in Cygnus A is still uncertain, there have been numerous observations, principally at the Leiden Observatory, of 21-cm emission lines in several relatively close galaxies. For example, Louise Volders at Leiden has investigated the neutral hydrogen in the spirals M 33 and M 101 and has found that, with reference to the local standard of rest, the radio observations of M 33 give a velocity of -176 km/sec, while the optical observations by Humason, Mayall, and Sandage give approximately -180 km/sec. In the case of M 101, the radio observations give $+253$ km/sec, while the optical observations give $+256$ km/sec. Although M 33 is a member of the local group of galaxies (a group of about a dozen galaxies in addition to the Milky Way, such as Andromeda galaxy and its two companions and the Magellanic Clouds), and therefore does not appear suitable for the test of the Doppler relation, with regard to the proportionality of $\Delta\lambda$ and λ, M 101 is probably sufficiently distant to serve as an indication of the proportionality in the cases of galaxies affected by the phenomenon of expansion of the universe.

The simplest way to explain the expansion phenomenon is to assume that (a) at some time in the very distant past all galaxies were relatively close together, perhaps even forming something G. Lemaître has described as the "primeval egg" of the universe; (b) at a particular time, usually designated the zero point in our time scale, all galaxies were propelled with different velocities from the egg's center; and (c) galaxies that initially had the largest velocities are now at the greatest distances from us. This hypothesis, which is related to what astronomers have called the "big-bang" theory of cosmology, implies that the reciprocal of the Hubble constant represents the age of the universe as measured from the arbitrary zero point. If the Hubble constant were approximately 100 km/sec per 1 million parsecs, the resulting age would be of the order of 10 billion years. Another vigorous proponent of the big-bang theory has been G. Gamow.

However, the big-bang theory is only one of several. It competes with the steady-state theory, which posits a gradual expansion of the system of galaxies and the continuous creation of matter within the observable volume of space to maintain a constant density of matter within that volume. H. Bondi, T. Gold, and F. Hoyle are most closely associated with the steady-state theory. Bondi and Gold have described the reasoning leading to it as follows:

. . . According to [the "cosmological principle"] all large-scale averages of quantities derived from astronomical observations (i.e., determination of the mean density of space, average size of galaxies, ratio of condensed to uncondensed matter, etc.) would tend statistically to a similar value independent of the position of the observer, as the range of the observation is increased; provided only that the observations from different places are carried out at equivalent times.

. . . there is the qualification regarding the time of observation. The universe is still presumed to be capable of altering its large-scale structure, but only in such a way as not to upset its homogeneity. The result of a large-scale observation may hence be a measure of a universal time.

. . . As the physical laws cannot be assumed to be independent of the structure of the universe, and as conversely the structure of the universe depends upon the physical laws, it follows that there may be a stable position. We shall pursue the possibility that the universe is in such a stable, self-perpetuating state, without making any assumptions regarding the particular features which lead to this stability. We regard the reasons for pursuing this possibility as very compelling, for it is only in such a universe that there is any basis for the assumption that the laws of physics are constant; and without such an assumption our knowledge, derived virtually at one instant of time, must be quite inadequate for an interpretation of the universe and the dependence of its laws on its structure, and hence inadequate for any extrapolation into the future or the past.

Our course is therefore defined not only by the usual cosmological principle but by that extension of it which is obtained on assuming the universe to be not only homogeneous but also unchanging on the large scale. This combination of the usual cosmological principle and the stationary postulate we shall call the *perfect cosmological principle* and all our arguments will be based on it. The universe is postulated to be homogeneous and stationary in its large-scale appearance as well as its physical laws.[25]

Evaluation of theories of the origin and evolution of the universe is made more difficult because at very great distances, and for very large velocities, relativity effects may have to be considered. This would imply a curvature of space and a possible connection between the coordinates of space and of time. It must be concluded, therefore, that despite all the advances in our knowledge of the properties of the building blocks of the universe, astronomers still are unable to throw new light upon the cosmological problem by means of the existing optical and radio observations of galaxies.

APPENDIX

STELLAR SPECTROSCOPY*

In the 19th century stellar spectroscopists were mainly concerned with identifying the absorption lines in the spectra of stars and measuring the Doppler shifts in order to determine radial velocities. These tasks are by no means completed. Even the sun's spectrum has thousands of unidentified lines, but no one now doubts that they are produced by common atoms and molecules known from laboratory experiments; P. W. Merrill's discovery of strong absorption lines of technetium—an element of short lifetime—constitutes a major achievement of the 20th century in this field. As the 19th century came to a close, however, several new problems arose that greatly enhanced the scope of stellar spectroscopy.

Our knowledge of the atmospheres of the stars followed two independent paths. On the one side there were the observers who obtained photographs of stellar spectra and attempted to explain the multitude of features seen on these photographs while on the other side theoretical astrophysicists developed the theory of the transfer of radiation through the outermost layers of a star. Although there were frequent occasions

---

* This material is presented as an illustration of growth in a fairly narrow field of astrophysics—the one with which the authors of this book are most familiar. It was originally a paper by Dr. Struve presented at a joint meeting of Sections B and D of the American Association for the Advancement of Science in Minneapolis, Minnesota, on June 25, 1935. It was later published as a three-part article, "Some new Trends in Stellar Spectroscopy," in *Popular Astronomy*, Vol. 43, Oct., Nov., and Dec., 1935. New material has been italicized to distinguish it from the previously published matter, and original material no longer considered pertinent has been omitted. Some of the historical information has been mentioned briefly in Chaps. IV and XI, and is expanded here.

when the results of the observations were used by the theoreticians many observed effects remained outside the domain of theory.

In discussing the history of stellar spectroscopy it is convenient to divide it into four somewhat overlapping stages of development. The first stage of early observations and of preliminary attempts to give a theoretical interpretation of stellar spectra started with Fraunhofer's work in 1814 and reached its culmination in 1850 with the famous theoretical work of Kirchhoff.

The second stage was devoted to a systematic classification of the spectra of the stars and involved the enormous task of measuring and identifying thousands of stellar absorption lines. The beginning of this period may properly be fixed at the year 1863 when Huggins made his early spectroscopic observations.

The third . . . phase in stellar spectroscopy began in 1843 with Christian Doppler's publication *"Über das farbige Licht der Doppelsterne."* Doppler's principle was successfully applied to astronomy by Vogel in 1871, and resulted in the measurement of the solar rotation from the displacements of the spectral lines at the eastern and western limbs. In the years 1871 and 1872 Vogel in Germany and Huggins in England obtained the first measurements of radial velocities from stellar spectra. . . . The radial velocity epoch of stellar spectroscopy is by no means over. Radial velocity determinations of faint stars are now under way at several observatories, and detailed investigations of spectroscopic binaries, convection currents in stellar atmospheres, etc., occupy a considerable share of the observing hours at the larger astronomical institutions. *It is, however, symptomatic that the Commission on Stellar Radial Velocities of the International Astronomical Union has shrunk to a very small number of members, while at one time, about 30 years ago, it was one of the largest and most active in the Union. Apparently, mass determinations of radial velocities are now being conducted at very few observatories. France, with Fehrenbach at the head, and two or three southern observatories are leaders in this field.*

In 1919 the fourth stage of development began. In that year the German physicist Eggert applied to the stars the theory of chemical equilibria. In 1920 Saha published in the *Philosophical Magazine* his fundamental paper on the ionization theory in stellar atmospheres. His work was followed by the theoretical investigations of Darwin, Fowler, and Milne in England, and of Russell in the United States. In recent years Miss Payne (*now Mrs. Payne-Gaposchkin*) at Harvard, and Adams and Russell at Mount Wilson have provided an adequate observational basis for the theory. Miss Payne's results, originally printed in numerous Harvard publications, were later summarized in her two monographs, "Stellar Atmospheres" and "Stars of High Luminosity." Russell . . . improved the theory and applied it to the study of the continuous absorption coefficient in the outer layers of the stars. Wildt, Swings, and especially Russell have extended the theory of gaseous equilibria to molecular spectra and have succeeded in explaining the more important band spectra in later type stars.

BROADENING OF STELLAR ABSORPTION LINES

Whenever a great advance is made in a field of science a number of phenomena are usually found which are not accounted for by the new theory but which come into prominence after the more essential features of the observational data have been satisfactorily explained by it. It is to such phenomena, resulting from the theory of ionization but not explained by it, that we shall now turn our attention. We shall discuss here only a few of the problems which have recently arisen. Some of these form a fairly connected story of the gradual progress in stellar spectroscopy and illustrate the slow and difficult process of searching for new truths.

Some of the older astrophysicists will remember the almost hopeless feeling they experienced in examining a stellar spectrogram before Saha's ionization theory became known. Many lines had been satisfactorily identified by Lockyer and his associates but a much greater number remained unknown. For radial velocity determination this lack of identification was not especially serious. In the later spectral types, and even in the earlier ones, enough identifications were available to obtain a satisfactory number of individual measurements. But the appearance of the stellar lines was so different from that of the laboratory comparison spectra that it was difficult to suppress a feeling of uncertainty. After all, what right did we have to apply Doppler's principle to hydrogen lines several hundred angstroms wide or to lines complicated by central reversals which often were variable and not even symmetrical? How reliable were conclusions based upon measurements of metallic lines ten angstroms or more in width having central absorptions of not more than ten per cent of the star's continuous radiation spectrum?

The theory of ionization succeeded in explaining the more important differences between the spectra of different stars. Moreover, in doing so, it taught us an important lesson, for it clearly demonstrated that the ordinary laws of physics could be safely and successfully applied to the study of stellar spectra. With surprising success Fowler and Milne computed the maxima of the absorption lines *or their marginal appearance* in the sequence of stellar spectra and the basis of their work was a formula derived from the laws of physics. In spite of the many individual differences in the intensities and shapes of stellar absorption lines, all major features of the Henry Draper classification and of the giant and dwarf criteria were satisfactorily accounted for by two physical variables: temperature and pressure.

It was reasonable to expect that other phenomena not directly accounted for by the theory of ionization would also find their explanation in simple physical laws. Perhaps the most interesting of these phenomena consisted of an amazing variety in the general appearance or contour of stellar absorption lines. It had been known for many years that while most of the Fraunhofer lines in the solar spectrum are narrow, there are many stars which exhibit ill-defined broad lines. There are, for example, the hydrogen lines in the hotter stars, especially in those of class A, which often are several hundred angstroms wide; there are the lines of ionized calcium H and K which are extremely strong and broad in stars of intermediate and late classes; there are lines of neutral calcium (λ 4227), of sodium (D_1 and D_2), of magnesium and of iron, which appear distinctly broadened in the later types. Finally, there are many stars of classes O, B, A, and F which have diffuse lines of iron, titanium, helium, silicon, etc.

In order to explain the causes of the broadening of stellar absorption lines it was first necessary to classify the observational results. It was not certain that a single physical cause was responsible for the observed effects. Russell had suggested that in the spectrum of the sun great line width is invariably associated with great total intensity and that, consequently, the abundance of atoms producing a given line is in some manner responsible for the observed broadening. This was an important result, but the explanation evidently does not apply to the spectra of A and B stars having many weak but ill-defined and broad lines of iron, helium, etc. Accordingly, it seemed reasonably certain that more than one physical cause contributed to the observed effects.

For the purpose of making an exhaustive test of the various known sources of broadening of spectral lines it will be useful to have at hand a chart of the various effects known or suspected to exist in the laboratory. These sources of broadening have been labeled "physical causes." All of them depend upon the form of the absorption coefficient and are therefore directly related to the abundance of atoms. The most fundamental of these broadening factors is what is usually termed radiation damping. It is known from theoretical considerations and from laboratory experiments that a spectral line, no matter how carefully produced, is never infinitely narrow. There is a natural width for any spectral line and this width is explained in the classical electron theory as being due to loss of energy in the oscillating atom through radiation. If a pulse of light produced by an oscillating electron can be represented by a Fourier analysis, then the loss of energy by radiation must produce a gradual diminution in the amplitude of the oscillation, and this, in the Fourier representation, corresponds to a broadening of the emitted radiation. The coefficient of absorption or emission thus derived is inversely proportional to the square of the value ($\lambda - \lambda_0$), where λ_0 is the center of the line. The absorption coefficient, accordingly, is very nearly equal to infinity at λ_0 and decreases as the square of the distance from λ_0.

Collisional damping results from the sudden interruptions in the wavetrains produced by collisions. An infinitely narrow line would correspond to an infinitely long wave-train of constant amplitude. If the amplitude is "damped" we observe "natural widening"; if the wave-train is interrupted, we observe "collisional broadening." In the laboratory this phenomenon is very important. . . .

The next effect is that discovered by A. H. Compton in X rays. It is included here because some years ago Franck suggested it in order to account for certain phenomena observed in novae and in stars of the P

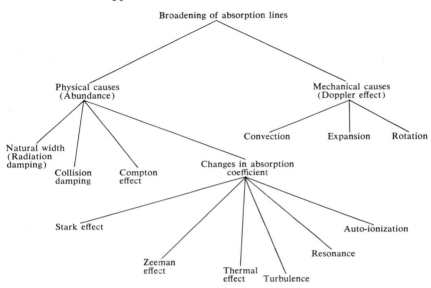

Cygni type. In spite of Franck's elegant treatment, the theory evidently does not apply to stellar spectra, and McCrea has given a better explanation of the observations. There is, however, no reason why an accummulated Compton effect should not be observable as a result of slow propagation of light through a nebula. If the optical depth of such a nebula is sufficiently great, a light quantum will collide many times with electrons and will gradually lose energy.

The last group of physical broadening factors is given under the title "changes in the absorption coefficient." We consider here various abnormal absorption coefficients, such as might result from ionic Stark effect, Zeeman effect, turbulence, thermal agitation, resonance, and auto-ionization.

In addition to this entire group of physical causes the astronomer is obliged to consider various mechanical causes produced by Doppler effect. It is true that thermal agitation and turbulence have already been considered among the physical causes but these factors are obviously affecting the form of the absorption coefficient. These are convection currents in the atmosphere of the star, expansion of the entire atmosphere, pulsation, and rotation. Expansion has for a number of years been considered the main cause of the great widths of the emission lines observed in novae. Pulsation is . . . regarded as the principal cause of radial-velocity variation in Cepheid variables. Convection currents have . . . been discussed by Adams and his collaborators in connection with radial velocity determinations of individual lines in certain bright stars.

Observational considerations have led us to suspect that more than one cause of broadening is active. Accordingly, an attempt must be made to classify the observational material and to establish a number of groups, each of which is probably dominated by one broadening factor alone. Three such groups may be readily recognized: 1) A single cause seems to be responsible for the broadening of all spectral lines in such stars as Altair. The spectrum of this star is of class A and is, therefore, similar to that of Vega. Now in Vega the spectral lines are sharp and narrow. The lines in Altair, though agreeing in position and in relative intensity with the lines of Vega, are several angstroms wide and are extremely shallow and diffuse. Approximately one-half of all B-type stars, a considerable number of A-type stars, and a fair sprinkling of F stars, show the same general appearance. 2) The second group of stars is of an entirely different nature. In these we observe broad hydrogen lines and occasionally broadened lines of helium, but the broadening is not related to that of the first group and may occur in the stars of that group having either sharp or broad lines. 3) The third group consists of stars of later type in which the lines of calcium are strong and broad. In this group the faint metallic lines are invariably sharp.

STELLAR ROTATION

We now proceed to test the various broadening agencies in the three groups of spectra. Consider first group one: among hundreds of stars having broad lines we find some of spectral class B in which the lines of Si III, $\lambda\lambda$ 4552, 4567, and 4574 are present. These three lines form a multiplet of relatively simple structure. The intensity rules for such multiplets indicate that the theoretical laboratory intensities of the three lines should be in the ratio 5:3:1. This evidently means that five times as many atoms participate in the production of line 4552 as in that of line 4574. We select three stars in which the lines appear to be of different widths. In γ Pegasi they are very sharp and narrow. In β Canis Majoris they are slightly broadened and in κ Orionis they are very broad and diffuse. We now measure the contours of the lines in all three stars and determine the total amount of energy absorbed in each line. Since the observed intensity of a beam of light ... decreases *roughly exponentially* in intensity when passing through an absorbing medium, we can write the following simple equation:

$$i = i_0 \, e^{-\sigma_1 l}$$

Here i indicates the observed intensity, i_0 is the intensity before absorption took place, σ_1 the absorption coefficient per centimeter in the case of λ 4552, and l the length of the path in the absorbing medium. Since i/i_0 is known, we can compute from our observations the value of $\sigma_1 l$. Since l is the same for all three lines and since the absorption coefficient is proportional to the number of observed atoms, we conclude that the absorption coefficient for line 4574 is $\sigma_3 = \sigma_1/5$. Knowing the two absorption coefficients we can compute the ratios of the total absorptions of λ4552 and λ4574. This is found to be approximately 5 in the case of κ Orionis and 2.2 in the case of γ Pegasi. The observations actually give 2.2 for all three stars, agreeing therefore with the computation for the narrow-line star but disagreeing in the case of broadened lines. It can be shown that a similar disagreement will be found in all cases of broadening listed in our chart under the heading "physical causes." It is not possible to attribute the broadening of weak stellar absorption lines to a peculiar form of the absorption coefficient without seriously violating well-established laws of physics. Recourse must, accordingly, be had to the Doppler effect.

Since the Doppler-shift is always proportional to the wave length, $\Delta\lambda = V \lambda/C$, where V is the velocity of the light source, λ the wave length and C the velocity of light. Accordingly, lines of similar intensity should have widths which are proportional to λ. For the stars of group one this relation was tested by *Struve* and was found to be true. An even more convincing set of measurements was . . . made by Shajn. Accordingly, this necessary condition of Doppler broadening is fulfilled.

It is now necessary to choose between the four mechanical causes listed in the chart, namely, convection, expansion, pulsation, and rotation. We therefore turn our attention to the spectroscopic binaries of classes A and B. These binaries are known to consist of two separate stars revolving around one another in a period ranging from a few hours to many thousands of years. It is generally believed that in very close systems the rotational periods of the two components agree with their periods of revolution. The spectral lines of the binaries are not all of the same width. In some stars the lines are narrow and sharp; in others they are of the character of those observed in Altair. If the spectroscopic binaries are arranged in order of increasing period it is found that, in general, the line-width decreases as the period increases. The broadest lines are invariably seen in spectroscopic binaries that have very short periods. Adams and Joy called attention to the fuzziness of the lines in W Ursae Majoris; Miss Maury found broad and diffuse lines in V Puppis and μ Scorpii. In these stars the absorption lines are so broad that they can hardly be measured; at the same time they are characterized by very short orbital periods. The conclusion seems justified that broadening of lines in spectroscopic binaries is correlated with orbital period. But this correlation has no physical sense. It is much more reasonable to suppose that . . . orbital period and rotational period are identical, *and that* the true correlation is between line-width and period of axial rotation. We, therefore, definitely incline, at least in the case of spectroscopic binaries, toward axial rotation. Whether rotation is the only cause of broadening is not yet known, but there are reasons to believe that it is the most important one. Since *most* binaries are not spectroscopically different from ordinary stars of group one, there appears to be no reason why rotation should not be considered the main cause of broadening in all of these objects.

In 1929 Elvey obtained accurate measurements of line contours for many stars of early type, and the problem was to test the shape of these contours by means of the rotational hypothesis. The theoretical derivation of the contours for stars in rapid rotation had been published a few years earlier by Shajn and *Struve*. Consider the circular disc of a rotating star and let the axis of rotation be perpendicular to the line of sight. It is easy to show that all points on the disc which lie at the same distance from the axis must have the same radial component of their rotational motion. Accordingly, we consider the star disc to be divided into a number of narrow strips lying parallel to its axis. The radial velocity of all points in a given section will be the same. The central section has all of its motion at right angles to the line of sight. Consequently, it will contribute a portion to the composite line, which is undisplaced, but which is diminished in depth with respect to the original line of a non-rotating star in the same proportion as that which the area of the section bears to the area of the entire disc. The diminution is, of course, caused by the continuous spectra of other sections, which in a rotating star overlap with the line of the central section. The two adjoining sections produce spectral components which are slightly shifted toward the violet *or* toward the red of the original wave length. The depth of this contribution will again be proportional to the area of each section in terms of the area of the disc. Proceeding in this manner toward the other sections of the disc, we obtain a graphical integration of our original line, and the sum of the ordinates of the various contributing components will give us the theoretical contour of the rotational line. The total absorption of the broadened line measured as the area between the line contour and the continuous spectrum will be identical with that of the original unbroadened line. By means of this graphical procedure, Elvey was able to construct a number of theoretical lines corresponding to different rotational velocities and to different initial lines such as would have been observed in non-rotating stars. The agreement in the shape of the theoretical contours with those observed by Elvey was most striking and served as an additional argument in favor of the rotational hypothesis. *An ingenious* investigation by John Carroll for a few stars *has* confirmed these results: the character of the broadened lines is such as can only be produced by rotation.

While we do not exclude the possibility of effects other than those caused by rotation in stars of group one, it is interesting to investigate the problem further by making the express assumption that rotation alone is present. Should other causes of broadening be found . . ., these results will have to be revised. In the meantime, however, we are able to gather data concerning the probable distribution of stellar rotational velocities. Perhaps the most surprising result is the fact that no star has a velocity at its equator in excess of about 300 km/sec. Actual measurements have given values ranging all the way from zero to . . . more than 250 km/sec. It is, of course, obvious that the axes of the stars are not always perpendicular to the line of sight. There is . . . no reason to assume that these axes have a preferential orientation in space. In making this assertion we think primarily of the orbit planes of visual and spectroscopic binaries. These have not been found to have a preferential orientation with respect to the Milky Way. Assuming, then, that the axes are distributed at random we are able to compute the theoretical distribution of apparent rotational velocities. Suppose for a moment that all stars rotate with the same velocity of 250 km/sec. It is clear that there will be very few stars having their axes in or near the line of sight and that the number will be a maximum for stars having axes approximately 90° from the line of sight. Expressed mathematically, we should say that the probability of observing a star with an inclination of its axis equal to α degrees is proportional to $\cos\alpha$. This would give us a curve with a minimum at 0 and a maximum at 250 km/sec. The ordinate represents the number of stars and the abscissa is the velocity of rotation at the equator, or rather its projection upon the line of sight. The true distribution curve of the observed rotational velocities shows a maximum at intermediate velocities. There is no resemblance in shape to the theoretical curve. One of our assumptions must, therefore, be in error. We naturally suspect that the stars do not all rotate with the same velocity of 250 km/sec. For example, our own sun has a velocity of rotation of only 2 km/sec and it is entirely reasonable to expect that the true rotational velocities of the stars will range from zero to the maximum of 250 km/sec.

We can arbitrarily assign the percentages of stars having true equatorial velocities within certain ranges. For each such range a curve is obtained which is similar in shape to the $\cos\alpha$ curve, but in which the abrupt drop occurs at a different value of V. The sum of all such curves should give the expected distribution. If it does not agree with the observed curve we proceed by trial and error until the percentages are properly chosen to give the correct representation. This work was carried out by Miss Christine Westgate at the Yerkes Observatory.

In spectral class B approximately 27 per cent of the stars were found to have velocities averaging 50 km/sec, 53 per cent have velocities of approximately 100 km/sec, 15 per cent have velocities of 150 km/sec, and only 5 per cent have true velocities in excess of 200 km/sec. For the A stars a somewhat similar distribution of velocities was found, while for the F's the proportion of slower rotations is much greater. Finally, for stars of classes G, K, and M the proportion having measurable rotational velocities is entirely negligible.

The result that all rotational velocities fall below the limit of *about* 300 km/sec is evidently not accidental. It must have its origin in the balance between centrifugal force and force of attraction. The acceleration due to the attraction of *the* earth is 10 m/sec². The sun has a mass of approximately 3×10^5 times that of the earth. Since acceleration due to gravity is proportional to the mass and inversely proportional to the square of the radius, we find that the acceleration of gravity on the surface of the sun is 3×10^4 cm/sec². For an ordinary star of early type the mass may be considered approximately 5 times that of the sun, while the radius would be of the order of 3 solar radii. Accordingly, the acceleration of gravity on the surface of such a star would also be in the neighborhood of 10^4 cm/sec². The acceleration due to centrifugal force is equal to the square of the velocity divided by the radius. Assuming a maximum velocity of 300 km/sec and a radius of 2×10^{11} centimeters, we find for the centrifugal force a value of approximately $\frac{1}{2} \times 10^4$ cm/sec². Accordingly in such a star gravity is only twice as strong as the centrifugal force, and if radiation pressure is supporting an appreciable portion of the star's atmosphere, the balance between gravity and centrifugal force may perhaps be reached or even surpassed in such stars as Altair. For comparison we might mention that the ratio of the centrifugal force to the force of attraction is 1/300 in the case of the earth and 1/6 in the case of Saturn. Saturn has an oblateness of about 1/10. It would be reasonable to expect an appreciable rotational flattening in the case of rapidly rotating stars, but this effect has not yet been *directly* observed. One might suppose that an accurately determined contour would provide a test of the oblateness of rotating stars, but it so happens that the rotational contour produced by an elliptical disc is exactly the same as that produced by a circular disc. Incidentally, the period of rotation of the star Altair is approximately 6 hours. Contrast this with the period of the sun which is about one month.

It may seem surprising that stellar rotation was not discovered long ago. The reason for the delay may be found in the enormous weight carried by the opinion of H. C. Vogel who for many years dominated all thought in this field of astrophysics. In 1877 Abney had suggested that axial rotation might be responsible for the great widths of certain stellar absorption lines. His paper was criticized by Vogel, who correctly pointed out that it was not sufficient to observe broad hydrogen lines, but that all stellar absorption lines should be broadened if rotation were actually present. Incorrectly, however, Vogel stated that there were no stars in which all absorption lines were broadened. He was apparently thinking of the broad hydrogen and calcium lines and it is, of course, obvious that these cannot be explained by Doppler effect. There is no doubt, however, that Vogel must have known the spectrum of Altair and that he must have been aware of the broadening of all metallic lines in it. Incidentally, Vogel's paper contains the following statement in regard to the photographic method suggested by Abney: "It is quite impossible for me to understand how Mr. Abney can express the hope that the photography of stellar spectra could ever become of importance in the problem considered by him. For such faint objects as we generally find in the case of stellar spectra the method of photography will always be inferior to that of visual observation. Photography can be of importance only because it makes accessible the violet and ultra-violet parts of the spectrum which are difficult to observe visually and makes it possible to observe in these regions the stronger absorption lines. However, even on the most successful photograph only relative measures of lines among one another would be possible in regard to their width, so that no conclusions could be obtained in regard to rotation; the widths of lines on different photographic plates would depend upon the length of exposure, the sensitivity of the plate and the length of development."

What an irony that only a few years after this emphatic prediction Vogel himself introduced the photographic method into astrophysics *and in a later paper re-discovered the phenomenon of stellar rotation—only to see it forgotten almost immediately.*

The correct interpretation of the broadening influence in the stars of our first group has made possible a number of related investigations. There are among the early-type stars some in which we observe not only absorption lines but also emission lines of hydrogen, iron, magnesium, etc. The origin of these bright lines was not known and they were not explained by the theory of ionization. In fact, . . . there was considerable uncertainty as to the region in the stars' atmospheres where the bright lines have their origin. Some astronomers were of the opinion that the emission lines are produced in the deeper and denser portion of the stars' atmospheres, others maintained that they originate in the normal Fraunhofer layer as do the absorption lines, while still others held the opinion that they come from extremely rarified outer nebulous shells.

The emission lines present a problem that is somewhat analogous to that just discussed in the case of the absorption lines. They, too, are not always sharp and narrow but often have appreciable widths. Measurements made principally by R. H. Curtiss established the fact that the widths of the hydrogen emission lines are proportional to the wavelengths. Earlier in this paper we mentioned a similar relation for the broadened absorption lines and have regarded it as an argument in favor of Doppler effect. Similarly the suggestion, originally made by Curtiss and supported by Merrill and Wilson, and by *Struve*, that the emission lines are broadened by Doppler effect, appears reasonable.

An interesting result was obtained when the widths of the hydrogen emission lines were compared with the widths of the helium absorption lines. It appeared that there was a close correlation between the two types of line widths. This has been confirmed by Merrill at the Mount Wilson Observatory, and seems to prove that there is a connection between rotational velocity as determined from the absorption lines and the Doppler broadening of the emission lines.

One might be tempted to suggest that emission lines as well as absorption lines are broadened by rotation in the same atmospheric layer. But this is disproved by the fact that the actual velocity of rotation for the two types of lines is not the same. Consequently, if rotation is responsible for the broadening of the emission lines, their origin cannot be in the Fraunhofer layer. It is interesting, in this connection, that emission lines of different elements may give different velocities. Consequently, different elements give rise to emission lines in different layers. The absorption lines, on the contrary, all give the same velocity, and therefore originate in the same layer.

Perhaps we will be pardoned if we indulge in a brief speculation on the origin of the emission lines. Is it possible that they are due to gravitational instability in rapidly rotating stars? We have found before that stars like Altair are near the point of breaking up at the equator even if we disregard the effect of radiation pressure. Accordingly, it is not unreasonable to suppose that atoms are driven away by centrifugal force in the vicinity of the star's equator and that they form a ring or shell at a considerable distance from the reversing layer of the star. If this is true, all

Be stars must be rotating with velocities near . . . V=250 km/sec. Those having narrow lines would be explained by inclination. Unfortunately, the number of Be stars is not large enough to apply the statistical test of the cosα law to the frequency curve of stars having different observed line widths. It is not quite clear, however, why only some rapidly rotating stars have emission lines.

The actual physical process which produces bright lines is called fluorescence; this has been investigated by Rosseland. Some stars show double emission lines, and these could be explained on the assumption of gaseous rings which rotate according to Kepler's laws around their central stars. McLaughlin has improved and enlarged this hypothesis and has combined it with the assumption of pulsating motions by means of which he *was* able to account for variations in the intensities of the bright lines. Finally, in a series of important papers, Gerasimovič has combined the rotational hypothesis with that of an expanding shell. According to him rotational instability is insufficient for the formation of an outer shell and for various reasons "the revival of the old Laplacian ideas in a modern disguise can hardly appeal to the astrophysicist of our days." Instead, Gerasimovič suggested that "in the Be stars . . . this radiative dissipation is facilitated by stellar rotation working against gravity." Radiation pressure is primarily responsible for the outward motion of the shell. As soon as the shell is completely developed, the inward flux of radiation stops the outflow, and the latter can begin only after the shell has been sufficiently dispersed. By this mechanism Gerasimovič *was* able to give a quantitative explanation of the observed variations in Be stars.

In a rotationally broadened absorption line each point corresponds effectively to a definite portion of the star's disc. Accordingly, by observing different portions of a rotational contour we are able to gain information concerning the distribution of light on the apparent disc of the star. Suppose, for example, that a rotating star is not uniformly bright. In that case the rotational contour would show periodic variations in shape and the lines would at times be unsymmetrical. No such asymmetries have been observed in the lines of single stars. In double stars, however, the two components act as reflectors so that their inner sides are brighter than those portions which are not illuminated. This reflection effect has been known for a long time and has been investigated in the light curves of eclipsing variables. It is now possible to compute the effect of unequal light distribution in spectroscopic binaries and to predict the amount of asymmetry in the spectral lines of such stars. . . . E. L. McCarthy of the Yerkes Observatory has shown that in some of the closest binaries, such as V Puppis and u Herculis, the predicted asymmetry due to the combined effect of rotation and reflection must be large enough to show in accurate measurements of their contours. The systematic error in radial velocity determinations from such unsymmetrical lines has been found to be relatively small and insignificant. . . .

An interesting modification of the rotational method of studying line contours is provided by the eclipsing binaries. In 1909 Schlesinger noticed that in certain eclipsing binaries the radial velocities were systematically in error just preceding the middle of the eclipse and immediately following it. The values, measured minus computed velocity, were positive before middle eclipse and negative after central phase. This effect was later discussed by Forbes and by Hellerich. It was thoroughly investigated in β Lyrae by Rossiter and in Algol by McLaughlin. All of these investigations were based upon spectrograms of small dispersion, and the unsymmetrical effect resulting from the fact that part of the star's disc is covered during eclipse by the fainter component merely produces a spurious shift of the spectral lines. Struve and Elvey have obtained high dispersion spectrograms of Algol with the Bruce spectrograph of the Yerkes Observatory and have measured the unsymmetrical contours of the lines during eclipse. Computations made for several other stars indicate that the shape of the contour undergoes marked variations with phase. Thus, in stars having annular eclipses the lines may even become double near the central phase. The reason for this is that the central part of the line, corresponding to the middle section of the star's disc, is partly blocked out by the disc of the eclipsing star, the surface brightness of which must be fainter than that of the eclipsed star. . . .

We have seen before that in stars of rapid axial rotation the force of gravity is almost balanced by the centrifugal force. The question naturally arises: What will be the effect of this reduction in gravity upon the conditions of ionization and of excitation in the atmosphere of the star? One might expect that the reduced gravity at the equator would produce an earlier type of spectrum in the equatorial regions and a later type in the polar regions. Since in ordinary stars we observe the integrated spectrum of the entire disc we should expect that the spectrum of a rapidly rotating star would be a superposition of spectra corresponding to different absolute magnitudes. No conclusive observational test of this effect is as yet available but there are certain possibilities which have not yet been investigated. For example, it is clear that if we observe a stellar spectrum with sharp lines, the star must either be rotating slowly or must have its axis in the line of sight. The absolute magnitude effect produced by rapid rotation may perhaps serve to *distinguish* between inclination of axis and true velocity. . . .

Since the foregoing paragraphs on stellar rotation were written in 1935, considerable progress has been made, both on the observational and the theoretical aspects of the problems. The occurrence of double emission lines of hydrogen, and sometimes of other elements, in B-type stars has been explained as the consequence of the formation of a gaseous ring in the equatorial plane of a rapidly rotating star. An independent confirmation of this hypothesis was obtained first by A. H. Joy when he observed the eclipse of the emitting ring in the binary system RW Tauri: Before the onset of the geometrical eclipse, the darker companion first obscures the approaching limb of the ring, causing the disappearance of the violet-displaced emission component. After mid-eclipse the receding emission component disappears because of the eclipse. Several dozen other binary systems have since been discovered in which one component star—usually the brighter, more massive but smaller—is surrounded by a gaseous ring.

The earlier speculations concerning the formation of gaseous rings merely stated that in rapidly rotating stars the force of gravitation is sometimes balanced by the centrifugal force. No attempt was made to fit this phenomenon into the broad picture of stellar evolution. The work of J. H. Jeans had indicated that, in a contracting gaseous sphere, preservation of angular momentum would at a certain stage result in the formation of an equatorial ring. This, obviously, did not apply to the more prominent emission-line B-type stars. Some of this type—for example, Pleione and other hot stars in the Pleiades—are not now in the contracting stage of their evolution, but are in the process of expansion that carries the representative point of such a star in the H-R diagram from the main sequence toward the right side of the diagram. F. Hoyle and D. J. Crampin have succeeded in explaining the occurrence of bright lines in Be stars such as Pleione. Although the star as a whole increases in size and gradually assumes the properties of a giant, the internal structure is changed in such a manner that for homogeneous stars expansion would imply a decrease in the rotational velocity. This will not be the case in real B-type stars that have departed from the main sequence, because only a very tenuous outer shell of the star participates in the expansion. At the same time the dense central nucleus condenses, producing an over-all effect of an increasing ratio of centrifugal force to gravitational force at the equator.

On the observational side, D. B. McLaughlin noticed long ago that an important phenomenon in the bright hydrogen lines is their tendency to possess violet and red components of unequal intensity, a phenomenon that he has described as V/R variation. McLaughlin, therefore, suggested that, in addition to rotation, the gaseous rings also participate in radial motions, sometimes directed away from the star, while at other times they are directed toward the center. The theory of moving envelopes of stars was worked out by V. V. Sobolev in 1947 and in a number of subsequent investigations. His book, first published in Russian, was translated into English by S. Gaposchkin in 1960. A comparison of the translation with the original Russian book indicates the difficulty of preserving the historical facts, even when the interval of time is short and both the author and the translator are able to compare their respective writings. For example, on P. 37 of the English translation, Struve's hypothesis "that double bright lines occur in the transparent gaseous ring which is rotating about the star," is stated to be "completely unsatisfactory."[1] The Russian original, when correctly translated, reads as follows: "However for the explanation of all characteristics of these spectra, Struve's hypothesis is insufficient."

Arne Slettebak has measured the equatorial rotational velocities, v sin i, in a large number of stars, and has made allowances for limb darkening and other possible effects. George Herbig and several other astronomers have discovered that the sharp discontinuity in rotational velocity at spectral type F 5 does not occur among the giant stars but is essentially limited to stars on the main sequence. Thus even a late F-type star may have a rotational velocity at the equator of the order of 50 or even 100 km/sec, despite the fact that a star of similar type on the main sequence has a rotational velocity that never exceeds about 10 km/sec. This result has been interpreted by Sandage and others as a result of the conservation of angular momentum in a star that may have had a spectral type of approximately A 5 when it was on the main sequence, with a rotational velocity at the equator of the order of 200 km/sec. Hence, even though the rotational velocity decreases as such a star moves away from the main sequence and becomes a late F-type giant, it may still exceed the rotational velocity of a main sequence star of spectral type late F. Similarly, Herbig has shown that there appears also to be conservation of angular momentum in the very young, cool variable stars of the T Tauri type. These stars are now above the main sequence and they are still in the process of Helmholtz contraction. The rotational velocity of such a star increases as the star contracts still further, and it may end up on the main sequence with a spectral type of late A or early F. In this case, its rotational equatorial velocity would be larger than it is at present, but would not be inconsistent with the rotational velocities of late A-type stars that are now located on the main sequence. Thus there appears to be good evidence for assuming that the angular momentum of a star, caused by its own axial rotation, is preserved over long intervals of time. It also can be assumed that, presumably, the discontinuity on the main sequence at F5 is not caused by the braking action of magnetic fields or by other phenomena that would operate smoothly along the entire spread of the H-R diagram, but that the discontinuity represents a rather fundamental difference in the manner in which the stars have been formed. Presumably main-sequence stars, of spectral type F5 and later, have formed planetary systems that have absorbed most of the angular momentum of the original protostar; stars of earlier spectral type are either devoid of planetary systems or have at least preserved within the star itself the major part of its original angular momentum.

Still another important advance was made by D. H. McNamara and his assistants at Brigham Young University in the study of pulsating variable stars of the type of β Canis Majoris and of δ Scuti. It appears that in these pulsating stars the absorption lines are relatively narrow and the corresponding equatorial rotational velocities are small. Thus rapid axial rotation and pulsation seem to be mutually exclusive. We return to the 1935 discussion.

STARK EFFECT

We have seen that axial rotation accounts satisfactorily for a number of phenomena observed in stars of group one. However, a minute examination of spectra of B-type stars reveals cases of line broadening which are not accounted for by this theory. Consider, for example, the star γ Pegasi, of spectral class B2. The lines are in general narrow with the exception, of course, of the Balmer lines, which are broad and diffuse. But the hydrogen lines are considered in group two of our observational data. If we examine carefully the lines of SiIII, O II, N II, etc., we find that their widths are as narrow as can be obtained with any stellar spectrograph now in existence. Plates taken with a dispersion of 5 angstroms per millimeter at the Coudé focus of the 100-inch telescope at Mount Wilson show that the true line widths must be below the resolving power of the instrument. When we examine the helium lines of γ Pegasi we find that some of them are also sharp and narrow, for example, $\lambda\lambda$ 3965, 4121, 4169. However, other lines of helium, for example, $\lambda\lambda$ 3872, 3927, 4009, 4026, 4388, 4472, are appreciably broadened and have diffuse edges.

Since rotational broadening must affect all lines in a star's spectrum a different explanation must be looked for in the case of the helium lines. Furthermore, Doppler effect produces line widths which are proportional to the wave lengths. In the helium lines, on the contrary, the broadening seems to increase toward the violet. For example, λ 3872 is much broader than λ 4922 of the same spectral series. An examination of the helium lines which are subject to broadening in such stars as γ Pegasi, δ Ceti, and γ Orionis, reveals the interesting fact that all of them belong to two spectral series: 2^3P-n^3D and 2^1P-n^1D. All members of the other helium series are sharp. The two series having broadened lines are characteristically designated as the diffuse series of helium triplets and the diffuse series of singlets. These names, assigned long ago on the basis of laboratory experiments, suggest that even in the discharge tube these lines have a tendency to be broad and diffuse. Accordingly, we are justified in turning to physics for an appropriate explanation of the observed effects. These have been found to be the result of inter-ionic Stark effect produced between charged particles and helium atoms. The helium lines of the two diffuse series are easily split into a number of components if the vapor is kept in an electric field. This phenomenon was discovered in the laboratory by J. Stark in 1913 and has since been carefully investigated by a number of physicists. The most complete laboratory investigation of the Stark effect in helium is that of J. S. Foster of McGill University.

In the atmospheres of the stars the gases are known to be highly ionized. From a study of their spectral lines we find that most atoms have lost at least one electron and many have lost two, three, or even more. All of these free electrons are moving about in the gas and each is charged with a minute quantity of negative electricity equal to 5×10^{-10} electrostatic unit. The remaining ions contain equal amounts of positive electricity. Now suppose that in its flight through the atmosphere of a star such a charged particle, ion or electron, happens to pass near a helium atom that is about to radiate the line 4472. Naturally the electric charge will cause perturbations in the electronic orbits of the radiating atom and the emitted line should display the characteristic features of the Stark effect. The motions of the atoms, ions, and electrons are distributed at random. Consequently, some atoms will be under the influence of nearby charged particles, while other atoms will be relatively free of disturbing effects.

The observed appearance of a spectral line in such a gas must, therefore, correspond to the superposition of a large number of individual Stark patterns. The line will appear broadened and the amount of broadening will depend upon the average distance between atoms and charged particles.

Physicists have shown theoretically that only the lines of the diffuse series in helium are subject to a large Stark effect. In the other lines the Stark effect can be observed only when the electric fields are enormously high. The average distance between the charged particles and an atom must naturally depend upon the pressure of the gas, and this is again related to the surface gravity. Now the surface gravity of a dwarf star is much greater than that of a giant. Accordingly, if our explanation is correct, Stark broadening should display a correlation with absolute magnitude. Such a correlation actually exists: γ Pegasi, δ Ceti, and γ Orionis are all comparatively faint stars; the more luminous B stars, such as 67 Ophiuchi, ε Canis Majoris and ζ Persei do not show broadening in the diffuse helium lines.

Stark discovered another important phenomenon produced by electric fields. When an atom radiates in the presence of such a field, the ordinary selection principles of the quantum theory are violated and transitions between spectral terms are observed which are not present in ordinary spectra. In the case of helium the violation of selection rules is confined largely to the choice of azimuthal quantum numbers. Under ordinary circumstances the azimuthal quantum number must change by one unit. Transitions corresponding to no change or to a change greater than one are forbidden. For example, the line 4472 involves a change from state ^3P to state ^3D. The corresponding transition from state ^3P to state ^3F is forbidden. Were it permitted, a line would be observed at λ 4470, in the immediate vicinity of the permitted line 4472. The two terms, 4^3D and 4^3F differ very slightly and therefore the difference in wave length between the permitted and the forbidden line is only two angstroms. The forbidden line was observed by Stark and was found by him and by others to occur in relatively weak electric fields. In γ Pegasi and in other B-type dwarfs a line at λ 4470 is actually observed and, similarly, other forbidden lines of helium are found in the vicinity of helium λλ 4026, 4388, and 4922. The wave length of the forbidden line agrees exactly with that computed, from laboratory experiments, for rather weak electric fields. If there is any discrepancy between theory and observation it is in the surprisingly great intensity of the stellar forbidden lines. Foster and Douglas have recently shown that it is difficult to reconcile the intensities, even allowing for the fact that absorption lines, especially those in the reversing layers of the stars, show less difference in intensity than do the corresponding emission lines.

We agree with Foster and Douglas that the average electric field computed from the broadening of the diffuse lines would not be expected to produce as strong a forbidden line as λ 4470 with as little violet shift as has actually been observed in several stars. There is probably no reason to suspect that anything is wrong with the theory of Stark effect in stellar atmospheres, but it is quite possible that other causes tend to overthrow selection rules and that, consequently, λ 4470 can appear at lower average electric fields than we have heretofore considered probable. A rough computation shows that the average field in a stellar atmosphere produced by the ions is between 1000 and 10,000 volts per centimeter. Such a field would not be considered strong from the laboratory point of view, where fields of several hundred thousand volts per centimeter are produced. Knowing the average field intensity in a stellar atmosphere we can compute the pressure of the gas. The result is in . . . agreement with Russell's value for the average pressure in a stellar atmosphere.

It is evident that the Stark effect can be used to discriminate between stars of high and low luminosity. This method has been successfully used for a number of stars, but in practice it is limited by the fact that rotationally broadened lines fail to show the minor broadening of the diffuse helium lines.

Our results concerning Stark effect in helium lines bring us naturally to the consideration of those stars which we included in our group two. These are characterized by extremely wide Balmer lines of hydrogen. They belong to spectral classes B, A, and F and show a marked variation for different stars. For example, Vega has hydrogen lines which are several hundred angstroms wide, while α Cygni, of approximately the same spectral class, has narrow and sharp lines. This effect is evidently related to absolute magnitude: Vega is not very luminous, while α Cygni is a typical supergiant. The broadening of the hydrogen lines has for a number of years been tentatively attributed to Stark effect. Hulburt, Vasnecov, and especially Russell and Stewart, have made computations showing that under the pressures believed to exist in stellar atmospheres, broadening of the Balmer lines should be observable. Our results for the helium lines strengthen this belief. Since there are no lines in hydrogen devoid of Stark effect and since there are no forbidden lines of hydrogen which make their appearance in electric fields it is impossible to make as convincing a test as was made in the case of helium. The observational evidence is therefore limited to the contours of the Balmer lines. These have been investigated at the Yerkes Observatory and the results have been found to be in fair agreement with the requirements of the theory.

The Stark patterns in hydrogen are always symmetrical. Thus Hβ, if produced in an electric field, splits into two stronger and many fainter components. For Hγ the number of strong components is four. A charge equal to one unit on the electrostatic system, placed at a distance of one centimeter from the radiating gas, will displace the outermost components of the Hβ line by an amount equal to 0.06 angstrom.

In a paper published some years ago by Elvey and *Struve* a computation was carried out to determine the theoretical contour of a hydrogen line broadened by Stark effect. The assumption was made that the line Hγ if devoid of Stark effect would have the same shape as that observed in the giant star η Leonis. It was next assumed that the pressure in the atmosphere of the star varies in accordance with a formula suggested by Milne. For different layers in the star's atmosphere having different pressures, the corresponding mean electric fields were then computed and the average Stark pattern was determined for Hγ. The assumption was next made, in agreement with the work of Unsöld, that the electrons and atoms are distributed at random, and the corresponding effect of broadening was computed for each layer. The combined absorption of all layers was then determined with the help of an equation derived by Eddington. The result shows what would happen to the Hγ line of η Leonis if it were subjected to conditions believed to exist in ordinary dwarf stars. The results are distinctly encouraging and agree in general with the observations: Normal pressures produce appreciable modifications in the contour of Hγ. The total absorptions of the hydrogen lines are greatly increased by the Stark effect and the general contour of the computed lines bears a marked resemblance to the observed contours in dwarf stars like γ Pegasi.

Since the Stark effect in hydrogen increases with the serial number we should expect that the total absorptions of successive members of the Balmer series would not decline as rapidly as do the intensities of emission lines in laboratory spectra. In fact we may even have an increase in total absorption as we approach the limit of the Balmer series. This is one of the outstanding characteristics of the observational results in all stellar hydrogen lines. Furthermore, our computations show that the spread of the wings must be much greater in the dwarfs than in the giants and, accordingly, there should be an absolute-magnitude effect for hydrogen. While all major characteristics of the observed contours are satisfactorily accounted for, there emerge from a detailed study certain results which indicate the presence of other unknown effects. For example, it was found that the observed contour of Hδ in the spectrum of the dwarf ι Herculis cannot be produced by Stark effect from the observed contour of the same line in the giant 67 Ophiuchi. These two stars are of approximately the same type and there is no obvious reason why the theory should not apply. Apparently the hydrogen lines are subject to an additional absolute-magnitude effect. . . . On the other hand, if we compare the observed contours in ε Aurigae, a well-known supergiant, with those in γ Pegasi, a typical dwarf, we find that the theoretical prediction is well supported.

Before we leave the subject of the hydrogen lines, attention must be called to the fact that the existence of Stark broadening in hydrogen and helium may appreciably alter results based upon the theory of ionization. It is not permissible to consider the total intensities or the central intensities of the hydrogen lines as functions of numbers of atoms alone. The Stark effect must increase with temperature, and the total absorptions of the hydrogen lines will therefore be increased in the direction of the hotter stars, thereby producing a systematic departure from the theoretical curves given by the ordinary ionization formulae.

The only other atom that is subject to a pronounced Stark effect is that of ionized helium. In the O-type stars such as 10 Lacertae, a number of He II lines have been measured and the broadening of λ 4200 is clearly seen on the plates. Accurate contours of the He II lines have not been observed, but rough measurements of line widths have been tested theoretically and have been found to be in agreement with theory. It is of considerable interest to compare the Stark effect for members of the Fowler series with that for members of the Pickering series. The theory of the Stark effect suggests that the lines 4200 and 4542 should show a much greater width than λ 4686. This seems to be in accordance with *observations*. A comparison can also be made between the Balmer lines and the Fowler lines of He II. Theoretically, the Stark broadening of the Fowler lines should exceed that of H$_\epsilon$ and would be equalled only by the broadening in the higher members of the Balmer series where blending and confluence of the wings would make it impossible to study the contours in detail. In actual practice the Balmer lines are so much stronger than the He II lines that a qualitative comparison is useless. However, it seems quite consistent with the observations to say that the Fowler lines are relatively broader than the corresponding hydrogen lines of the same total intensity. The broadening of the He II lines should, of course, also be sensitive to differences in absolute magnitude. The observational data are limited to very few stars, but a comparison of the giant 9 Camelopardalis with the dwarf 10 Lacertae indicates that this effect is present. The broadening of the Fowler series has been observed in the laboratory by Paschen, whose work was limited to the extreme ultra-violet part of the spectrum. . . .

Since 1935 the most spectacular Stark-broadened hydrogen absorption lines have been discovered in several white dwarfs by J. L. Greenstein, B. Lynds, and others. However, not all white dwarfs have extremely broad lines; those that do not may possess rather tenuous outer envelopes.

The ideas of Foster and Douglas, and later of A. B. Underhill, concerning the nature of the absorpton line at λ 4470 were quite ingenious. They attributed it to the effect of diminished induced emission of the permitted line λ 4472 in the violet wing of that line (λ 4470)—in other words, to a rather conspicuous departure from thermodynamic equilibrium, resembling the cyclic processes first investigated by S. Rosseland. But such departures are not very probable in ordinary main-sequence stars: They occur conspicuously in shell spectra, spectra of novae, etc. According to A. Unsöld's discussion in his book Physik der Sternatmosphären *("Physics of Stellar Atmospheres"),[2] the line at λ 4470 is undoubtedly the forbidden line* $^3P - {}^3F$.

The Stark broadening of the hydrogen lines has been successfully used by R. M. Petrie and W. W. Morgan, among others, as a criterion for estimating the intrinsic luminosities (or absolute magnitudes) of the B and A stars. This method is less useful in the O-type stars, for which A. B. Underhill has developed other criteria.

NATURAL WIDTH

We now turn to the third group of stars, namely those of late class, in which the lines of Ca II are strong and broad. The correct explanation of these line widths was first given by Russell, who showed that all strong lines in the atmospheres of the sun and stars are "winged." In a far-reaching investigation Unsöld, in 1927, combined the theory of radiation damping with that of a stellar atmosphere. It is difficult to understand why this theory, well known to physicists *many* years ago had failed to make an impression in astrophysics prior to the work of Unsöld. The explanation may perhaps be the misleading statement, often found in text books, that the natural width of a line is a minute fraction of one angstrom (0.000116 A) and is, therefore, below the resolving power of any stellar spectrograph. What was overlooked in this statement was the difference between emission and absorption lines. The natural width of a line defined, let us say, as the width measured at an ordinate one-half the maximum intensity, is constant for any given emission line no matter how long the exposure. If we have a faint emission line the central intensity is small and the line width is measured at a low value of the intensity. If we increase the exposure, we thereby increase the maximum intensity and the line width is measured at a greater intensity. Were our measurements confined to a constant value of the intensity or plate blackening, the width of the emission line would, of course, increase in agreement with the factor $(\lambda - \lambda_0)^2$ in the emission coefficient. In practice such measurements would be hopeless because the over-exposure of the central portions of the line would cause spurious photographic effects. It is clear, therefore, that natural line widths cannot be measured in emission lines photographed with stellar spectrographs. Conditions are entirely different if we consider an absorption line. Radiation damping causes such a line to be intense in the middle, where almost all the light of the continuous spectrum is removed. The wings extend toward the red and the violet, in accordance with the term $(\lambda - \lambda_0)^2$. For a very weak line, the width measured, let us say, at a point where the absorption is 0.5, would be so small as to be below the resolving power of the instrument. For a stronger line the central absorption increases but slightly since it can never exceed the value of 1.0. The wings, however, spread out in proportion to the square root of the total number of atoms present in the absorption chamber. Accordingly, our line width will increase as the square root of N [*number of atoms per cm³*] and can be made as large as is desired. Minkowski at Hamburg, Stewart and his associates at Princeton, and other physicists, have actually measured this broadening in laboratory absorption lines. Unsöld applied the theory to the case of absorption in a stellar atmosphere and derived the numbers of atoms per square centimeter that are active in producing the H and K lines of the solar spectrum. Miss Payne [*Cecilia Payne-Gaposchkin*] has tested the contours of the calcium lines in numerous stellar spectra and has found them to be in fair agreement with Unsöld's theory. Similar results have also been obtained at the Yerkes Observatory and the only serious discrepancies were found in stars known to be subject to rapid rotation. It should be mentioned in this connection that the central intensities of stellar lines are not equal to zero, as would be demanded by Unsöld's formula. Miss Payne has given convincing observational evidence for this departure, and Unsöld and Pannekoek have discussed the problem theoretically.

An interesting test can be made of Unsöld's theory by considering the relative intensities of different lines. His formula is essentially that proposed by Schwarzschild and by Schuster for the case of a scattering atmosphere: $i = i_0/1 + \sigma l)$. This expression takes care of the effect of re-radiation by the various atoms. Were there no such re-emission the formula would be:

$$i = i_0 \, e - \sigma l.$$

In both expressions 1 is the length of the absorbing column. The exponential formula is that usually given in elementary textbooks; it assumes that in each centimeter of path in the absorbing medium a fraction σ of the light is lost, that is—transformed into heat. The quantity σ is called the absorption coefficient. For each atom it is inversely proportional to $(\lambda - \lambda_0)^2$, and for N atoms per cubic centimeter it is proportional to N. Hence we may write $\sigma = (\text{Const. N})/(\lambda - \lambda_0)^2$. The total absorption of a line is obtained by integrating i over all wave lengths from minus infinity to plus infinity:

$$W = \int (1 - i) \, d\lambda$$

This is the area enclosed by the horizontal line i = 1 at the top, and by the contour of the line at the bottom. The quantity W is usually expressed in angstrom units of "equivalent breadth." In other words, the area W is measured by the width of an equal area bounded by the intensity of the continuous spectrum at the top, the zero axis at the bottom, and two vertical lines at the sides.

No matter whether we use the Schuster-Schwarzschild expression or the ordinary exponential formula, W is found to be proportional to the square root of N. In the case of a multiplet, the relative values of N are known. For example, K and H have theoretical intensities of 2 : 1. Accordingly, the total absorptions of these two lines should be in the ratio $\sqrt{2} : \sqrt{1}$ or 1.42. The measurements made by Unsöld, by Miss Payne and by other workers at Harvard and at the Yerkes Observatory, have confirmed the square-root law for all the stronger calcium lines and for many other members of multiplets in stellar spectra. For example, the silicon lines 4552, 4567, and 4574 were found to be approximately in the ratio $\sqrt{5} : \sqrt{3} : 1$.

THERMAL AGITATION

The square-root law for the total intensities of absorption lines was tested for the solar spectrum by numerous observers. Minnaert and Woolley independently found large departures in the case of the fainter Fraunhofer lines. On the other hand, laboratory measurements by Korff, as well as measurements of the atmospheric lines in the solar spectrum by Childs, von Klüber, and others, confirmed the theory.

Evidently the contours of the fainter solar lines were not wholly defined by the natural width caused by radiation damping. Damping due to collisions, first investigated by Lorentz, may be present. In stellar spectra this type of damping should show a marked relation to absolute magnitude. . . ,

There is, however, another effect which cannot be disregarded. Long ago Michelson pointed out that the random motions of the molecules in a gas at ordinary temperatures would be sufficient to cause a marked broadening of the lines. Since the motions of the atoms are distributed at random in accordance with Maxwell's law, the absorption coefficient may be represented in the following way:

$$\sigma = \text{const. N} e^{-(\lambda - \lambda_0)^2/a^2},$$

where

$$\alpha = \lambda_0 \, v_0 / C \text{ and } v_0 = \sqrt{(2kT/m)}$$

Here N is the number of atoms per cm^3; λ_0 is the normal wave length of the line; C the velocity of light and v_0 the most probable velocity of the atoms, corresponding to the temperature of the gas T and the atomic weight m.

The above expression for the absorption coefficient simply states the fact that the motions of the atoms are distributed in accordance with the laws of kinetic theory of gases. Each atom, of course, has its own absorption coefficient depending upon radiation damping, but for the moment we shall assume that "natural width" is negligible in comparison with thermal Doppler broadening.

Substituting the expression for σ in our exponential absorption formula, we have

$$I = I_0 \, e^{-\sigma l} = I_0 \, e^{-\text{CN}l e^{-(\lambda - \lambda_0)^2/a^2}}.$$

If the line is faint, we can expand this expression into a power series with rapidly diminishing terms. Retaining only the first, we get:

$$I/I_0 = 1 - \text{CN}l e^{-(\lambda - \lambda_0)^2/a^2}.$$

It is clear from this expression that the width of the line $2(\lambda - \lambda_0)$ for any given value of I/I_0 is proportional to

$$\sqrt{\log (\text{const. N})}.$$

For the case of pure radiation damping we have found that $(\lambda - \lambda_0)$ is proportional to $\sqrt{N}$. Evidently, if N is increased the Doppler type of broadening proceeds more slowly than natural widening.

In reality, both types of broadening must be considered simultaneously. This was done by Voigt and others, and was applied by Schütz to the problem of laboratory absorption lines. Unsöld, Struve, and Elvey made an application of Schütz' results to the contours of interstellar calcium lines, while Pannekoek, Minnaert and Slob, and others developed the theory to account for the behavior of stellar and solar absorption lines.

Pannekoek found from Voigt's expression of the absorption coefficient, that the contour of a very faint line is determined almost entirely by thermal Doppler effect. For stronger lines, corresponding to larger values of N, the contour gradually deepens, and the total absorption increases in direct proportion to N. After the center of the line has become deep enough, the increase of the total absorption with N becomes slower and ceases almost completely. For a certain range of N the total absorption is practically independent of N. Then, as N is increased still more, radiation damping begins to dominate. Broad wings appear which spread out in accordance with the law $\sqrt{N}$ and the total absorption also increases as $\sqrt{N}$. The center of the line, however, continues to show a nucleus which is defined by Doppler effect and which is broader than the corresponding portion of the Unsöld contour.

For atomic weight 1, T = 6000° and λ_0 = 4000 A, Pannekoek finds a Doppler core of approximately 1 A in width. Now the hydrogen lines in the sun are, according to Unsöld, broadened by Stark effect so that the Doppler core cannot be measured. For other elements, such as calcium, the atomic weight is large, the thermal motions are correspondingly small, and the Doppler core has a width of only 0.18 A.

The best chance of finding the thermal cores of spectral lines is in the hottest stars. We have seen that the core is proportional to $\sqrt{2kT/m}$. Accordingly, for a ... star in which T = 24,000°, the core is twice that found by Pannekoek for the sun. The hydrogen lines should have a core of 2 A and the He lines a core of 1 A.

Hydrogen is again unsuitable for this test. But helium is more promising. We have seen before that only some of the He I lines show a measurable amount of Stark effect. Such lines as $\lambda\lambda$ 4438, 4169, 4121, 3965, and 3868 are practically free of complications arising from electric fields, and are therefore eminently suitable for a test of thermal Doppler effect.

Observations of the spectra of B stars, made by Struve and Dunham, give no conclusive results. The lines 4438 and 3965 are probably a trace wider than similar lines of other elements, but actual measurements show only that the core is not larger than is predicted by the theory. The other helium lines are blended with faint lines of O II and of other elements and cannot be used. A dispersion slightly greater than that available at λ 3965, namely 7.8 A/mm, would doubtless be sufficient to measure the thermal broadening of the helium lines.

For the Fraunhofer lines in the sun, Minnaert and Mulders constructed a "curve of growth" in which they plotted the total absorptions of the lines against the relative numbers of atoms. The latter were inferred from the theoretical multiplet intensities. The curve shows for small N a stretch which is directly proportional to N. Then follows an almost horizontal stretch, where the total absorption is almost independent of N and remains approximately equal to 0.1 A of the continuous spectrum (or Rowland intensity 3), and this is followed by a stretch in which W is proportional to $\sqrt{N}$. The horizontal part of the curve agrees with the requirements of the theory. To be exact, it should be at W = 0.1 A for an element of m = 50 and T = 10,000°. For the sun, T = 6000°, and the horizontal part should fall slightly below W = 0.1 A.

For the hotter stars the horizontal part shifts slightly towards larger values of W, but the shift is not very sensitive to temperature. At any rate, for stars of T $\leqq$ 10000° the conclusion is justified that practically all lines stronger than W = 0.1 A would conform to the square-root law: W is proportional to $\sqrt{N}$.

TURBULENCE

With the accumulation of accurate measurements, departures from the square-root law were recorded at various observatories. At the Yerkes Observatory numerous cases of such departures were found by Struve, Elvey, Morgan, and Hynek. Shajn at Simeis and Thackeray at Cambridge announced similar results. The discussion and interpretation of the observational data presented considerable difficulty.

The theory of Schütz was carefully tested in the laboratory and found to be correct. Minnaert definitely confirmed it for the sun. Yet, there were stars which gave distinctly discordant results. Particularly striking is a comparison of 17 Leporis, ϵ Aurigae, α Persei, and Procyon. If we examine the same multiplet, say one of Fe II, in these four stars, and plot the observed intensity against the theoretical multiplet intensity, we obtain for each star an inclined line. The gradient of this line is steep for 17 Leporis, less steep for ϵ Aurigae, and still flatter for α Persei and Procyon.

Similar results were found for the gradients of the O II lines in B stars and of the Fe I lines in F stars. The phenomenon was apparently quite complicated, and a detailed investigation had to be undertaken in order to solve it.

Struve and Elvey obtained accurate measurements of many lines in a number of stars and constructed for each spectrum a "curve of growth." The results were very enlightening. In most cases the curves resembled in shape those obtained by Minnaert and Slob for different temperatures. But in 17 Leporis all points were on the first branch of the curve, where W is proportional to N. For ϵ Aurigae the flat part of the curve fell at $W = 1.0$ A, and for α Persei at $W = 0.4$ A. The resulting temperatures, namely 3×10^7 degrees for 17 Leporis, 2×10^6 degrees for ϵ Aurigae, and 3×10^5 for α Persei are, of course, impossible, being readily disproved by the theory of ionization. We were forced to conclude that, notwithstanding the agreement in the shapes of the curve with the theory by Schütz, thermal Doppler-effect cannot be responsible for the different gradients in the stellar lines.

The only satisfactory explanation that has thus far been suggested is that there are violent turbulent motions in the atmospheres of some stars, and that these motions are responsible for the upward shift of the curves of growth. The formulae remain practically the same as in the case of thermal agitation, the only difference being that turbulence does not depend on atomic weight or temperature. The most probable turbulent velocity is 67 km/sec for 17 Leporis, 20 km/sec for ϵ Aurigae, and 7 km/sec for α Persei. It is zero for the sun, Sirius, Vega, τ Scorpii, γ Pegasi, etc.

... Dunham has announced similar results for α Persei, for which he finds a turbulent velocity of 5 km/sec—about twice what would be expected from thermal Doppler effect. An important confirmation of the theory was also obtained by Berman, who derived a turbulent velocity of 10 km/sec for R Coronae Borealis. In this work Berman made use of theoretical intensities of "super-multiplets" derived by Goldberg and by Menzel at the Harvard Observatory.

An interesting test of the theory of turbulence should be possible in the study of the line-contours. These should, of course, give Doppler-contours or Doppler-cores which are easily observable . . . and the widths of the lines in turbulent stars are in . . . agreement with the theory. Moreover, the stronger metallic lines in 17 Leporis and in ε Aurigae are definitely not of the Unsöld type and, qualitatively at least, agree with the Doppler contour.

Astrophysically, the study of turbulence in stellar spectra promises to lead to many interesting developments. . . . turbulence is more pronounced in the supergiants than in the normal giants or in the dwarfs. . . .

In the derivation of turbulent velocities at the Yerkes Observatory the assumption was made that the motions in the line of sight are distributed according to the law of Maxwell. For thermal motions this assumption is necessary. For turbulent motions affecting large volumes of gas the distribution of velocities need not be Maxwellian.

The shape of the curve of growth depends upon the assumed velocity distribution. For a Maxwellian distribution the curve never becomes completely horizontal, but approaches a definite slope in its central portion. For a velocity distribution which is a constant between zero and a maximum value V, the curve is horizontal in the limiting case. Such a distribution of velocities would be observed in a gas in which equal volume-elements are all moving with the same velocity, but in random directions. In nature this type of motion is realized in the case of interstellar gases. The absorption lines produced by a gas that participates in the rotation around the massive center of the galaxy are identically the same as those produced by a gas in which the motions are all equal but the directions are distributed at random.

It is now of interest to invert the problem and to derive the law of turbulent motions in stellar atmospheres from the observed curves of growth. This involves the solution of an integral equation, but in view of the great uncertainty of existing observational material no refinements are required in the solution. . . . An admirable summary of certain phases of the problem was given by Minnaert in . . . The Observatory.[3]

Many phenomena that have been puzzling us in the past are now satisfactorily explained. The star 17 Leporis, for example, is undergoing changes in the appearance of its lines. At times the metallic lines are fairly narrow and sharp while at other times they are broad and diffuse. There is good reason to attribute the absorption lines to expanding shells—like in stars of the P Cygni type—but the puzzle is this: When the lines are narrow most of them are much more conspicuous than when they are broad. The hydrogen lines, however, are strongest when these metallic lines are broad and inconspicuous and several strong lines of iron . . . do not change a great deal in intensity, but remain quite strong even when other lines of iron, for example λ 4508, 4520, and others, are practically invisible.

The explanation of this interesting phenomenon is quite simple once we accept the turbulence hypothesis. When the lines are narrow the turbulence is relatively small and the curve of growth reaches its flattest portion at a relatively low total absorption. When the lines are broad the turbulent velocities are large and the curve of growth continues along the left hand branch where W is proportional to N, until much larger values of W have been reached. In other words, strong lines which are saturated no matter what the dispersion in velocities are strengthened in the broad-line stage of the star, while weak lines are reduced in central intensity and thereby are made inconspicuous. . . .

The advances since 1935 have been fully discussed by A. Unsöld in the second edition of Physik der Sternatmosphären[1], *and much important work is being done in this field. Since the opinions and results of different groups of astrophysicists are somewhat discordant, it may be sufficient to list here a few of the principal groups:*

1. M. Hack of Italy (in collaboration with O. Struve) is preparing for publication a book on the observational aspects of stellar spectroscopy.

2. The French group, with the two Peckers, E. Schatzman, D. Chalonge, and his collaborators, the Andrillats and others have made notable theoretical and observational contributions and some of their ideas have found their way in to the 1959 textbook Astrophysique Générale (*"General Astrophysics"*)[4], *by J. C. Pecker and E. Schatzman.*

3. An American group, centered around R. N. Thomas, R. Grant Athay, and several others, has developed interesting theoretical ideas primarily with regard to the spectrum of the sun, but also applicable to stellar spectra.

4. The most fruitful combination of observational work and theoretical insight in stellar spectroscopy is now found mainly at Mount Wilson-Palomar Observatory. This body of work consists of H. W. Babcock's work on stellar magnetic fields, J. L. Greenstein's monumental study of atomic abundances in stellar atmospheres, A. J. Deutsch's long series of articles on the spectrum variables, O. C. Wilson's study of Ca II emission lines in late-type stars, and other contributions. Other principal centers of study and research are the Dominion Astrophysical Observatory in Victoria, Canada, where A. B. Underhill is comparing the observed intensities of stellar absorption lines with those predicted by model atmospheres, and K. O. Wright is exploring the curves of growth of different types of stars; at the University of Michigan—L. H. Aller wrote his 1953 book The Atmospheres of the Sun and Stars[5], *at this university—and at the Lick Observatory, where G. Herbig, W. P. Bidelman and G. W. Preston have explored the spectra of many faint variable stars.*

Of special interest to astrophysicists is P. W. Merrill's monograph, Lines of the Chemical Elements in Astronomical Spectra.[6]

NOTES

Chapter I

1.   A. I. Slastenov, *Astronomiia v Khar'kovskom Universitete za 150 let, 1805–1955* ("Astronomy at the University of Kharkov for 150 years, 1805–1955"). Kharkov: Publ. Kharkov State University (1955).

2.   F. Reif, "The Competitive World of the Pure Scientist," *Science*, Vol. 134 (1961), p. 1957.

3.   J. L. Greenstein (private communication).

4.   A. Sandage (private communication).

5.   V. A. Ambarzumian, "Discours Introductif au Symposium sur l'evolution des étoiles" ("Introductory Talk to the Symposium on Stellar Evolution"), *Transactions of the International Astronomical Union*, Vol. 8 (1954), p. 678. Author's translation.

6.   B. V. Kukarkin, "Nekotorie Metodologicheskie Voprosi Istorii Astronomii" ("Some Methodological Questions of History of Astronomy"), in *Istoriko-Astronomicheskie Issledovania* ("Investigations of the History of Astronomy"), part 7 (1961); Moscow: State Publishing House, pp. 131–146.

7.   G. Abetti, *The History of Astronomy*, trans. Betty B. Abetti. New York: H. Schuman (1952), 345 pp.

8.   A. H. Compton, "The First of the Sciences," *Popular Astronomy*, Vol. 47 (1939), p. 352.

9.   E. B. Frost, *An Astronomer's Life*. Boston and New York: Houghton Mifflin Co. (1933), p. 276.

10.   P. P. Parenago, *Mir Zvezd* ("The World of Stars"). Moscow: Publ. House of the Academy of Sciences of the U.S.S.R. (1951), p. 109.

Chapter II

1.   S. Newcomb, Remarks at the meeting of the American Astronomical Society, *American Astronomical Society Publications*, Vol. 1 (1910), pp. 130–131.

2.   S. J. Brown, "International Astrographic Conference of July, 1900," *Popular Astronomy*, Vol. 8 (1900), p. 355.

3.   Appendix. *Monthly Notices of the Royal Astronomical Society*, hereafter *M. N.*, Vol. 60 (1900).

4. H. Poincaré, *Les Méthodes Nouvelles de la Mécanique Céleste* (New Methods of Celestial Mechanics"). Paris: Gauthier-Villars et fils (1892–1899).

5. G. Darwin, "Presidential Address," *M. N.*, Vol. 60 (1900), p. 415.

6. H. Poincaré, *Leçons sur les hypothèses cosmogoniques* ("Lectures on Cosmogonical Hypotheses"). 1st ed., Paris: Hermann et fils, 1911; 2nd ed., 1913.

7. K. Schwarzschild, "Über das zulässige Krümmungsmass des Raumes," ("On the Possible Curvature of Space"), *Vierteljahrsschrift der Astronomischen Gesellschaft* ("Quarterly of the Astronomical Society"), Vol. 35 (1900), pp. 337–338. Authors' translation.

8. *Ibid.*, pp. 344–345.

9. J. E. Keeler, "The Crossley Reflector of the Lick Observatory," *Astrophysical Journal*, hereafter *Ap. J.*, Vol. 11 (1900), p. 325.

10. W. W. Campbell, "James Edward Keeler," *Ap. J.*, Vol. 12 (1900), pp. 243–253.

11. H. C. Vogel, "Progress Made in the Last Decade in Determination of Stellar Motions in the Line of Sight," *Ap. J.*, Vol. 11 (1900), pp. 373–393.

12. F. R. Moulton, "An Attempt to Test the Nebular Hypothesis by an Appeal to the Laws of Dynamics," *Ap. J.*, Vol. 11 (1900), p. 103.

13. F. R. Moulton, "A Meteoric Theory of the Gegenschein," *Astronomical Journal* hereafter *A. J.*, Vol. 11 (1900), p. 17.

Chapter III

1. P. Fox, *Journal of the Tennessee Academy of Sciences*, Vol. 3, No. 1 (January, 1928).

2. Thomas Dick, *Practical Astronomer*. New York: Harper and Brothers (1845), 487 pp.

3. M. R. Calvert, *Journal of the Tennessee Academy of Sciences*, Vol. 3, No. 1 (January, 1928).

4. E. E. Barnard, "Development of Photography in Astronomy," *Popular Astronomy*, Vol. 6 (1898), p. 439.

5. E. E. Barnard, "Photographs of the Milky Way and of Comets Made with the Six-inch Willard Lens and Crocker Telescope during the Years 1892 to 1895 by E. E. Barnard," *Lick Observatory Publications*, Vol. 11 (1913).

6. E. E. Barnard, *A Photographic Atlas of Selected Regions of the Milky Way by Edward Emerson Barnard*, ed. Edwin B. Frost and Mary R. Calvert. Washington, D.C.: Carnegie Institution of Washington (1927).

7. A. Clerke, *A Popular History of Astronomy during the Nineteenth Century*. Edinburgh: Adam & Charles Black; New York: The Macmillan Company (1885), 502 pp. *The System of the Stars*. London: Longmans, Green and Co. (1890); *Problems of Astrophysics*. London: Adam and Charles Black (1903).

8. A. Clerke, *Problems of Astrophysics*. London: Adam and Charles Black (1903), p. 541.

9. E. E. Barnard, "On the Dark Markings of the Sky," *Ap. J.*, Vol. 49 (1919), p. 12.

10. D. S. Khavtasi. *Atlas Galakticheskikh Temnikh Tumanostei* ("Atlas of Galactic Dark Nebulae"), Abastumani Astrophysical Observatory—Academy of Science, Georgian S.S.R. (1960).

11. W. Becker, *Materie im Interstellaren Raume* ("Matter in Interstellar Space"). Leipzig: J. A. Barth (1938), 78 pp.

Chapter IV

1. W. W. Campbell, *Stellar Motions*. New Haven: Yale University Press (1913), 315 pp.

2. W. Huggins, "Celestial Spectroscopy," *Essays in Astronomy by Great Astronomers*, ed. R. Johnson. New York: D. Appleton & Co. (1900), p. 426.

3. R. E. Wilson, *General Catalogue of Stellar Radial Velocities*. Washington, D.C.: Carnegie Institution of Washington (1953).

Chapter V

1. S. I. Bailey, *History of the Harvard Observatory*, Harvard Observatory Monograph No. 4. New York: McGraw-Hill Book Company, Inc. (1931), p. 130.

2. E. C. Pickering, A. Searle, and O. C. Wendell, "Observations with the Meridian Photometer during the Years 1879–1882," *Annals of the Astronomical Observatory of Harvard College*, hereafter *Harvard Annals*, Vol. 14 (Part I—1884; Part II—1885). Also referred to as "Harvard Photometry."

3. G. Müller and P. Kempf, *Photometrische Durchmusterung des Nördlichen Himmels, enthaltend die Grössen und Farben aller Sterne der B.D. bis zur Grösse 7.5* ("Photometric Catalogue of the Northern Sky, Containing the Magnitudes and Colors of all Stars of the B.D. to Magnitude 7.5"). Potsdam: Potsdam Publications, Vols. 9, 13, 14, 16, and 17 (1894–1907).

4. E. C. Pickering, "Revised Harvard Photometry," *Harvard Annals*, Vol. 50 (1908).

5. J. Stebbins, "Early Photometry at Illinois," *Publications of the Astronomical Society of the Pacific*, hereafter *Pub. A. S. P.*, Vol. 69 (1957), p. 506.

6. *Ibid.*, pp. 507–508.

7. *Ibid.*, p. 508.

8. J. Stebbins, "The Washburn Observatory, 1878–1958," *Pub. A. S. P.*, Vol. 70 (1958), pp. 441–442.

9. J. Stebbins, "Early Photometry at Illinois," *op. cit.*, p. 509.

10. I. S. Bowen, "Problems in Future Telescope Design," *Pub. A. S. P.*, Vol. 73 (1961), p. 114.

11. A. C. B. Lovell, *The Individual and the Universe*. New York: Harper and Brothers (1958), p. 3.

Chapter VI

1. K. G. Jansky, "Directional Studies of Atmospherics at High Frequencies," *Proceedings of the Institute of Radio Engineers*, hereafter *Proc. Inst. Radio Engrs.*, Vol. 20 (1932), p. 1920.

2. K. G. Jansky, "Electrical Disturbance of Extraterrestrial Origin," *Proc. Inst. Radio Engrs.*, Vol. 21 (1933), p. 1388.

3. *Ibid.*, p. 1398.

4. K. G. Jansky, "Directional Studies of Atmospherics at High Frequencies," *Proc. Inst. Radio Engrs.*, Vol. 20 (1932), pp. 1920–1932; "Electrical Disturbances of Extraterrestrial Origin," *Proc. Inst. Radio Engrs.*, Vol. 21 (1933), pp. 1387–1398.

5. K. G. Jansky, "Electrical Phenomena that Apparently Are of Interstellar Origin," *Popular Astronomy*, Vol. 41 (1933), pp. 549-555.

6. G. Reber, "Cosmic Static," *Proc. Inst. Radio Engrs.*, Vol. 28 (1940), pp. 68–71; "Cosmic Static," *Proc. Inst. Radio Engrs.*, Vol. 30 (1942), pp. 367–378.

7. G. Reber, "Cosmic Static," *Ap. J.*, Vol. 91 (1940), pp. 621–624.

8. G. Reber, "Cosmic Static," *Ap. J.*, Vol. 100 (1944), pp. 279–287.

9. G. C. Southworth, "Microwave Radiation from the Sun," *Journal of the Franklin Institute*, Vol. 239 (1945), p. 285.

10. G. Reber, *op. cit.*, p. 284.

11. J. S. Hey, "Solar Radiation in the 4–6 Meter Radio Wave-length Band," *Nature*, Vol. 157 (1946), p. 47.

12.   F. T. Haddock, "Introduction to Radio Astronomy," *Proc. Inst. Radio Engrs.*, Vol. 46 (1958), p. 5. This issue was devoted entirely to radio astronomy.

13.   J. S. Hey, "The First Discovery of Point Sources," *Paris Symposium on Radio Astronomy*, ed. R. N. Bracewell. Stanford, Calif.: Stanford University Press (1959), p. 295.

14.   J. S. Hey, S. J. Parsons, and J. W. Phillips, "Fluctuations in Cosmic Radiation at Radio Frequencies," *Nature*, Vol. 158 (1946), p. 234.

15.   H. C. van de Hulst, "Studies of the 21-cm Line and Their Interpretation," *Radio Astronomy*, International Astronomical Union Symposium No. 4. New York: Cambridge University Press (1957), p. 3.

16.   H. C. van de Hulst, "Origin of the Radio Waves," *Source Book in Astronomy, 1900–1950*, ed. H. Shapley. Cambridge, Mass.: Harvard University Press (1960), p. 292. Translation from original paper in *Ned. Tijd. v. Natuurkunde*, Vol. 2 (1945), p. 201.

17.   H. I. Ewen, "Radio Waves from Interstellar Space," *The New Astronomy*, ed. *Scientific American*. New York: Simon & Schuster, Inc. (1955), p. 235.

18.   J. G. Bolton, "Radio Telescopes," in *Telescopes*, Vol. I of "Stars and Stellar Systems," eds. G. P. Kuiper and B. Middlehurst. Chicago: University of Chicago Press (1960), pp. 182–183.

19.   *Ibid.*, p. 192.

20.   B. Lockspeiser, Introductory remarks to "Radio Astronomy," lecture by A. C. B. Lovell, *Journal of the Royal Society of Arts*, Vol. 103 (1955), p. 666.

21.   J. D. Kraus, "Radio Telescope Antennas of Large Aperture," *Proc. Inst. Radio Engrs.*, Vol. 46 (1958), p. 92.

22.   *Ibid.*, p. 96.

23.   S. von Hoerner, "The Search for Signals from Other Civilizations," *Science*, Vol. 134 (1961), pp. 1839–1843.

Chapter VII

1.   H. H. Turner, "Presidential Address," *M. N.*, Vol. 64 (1904), p. 388.

2.   H. Deslandres, "Recherches sur l'atmosphère solaire et appareils enregistreurs des couches de vapeurs superposées qui la composent," translated by Michael Reck, *Bulletin Astronomique*, Vol. 22 (1905), pp. 332–333.

3.   G. E. Hale, "Reply to Recent Statements by M. Deslandres," *Ap. J.*, Vol. 23 (1906), pp. 92–93.

4.   F. W. Dyson, "Presidential Address," *M. N.*, Vol. 73 (1913), pp. 317–318.

5.   G. E. Hale, "Autobiographical Notes," unpublished, p. 3. Courtesy Miss H. Wright.

6.   *Ibid.*

7.   *Ibid.*

8.   G. E. Hale, *The Study of Stellar Evolution*. Chicago: The University of Chicago Press (1908), pp. 3–4.

9.   G. E. Hale and S. B. Nicholson, *Magnetic Observations of Sunspots at Mt. Wilson, 1917–1924, Part I*, Carnegie Institution of Washington Publication No. 498. Washington, D.C.: Carnegie Institution of Washington (1938), p. 1.

10.   G. E. Hale, "Solar Vortices," *Mount Wilson Solar Observatory Contributions*, No. 26 (1908), pp. 15–16.

11.   D. H. Menzel, *Our Sun*. Philadelphia: Blakiston Co. (1949), 326 pp.; rev. ed., Cambridge, Mass.: Harvard University Press (1959), 350 pp.

12.   G. E. Hale, "A 100-inch Mirror for the Solar Observatory," *Mount Wilson Solar Observatory Contributions*, No. 13 (1906), p. 5.

13.   G. E. Hale, *The New Heavens*. New York: Charles Scribner's Sons (1922), p. 26.

14.   G. E. Hale, *Signals from Stars*. New York: Charles Scribner's Sons (1931), p. 56.

15.   G. E. Hale, Letter to Dr. Wickliffe Rose, President, International Education Board (April 16, 1928). Courtesy Miss H. Wright.

Chapter VIII

1.   A. L. Lowell, *Biography of Percival Lowell*. New York: The Macmillan Company (1935), p. 5.
2.   *Ibid.*, p. 60.
3.   P. Lowell, *Mars*. Boston: Houghton Mifflin Company (1895), Preface.
4.   *Ibid.*
5.   P. Lowell, *Annals of the Lowell Observatory*, Vol. 1 (1897).
6.   P. Lowell, *Mars*, p. 228.
7.   P. Lowell, *Mars and Its Canals*. New York: The Macmillan Company (1906), 393 pp.
8.   P. Lowell, *Mars as the Abode of Life*. New York: The Macmillan Company (1908), 288 pp.
9.   P. Lowell, *Mars*, p. 75.
10.   *Ibid.*, p. 122.
11.   *Ibid.*, pp. 131–132.
12.   *Ibid.*, p. 173.
13.   *Ibid.*, p. 137.
14.   *Ibid.*, p. 177.
15.   *Ibid.*, p. 201.
16.   *Ibid.*, p. 208.
17.   H. Spencer Jones, *Life on Other Worlds*. New York: The Macmillan Company (1940), p. 222.
18.   *Ibid.*, p. 225.
19.   R. L. Waterfield, *A Hundred Years of Astronomy*. New York: The Macmillan Company (1940), p. 50.
20.   A. L. Lowell, *op. cit.*, p. 192.
21.   *Ibid.*
22.   C. Tombaugh, "The Search for the Ninth Planet, Pluto," *Astronomical Society of the Pacific Leaflet*, hereafter *A. S. P. Leaflet*, No. 209 (1946), p. 7.
23.   H. N. Russell, *Scientific American* (December, 1930), quoted by A. L. Lowell, *op. cit.*, p. 197.
24.   H. N. Russell, as quoted by A. L. Lowell, *op. cit.*, Appendix
25.   C. W. Allen, *Astrophysical Quantities*. University of London: The Athlone Press (1955), pp. 155–159; O. Struve, B. Lynds, and H. Pillans, *Elementary Astronomy*. New York: Oxford University Press (1959), p. 116.
26.   H. C. Urey, "The Atmospheres of the Planets," *Encyclopedia of Physics*, ed. S. Flügge. Berlin: Springer-Verlag, Vol. 52 (1959), p. 413.
27.   A. Dollfus, "Polarization Studies of Planets," *The Solar System*, eds. G. P. Kuiper and B. Middlehurst. Chicago: University of Chicago Press (1961), Vol. 3, p. 350.
28.   C. H. Mayer, "Radio Emission of the Moon and Planets," *Ibid.*, p. 442.
29.   W. C. de Marcus, "Planetary Interiors," *Encyclopedia of Physics*, ed. S. Flügge. Berlin: Springer-Verlag, Vol. 52 (1959), p. 440.
30.   R. Wildt, "The Constitution of the Planets," *M. N.*, Vol. 107 (1947), p. 86.
31.   *Ibid.*, p. 92.
32.   *Ibid.*, p. 96.
33.   N. T. Bobrovnikov, "Comets," *Astrophysics*, ed. J. A. Hynek. New York: McGraw-Hill Book Company, Inc. (1951), pp. 303–304.
34.   K. Schwarzschild and E. Kron, "On the Distribution of Brightness in the Tail of Halley's Comet," *Ap. J.*, Vol. 34 (1911), p. 348.
35.   A. McKellar, "Rotational Distribution of CH Molecules in the Nucleus of Comet Cunningham (1940c)," *Ap. J.*, Vol. 98 (1943), p. 1.

36.   P. Swings, "Complex Structure of Cometary Bands Tentatively Ascribed to Contour of the Solar Spectrum," *Lick Observatory Bulletin*, Vol. 19 (1941), p. 136.

Chapter IX

1.   F. R. Moulton, "Evolution of the Solar System," *Ap. J.*, Vol. 22, (1905), p. 166.
2.   J. H. Jeans, *The Universe Around Us*. 4th ed. New York: Cambridge University Press (1944), p. 233.
3.   H. N. Russell, *The Solar System and Its Origin*. New York: The Macmillan Company (1935), pp. 95–96.
4.   H. Spencer Jones, *Life on Other Worlds*. New York: The Macmillan Company (1940), 269.
5.   *Ibid.*
6.   C. F. von Weizsäcker, "Über die Entstehung des Planetensystems" ("Regarding the Origin of the Planetary System"), *Zeitschrift für Astrophysik* ("Journal for Astrophysics"), Vol. 22 (1943), p. 319. Author's translation.
7.   G. Gamov and J. A. Hynek, "A New Theory by C. F. von Weizsäcker of the Origin of the Planetary System," *Ap. J.*, Vol. 101 (1945), p. 254.
8.   G. P. Kuiper, "On the Origin of the Solar System," *Astrophysics*, ed. J. A. Hynek. New York: McGraw-Hill Book Company, Inc. (1951), p. 365.
9.   *Ibid.*, p. 363.
10.   *Ibid.*, p. 364.

Chapter X

1.   A. Wolf, "Classification," *Encyclopedia Britannica*. Chicago: Encyclopedia Britannica, Inc. (1954), Vol. 5, p. 778.
2.   A. Secchi, *Report Brit. Ass.* (1868), p. 166.
3.   A. Clerke, *Problems of Astrophysics*. London: Adam and Charles Black (1903), pp. 179–180.
4.   E. W. Maunder, "Stars of the First and Second Types of Spectrum," *Astronomy and Astrophysics*, Vol. 11 (1892), p. 150.
5.   A. Clerke, *op. cit.*, p. 180.
6.   W. S. Adams, "The Past 20 Years of Physical Astronomy," *Pub. A. S. P.*, Vol. 40 (1928), p. 213.
7.   G. E. Hale, *The Study of Stellar Evolution*. Chicago: University of Chicago Press (1908), p. 200.
8.   *Ibid.*, pp. 207–208.
9.   R. L. Waterfield, *A Hundred Years of Astronomy*. New York: The Macmillan Company (1938), p. 65.
10.   "The Draper Catalogue of Stellar Spectra," *Harvard Annals*, Vol. 27 (1890).
11.   A. J. Cannon and E. C. Pickering, "The Henry Draper Catalogue," *Harvard Annals*, Vols. 91–99 (1918–1924).
12.   H. N. Russell, C. H. Payne-Gaposchkin, and D. H. Menzel, "The Classification of Stellar Spectra," *Ap. J.*, Vol. 81 (1935), p. 108.
13.   R. H. Curtiss, "Classification and Description of Stellar Spectra," *Handbuch der Astrophysik* ("Encyclopedia of Astrophysics"). Berlin: Julius Springer Verlag (1932), Vol. V/1, p. 25.
14.   A. C. Maury, "Spectra of Bright Stars," *Harvard Annals*, Vol. 28 (1897), Part I, p. 5.
15.   *Ibid.*
16.   H. N. Russell, "Determinations of Stellar Parallax," *A. J.*, Vol. 26 (1910), pp. 153–154.
17.   H. N. Russell, "Some Hints on the Order of Stellar Evolution," *Science*, Vol. 32 (1910), p. 883.

18. H. N. Russell, "'Giant' and 'dwarf' stars," *Observatory*, Vol. 36 (1913), p. 325.

19. H. N. Russell, "The Spectra and Other Characteristics of the Stars," *Popular Astronomy*, Vol. 22 (1914), p. 342.

20. E. Hertzsprung, "Über die Verwendung photographischer effektiver Wellenlängen zur Bestimmung von Farbenequivalenten" ("Regarding the Use of Photographic Effective Wavelengths in the Determination of Color Equivalents"), *Publikationen des Astrophysikalischen Observatoriums zu Potsdam* ("Publications of the Potsdam Astrophysical Observatory"), Vol. 22 (1911), pp. 6–7. Author's translation.

21. W. S. Adams, and A. Kohlschütter, "Some Spectral Criteria for the Determination of Absolute Stellar Magnitudes," *Ap. J.*, Vol. 40 (1914), p. 385.

22. *Ibid.*, p. 394.

23. *Ibid.*

24. *Ibid.*

25. W. W. Morgan, P. C. Keenan, and E. Kellman, *An Atlas of Stellar Spectra with an Outline of Spectral Classification*. Chicago: University of Chicago Press (1943).

26. *Ibid.*

27. A. Secchi, *Ibid.*

28. H. N. Russell, C. H. Payne-Gaposchkin, and D. H. Menzel, *op. cit.*, p. 109.

Chapter XI

1. C. A. Young, *The Sun*. New York: D. Appleton & Co. (1895), pp. 325–327.

2. *Ibid.*, pp. 333–334.

3. A. Fowler, "Solar and Stellar Photospheres," *Observatory*, Vol. 36 (1913), p. 183.

4. *Ibid.*, p. 185.

5. *Ibid.*

6. H. N. Russell and J. Q. Stewart, "Pressures at the Sun's Surface," *Ap. J.*, Vol. 59 (1924), p. 208.

7. A. S. Eddington, "The Formation of Absorption Lines," *M. N.*, Vol. 89 (1929), pp. 620–636.

8. R. O. Redman, "Centre to Limb Variation in Fraunhofer Line Intensity Over the Disc of the Primary Star of U Cephei and of U Sagittae," *M. N.*, Vol. 96 (1936), p. 489.

9. M. N. Saha, "Elements in the Sun," *Philosophical Magazine and Journal of Science*, hereafter *Phil. Mag.*, Vol. 40 (1920), p. 811.

10. *Ibid.*

11. M. N. Saha, "Ionization in the Solar Chromosphere," *Phil. Mag.*, Vol. 40 (1920), p. 479.

12. M. N. Saha, "On the Physical Theory of Stellar Spectra," *Proceedings of the Royal Society* (London), Series A, Vol. 99 (1921), p. 150.

13. *Ibid.*, p. 152.

14. O. Struve, B. Lynds, and H. Pillans, *Elementary Astronomy*. New York: Oxford University Press (1959), pp. 258 and 260.

15. H. N. Russell, "Ionization and the Sun-Spot Spectrum," *Ap. J.*, Vol. 55 (1922), p. 143.

16. C. H. Payne, *Stellar Atmospheres*. Cambridge, Mass.: Harvard University Press (1925).

17. C. H. Payne, *The Stars of High Luminosity*. New York: McGraw-Hill Book Company, Inc. (1930).

18. H. N. Russell, R. S. Dugan, and J. Q. Stewart, *Astronomy*. Boston: Ginn and Company (1927), p. 837.

19. *Ibid.*, p. 838.

20. I. S. Bowen, "The Origin of the Chief Nebular Lines," *Pub. A. S. P.*, Vol. 39 (1927), p. 295.

21.   B. Edlén, "An Attempt to Identify the Emission Lines in the Spectrum of the Solar Corona," *Arkiv för Matematik, Astronomi och Fysik* ("Journal for Mathematics, Astronomy, and Physics"), Vol. 28B (1942), p. 2.

22.   W. S. Adams and A. H. Joy, "The Orbits of Three Spectroscopic Binaries," *Ap. J.*, Vol. 49 (1919), p. 190.

23.   G. A. Shajn and O. Struve, "On the Rotation of the Stars," *M. N.*, Vol 89 (1929), p. 235.

24.   O. Struve, "A Study of Spectroscopic Binaries of Short Period," *The University of Chicago Abstracts of Theses*, Science Series, Vol. 2 (1923), p. 60.

25.   C. W. Allen, *Astrophysical Quantities*. University of London: The Athlone Press (1955), p. 186.

26.   H. N. Russell, "On the Composition of the Sun's Atmosphere," *Ap. J.*, Vol. 70 (1929), p. 11.

27.   H. N. Russell, "Molecules in the Sun and Stars," *Ap. J.*, Vol. 79 (1934), p. 317.

28.   H. N. Russell, R. S. Dugan, and J. Q. Stewart, *op. cit.*, revised edition, Vol. 2 (1938), p. 865.

29.   P. W. Merrill, "Technetium in the Stars," *Science*, Vol. 115 (1952), p. 484.

Chapter XII

1.   R. Emden, *Gaskugeln* ("Gaseous Spheres"). Leipzig: B. G. Teubner (1907).

2.   A. S. Eddington, *The Internal Constitution of the Stars*. London: Cambridge University Press; New York: The Macmillan Company (1926), p. 1.

3.   *Ibid.*, p. 9.

4.   *Ibid.*, pp. 19–20.

5.   A. S. Eddington, *Stars and Atoms*. New Haven: Yale University Press (1927), p. 26.

6.   A. S. Eddington, "On the Relation between the Masses and Luminosities of the Stars," *M. N.*, Vol. 84 (1924), p. 332.

7.   A. S. Eddington, *Stars and Atoms*. New Haven: Yale University Press (1927), p. 50.

8.   H. N. Russell, "Notes on White Dwarfs and Small Companions," *A. J.*, Vol. 51 (1944), p. 13.

9.   W. S. Adams, "The Relativity Displacement of the Spectral Lines in the Companion of Sirius," *Proceedings of the National Academy of Sciences*, Vol. 11 (1925), p. 387.

10.   H. N. Russell, "The Problem of Stellar Evolution," *Nature*, Vol. 116 (1925), p. 209.

11.   H. N. Russell, R. S. Dugan, and J. Q. Stewart, *Astronomy*. Boston: Ginn and Company (1927), pp. 909–910.

12.   *Ibid.*, p. 910.

13.   *Ibid.*, p. 911.

14.   *Ibid.*, p. 912.

15.   *Ibid.*, p. 915.

16.   *Ibid.*

17.   *Ibid.*, p. 917.

18.   *Ibid.*, p. 923.

19.   *Ibid.*, p. 908.

20.   A. S. Eddington, *Stars and Atoms*. New Haven: Yale University Press (1927), pp. 99–103.

21.   *Ibid.*, p. 111.

Chapter XIII

1.   R. J. Trumpler, "Spectral Types in Open Clusters," *Pub. A. S. P.*, Vol. 37 (1925), pp. 313–314.

2.   *Ibid.*, p. 317.

3.   G. P. Kuiper, "On the Hydrogen Content of Clusters," *Ap. J.*, Vol. 86 (1937), pp. 176–197.

4.   *Ibid.*, pp. 176–177.

5.   H. Shapley, *Star Clusters.* New York: McGraw-Hill Book Company, Inc., (1930).

6.   H. Shapley, "A Half Century of Globular Clusters," *Popular Astronomy*, Vol. 57 (1949), pp. 214–215.

7.   J. H. Oort, "Dynamics and Evolution of the Galaxy," *Stellar Populations*, ed. D. J. K. O'Connell. New York: Interscience Publishers (1957), p. 419.

Chapter XIV

1.   O. J. Eggen, "Sherburne Wesley Burnham and his Double Star Catalogue," *A. S. P. Leaflet*, No. 295 (1953), p. 3.

2.   S. W. Burnham, *A General Catalogue of Double Stars within 121° of the North Pole.* 2 vols. Washington, D.C.: Carnegie Institution of Washington (1906).

3.   R. G. Aitken, *New General Catalogue of Double Stars within 120° of the North Pole.* 2 vols. Washington, D.C.: Carnegie Institution of Washington (1932).

4.   R. T. A. Innes, with collaboration of B. H. Dawson and W. H. van den Bos, *Southern Double Star Catalogue, −19° to −90°.* Johannesburg, So. Africa: Union Observatory (1927); mimeographed, limited circulation.

5.   F. W. A. Argelander, "Bonner Sternverzeichnis," referred to usually as "Bonner Durchmusterung" ("Bonn Star List"), *Bonn Astronomische Beobachtungen* ("Bonn Astronomical Observations"), Vols. 3, 4, and 5 (1859–1862). Extension by E. Schönfeld, Vol. 8 (1886).

6.   J. E. Merrill, *Tables for Solution of Light Curves of Eclipsing Binaries.* Contributions of Princeton University Observatory, No. 23 (1950).

7.   Z. Kopal, *Close Binary Stars.* New York: John Wiley & Sons, Inc. (1959).

8.   J. Stebbins, "Selenium Photometry of Stars," *Ap. J.*, Vol. 32 (1910), p. 213.

9.   J. H. Moore and F. J. Neubauer, *Fifth Catalogue of the Orbital Elements of Spectroscopic Binary Stars.* Lick Observatory Bulletin No. 521 (1948).

10.   R. E. Wilson, *General Catalogue of Stellar Radial Velocities.* Washington, D.C.: Carnegie Institution of Washington (1953).

11.   R. M. Petrie, "Probable Errors of Stellar Radial Velocities and the Frequency of Variable Velocities," *Annales d'Astrophysique* ("Annals of Astrophysics"), Vol. 23 (1960), p. 748.

12.   N. C. Dunér, "Calculation of Elliptical Elements of the System of Y Cygni," *Ap. J.*, Vol. 11 (1900), p. 190.

13.   G. Herbig, "Observations and an Interpretation of VV Puppis," *Ap. J.*, Vol. 132 (1960), p. 86.

14.   A. Clerke, *The System of the Stars.* London: Adam and Charles Black, 2nd ed., (1905), p. 105.

15.   *Ibid*

16.   G. P. Kuiper, O. Struve, and B. Strömgren, "The Interpretation of ϵ Aurigae," *Ap. J.*, Vol. 86 (1937), pp. 570–612.

Chapter XV

1.   A. Clerke, *Problems in Astrophysics.* London: Adam and Charles Black (1903), p. 319.

2.   S. Rosseland, *The Pulsation Theory of Variable Stars.* Oxford: Clarendon Press (1949), p. 4.

3.   H. Shapley, "On the Nature and Cause of Cepheid Variation," *Ap. J.*, Vol. 40 (1914), p. 459.

4.   *Ibid.*, p. 460.

5.   O. Struve, B. Lynds, and H. Pillans, *Elementary Astronomy*. New York: Oxford University Press (1959), Table 30.1.

6.   E. C. Pickering (presenting a report prepared by H. S. Leavitt). "Periods of 25 Variable Stars in the Small Magellanic Cloud, Harvard College Observatory Circular" No. 173 (1912), p. 3.

7.   *Ibid.*, p. 1.

8.   R. E. Wilson, "The Zero Point of the Period-Luminosity Curve," *Ap. J.*, Vol. 89 (1939), p. 218.

9.   "Report of Meeting—Commission des Nebuleuses Extragalactiques" ("Commission on Extragalactic Nebulae"), *Transactions of the International Astronomical Union*, Vol. 8 (1954), p. 398.

10.   *Ibid.*, p. 397.

Chapter XVI

1.   S. Gaposchkin, "The Elusive Maximum of S Andromedae," *Sky and Telescope*, Vol. 21 (1961), p. 327.

2.   E. B. Frost, *An Astronomer's Life*. Boston: Houghton Mifflin Company (1933), p. 45.

3.   *Ibid.*

4.   H. Shapley and H. D. Curtis, "The Scale of the Universe," *Bulletin of the National Research Council*, Vol. 2 (1921), p. 215.

5.   C. H. Payne-Gaposchkin, *Galactic Novae*. New York: Interscience Publishers (1957), p. 267.

6.   *Ibid.*

7.   N. U. Mayall and J. H. Oort, "Further Data Bearing on the Identification of the Crab Nebula with the Supernova of 1054 A.D." *Pub. A. S. P.*, Vol. 54 (1942), p. 96.

8.   R. Minkowski, "Optical Observations of Nonthermal Galactic Radio Sources," *Paris Symposium on Radio Astronomy*, ed. R. N. Bracewell. Stanford, Calif.: Stanford University Press (1959), pp. 319–320.

9.   I. S. Shklovsky, *Cosmic Radio Waves*, translated from 1956 Russian edition by R. B. Rodman and C. M. Varsavsky. Cambridge, Mass.: Harvard University Press (1960).

10.   I. S. Shklovsky, "O vozmozhnom vekovom izmenenii potoka i intensivnosti radio-izluchenia ot nekotorykh diskretnykh istochnikov" ("Possible Secular Variations of the Flux and Intensity of Radio Emission from Discrete Sources"), *Astronomicheskii Zhurnal* ("Astronomical Journal"), Vol. 37 (1960), p. 258.

11.   Burbidge, G. R., "Galactic Explosions as Sources of Radio Emission," *Nature*, Vol. 190 (1961), pp. 1053–1056.

12.   F. J. M. Stratton and W. H. Manning, *Atlas of Spectra of Nova Herculis 1934*. London: Cambridge University Press (1939).

Chapter XVII

1.   P. Lebedeff, "On the Apparent Dispersion of Light in Space," *Ap. J.*, Vol. 29 (1909), p. 102.

2.   H. Shapley, *Note on the Velocity of Light*, Harvard College Observatory Bulletin, No. 763 (1922), p. 1.

3.   W. de Sitter, "Investigation of the Systematic Difference between the Photographic and Visual Magnitudes of the Stars," *Publications of the Astronomical Laboratory at Groningen*, Vol. 12 (1904), p. 119.

4.   H. H. Turner, "On the Diminution of Light in Its Passage through Interstellar Space," *M. N.*, Vol. 69 (1908), p. 61.

5.   A. C. Maury, "Spectra of Bright Stars," *Harvard Annals*, Vol. 28 (1897), Part I.

6. J. C. Kapteyn, "On the Absorption of Light in Space," *Ap. J.*, Vol. 29 (1909), p. 52.

7. W. S. Adams and A. Kohlschütter, "Some Spectral Criteria for the Determination of Absolute Stellar Magnitudes," *Ap. J.*, Vol. 40 (1914), p. 387.

8. J. C. Kapteyn, "Remarks on the Determination of the Number and Mean Parallax of Stars of Different Magnitude and the Absorption of Light in Space," *A. J.*, Vol. 24 (1904), p. 121.

9. R. J. Trumpler, *Preliminary Results on the Distances, Dimensions, and Space Distribution of Open Star Clusters*, Lick Observatory Bulletin, No. 420 (1930).

10. *Ibid.*, p. 163.

11. *Ibid.*, p. 165.

12. *Ibid.*, p. 167.

13. F. H. Seares, "The Dust of Space," *Pub. A. S. P.*, Vol. 52 (1940), p. 114.

14. W. A. Hiltner, "Report on Grant," *American Philosophical Society Yearbook, 1947*, p. 120.

15. W. A. Hiltner, "Polarization of Light from Distant Stars by the Interstellar Medium," *Science*, Vol. 109 (1949), p. 165.

16. W. A. Hiltner, "Interstellar Polarization," *Vistas in Astronomy*, ed. A. Beer. London and New York: Pergamon Press, Vol. 2 (1956), pp. 1084–1086.

17. J. Hartmann, "Investigations on the Spectrum and Orbit of δ Orionis," *Ap. J.*, Vol. 19 (1904), p. 274.

18. O. Struve, "On the Calcium Clouds," *Popular Astronomy*, Vol. 34 (1926), p. 10.

19. A. S. Eddington, "Diffuse Matter in Interstellar Space," *Proceedings of the Royal Society* (London), Series A, Vol. 111 (1926), p. 445.

20. W. S. Adams, "Observations of Interstellar H and K, Molecular Lines, and Radial Velocities in the Spectra of 300 O and B Stars," *Ap. J.*, Vol. 109 (1949), p. 354.

21. G. Münch and H. Zirin, "Interstellar Matter at Large Distances from the Galactic Plane," *Ap. J.*, Vol. 133 (1961), p. 13.

Chapter XVIII

1. V. M. Slipher, "On the Spectrum of the Nebula in the Pleiades," *Popular Astronomy*, Vol. 21 (1913), p. 187.

2. E. P. Hubble, "A General Study of Diffuse Galactic Nebulae," *Ap. J.*, Vol. 56 (1922), p. 162.

3. *Ibid.*, p. 189.

4. H. Zanstra, "The Gaseous Nebula as a Quantum Counter," *The Quarterly Journal of the Royal Astronomical Society*, Vol. 2 (1961), p. 137.

5. *Ibid.*, p. 148.

6. O. Struve and C. T. Elvey, "Emission Nebulosities in Cygnus and Cepheus," *Ap. J.*, Vol. 88 (1938), p. 368.

7. B. A. Vorontsov-Velyaminov. "Course of Practical Astrophysics," Moscow-Leningrad: State Publishing House (1940), 648 pp.

8. D. S. Khavtasi, *Atlas of Dark Nebulosities*. (See ref. 10, Chap. 3)

9. B. Lynds, "Catalogue of Dark Nebulae," *Ap. J. Supplement*, Vol. 7, pp. 1–52.

10. L. Spitzer, Jr., "Behavior of Matter in Space," *Ap. J.*, Vol. 120 (1954), p. 13.

11. S. Pottasch, "A Study of Bright Rims of Emission Nebulae," *Bulletin of the Astronomical Institute of the Netherlands*, Vol. 13 (1956), p. 77.

12. G. Herbig, "T Tauri and Hind's Nebula," *A. S. P. Leaflet*, No. 293 (1953), p. 7.

13. *Ibid.*, p. 8

14. J. G. Hagen, "Rasségna delle nebulose oscure, Parte I" ("A List of the Dark Nebulae, Part I"), *Specola Astronomica Vaticana 14* ("Publications of the Vatican Observatory, Vol. 14"), (1931).

15. F. Becker and J. Meurers, "The Problem of Hagen's Clouds," *Vistas in As-*

tronomy, ed. A. Beer. London and New York: Pergamon Press (1956), Vol. 2, p. 1069.

16.   H. Shapley, *Note on Obscuring Cosmic Clouds in High Galactic Latitudes*, Harvard College Observatory Circular, No. 281 (1925), pp. 3–4.

17.   C. T. Elvey and P. Rudnick, "Note on the Sky Brightness of Two Regions of Hagen's Cosmic Clouds," *Ap. J.*, Vol. 78 (1933), p. 158.

18.   K. Haidrich, "Bemerkungen zu den Kritiken meiner astrophotographischen Arbeiten" ("Notes on the Criticisms of My Astrophotographic Works"), *Astronomische Nachrichten* ("Astronomical News"), Vol. 260 (1936), pp. 281–286.

19.   F. Becker and J. Meurers, *op. cit.*, p. 1073.

20.   *Ibid.*, p. 1072.

21.   *Ibid.*, pp. 1072–1073.

22.   W. Becker, *Sterne und Sternsysteme* ("Stars and Stellar Systems"). 2nd rev. ed. Dresden: T. Steinkopff (1950).

23.   S. Gaposchkin, "The Visual Milky Way," *Vistas in Astronomy*, ed. A. Beer. London and New York: Pergamon Press, Vol. 3 (1960), p. 290.

Chapter XIX

1.   C. H. Payne-Gaposchkin, *Introduction to Astronomy*. New York: Prentice-Hall, Inc. (1954), p. 436.

2.   H. Shapley and H. D. Curtis, "The Scale of the Universe," *Bulletin of the National Research Council*, Vol. 2 (1921), p. 182.

3.   *Ibid.*, p. 180.

4.   *Ibid.*, p. 206.

5.   *Ibid.*, p. 210.

6.   B. Lindblad, "Star Streaming and the Structure of the Stellar System," *Arkiv för Matematik, Astronomi och Fysik* ("Journal for Mathematics, Astronomy and Physics"), Vol. 19A, No. 21 (1925), pp. 1–2.

7.   J. H. Oort, "Observational Evidence Confirming Lindblad's Hypothesis of a Rotation of the Galactic System," *Bulletin of the Astronomical Institutes of the Netherlands*, Vol. 3 (1927), p. 276.

8.   R. L. Waterfield, *A Hundred Years of Astronomy*. New York: The Macmillan Company (1938), pp. 319–321.

9.   C. Easton, "A New Theory of the Milky Way," *Ap. J.*, Vol. 12 (1900), p. 157.

10.   *Ibid.*

11.   H. Shapley, *Star Clusters*. Harvard Observatory Monograph No. 2. New York: McGraw-Hill Book Company, Inc. (1930), p. 194.

12.   *Ibid.*, pp. 209–210.

13.   B. Bok, *The Distribution of the Stars in Space*. Chicago: University of Chicago Press (1937), p. 123.

Chapter XX

1.   A. Clerke, *The System of the Stars*. London: Longmans, Green & Company (1890), p. 368.

2.   V. M. Slipher, "On the Spectrum of the Nebula in the Pleiades," *Popular Astronomy*, Vol. 21 (1913), pp. 187–188.

3.   G. W. Ritchey, "On Some Methods and Results in Direct Photography with the 60-inch Reflecting Telescope of the Mount Wilson Solar Observatory," *Ap. J.*, Vol. 32 (1910), p. 32.

4.   F. H. Seares, "The Surface Brightness of the Galactic System as Seen from a Distant External Point and a Comparison with Spiral Nebulae," *Ap. J.*, Vol. 52 (1920), p. 162.

5.   J. H. Reynolds, "Photometric Measures of the Nuclei of Some Typical Spiral Nebulae," *M. N.*, Vol. 80 (1920), p. 753.

6. H. Shapley and H. D. Curtis, "The Scale of the Universe," *Bulletin of the National Research Council*, Vol. 2 (1921), p. 217.

7. *Ibid.*, p. 192.

8. *Ibid.*, p. 212.

9. *Ibid.*, p. 213.

10. *Ibid.*, p. 214.

11. E. Hubble, "Angular Rotations of Spiral Nebulae," *Ap. J.*, Vol. 81 (1935), pp. 334–335; A. van Maanen, "Internal Motions in Spiral Nebulae," *Ibid.*, pp. 336–337.

12. A. S. Eddington, *Stellar Movements and the Structure of the Universe*. London: Macmillan and Company, Ltd. (1914), pp. 242–243.

13. K. Lundmark, "The Relations of the Globular Clusters and Spiral Nebulae to the Stellar System," *Kungl. Svenska Vetenskaps Akademiens Handlingar* ("Transactions of the Swedish Academy of Science"), Vol. 60 (1920), No. 8, p. 62.

14. E. Hubble, "The Spiral Nebula as a Stellar System—M 33," *Ap. J.*, Vol 63 (1926), p. 236.

15. K. Lundmark, *Studies of Anagalactic Nebulae*, Meddelanden från Astronomiska Observatorium Upsala ("Bulletin of the Astronomical Observatory at Upsala"), No. 30 (1926), p. 19.

16. W. Baade, "NGC 147 and NGC 185, Two New Members of the Local Group of Galaxies," *Ap. J.*, Vol. 100 (1944), pp. 147–150.

17. E. Hubble, *The Realm of the Nebulae*. New Haven: Yale University Press (1937).

18. W. W. Morgan, "Some Characteristics of Galaxies," *Ap. J.*, Vol. 135 (1962), p. 2.

19. A. Sandage, *The Hubble Atlas of Galaxies*. Washington, D.C.: Carnegie Institution of Washington, Publ. 618 (1961), p. 7.

20. *Ibid.*, p. 5.

21. *Ibid.*, p. 6.

22. W. W. Morgan, *loc. cit.*

23. E. M. Burbidge, and G. R. Burbidge (private communication).

24. A. E. Lilley and E. F. McClain, "The Hydrogen Line Red Shift of Radio Source Cygnus A," *Ap. J.*, Vol. 123 (1956), p. 172.

25. H. Bondi and T. Gold, "The Steady State Theory of the Expanding Universe," *M. N.*, Vol. 108 (1948), pp. 253–254.

Appendix

1. V. V. Sobolev, *Moving Envelopes of Stars*, translated by S. Gaposchkin, Harvard University Press (1960), p. 37.

2. A. Unsöld, *Physik der Sternatmosphären* ("Physics of Stellar Atmospheres"). 1st ed., Berlin: Julius Springer Verlag (1938), 500 pp.; 2nd ed., Berlin: Springer Verlag (1955), 866 pp.

3. Minnaert, "The Measurement of Equivalent Width as a Method for the Investigation of Line Profiles," *The Observatory*, Vol. 57 (1934), p. 328.

4. J. C. Pecker and E. Schatzman, *Astrophysique Generale* (General Astrophysics"). Paris: Masson et Cie. (1959).

5. L. H. Aller, *Astrophysics, The Atmospheres of the Sun and the Stars*. New York: Ronald Press Co. (1953), 412 pp.

6. P. W. Merrill, *Lines of the Chemical Elements in Astronomical Spectra*, monograph. Washington, D.C.: Carnegie Institution of Washington, Publication No. 610 (1956).

GLOSSARY

Absolute Magnitude   See Magnitude.

Absolute Zero $-273°$ C, zero on the Kelvin scale (see Kelvin temperature).

Absorption Coefficient   The fraction of continuous radiation absorbed at a certain wavelength per unit distance of depth, or per unit mass in the stellar atmosphere.

Absorption Lines   See Spectrum.

Albedo   The ratio of total light reflected from a sphere to the total light incident on it.

Altitude   See Coordinates.

Angstrom Unit   A unit of length equal to 10^{-8} cm, and usually abbreviated "A." This unit is commonly used in astronomy, particularly in reference to the wavelength of light. It is named for the 19th-century Swedish physicist A. J. Ångström.

Angular Momentum   The product of the mass of a moving particle and the area swept out in unit time by the line joining it to a given point. For a planet moving in a circular orbit, the angular momentum is the product of its mass, its distance from the sun, and its orbital velocity. For a rotating body, it is the sum of the products of the mass of each particle, its distance from the axis of rotation, and its rotational velocity. The total angular momentum of a system can be changed only by an outside force.

Annular Eclipse   See Eclipsing Binary.

Aperture   The effective diameter of the objective lens or mirror of a telescope.

Aphelion   The point in the orbit of a body in the solar system at which it is farthest from the sun.

Apparent Magnitude   See Magnitude.

APPARENT ORBIT   See VISUAL BINARY.

ASSOCIATION (STELLAR)   A loose grouping of stars in the galaxy, which some astronomers believe to expand with velocities of about 10 km/sec.

ASTROMETRIC BINARY   A pair of stars whose binary nature is inferred from a common proper motion.

ASTRONOMICAL UNIT   The mean distance between the earth and the sun, equal to 150 million km or 93 million miles, abbreviated a.u.

ATMOSPHERE   The gaseous outer layers of a star or other celestial body. The observed radiation of a star originates in the deepest layer of the stellar atmosphere, the *photosphere*. Two more tenuous layers, the *chromosphere* and the *corona*, extend above the photosphere. The top layer of the photosphere (below the chromosphere), which is primarily responsible for the absorption lines in the stellar spectrum is referred to as the *reversing layer*.

AZIMUTH   See COORDINATES.

BALMER SERIES   Hydrogen lines associated with the second energy level of the atom (see spectral series). The transitions between the second and third level produce the Balmer α line (Hα) at 6563 A. The limit of the Balmer series is at 3646 A.

BINARY OR DOUBLE STAR   Two stars in relative orbital motion due to their mutual gravitational attraction, known as binary stars. Binaries are classified as visual, spectroscopic, eclipsing, and astrometric.

BLACK-BODY RADIATION   See THERMAL RADIATION.

BOLOMETRIC MAGNITUDE   See MAGNITUDE.

CELESTIAL SPHERE   An imaginary sphere, of infinite radius, surrounding the earth, onto which all the objects in the heavens are projected.

CEPHEIDS   A group of pulsating variable stars, named after their prototype, δ Cephei.

CHROMOSPHERE   See ATMOSPHERE.

CLUSTER   A relatively stable group of stars, held together by their gravitational attraction. *Galactic* or open clusters contain, on the average, a few hundred stars, rather loosely grouped, with little concentration toward the center. *Globular* clusters are quite compact, roughly spherical in shape, with a strong central concentration; they contain, on the average, several hundred thousand stars.

COLLIMATOR   See SPECTROGRAPH.

COLOR EXCESS   The difference between the observed color index of a star and its normal color index, as inferred from the star's spectral type.

COLOR INDEX   The difference between the photographic and visual magnitude of a star ($\text{mag}_{\text{phot.}} - \text{mag}_{\text{visual}}$). Color index is set equal to zero for stars of spectral type A0, of surface temperature 10,000°; it is negative for hotter stars, positive for cooler stars.

COMA   Distortion of image in a reflecting telescope, producing elongated, comet-shaped images at the outer edges of the field.

CONTINUUM OR CONTINUOUS SPECTRUM   See SPECTRUM.

COORDINATES (CELESTIAL)   Two angles, measured in mutually perpendicular directions, uniquely determining the position of a celestial body on the celestial sphere. Astronomical coordinates are usually given as (1) angular distance perpendicular to a fundamental plane and (2) angular distance along a great circle in the fundamental plane, from a fixed reference point to a great circle perpendicular to it and passing through the star. Several coordinate systems are employed:

CORONA   See ATMOSPHERE.

DECLINATION   See COORDINATES.

DIFFRACTION GRATING   See SPECTROGRAPH.

DISPERSION   The amount of separation of light of different colors by the spectrograph. For example, a dispersion of 3 A/mm means that 2 absorption lines whose wavelengths differ by 3 A are recorded on the photographic plate with a separation of 1 mm. A value similar to this is referred to as "high dispersion," and is achieved only with some of the largest instruments for relatively bright stars. A "low-dispersion" spectrogram may have, for example, 250 A/mm, that is, two lines differing in wavelength by 250 A are separated by 1 mm.

DOPPLER EFFECT   Shift in wavelength of light (or sound) due to relative motion of the source and the receiver: a decrease in wavelength in the case of approach, an increase in the case of recession.

DOUBLE STARS   See BINARIES.

DWARF STARS   Stars belonging to the main sequence of the Hertzsprung-Russell diagram.

EARLY SPECTRAL TYPE   See SPECTRAL TYPE.

ECLIPSING BINARY   A pair of stars whose binary nature is detected photometrically, from periodic variations in its brightness when one component passes in front of the other. At the time of *primary eclipse* (greatest decrease in light of the system), the component of greater surface brightness is eclipsed by the one of lower surface brightness. The fainter is eclipsed by the brighter during *secondary eclipse*. If one component is completely hidden from view, a *total eclipse* results; when it is only partially hidden, a *partial eclipse*. In an *annular eclipse,* a smaller component obscures the central part of a larger component, leaving an unobscured ring. At *mid-eclipse*, the two stars are along the line of sight if the orbital plane is at right angles to the celestial sphere.

ECLIPTIC   See COORDINATES.

ELECTRON VOLT   A very small unit of energy, commonly used in nuclear and atomic physics.

ELONGATION   Angular distance of a body of the solar system from the sun, or of a satellite from its parent planet.

EMISSION LINES   See SPECTRUM.

EMISSION NEBULA   See NEBULAE (Galactic).

Coordinate system	Fundamental Circle	Reference Point	Coordinates Along Fundamental Circle	Perpendicular to Fundamental Plane
EQUATORIAL	Celestial equator—The intersection of the plane of the earth's equator with the celestial sphere	Vernal equinox—the intersection of the celestial equator and the ecliptic	Right ascension—α—arc along the celestial equator, from vernal equinox, measured eastward	Declination—δ—angular distance north or south of the celestial equator; it is considered positive in the northern hemisphere, negative in the southern hemisphere
HORIZONTAL	Horizon—the great circle, 90° from the zenith	South point on the horizon	Azimuth — measured westward from south point along horizon completely around the circle	Altitude—distance above the horizon
ECLIPTIC	Ecliptic—the apparent path of the sun on the celestial sphere	Vernal equinox	Longitude, measured eastward along the ecliptic, from vernal equinox	Latitude—distance north or south of the ecliptic
GALACTIC	Galactic equator—the intersection of the plane of the Milky Way and the celestial sphere	Old definition: Intersection of galactic and celestial equator. New definition: Direction toward the center of the Milky Way, in the constellation of Sagittarius	Galactic longitude—measured eastward	Galactic latitude

ENERGY LEVEL OF AN ATOM   The energy corresponding to the different shells an electron can occupy in the Bohr model of the atom, which conceives of the electrons revolving around the central nucleus as being arranged in shells, each containing a certain number of electrons. The jump of an electron to a shell having an orbit of smaller energy is accompanied by a radiation emission. In order to move an electron from a shell of larger radius, energy must be supplied.

ENERGY CURVE   Plot of the intensity of the continuous spectrum against the wavelength.

EQUATOR   See COORDINATES.

EXTRAGALACTIC NEBULAE   See GALAXIES.

F-NUMBER   The ratio of a telescope's focal length to its aperture.

FACULAE   Luminous areas seen near the limb of the sun in white light (see FLOCCULI).

FLARE   Sudden brightening of a region in the vicinity of a sunspot.

FLASH SPECTRUM   The emission spectrum of the solar chromosphere, observed for an instant during solar eclipse.

FLOCCULI   Regions of high luminosity, surrounding sunspots, visible in the light of hydrogen or of ionized calcium. These areas, when observed in white light near the limb of the sun, are known as FACULAE.

FLUORESCENCE   Absorption of radiation with subsequent re-emission of the equivalent amount.

FORBIDDEN LINE   Spectral line originating from a metastable energy level of an atom and observed only in an extremely rarefied medium.

FRAUNHOFER LINES   The dark lines in the solar spectrum (and stars of similar spectral type).

GALACTIC EQUATOR   See COORDINATES.

GALACTIC CENTER   See COORDINATES.

GALACTIC NEBULAE   See NEBULAE (GALACTIC).

GALAXY   A large aggregate of stars, nebulae, and interstellar matter. Galaxies are also referred to as *extragalactic* or *anagalactic nebulae*.

GIANT STARS   Luminous stars, of about zero absolute magnitude, low density, and relatively large size.

GROUND STATE   The lowest energy state of an electron.

H LINE OF CALCIUM   The line of ionized calcium at 3,968 A.

HIGH-VELOCITY STARS   Stars having velocities in excess of 60 km/sec with respect to the sun.

HERTZSPRUNG-RUSSELL DIAGRAM (H-R DIAGRAM)   A plot of the absolute (or apparent) magnitudes of stars against their spectral types (or colors).

IMAGE CONVERTER   An instrument capable of forming an electronic image of a field of stars and nebulae, also referred to as *image intensifier tube*.

INTERFEROMETER   An instrument utilizing the phenomenon of interference, which is the modification of intensity obtained by the superposition of two or more beams of light, derived from the same source.
Depending on the type of interferometer used, alternating dark and
light lines or rings are observed. The spacing of the *maxima* (or *fringes)*
depends on the angle of incidence, the separation of the beams, and
the wavelength. In the case of two sources with small angular separation or an extended source with nonuniform intensity, the fringe
patterns are modified in a way depending upon the separation of the
sources or the intensity distribution of a single extended source.
INTERSTELLAR REDDENING   The reddening of star light due to scattering
by small interstellar dust particles.
ISOTOPES   Atoms of the same element having different atomic weights.
That is, they have the same number of electrons and hence identical
atomic numbers and chemical behavior, but different nuclear masses.

KAPTEYN UNIVERSE   A model of the Milky Way galaxy, ascribing to it
small dimensions, with the sun located at or near the center.
KELVIN (HELMHOLTZ) CONTRACTION   The hypothesis proposed in the
19th century to account for the radiation emitted by the sun and stars.
According to it, stars tend to cool down and contract during their lifetimes and in doing so are converting gravitational potential energy into
heat.
KELVIN TEMPERATURE   A temperature scale with the same divisions as
centigrade scale, and zero point at $-273°$C.
KEPLER'S THIRD LAW   General: the product of the total mass of two
bodies times the square of the orbital period is proportional to the
cube of the semimajor axis of the orbit. Special case, applicable to
planetary orbits: the squares of the orbital periods of the planets are
proportional to the cubes of their mean distances from the sun.
KIRCHHOFF'S LAWS OF SPECTRUM ANALYSIS   Continuous spectrum is produced by a glowing solid, liquid, or gas under high pressure; *emission
spectrum*—by a glowing gas under low pressure; *absorption spectrum*
—by a continuous source with cooler gases at low pressure in front of it.
K LINE OF CALCIUM   The line of ionized calcium at 3,933 A.

LATE SPECTRAL TYPE   See SPECTRAL TYPE.
LIGHT CURVE   A plot showing the variation of the brightness of a star
against time.
LIGHT-YEAR   The distance traveled by light in a vacuum, in a year:
9.5×10^{17} cm, or 5.9×10^{12} mi, or 6.3×10^{4} a.u.
LUMINOSITY FUNCTION   The number of stars per unit of volume, in successive intervals of absolute magnitude.
LYMAN SERIES   The spectral series of the hydrogen atom, associated
with the first energy level (see SPECTRAL SERIES). The Lyman-α line is
at 1,216 A, the series limit at 912 A.

MAGNITUDE   Unit of stellar brightness. Two stars differing by 1 mag differ in luminosity by a factor of about 2.5. *Apparent magnitude* refers to the observed brightness of a celestial object. *Absolute magnitude* is the apparent magnitude an object would have at a distance of 10 parsecs from the sun. Different magnitude scales result from different methods of observation. *Visual magnitudes* are determined by visual observations; *photographic magnitudes,* on blue-sensitive photographic plates; *photovisual,* on photographic plates most sensitive to the same wavelength range as the eye. *Bolometric magnitude* corresponds to the total amount of energy radiated in all wavelengths.

MAIN SEQUENCE   The concentration of representative points in the H-R diagram in a band running diagonally from the hot, luminous stars at the upper left-hand corner to cool, faint stars in the lower right-hand corner.

MASS-LUMINOSITY RELATION   A theoretical relation between the masses and luminosities of stars to which most stars conform during the stable stages of their evolution.

MERIDIAN   The great circle passing through the zenith of an observer and the north and south points on the celestial sphere.

METASTABLE STATE (LEVEL)   An atomic energy level of a relatively long lifetime; under normal conditions the atom is usually disturbed by collisions before spontaneous emission from a metastable level can occur.

MID-ECLIPSE   See ECLIPSING BINARY.

MILKY WAY   The name used to describe the conspicuous band of dense star clouds that forms almost a complete circle around the sky. It is also used to denote the large, strongly flattened aggregate of stars, nebulae, and dust, the Milky Way galaxy. The appearance of the Milky Way band results from the greater concentration of stars and the larger extent of the system in this plane, near which the sun is located. The Milky Way galaxy is also referred to simply as "the galaxy" or "our galaxy."

NEBULAE (EXTRAGALACTIC)   See GALAXIES.

NEBULAE (GALACTIC)   Aggregates of interstellar matter, consisting of gas and dust, in the Milky Way. Dark nebulae are clouds of obscuring matter detected from the dimunition of light from the stars shining through them. If a star is located in or near a nebula, a bright *emission* or *reflection* nebula is produced; the spectrum of the former is characterized by *emission lines*, that of the latter by *absorption lines*.

NICOL PRISM   See POLARIZATION OF LIGHT.

NOVA   A star suddenly increasing in brightness, due to a catastrophic expansion. The increase is about 10 mag on the average.

OBJECTIVE PRISM   A prism placed in front of the objective of a telescope, producing spectra of all stars in the field of view that are sufficiently bright.

OBLATENESS   Ratio of the difference between the equatorial and polar radius of a planet (or star) to its equatorial radius.

ORBIT   The path in which one body revolves around another.

PENUMBRA   See SUNSPOTS.

PERIHELION   Closest approach to the sun of a body in the solar system.

PARALLAX (GEOCENTRIC)   The angle subtended by the radius of the earth at an object.

PARALLAX (HELIOCENTRIC)   The angle subtended at a star by the semi-major axis of the earth's orbit. (1 a.u.).

PARSEC   The distance at which a star would have a parallax of 1″. 1 parsec equals 2.1×10^5 a.u., or 3.3 light-years.

PERIOD-LUMINOSITY RELATION   Relationship between periods and luminosities of several types of variable stars, used to estimate their absolute brightnesses and hence distances.

PHOTOGRAPHIC MAGNITUDE .   See MAGNITUDE.

PHOTOMETER   A device used to determine the brightness of a celestial object by comparison with another object of known brightness.

PHOTOMETRY   The measurement of stellar magnitudes. Depending on the method employed, is spoken of as visual, photographic, and photoelectric photometry.

PHOTOELECTRIC CELL   A device employed in photometry in which an electric current is generated by the ejection of electrons from a metal surface exposed to light.

PHOTOMULTIPLIER TUBE   A device used in photometry that takes advantage of the fact that electrons released by light rays in a photoelectric cell will release additional electrons when they strike another suitable metal surface. Several such stages of multiplication may be used in a photomultiplier tube, increasing greatly its sensitivity.

PHOTOSPHERE   See ATMOSPHERE.

PHOTOVISUAL MAGNITUDE   See MAGNITUDE.

PLANCK CURVE   See THERMAL RADIATION.

POLARIZATION OF LIGHT   Light may be considered as consisting of transverse waves, vibrating at right angles to the direction of propagation. Star light usually is made up of vast numbers of electromagnetic waves, each having its own plane of vibration. When all planes of vibration are present, the light is said to be unpolarized; if only one plane is present, the light is plane-polarized. Polarized light can be detected with a *Nicol prism,* an optical device made from a calcite crystal, which transmits only one plane of vibration.

POPULATIONS I AND II   A rough division of stars into two groups, proposed by W. Baade. Population I denotes relatively young stars, found in the spiral arms of a galaxy, usually associated with gas and dust. Population II stars are older and are found principally in regions devoid of dust and gas, such as globular clusters and nuclei of galaxies.

PRECESSION   Conical motion of the axis of rotation of the earth around a line perpendicular to the ecliptic, resulting in a shift of the vernal equinox westward along the ecliptic by 50"/yr.

PRIMARY ECLIPSE   See ECLIPSING BINARY.

PROMINENCES   Masses of luminous gas rising high above the solar photosphere and best seen projected against the sky at the edge of the
solar disk.

PROPER MOTION   Apparent angular rate of motion of a star on the
CELESTIAL SPHERE.

RADIAL VELOCITY   Velocity along the line of sight, toward or away
from the observer. Velocities toward the observer usually are designated as negative, away from the observer as positive.

RECIPROCITY FAILURE OF A PHOTOGRAPHIC EMULSION   The photographic
density of a stellar image is not solely a product of the intensity of the
source and the duration of the exposure. It is a function, $I \times t^p$, where
I is the intensity of the source, t is the length of the exposure, and p is
a constant for a given photographic emulsion, whose average value is
about 0.8.

REDSHIFT   Displacement toward longer wavelengths of the spectral features of a light source.

REFLECTION NEBULA   See NEBULAE (GALACTIC).

REFLECTING TELESCOPE   A telescope employing a spherical or parabolic
mirror as light-gathering element.

REFRACTING TELESCOPE   A telescope employing glass lenses as light-
gathering element.

REVERSING LAYER   See ATMOSPHERE.

RIGHT ASCENSION   See COORDINATES.

RR LYRAE VARIABLES   A group of short-period pulsating variables with
periods less than 1 day and absolute magnitudes close to zero. Also
referred to as *short-period* or *cluster variables*.

SECONDARY ECLIPSE   See ECLIPSING BINARY.

SEEING   A term denoting the atmospheric conditions affecting the quality of a stellar image. In good seeing, atmospheric turbulence is low
and stellar images are of small diameter. In poor seeing, the images
become blurred.

SHORT-PERIOD VARIABLES   See RR LYRAE VARIABLES.

SPECTRAL CLASS   See SPECTRAL TYPE.

SPECTRAL SEQUENCE   The sequence of spectral types O, B, A, . . . (see
SPECTRAL TYPE).

SPECTRAL SERIES   All spectral lines in an atom having a common lower
energy level form a series. The transition between the ground state
and the next higher level gives rise to the absorption line with the
longest wavelength. The lines of a series become more closely spaced
toward the violet and converge to a *series limit,* which represents the
amount of energy required to dissociate the electron from the atom. If
more than this amount of energy is absorbed, the electron acquires
some kinetic energy; since there can be a continuous distribution of

kinetic energies, light of all wavelengths toward the violet end of the series limit can be absorbed, resulting in the *series continuum*. The transition at the series limit is often referred to as the *"jump."* The same processes result in emission lines and an emission continuum if the electron drops to the lower level of series and gives up energy.

SPECTRAL TYPE (OR CLASS)   Groups of stars, classified according to their spectral features, depending primarily on the temperature of the surface layers of the star. The principal spectral class designations now in use, O, B, A, F, G, K, and M, were introduced at the Harvard Observatory and represent a sequence extending from hot, blue stars (O) to cool, red stars (M). The hot stars are also often referred to as "early"; the cool, as "late."

SPECTROGRAPH   An instrument used to disperse and photograph light. The conventional spectrograph has five essential parts: the *slit*, which is a narrow opening; the *collimator*, which renders the light parallel before it reaches the dispersing unit; the *dispersing unit*, which is a *prism* or a *grating*; a *camera* that focuses the dispersed light; and the *photographic plate* or other recording instrument.

SPECTROHELIOGRAPH   An instrument used to photograph the sun in the light of a discrete spectral line.

SPECTROSCOPIC BINARY   A pair of stars whose binary motion is detected from periodic shifts of the absorption lines in their spectra. In double-line binaries, the components are of comparable luminosity and spectral features of both stars are recorded. In single-line binaries, only one spectrum is seen, the other being too faint.

SPECTRUM OF A STAR   The spectrum as recorded by a conventional spectrograph consists of a continuous bright background: the *continuous spectrum*. It ranges from red, for the longest visible wavelengths, to violet, for the shortest; the continuous spectrum is crossed by narrow dark or bright lines: the *absorption* or *emission lines*, respectively.

SPHERICAL ABERRATION   The failure of light rays at the center and edges of the field of a telescope to converge at one point.

SPIRALS   Galaxies with spiral structure. Since this is a very common and easily recognized type of galaxy, for some time galaxies were referred to as spirals.

SUNSPOTS   Relatively dark, roughly circular regions on the solar surface. The inner, dark center is called the *umbra*, the surrounding lighter areas the *penumbra*.

SUPERGIANTS   Extremely luminous stars of large size and very low density.

SUPERNOVA   A star increasing in brightness suddenly by as much as 15 to 20 mag due to a catastrophic expansion of its outer layers.

SYNCHROTRON RADIATION   Radiation emitted by high-velocity (relativistic) electrons spiraling along magnetic lines of force.

THERMAL OR BLACK BODY RADIATION   A particular type of intensity distribution in the spectrum, characteristic of the "perfect radiator," that is, one radiating the maximum amount of energy at any given temperature and being perfectly black when cold. This intensity distribution can be calculated from a formula developed in 1901 by M. Planck. Decrease in temperature affects the energy curve (*Planck curve*) in two ways: (1) the total amount of energy radiated per square centimeter of surface decreases, and (2) the maximum of the energy curve shifts to longer wavelengths. For most stars, the maximum occurs within or close to the visible region, and the curve drops first rapidly, then more gradually, toward longer wavelengths.

THERMOCOUPLE   An instrument consisting of wires or strips of two dissimilar metals, soldered at their junction and connected to an ammeter, used to determine the temperature of a celestial body.

T TAURI STARS   A group of irregular variable stars, named after their prototype T Tauri, usually associated with dark nebulosities and believed to be stars in the early stages of their evolution.

TOTAL ECLIPSE   See ECLIPSING BINARY.

UMBRA   See SUNSPOTS.

VERNAL EQUINOX   See COORDINATES.

VISUAL BINARY   A pair of stars whose binary character is determined from direct observations of the changes in their relative positions on the CELESTIAL SPHERE (either visually or photographically). The observations give the *apparent orbit* of the binary, that is, a projection of the true orbit on the CELESTIAL SPHERE.

VISUAL MAGNITUDE   See MAGNITUDE.

WHITE DWARFS   Stars of absolute magnitudes between about +10 and +16, of high surface temperature, small size, and enormous density, believed to be the end-products of stellar evolution.

ZEEMAN EFFECT   The splitting of a spectral line into several components, with distinct polarization characteristics, resulting when a source of light is in a magnetic field.

ZENITH   The point at which the direction indicated by the plumb line, extended infinitely upward, pierces the CELESTIAL SPHERE.

ZONE OF AVOIDANCE   An irregular zone, along the galactic equator, in which galaxies are obscured by the interstellar dust concentrated in the plane of the Milky Way.

THE CONSTELLATIONS

ANDROMEDA	And	The Chained Lady
ANTLIA	Ant	The Air Pump
APUS	Aps	The Bird of Paradise
AQUARIUS	Aqr	The Water Carrier
AQUILA	Aql	The Eagle
ARA	Ara	The Altar
ARIES	Ari	The Ram
AURIGA	Aur	The Charioteer
BOÖTES	Boo	The Herdsman
CAELUM	Cae	The Graving Tool
CAMELOPARDALIS	Cam	The Giraffe
CANCER	Cnc	The Crab
CANES VENATICI	CVn	The Hunting Dogs
CANIS MAJOR	CMa	The Greater Dog
CANIS MINOR	CMi	The Smaller Dog
CAPRICORNUS	Cap	The Goat
CARINA	Car	The Keel
CASSIOPEIA	Cas	The Lady in the Chair
CENTAURUS	Cen	The Centaur
CEPHEUS	Cep	Cepheus
CETUS	Cet	The Sea Monster
CHAMAELEON	Cha	The Chameleon
CERCINUS	Cir	The Pair of Compasses
COLUMBA	Col	The Dove
COMA BERENICES	Com	Berenice's Hair
CORONA AUSTRALIS	CrA	The Southern Crown
CORONA BOREALIS	CrB	The Northern Crown
CORVUS	Crv	The Crow
CRATER	Crt	The Cup
CRUX	Cru	The Cross
CYGNUS	Cyg	The Swan
DELPHINUS	Del	The Dolphin
DORADO	Dor	The Swordfish
DRACO	Dra	The Dragon
EQUULEUS	Equ	The Colt
ERIDANUS	Eri	The River

GEMINI	Gem	The Twins
GRUS	Gru	The Crane
HERCULES	Her	The Kneeling Man
HOROLOGIUM	Hor	The Clock
HYDRA	Hya	The Sea Serpent
HYDRUS	Hyi	The Water Snake
INDUS	Ind	The Indian
LACERTA	Lac	The Lizard
LEO	Leo	The Lion
LEO MINOR	LMi	The Lion Cub
LEPUS	Lep	The Hare
LIBRA	Lib	The Scales
LUPUS	Lup	The Wolf
LYNX	Lyn	The Lynx
LYRA	Lyr	The Lyre
MICROSCOPIUM	Mic	The Microscope
MONOCEROS	Mon	The Unicorn
OPHIUCHUS	Oph	The Serpent Bearer
ORION	Ori	The Hunter
PAVO	Pav	The Peacock
PEGASUS	Peg	The Flying Horse
PERSEUS	Per	The Hero
PHOENIX	Phe	The Phoenix
PISCES	Psc	The Fishes
PISCIS AUSTRINUS	PsA	The Southern Fish
PUPPIS	Pup	The Stern
PYXIS	Pyx	The Compass
SAGITTA	Sge	The Arrow
SAGITTARIUS	Sgr	The Archer
SCORPIUS	Sco	The Scorpion
SCULPTOR	Scl	The Sculptor's Tools
SCUTUM	Sct	The Shield
SERPENS	Ser	The Serpent
SEXTANS	Sex	The Sextant
TAURUS	Tau	The Bull
TELESCOPIUM	Tel	The Telescope
TRIANGULUM	Tri	The Triangle
TRIANGULUM AUSTRALE	TrA	The Southern Triangle
TUCANA	Tuc	The Toucan
URSA MAJOR	UMa	The Greater Bear
URSA MINOR	UMi	The Smaller Bear
VELA	Vel	The Sail
VIRGO	Vir	The Virgin
VOLANS	Vol	The Flying Fish
VULPECULA	Vul	The Fox

GREEK ALPHABET

	Capital	Small
Alpha	A	α
Beta	B	β
Gamma	Γ	γ
Delta	Δ	δ
Epsilon	E	ϵ
Zeta	Z	ζ
Eta	H	η
Theta	Θ	θ
Iota	I	ι
Kappa	K	κ
Lambda	Λ	λ
Mu	M	μ
Nu	N	ν
Xi	Ξ	ξ
Omicron	O	o
Pi	Π	π
Rho	P	ρ
Sigma	Σ	σ
Tau	T	τ
Upsilon	Υ	υ
Phi	Φ	ϕ
Chi	X	χ
Psi	Ψ	ψ
Omega	Ω	ω

BIBLIOGRAPHY

Most of the material upon which this book is based was originally published in astronomical periodicals. Following is a list of the publications:

Annales d'Astrophysique, Astrophysical Journal, and *Zeitschrift für Astrophysik* are the most important, highly technical periodicals in the field of astrophysics, published in France, the United States, and Germany, respectively.

Monthly Notices of the Royal Astronomical Society includes many highly technical articles and also the transactions of the Society, reports of the meetings, and other similar information.

Astronomical Journal is devoted to articles on positional and statistical astronomy, also of a specialized nature. In addition, the journal prints the abstracts of papers presented at meetings of the American Astronomical Society. The German *Astronomische Nachrichten* has a similar scope as this American journal.

An important periodical is the highly technical *Astronomicheskii Zhurnal* ("Astronomical Journal"), issued by the Academy of Sciences of the U.S.S.R. It is now being translated into English by the American Institute of Physics, under the title *Soviet Astronomy, A. J.*

Publications of the Astronomical Society of the Pacific covers a wide range of subjects. The articles are written on a somewhat less technical level than the preceding publications. The *Leaflets of the Astronomical Society of the Pacific* are summary articles on some particular problem.

Sky and Telescope is the most outstanding semipopular periodical in astronomy. It contains extensive articles on special subjects as well as short summaries of important papers presented at astronomical meetings and published in the more technical journals.

Observatory and *Popular Astronomy* (discontinued in 1952) are of a more popular nature.

The following is a selected list of books used in the preparation of this work:

ABETTI, G. *The History of Astronomy.* New York: H. Schuman, 1952.

ALLEN, C. W. *Astrophysical Quantities.* University of London: The Athlone Press, 1955.

ARMITAGE, A. *A Century of Astronomy.* London: Sampson Low, 1950.

BAKER, R. H. *Astronomy.* 7th ed. New York: D. Van Nostrand Company, Inc., 1959.

BEER, A. (ed.) *Vistas in Astronomy.* London and New York: Pergamon Press. 4 vols., 1956–1962.

BOK, B. J. *The Astronomer's Universe.* London: Cambridge University Press, 1958.

——.*The Distribution of the Stars in Space.* Chicago: University of Chicago Press, 1937.

BOK, B. J. and BOK, P. F. *The Milky Way.* Cambridge, Mass.: Harvard University Press, 1957.

BRACEWELL, R. N. (ed.) *Paris Symposium on Radio Astronomy.* Stanford, Calif.: Stanford University Press, 1959.

CHANDRASEKHAR, S. *An Introduction to the Study of Stellar Structure.* New York: Dover Publications, Inc., 1957.

CLERKE, A. M. *Problems of Astrophysics.* London: A. & C. Black, 1903.

——. *A Popular History of Astronomy during the Nineteenth Century.* 3rd ed. London: A. & C. Black, 1893.

——. *The System of the Stars.* London: A & C. Black, 1890.

DAVIES, R. D. and PALMER, H. P. *Radio Studies of the Universe.* New York: D. Van Nostrand Company, Inc., 1959.

DE VAUCOULEURS, G. *Discovery of the Universe.* New York: The Macmillan Company, 1957.

EBERHARD, G., KOHLSCHÜTTER, A. and LUDENDORFF, H. (eds.) *Handbuch der Astrophysik* ("Encyclopedia of Astrophysics"). 7 vols. Berlin: Julius Springer Verlag, 1928–1936.

EDDINGTON, A. S. *The Internal Constitution of the Stars.* London: Cambridge University Press, 1926; New York: Dover Publications, 1959.

——. *Stars and Atoms.* New Haven: Yale University Press, 1927.

——. *Stellar Movements and the Structure of the Universe.* London: Macmillan & Co., Ltd., 1914.

EMDEN, R. *Gaskugeln* ("Gaseous Spheres"). Leipzig: B. G. Teubner, 1907.

FLÜGGE, S. (ed.) *Handbuch der Physik* ("Encyclopedia of Physics") Vols. 50–53. Berlin: Springer Verlag, 1959.

HALE, G. E. *Beyond the Milky Way.* New York: Charles Scribner's Sons, 1926.

——. *Depths of the Universe.* New York: Charles Scribner's Sons, 1924.

——. *New Heavens.* New York: Charles Scribner's Sons, 1922.

——. *Signals from the Stars*. New York: Charles Scribner's Sons, 1931.

——. *The Study of Stellar Evolution*. Chicago: The University of Chicago Press, 1908.

HUBBLE, E. P. *The Realm of the Nebulae*. New Haven: Yale University Press, 1936.

HYNEK, J. A. (ed.) *Astrophysics*. New York: McGraw-Hill Book Company, Inc., 1951.

JEANS, J. H. *Astronomy and Cosmogony*. Cambridge: Cambridge University Press, 1929.

——. *The Universe Around Us*. New York: The Macmillan Company, 1929.

KING, H. C. *The History of the Telescope*. London: Charles Griffin, 1955.

KUIPER, G. P. and MIDDLEHURST, B. (eds.) *The Solar System*. Chicago: University of Chicago Press. Vol. I, *The Sun*, 1953. Vol. III, *Planets and Satellites*, 1961.

KUIPER, G. P. and MIDDLEHURST, B. (eds.) *Stars and Stellar Systems*. Chicago: University of Chicago Press. Vol. I, *Telescopes*, 1960.

LOWELL, P. *Mars*. Boston: Houghton, Mifflin & Co., 1895.

——. *Mars and Its Canals*. New York: The Macmillan Company, 1906.

MENZEL, D. H. *Our Sun*. Cambridge, Mass.: Harvard University Press, 1959.

PANNEKOEK, A. *A History of Astronomy* (first published in Dutch in 1951). New York: Interscience Publishers, 1961.

PAWSEY, J. L. and BRACEWELL, R. N. *Radio Astronomy*. Oxford: Clarendon Press, 1955.

PAYNE, C. *Stellar Atmospheres*. Cambridge, Mass.: Harvard University Press, 1925.

PAYNE, C. *The Stars of High Luminosity*. New York: McGraw-Hill Book Company, Inc., 1930.

PAYNE-GAPOSCHKIN, C. *Introduction to Astronomy*. New York: Prentice-Hall, Inc., 1954.

RUSSELL, H. N. *The Solar System and its Origin*. New York: The Macmillan Company, 1935.

RUSSELL, H. N., DUGAN, R. S., and STEWART, J. Q. *Astronomy*. 1st ed. Boston: Ginn & Company, 1926–1927; 2nd ed., 1938–1945.

SANDAGE, A. *The Hubble Atlas of Galaxies*. Washington, D.C.: Carnegie Institution of Washington, 1961.

SHAPLEY, H. *Star Clusters*. New York: McGraw-Hill Book Co., Inc., 1930.

——. (ed.) *Source Book in Astronomy*, 1900–1950. Cambridge, Mass.: Harvard University Press, 1960.

STRUVE, O., LYNDS, B. and PILLANS, H. *Elementary Astronomy*. New York: Oxford University Press, 1959.

VAN DE HULST, C. H. (ed.) *Radio Astronomy*. International Astronomical Union Symposium No. 4. New York: Cambridge University Press, 1957.

WATERFIELD, R. L. *A Hundred Years of Astronomy*. New York: The Macmillan Company, 1938.

WRIGHT, H. *Palomar*. New York: The Macmillan Company, 1953.

INDEX